Intellectual Mastery of Nature

Intellectual

VOLUME *1*

Christa Jungnickel
and
Russell McCormmach

Mastery of Nature

Theoretical Physics from Ohm to Einstein

The Torch of
Mathematics
1800–1870

THE UNIVERSITY OF CHICAGO PRESS

Chicago and London

The University of Chicago Press, Chicago 60637
The University of Chicago Press, Ltd., London
© 1986 by The University of Chicago
All rights reserved. Published 1986
Printed in the United States of America
95 94 93 92 91 90 89 88 87 86 54321

Library of Congress Cataloging-in-Publication Data

Jungnickel, Christa.
  Intellectual mastery of nature.

  Bibliography: v. 1, p.
  Includes index.
  Contents: v. 1. The torch of mathematics, 1800–1870.
  1. Physics—History. 2. Mathematical physics—
History. I. McCormmach, Russell. II. Title.
QC7.J86 1986   530′.09′034   85-16507
ISBN 0-226-41581-3 (v. 1)

FOR OUR PARENTS

Contents

Volume 2: The Now Mighty Theoretical Physics, 1870–1925

List of Illustrations

Preface

"Even the formulation of this concept is not entirely without difficulty," Ludwig Boltzmann wrote in 1895.[1] The concept was that of a "theoretical physicist," which Boltzmann introduced so that his readers would better understand what he was going to say about his teacher Josef Stefan. We have taken on a task similar to Boltzmann's, only with reference to the many physicists who worked in and taught theoretical physics in Germany.

The interest of one of us—we resort to the first person singular here—in theoretical physics goes back to a demanding course on the subject I took at Washington State College. Its teacher, the theoretical physicist William Band, observed that in recent decades—I now refer to the textbook based on his lectures—theoretical physics had moved from its "classical" emphasis on mechanical constructions toward a more abstract mathematical approach, and his course accordingly surveyed "theoretical physics from a modern unified point of view." There was at the same time a continuity from the classical period in one of the modern theorist's primary goals: he sought, Band said, the one "universal law embracing the whole of physical reality," borne by a "faith that such a universal law does exist and is comprehensible to the human mind."[2] One reason I later chose the history of science as my field of study was to understand the history of theoretical physics, which in Band's presentation had impressed me with its power to describe mathematically disparate phenomena in a uniform way. As I studied early works in theoretical physics, I became increasingly interested in the "theoretical physicist" of the late nineteenth century and beyond—Boltzmann's difficult concept—and in his search for universal laws encompassing all of the physical world. I became interested in Einstein not only as the author of the theory of relativity but also as a theoretical physicist. For my part,

1. Ludwig Boltzmann, "Josef Stefan," speech given on 8 Dec. 1895, reprinted in Boltzmann's *Populäre Schriften* (Leipzig: J. A. Barth, 1905), 92–103, on 94.
2. William Band, *Introduction to Mathematical Physics* (Princeton: Van Nostrand, 1959).

I have undertaken this study largely to answer my questions about the historical circumstances that gave rise to the theoretical physicist and about what it meant for someone to become a specialist of that kind.

This book is a result of the complementary, as well as overlapping, interests of its authors. The early interest of the other author—we use the first person singular again—was that of a student of the mathematical sciences who wanted to see the history of science integrated into general history. My interest in the problem arose out of my studies and work with the German historian Jacqueline Strain, whose example impressed me with the need for historians to incorporate the work of specialists in the history of science into the materials of general history. I wanted to test the idea by studying nineteenth-century German educational and cultural institutions and, at the same time, science. In particular, I wanted to study physics, one of the earliest sciences to partake of what, in other contexts, might be considered a characteristically German cultural aspiration, the attainment of a unified and comprehensive vision. Along with many other persons today who are concerned with German history, I also turned to the general subject of German education, culture, and science with the wish to contribute, however remotely, to the understanding of what went wrong, of what produced the German culture that, despite all of its intellectual and artistic accomplishments, in many respects failed so horribly in the middle years of the twentieth century.

As a historical subject, theoretical physics from Ohm to Einstein needs to be explained. Although there had been a body of physical theories for centuries, in Ohm's day, the early nineteenth century, theoretical physics was not a specialized field of study, and it was not to emerge as one for a good part of the century, until nearly the time of Einstein. So for much of the period covered by our study, our subject, strictly speaking, did not exist. But of course it did, in a practical sense, right from the start. Major contributions to physical theory were made by Ohm and his contemporaries and by their successors throughout the nineteenth century. In the second half of the century, teaching positions were gradually created for theoretical physics—Ohm himself at the end of his career received one of the first—and these positions laid the foundation for the partial separation of physics into the fields of experimental physics and theoretical physics. Our study of theoretical physics in the nineteenth and early twentieth centuries is a study of the various forms it took within physics, which itself was changing throughout the period, and it ends with an account of the mature form that theoretical physics assumed by the turn of the century.

Our book discusses the development of theoretical physics in one country, Germany, which is not to imply that the subject was created there. German physicists played an important part in its creation, but so did physicists in Britain, France, and other countries. To avoid any serious misrepresentation of our subject, we show the many points at which German physicists brought to their own work the work of their colleagues abroad. This work includes not only the content of physics but also its organization, for which France especially suggested early models. There is a proper sense in which we may define our subject as, and delimit it to, German

theoretical physics. In the course of the nineteenth century, German physicists organized their field as a university discipline, and it was within that "German" institutional framework that the specialties of experimental and theoretical physics
emerged. (We speak of the framework as "German" in quotation marks, since it
could be found also in a few, frequently German-speaking, locations outside of Germany.)

At the beginning of the nineteenth century, the German universities had no
function that called for more than elementary physics lectures for students seeking a
general education before going on to professional studies in medicine, law, or theology. Consequently they made no institutional provisions for any of the things we
have come to associate with a scientific university discipline such as physics: a comprehensive course of study, advanced training in research, and research by the established scientists. Gradually the German universities underwent an important internal
revitalization through the addition of the new function of research. The idea that
the creation of new knowledge could lift these state institutions to a higher plateau
and thereby raise the cultural and political reputation of the German states that
maintained them supplied the main argument for educational reform during and
following the Napoleonic wars. It was also an idea that, at least where the natural
sciences were concerned, had almost no hope of being formally realized at that time.
For providing the means for research would have required relatively large amounts
of money, which the then beleaguered and impoverished German states had far more
urgent uses for. It also would have required an understanding of whose business it
was to provide the money and what, in fact, research in the natural sciences consisted of. That information was not sought from scientists but from bureaucrats and
educators who were not experimental scientists and who had little interest in promoting experimental science. The debate among university people and other educators over whether or not research even belonged at the German universities continued until well into the nineteenth century. In time, the idea succeeded,
becoming a commonplace in fact, and the union of teaching and research in the
form it .took at the German universities became a chief characteristic defining a
"German" university and, by implication, a "German" university discipline. That is
the main sense in which we speak of "German" theoretical physics. The practice
and content of physics were, as we shall see, influenced by the universities' system
of organization.

The development of theoretical physics into a separate field of teaching and
research is, of course, an instance of specialization within the natural sciences. The
designation of new specialized fields was common at German universities during the
period of our study. The specific form that specialization took within physics was the
division into theoretical and experimental specialities by the partially different methods they applied to a common subject. The subdivision of a natural science by
method was not unique to physics: astronomy acquired a few "theoretical" professorships alongside the "practical," and chemistry acquired a third branch, physical
chemistry, which was sometimes described as "theoretical" chemistry. Every empirical science was understood to require theoretical guidance, but as one of our physi-

cists observed, it was only in physics that theoretical work developed into a major teaching and research specialty in its own right.[3] The division of physics into theoretical and experimental physics perpetuated arrangements that had arisen out of practical necessity and elevated them into something of an ideal of scientific cooperation. The physicists' desire and at times need for comprehensive theories were not disturbed by the multiplicity of their actual researches. Outwardly their science was still one, united through the usually complementary, if occasionally strained, interaction of experimentalists and theorists.

The goal of our study of German theoretical physics is to give an integrated account of the scientific work and its institutional setting. To accomplish this, to draw as complete a portrait as possible of the working lives of the physicists, we divide their occupational activities into two categories.[4] First, we study the individual physicist and his relations with others working with him in the same field. In the German universities of our period, physics was usually represented by only one senior physicist, which meant that his interactions with fellow physicists of equal rank occurred by correspondence, visits, occasional formal meetings, and publication in a few specialized journals or academy proceedings. Second, we study the individual physicist and his relations with others within the institution employing him, usually his university, and within the bureaucracy of the state in which he worked. In the university, he dealt with fellow faculty members who were not physicists but who nevertheless could influence important decisions regarding his subject. These decisions included, for example, appointments and promotions affecting physics, the allocation of funds between physics and other subjects taught by the faculty, and the allocation of university space for teaching and, in some instances, research. As an employee of the state—that is, as a university teacher and as a director of the university physics instrument collection or physics institute—he dealt with a hierarchy of persons ranging from the lowest laboratory servant to his state's minister of education or even his monarch. We outline these relations in a few words here; in practice, as we show throughout this book, they varied greatly with each German state, often with each university, and certainly with time. If the German university physicist was to succeed in both kinds of relationships, he had to arrange his work so that the practical tasks of his employment served the scientific tasks that he wished to pursue as a researcher, and conversely he had to represent his scientific work as important for carrying out his teaching obligations. This balancing of the parts of the physicists' work is central to our study; by tracing the many ways in which physicists achieved this balance, we show how they ultimately arrived at a well-defined field with well-understood and generally accepted goals and needs.

Of equal importance to our study as the physicists' institutional activities is their scientific work, for the problems that interested the physicists largely determined the

3. Wilhelm Wien, "Ziele und Methoden der theoretischen Physik," *Jahrbuch der Radioaktivität und Elektronik* 12 (1915): 241–59, on 241.
4. As done, for example, in Edward Gross, *Work and Society* (New York: Thomas Y. Crowell, 1967), 12.

arrangements they made for their research, shaped their relations with one another, and suggested the classes they offered to advanced students. We accordingly devote substantial discussion to the researches in theoretical physics by the German physicists of our period. We do not give a complete and continuous history of their work, since many studies have set out to do just that; little purpose would be served if we were to go over the same ground, and in any case we could not do the subject justice in a work of this length. Instead we discuss a limited number of theoretical researches by physicists in the several principal branches of physics, stressing the physicists' characteristic methods and their larger conceptions of physics and the physical world. We take care to locate the physicists' researches within their workplace and their other activities in physics. Only in this way can we show the complex relationships between the state of physics, the problems individual researchers addressed, the methods they used, and their local working conditions. Beyond that, we show how theoretical physics was seen by, and how it entered the lives of, physicists at all levels. Through periodic surveys of the literature of physics, especially the chief journals for physics, we give summary accounts of the work of physicists in and out of the universities and at all levels within the universities. In addition, through surveys of lectures and textbooks, we show how physics was defined for the next generation of physicists, and how the leaders of theoretical physics presented and integrated the branches and the whole of their science at different times throughout our period.

By selecting the physicists' work as our organizing principle, we take into account what is specific to physics among the sciences and, within physics, what is specific to the individual researcher. Physics calls for distinct capabilities and interests not necessarily found in other natural sciences. Max Planck, the first German specialist in theoretical physics (in a sense which our study makes clear), devoted much work to understanding chemical reactions from the standpoint of heat theory, conscious that it was "often not easy for a theoretical physicist to fit his manner of thinking and expression to the chemists' viewpoint."[5] Hermann von Helmholtz, who contributed to several natural sciences including theoretical physics, observed that "every man of conspicuous ability has his own special mental constitution, which fits him for one line of thought rather than for another." He explained: "If you compare, for example, the work of two contemporary investigators, even in closely allied branches of science, you can generally see that the more distinguished the men are, the more clearly their individuality comes out and the less qualified either of them would be to carry on the researches of the other."[6]

The individual researches we choose to discuss are, in the main, associated with new methods. Innovation in methods of research—mathematical, experimental, and observational—is characteristic of the period we consider. By discussing certain of

5. Max Planck, "Über das Princip der Vermehrung der Entropie. 1. Abhandlung," Ann. 30 (1887):562–82, in Planck's Physikalische Abhandlungen und Vorträge (Braunschweig: F. Vieweg, 1958), 1:196–216, on 216.

6. Hermann von Helmholtz, "The Relation of the Natural Sciences to Science in General," talk given at Heidelberg University on 22 Nov. 1862, trans. in Selected Writings of Hermann von Helmholtz, ed. R. Kahl (Middletown, Conn.: Wesleyan University Press, 1971), 122–43, on 129.

the new methods that became available to physicists, we give a sufficient idea of how theories were constructed by different physicists at different times.

For some categories of workers, it has been observed, work is "synonymous with life itself." Not all physicists showed that degree of identification with their work, but that at least some of them did is borne out by Einstein's choice of writing about his work when he was asked for an autobiography. The specific character of a physicist's commitment to his work is a psychological—we would prefer to call it common sense—hypothesis that can, in certain limited respects, be tested against practical actions and decisions within a historical setting. But the quality of the physicist's working experience, the feel of it, the gratification of accomplishment and the frustration of failure, the joy accompanying hard-won understanding and the perplexity when it does not come, the excitement and the tedium of research, all of this is a highly subjective matter, for which other approaches than ours are better suited.[7]

In Germany during out period, the usual setting of the physicists' work was the university physics institute. The control of a physics institute was an objective of most physicists, promising them scientific independence and reputation. The physics institute is the primary institution for our study; most of the relationships we analyze—scientific, organizational, and political—came together in it. By examining the physicist's work within his institute, we are able to give a realistic portrayal of German physics in our period.

We have organized our subject chronologically according to what emerges as its inner clock. In the complex development we describe, there are no sharply fixed turning points; even an important scientific discovery requires time to be prepared and time to affect the rest of physics afterward. But there are certain periods during which institutional changes or scientific ideas that once needed to be championed or justified are no longer even discussed but are treated as a matter of fact, while their consequences now preoccupy the physicists, university faculties, and government officials. These are the periods we use to divide our subject. There are four.

The first period, which extends to about 1830, we include primarily to describe physics in Germany at the beginning of our study; we depict the state of affairs to which we refer subsequent changes. The disruptions of war, political reforms, and social realignments of the first decades of the nineteenth century affected the German universities as they did most aspects of German life. Physics professors, as everyone else, kept going as best they could. Outside of Germany, particularly in France, these same decades produced an important body of mathematical physics along with major experimental discoveries. This foreign work entered German physics as it appeared, but it did not have important consequences until, roughly speaking, after 1825. It was then that the first German physicists who had grown up with the new physics attained university professorships and scientific independence.

In our second period, 1830–70, German physicists worked out the new possibil-

7. For one example: Russell McCormmach, *Night Thoughts of a Classical Physicist* (Cambridge, Mass.: Harvard University Press, 1982).

ities for physics, both scientifically and institutionally. We show how German universities acquired elementary physics laboratories and advanced, or "higher," physics instruction, how certain forms of specialized physics activities came about, and how the classical theories of physics were established and advanced in Germany.

Our third period extends from 1870 to around the end of the century. Early in this period, Gustav Kirchhoff moved to Berlin as a theoretical physicist, joining Helmholtz, who held the professorship for experimental physics there. This signaled the impending systematic separation of the two parts of physics, even though Kirchhoff's move did not have that design. Indicative of a general change in outlook, it marked the end of an era in German physics in the sense that the physicists who had embarked on their careers in the 1830s or thereabouts, with the goal of making a place for their experimental science at the universities, were now reaching the end of their careers and successfully concluding their efforts on behalf of physics. Scarcely anyone any longer questioned that physics laboratories belonged at universities, that students of physics should do more than just watch experiments and listen to lectures, or that physics was an intellectual discipline comparable in value to the humanistic sciences. The results of the work of physicists during the middle of the century now came into the hands of new men who no longer needed to promote their subject as their predecessors had had to. They built upon what had become accepted fact, which had practical consequences: for example, physicists could make a more effective case than before for physics education for different kinds of students, strengthening their claim on government support; more students for physics meant more teachers in subordinate positions, which were usually designated for theoretical physics, and this in turn meant more teachers seeking autonomy for theoretical physics as a teaching field. As a complement to the specialization of physics teaching, in the 1870s theoretical physics was increasingly recognized as a specialized area of research. This was indicated, for example, by the official designation of a theoretical researcher, Helmholtz, as the consultant on theoretical papers in the *Annalen der Physik*, the main German physics journal. By the end of the century, a degree of separation of the two parts of physics, if not yet equally realized at all German universities, was nevertheless completely accepted.

Most eminent German physicists of the nineteenth century, regardless of the designation of their university positions or their attention to experimental physics, owed their reputations primarily to fundamental contributions to theoretical physics. Theoretical physics acquired a distinction in Germany that was to be impressively affirmed in the twentieth century by the work of Einstein and Planck and by that of the young developers of the quantum and atomic theories. This era of achievement in physics, falling in the first quarter of the twentieth century, our final period, has received its due from historians of physics, which largely frees us from the task of undertaking extensive original research in it. We complete our story with the new atomic and field theories—who could forego such a conclusion?—but we limit ourselves to what our main subject requires. The reader interested only in the history of these new physical theories will find studies closer to his interest in the existing literature.

We had hoped to publish our study in a single volume. But because of its length, which our approach requires, our study appears in two volumes, the first treating 1800–1870 and the second 1870–1925. The different volumes may interest individual readers differently, but in design they are two volumes of a single book; in this preface, we wish to emphasize the unity of our study.

Our approach to the history of theoretical physics in Germany through the physicists' work does not preclude all consideration of "influences"; we acknowledge them when they contribute significantly to an understanding of our subject, but we do not begin with them. If we had begun by posing questions such as what influence German nature philosophy had on the intellectual directions of physics, or how German industrialization and unification influenced the institutions of physics, we believe we would have come up with a picture of German physics less faithful to the historical reality than the study we present here.[8]

Our portrayal of the working lives of the German physicists would have been impossible without the rich archival materials we uncovered in German university and state archives and libraries. By far the greater part of these sources has not been used before. In the historical literature, as Karl Neuerer points out in his recent work on nineteenth-century Bavarian higher education, these sources have "so far remained almost completely unnoticed." Because of the lack of earlier work in his subject, he proceeded almost exclusively from "hitherto unused documentary material."[9] Wilhelm Lorey, the historian of German mathematical education, made the same complaint long ago: the extensive historical studies of the German universities, for example, Friedrich Paulsen's, had left mathematics out of account, as well as, we hasten to add, the natural sciences.[10] Except for a few careful studies of particular subjects by German social historians, these archival sources remain largely unused in the history of science today; the result is that comprehensive studies of most scientific disciplines other than physics still remain to be done. Existing secondary work too often relies on a few, often already published, archival sources and on government-sponsored publications. We have found that in a hierarchical structure as many leveled and complex as the German university system, no single account of an event or situation, and least of all the officially published account, gives an adequate picture. What is now desirable is the kind of labor that is well demon-

8. An early draft of this book contained an entire part devoted to the relations between physics and German economic, political, social, and cultural developments. The preparation of that then still incomplete part required considerable research, and yet we had only the most superficial beginning of what was needed for a satisfactory discussion. To do the job properly would have required years more of research and certainly the space of another volume, and we decided not to burden the present work any further. We acknowledge industrial and other "connections" in appropriate places in the text, but we do not devote extensive discussion to them. The justification for a study limited largely to the work of a scientist, and the good sense of not trying to treat in a single book every philosophical, cultural, or whatever development that conceivably touched on the career of the scientist, can be appreciated from Stillman Drake's *Galileo at Work* (Chicago: University of Chicago Press, 1978).

9. Karl Neuerer, *Das höhere Lehramt in Bayern im 19. Jahrhundert* (Berlin: Duncker und Humblot, 1978), 6.

10. Wilhelm Lorey, *Das Studium der Mathematik an den deutschen Universitäten seit Anfang des 19. Jahrhunderts* (Leipzig and Berlin: B. G. Teubner, 1916), 2–3.

strated in the recent studies by Reinhard Riese of higher education in Baden and by Peter Borscheid of chemistry in Baden.[11] We have set out to do this for physics.

In an autobiographical sketch written toward the end of his career, Helmholtz told of what had originally drawn him to a life in science and, in particular, to physics. It had been his desire to gain an "intellectual mastery over nature," which an understanding of the laws of nature offered its possessor.[12] His colleagues often used this same expression when speaking of the results of physical research and of the specific contribution of physics to the ascendancy of culture over nature. Through a certain kind of inquiry and with a certain body of ideas, they said, physical nature could be mastered. The mastery they spoke of was in the first instance intellectual. From natural science, Helmholtz told the audience at his lectures on theoretical physics at Berlin University, the mind acquires the "only gift of prophecy that is given to man," a knowledge of the future course of natural events. The intellectual mastery of nature was followed by the material mastery, which was carried out by practical men: "by means of such preliminary knowledge of the laws, we are in a position to let natural forces work for us, after our will and wishes." As evidence for this, Helmholtz said: "The whole development of industry in recent times, and the whole change in the form of human life and activity connected with it, depend in an essential way on our mastery over the forces of nature."[13]

11. Reinhard Riese, *Die Hochschule auf dem Wege zum wissenschaftlichen Grossbetrieb. Die Universität Heidelberg und das badische Hochschulwesen 1860–1914*, vol. 19 of Industrielle Welt, Schriftenreihe des Arbeitskreises für moderne Sozialgeschichte, ed. W. Conze (Stuttgart: Ernst Klett, 1977). Peter Borscheid, *Naturwissenschaft, Staat und Industrie in Baden (1848–1914)*, vol. 17 of Industrielle Welt, Schriftenreihe des Arbeitskreises für moderne Sozialgeschichte, ed. W. Conze (Stuttgart: Ernst Klett, 1976).

12. Hermann von Helmholtz, "Autobiographical Sketch," 1891, in Helmholtz's *Popular Lectures on Scientific Subjects*, 2 vols., trans. E. Atkinson (London: Longmans, Green, 1908–12), 2:266–91, on 272.

13. Hermann von Helmholtz, *Vorlesungen über theoretische Physik*, vol. 1, pt. 1, *Einleitung zu den Vorlesungen über theoretische Physik*, ed. Arthur König and Carl Runge (Leipzig: J. A. Barth, 1903), 21.

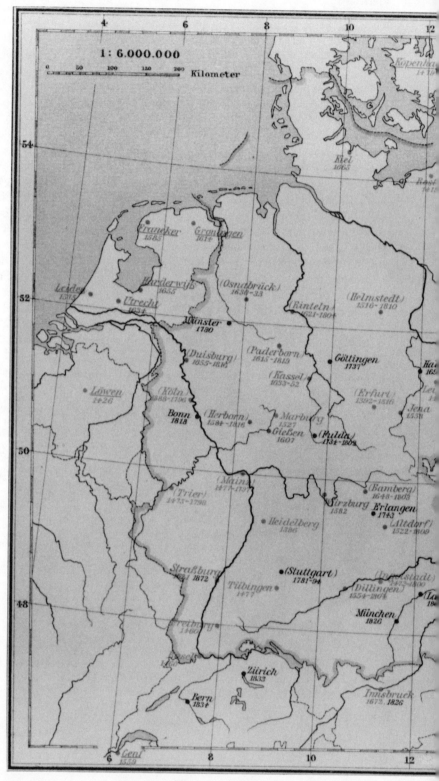

German Universities to the Beginning of the Twentieth Century.

Explanation. Founded before 1700: light type. Founded since 1700: dark type. Universities in parentheses have ceased. Universities underlined are not German-language universities. Reprinted from Franz Eulenburg, "Die Frequenz der deutschen Universitäten."

VOLUME *1*

The Torch of Mathematics 1800–1870

The Torch of Mathematics
1800–1870

Quietly and haltingly, theoretical physics made its appearance in Germany in the early nineteenth century. The first important result was Georg Simon Ohm's theory of galvanic currents, containing his now famous law, which he arrived at with the aid of a modest physics laboratory and, as he put it, the "torch of mathematics."[1] The laboratory was in the secondary school where Ohm taught, and the mathematics was from the best French writings of the day. He originally published his law in a journal devoted primarily to chemistry and only secondarily to physics. Shortly after, he published it again, this time in a book, a theoretically complete work. The latter was reviewed by a mathematician for a general science journal and by a teacher of geography and meteorology for a literary journal. The only physicist to review it did so for polemical purposes, writing for an ill-regarded science journal that propounded a certain philosophical direction. When Ohm's law at last aroused the interest of an academic physicist to undertake its experimental confirmation, it was at the hands of a junior professor who had been trained not in physics but in medicine and who had had no experience in experimental physics research.

The reception of his theory did not discourage Ohm. He looked for a position where he would have access to literature in his field and, above all, to physical apparatus. Since he had no money of his own, a teaching position was his best hope. He tried and failed to get a position at academies, universities, polytechnic schools, gymnasiums, and other secondary schools. Eventually he did get an improved teaching position, and he went on to become director of a polytechnic school and, toward

1. Georg Simon Ohm, *Aus Georg Simon Ohms handschriftlichem Nachlass. Briefe, Urkunden und Dokumente*, ed. Ludwig Hartmann (Munich: Bayerland-Verlag, 1927), 71. The expression Ohm used was familiar. For example, F. A. C. Gren said of J. T. Mayer, who stood out among German physicists at the time for using the calculus in his work, that he "seeks to enlighten a dark field of physics by the torch of mathematics." Review of Mayer's *Ueber die Gesetze und Modificationen des Wärmestoffs* (Erlangen, 1791) in Gren's *Journal der Physik* 4 (1791): 146.

the end of his life, professor at a university. His research, other than demonstrating the "literary" activity expected of a teacher who wanted to advance, had little to do with his early failure or with his later success in obtaining higher teaching positions. When it came to appointments as university professors of physics, researchers were treated no differently than writers of works that incorporated no research of their own. Ohm's introduction of a new direction for German research in physics went almost unnoticed, since everything else about him was so usual.

But that is not how his story is traditionally told. The circumstances of the publication and reception of Ohm's early work and his long struggle for a university appointment are portrayed as an exceptional case of neglect by German physicists and by government officials who had the power to place research scientists in German universities, where they presumably belonged. The story assumes that from the earliest decades of the nineteenth century, research in the natural sciences was supported in German universities as it came to be later in the century, and that German physicists of an earlier period acted in accordance with a view of physical research that was only established after Ohm and the physicists who soon followed him. When we compare Ohm's career with the careers of his contemporaries, we find, as we should expect, that his experience reflects the conditions under which scientists generally worked at the time. Ohm's career was in no way exceptional but for the type and quality of the work he did, and for this reason it is an instructive introduction to our study.

We see Ohm's career in its proper light when we recognize that for the first several decades of the nineteenth century, physics, like the other natural sciences, was principally two things: it was an elementary subject taught at universities and secondary schools as part of a general education; and it was a field of research open to persons with private means for maintaining and equipping their laboratories. As a result, physics was represented by persons in all kinds of positions and presented through all kinds of publications. The advent of significant German theoretical physics in the early nineteenth century in the form of Ohm's work, irregular as it may appear to us today, occurred under what was then perfectly normal circumstances.

1

Establishing Physics at the Universities

In Ohm's time, Germany was not one state but many separate states. Ohm spent most of his youth in the town of Erlangen, where he was born in 1789. At that time, Erlangen belonged to a Franconian principality. While Ohm was a student at the local gymnasium, Erlangen was Prussian; when he graduated from the local university, it was Bavarian. Ohm's early years coincided with the Napoleonic wars, when German frontiers changed frequently. The map of Germany was redrawn as the French extended their influence and rule, and it was redrawn again after the French were defeated. The settlement at the Congress of Vienna in 1815 left Europe with thirty-nine German states: thirty-five monarchies and four free cities. Prussia and Austria were the largest and most powerful; the rest varied greatly in size. Together they constituted Germany or, to observe the distinction we make in this study, Germany and Austria. For purposes of security, the German states formed the German Confederation, but each state retained sovereignty over its internal affairs such as the administration of any universities it might have.

Ideal of *Bildung* and Tasks of the Philosophical Faculty

The political changes at the beginning of the nineteenth century stimulated hopes and ideas for reform in many areas of public life, including the German universities. But the new purposes envisioned by reformers for the universities, such as research, did not then or for a long time to come supersede or even equal in importance their established function.[1] Their principal purpose remained the training of professionals needed by the German states: of physicians, lawyers, and government officials, who generally had to have a legal education, and of clerics and teachers, the two often being one and the same. To meet this purpose, a university existed in every German

---

1. Rudolph Wagner, "Schriften über Universitäten. Dritter Artikel," *Gelehrte Anzeigen* 3 (1836), cols. 993–97, 1001–6, 1013–16.

3

state that could afford one. The larger southern German states maintained more than one, and Prussia had six universities by 1818. Altogether, there were then nineteen German universities. Despite their different origins and state affiliations, they were all constituted in much the same way: each had "faculties"—professional schools—for medicine, law, and theology; in addition, each had a fourth faculty, the philosophical faculty, which represented the humanities, mathematics, and some of the natural sciences, and which supported the other three faculties by providing general education.

The several faculties of German universities were constituted of "ordinary" professors, who received salaries from the state to teach their fields and fees from students in their courses. Universities had other teachers who were not members of the faculties and who generally did not receive salaries but only student fees. They were the "extraordinary" professors and, below them, the lecturers known as Privatdocenten. These were the three ranks of university teachers, which in practice were varied to suit local needs and circumstances.

The philosophical faculty was the faculty that allowed German universities to present themselves as institutions of "pure science"—their practical purpose notwithstanding—and to claim superiority over "mere" professional schools or specialized institutions such as the military and engineering schools in France, a form of which was then beginning to be established in the German states. The philosophical faculty, according to this ideal view of its purpose, continued on a higher level the task of the humanistic German secondary school, the gymnasium, of giving students *Bildung*. *Bildung* consisted not only of fundamental knowledge but also of methods of inquiry. It enabled its professor to put all of his intellectual and emotional capacities to their best possible use, ennobling his character and refining his taste. *Bildung*, it was thought, was best acquired through classical studies: "A noble man in whose soul God has put the capacity of future greatness of character and high intellect will develop most splendidly through the acquaintance and the intimate intercourse with the lofty characters of Greek and Roman antiquity," Goethe said to J. P. Eckermann in 1827. For this reason, "one should not study those born and striving contemporaneously with oneself, but . . . above all the ancient Greeks and again and again the Greeks."[2] The study of classical antiquity prepared the gymnasium student to take responsibility for his future education and to value the pursuit of learning for its own sake. Including as it did all of the humanities and most of the natural sciences, the philosophical faculty then offered the student an opportunity to devote, in Wilhelm von Humboldt's words, "a number of years exclusively to scientific contemplation," enabling him to "grasp the unity of knowledge."[3]

This ideal program for the philosophical faculty, as for the gymnasium, could not work to the advantage of physics or of any of the other natural sciences represented in the philosophical faculty. *Bildung* had become so closely linked to classical philology that other interpretations of it were for a long time generally unacceptable,

2. Johann Wolfgang von Goethe, *Goethes Gespräche mit J. P. Eckermann*, ed. Franz Deibel (Leipzig: Insel-Verlag, 1908), 1:363.

3. Gerhardt Giese, *Quellen zur deutschen Schulgeschichte seit 1800*, vol. 15 of Quellensammlung zur Kulturgeschichte, ed. Wilhelm Treue (Göttingen: Musterschmidt-Verlag, 1961), 66.

even though, inevitably, they were proposed. "For now the principle still rules everywhere that there is only one way to higher education [*Geistesbildung*], namely, through the most thorough knowledge of the two ancient languges," Ernst Gottfried Fischer, a secondary school teacher of physics in Berlin, wrote with disapproval. "These take up by far the greatest part of the hours," an imbalance that Fischer's teaching and textbooks were meant to correct.[4] The natural scientists objected to a *Bildung* that looked to past cultures for the model of the present; the means by which this *Bildung* was to be achieved—despite loftier intentions, they usually amounted to incessant drilling in the classical languages—were antithetical to learning the modes of thought of the natural sciences.

Proper science instruction required learning by thinking and doing for oneself, which Ohm believed was a means of acquiring *Bildung*, too. When correctly taught, mathematics demanded the student's own inner striving and not merely his receptivity to things presented to him, an interpretation of *Bildung* that Ohm introduced in his book on the teaching of geometry. The book, it turned out, was scorned and then ignored. *Bildung* that would lead to a "new world . . . formed by active reason in man," as Ohm promised his teaching methods would achieve, must have seemed as undesirable to the authoritarian governments from whom he sought employment as to the humanists at gymnasiums with "an exclusively aesthetic interest" in human achievement.[5] The more successful scientists, particularly those outside Prussia, appealed to the interests of their governments rather than to those of their fellow teachers. They claimed usefulness for their subjects instead of the advancement of *Bildung*: the study of the natural sciences is now generally considered "extraordinarily important and useful as preparatory education," Georg Wilhelm Muncke wrote in 1817 to promote the establishment of a state-supported physical cabinet at Heidelberg University.[6]

The little contribution physics was allowed to make to higher *Bildung* was principally through the traditional course of lectures; Fischer recommended "for a fairly complete presentation of physics . . . at least a one-year course, of 4 to 6 hours weekly."[7] Another contribution was made through the systematic display of physical instruments, commonly located in the "academic museum."[8] But actively engaging

4. Ernst Gottfried Fischer, *Lehrbuch der mechanischen Naturlehre*, 3d ed., 2 vols. (Berlin and Leipzig, 1826–27), 1:xix.

5. Heinrich von Füchtbauer, *Georg Simon Ohm; ein Forscher wächst aus seiner Väter Art*, 2d ed. (Bonn: Ferdinand Dümmler, 1947), 115; *Ohms . . . Nachlass*, 37, 65–72.

6. Georg Wilhelm Muncke to Baden Ministry of the Interior, 1 June 1817, Bad. GLA, 235/3057. The *usefulness* of mathematics to civil servants and school teachers was a reason for proposing a mathematical seminar at Heidelberg in 1824. Heidelburg U. Curator Froehlich to Baden Ministry of the Interior, 23 Feb. 1824, Bad. GLA, 235/3228.

7. Fischer, *Lehrbuch* 1:xx.

8. This was a traditional use of the physical instruments. For accounts of arrangements accommodating the practice, see Wilhelm Weber to Göttingen U. Curator, 24 Apr. 1832, Göttingen UA, 4/V h/ 15; Otto Lehmann, "Geschichte des physikalischen Instituts der technischen Hochschule Karlsruhe," in *Festgabe zum Jubiläum der vierzigjährigen Regierung Seiner Königlichen Hoheit des Grossherzogs Friedrich von Baden* (Karlsruhe, 1892), 207–65, on 240; Academic Consistory to Pfaff, 25 Oct. 1842, LA Schleswig-Holstein, Abt. 47, Nr. 1235; instructions to Heidelberg U. dated 4 Aug. 1847, Bad. GLA, 235/352; *Handbuch der Architektur*, pt. 4, sect. 6, no. 2al, ed. H. Eggert, C. Junk, C. Körner, and E. Schmitt, 2d ed. (Stuttgart: A. Kröner, 1905), 194–95.

the student in learning physics did not fit the traditional idea of *Bildung,* as Wilhelm Weber discovered when he introduced experimental exercises to students of medicine, pharmacy, and chemistry, and to students preparing to become secondary school teachers of mathematics.[9] Students tended not to avail themselves of the opportunity,[10] and their major professors, especially those in the medical faculty, did not encourage them to.[11]

If the ideal task of the closely connected gymnasiums and philosophical faculties did not promote the intensive study of physics, neither did their real task of providing general education. Beginning university students as a rule took most of their lecture courses in the philosophical faculty. They were encouraged to do so, indeed, required to do so in Bavaria,[12] because the one-sided education they had received at the gymnasium had not prepared them adequately for professional studies, particularly professional studies requiring a knowledge of mathematics or the natural sciences. Under the best circumstances, in the gymnasium they had had only two hours per week of instruction in the natural sciences, which included a good deal of natural history and geography, and six hours per week in mathematics. A professor of mathematics at Leipzig University reported that he taught students who had never before had any mathematics.[13] The curator at Heidelberg University reported that otherwise well-educated young men lacked even an elementary knowledge of mathematics because of the superficiality and indifferences of mathematical instruction in the secondary schools.[14] A faculty report on the state of physics at Tübingen University listed the "lack of the necessary preliminary knowledge," especially in mathematics, as one of the reasons why students did not profit from their physics lectures and why they did not attend the mathematics lectures.[15] The professor of mathematics at Bonn University had to devote his lectures to elementary instruction, to arithmetic, Euclidean geometry, algebra, and trigonometry.[16] The Tübingen faculty noted that the "most famous universities" in Germany were no better off. However, when the physics professor at Freiburg University tried to remedy the problem by offering a course on the differential calculus or analytical geometry, no students attended.[17]

9. Weber to Göttingen U. Curator, 24 Apr. 1832, Göttingen UA, 4/V h/15.

10. Weber to Göttingen U. Curator, 10 May 1851, Göttingen UA, 4/V h/21.

11. The Göttingen medical faculty prevented Weber's "Praktikum" from becoming as effective as it could have been by refusing his participation in the physics examination of medical students. Exchange of letters between Weber and Göttingen U. Curator, and Medical Faculty and Curator in 1848, Weber Personalakte, Göttingen UA, 4/V b/95a.

12. E. K. J. von Siebold, review of A. F. Ringelmann's *Beyträge zur Geschichte der Universität Würzburg in den letzten zehn Jahren* (Würzburg, 1835), in *Göttingische gelehrte Anzeigen,* 1836, 65–73, on 67.

13. Moritz Wilhelm Drobisch, *Philologie und Mathematik als Gegenstände des Gymnasialunterrichts betrachtet, mit besonderer Beziehung auf Sachsens Gelehrtenschulen* (Leipzig, 1832), 71.

14. His purpose was to propose a mathematics seminar (at the request of the mathematics professor, F. Schweins). Heidelberg U. Curator Froehlich to Baden Ministry of the Interior, 23 Feb. 1824, Bad. GLA, 235/3228.

15. Report by Minister of the Interior and of Church and School Affairs von Otto, 16 Apr. 1821, Kabinettsakten, HSTA, Stuttgart, E11 Bü 52.

16. Debate by Bonn U. Philosophical Faculty, 16 Oct. 1827, Plücker Personalakte, Bonn UA. *Vorlesungen auf der Königlich Preussischen Rhein-Universität Bonn.*

17. The professor was Ludwig August Seeber. Helmuth Gericke, *Zur Geschichte der Mathematik an der Universität Freiburg i. Br.* (Freiburg i. Br.: E. Albert, 1955), 51.

Professors of physics who wrote textbooks to accompany their lectures regularly had to exclude mathematics, or at least the calculus and more advanced mathematics, because their students were unprepared. Heinrich Wilhelm Brandes's published lectures on physics were meant for readers who, like his students at Leipzig University, had no knowledge of mathematics.[18] Johann Tobias Mayer's, C. W. G. Kastner's, and G. G. Schmidt's textbooks on experimental physics could be studied with little mathematical preparation.[19] Although Kastner warned his readers that if they came to his lectures at Heidelberg University they would meet equations and calculations, even there the mathematical demands were not high; what he meant by mathematics as an "indispensable auxiliary study for the scientist and especially the physicist" was "at least arithmetic and geometry." Georg Freidrich Parrot, professor at Dorpat University, and Fischer both made a strong case for mathematics in their textbooks on theoretical and mechanical physics. Parrot recommended his mode of presentation for its "rigorous mathematical demonstrations," and Fischer described his subject as "almost completely mathematical."[20] But neither used the calculus, since they could not expect beginning students to know it. The chief task of physics professors was to give general introductory lectures, which were no more than surveys of the state of physical knowledge. For advanced courses on special areas of physics there were almost no students.[21]

Despite the nimbus of ideal learning it lent the German university as a whole, the philosophical faculty was not thought to be as important as the three professional faculties, to the detriment of the fields represented in it.[22] In some circles the philosophical faculty was considered not to be much above a secondary school, and physics and mathematics teachers, like their colleagues in the other natural sciences and the humanities, moved easily between the two kinds of institutions—and not just in one direction.[23] Ohm applied repeatedly for a simultaneous appointment to a teach-

18. Heinrich Wilhelm Brandes, *Vorlesungen über die Naturlehre zur Belehrung derer, denen es an mathematischen Vorkenntnissen fehlt*, 3 vols. (Leipzig, 1830–32), 1:iii.

19. Johann Tobias Mayer, *Anfangsgründe der Naturlehre zum Behuf der Vorlesungen über die Experimental-Physik*, 2d rev. ed. (Göttingen, 1805), vii; C. W. G. Kastner, *Grundriss der Experimentalphysik*, 2 vols. (Heidelberg, 1810), 1:viii, 58–59; Georg Gottlieb Schmidt, *Handbuch der Naturlehre zum Gebrauche für Vorlesungen*, 2d rev. ed. (Giessen, 1813), iv.

20. Georg Friedrich Parrot, *Grundriss der theoretischen Physik zum Gebrauche für Vorlesungen* (Riga and Leipzig, 1809–15), 1:xv; Fischer, *Lehrbuch* 1:3–4.

21. For example, at Göttingen University in 1810 C. L. Gerling found that although fifty to seventy students were interested in elementary lectures on the mathematical sciences, lectures on higher mechanics attracted only seven or eight. Gauss offered no advanced lectures at all unless two or three students expressed interest. Johann Friedrich Pfaff, *Sammlung von Briefen gewechselt zwischen Johann Friedrich Pfaff und Herzog Carl von Würtemberg, F. Bouterwek, A. v. Humboldt, A. G. Kästner und Anderen*, ed. Carl Pfaff (Leipzig, 1853), 275–76. Julius Plücker's ability to attract even a few students to his mathematical physics courses at Bonn University was taken as proof of his teaching ability and recommended him for promotion to extraordinary professor. Philosophical Faculty debate, and Philosophical Faculty to a Prussian government representative at Bonn U., 16 Oct. 1827, Plücker Personalakte, Bonn UA. See also our discussion of this problem in chapter 2 in connection with Franz Neumann and other later physicists.

22. See Christa Jungnickel, "The Royal Saxon Society of Sciences: A Study of Nineteenth Century German Science"(Ph. D. diss., Johns Hopkins University, 1978), 127–31, on the Saxon Society's hope to raise the status of the philosophical faculty to that of the professional faculties.

23. See, for example, the application for Weber's professorship at Göttingen University by Lambert, a gymnasium teacher from Wetzlar, dated 27 Jan. 1838, in J. B. Listing Personalakte, Göttingen UA, 4/ V b/108. Another example is the list of candidates in the report "Die Wiederbesetzung der Lehrstelle der

ing position at a secondary school and at the local university.[24] Even for an ordinary professor, the financial incentive might favor a move to a secondary school: Paul Erman's income as ordinary professor of physics at Berlin University was so much lower than that of a gymnasium teacher that he threatened to resign his professorship to return to secondary school teaching.[25] How little teachers and ministry officials distinguished between the philosophical faculties of universities and secondary schools can also be seen in their attitude toward the assignment of teaching equipment. The philosophical faculties and the teachers at nearby secondary schools saw each other as having much the same task with regard to science instruction, and they coveted each other's experimental apparatus for this purpose. For Ohm it was not unreasonable to fear that the new university at Bonn might claim the good collection of physical apparatus at the gymnasium in Cologne, just as it was not unreasonable for some gymnasiums in Baden to claim shared use of the physical apparatus of Heidelberg University.[26]

Tasks and Trials of Physics Professors

Because of their similar asks of providing elementary or general education in both secondary schools and philosophical faculties, professors in the early nineteenth century were still primarily teachers, as they had been in the eighteenth century. They were not specialists in a particular subject, who had qualified for it in a manner prescribed by the practitioners of the field. The list of candidates for the physics chair at Heidelberg University in 1816 shows the range of qualifications that applied: it names four university professors, an independent researcher who had the reputation of being an "extremely good" experimenter and a man of "genius," an assistant

---

Physik zu Heidelberg betrf.," 7 Dec. 1816, Bad. GLA, 235/3135. Altogether, during the first half of the nineteenth century, twenty-five university professors teaching physics at German universities—among them the physics chairholders Paul Erman (Berlin), K. D. M. Stahl and Thaddaeus Siber (Munich), J. S. C. Schweigger (Halle), G. F. Wucherer, L. A. Seeber, and Johann Müller (Freiburg), C. L. Gerling and Rudolph Kohlrausch (Marburg), Julius Plücker (Bonn), Karl Snell (Jena), Eduard Reusch (Tübingen), and Wilhelm Hankel (Leipzig)—taught at secondary schools at some time during their careers, several of them after they had already held university positions. Other sources of income were positions at technical schools and at military schools, then of a lower rank than the universities. Ten university teachers of physics—C. F. von Pfleiderer, Paul Erman, J. G. C. Nörrenberg, Georg Simon Ohm, L. A. Seeber, Heinrich Wilhelm Dove, August Seebeck, Hermann Karsten, Rudolph Clausius, and Wilhelm Beetz—simultaneously taught at military schools. Nine—G. F. Wucherer, Georg Simon Ohm, Heinrich Buff, August Seebeck, J. B. Listing, Wilhelm Beetz, Rudolph Clausius, Adolph Wüllner, and Eugen Lommel—moved from trade and technical schools to their university professorships.

24. Ohms . . . Nachlass, 137–38, 153, 155, 158–59.

25. Wilhelm Erman, "Paul Erman. Ein Berliner Gelehrtenleben 1764–1851," in Schriften des Vereins für die Geschichte Berlins 53 (1927): 1–264, on 122, 162.

26. Ohm was concerned because he had just been appointed to the gymnasium in Cologne when Bonn University was being set up in 1817. Ohms . . . Nachlass, 49. Heidelberg University at first agreed to share its apparatus with the secondary schools in Heidelberg, but when the secondary schools in other towns in Baden made similar demands, it rejected all sharing, pointing out that it needed the apparatus for its own lectures on physics and applied mathematics, and that frequent transportation would damage the apparatus. Heidelberg UA, IV 3e Nr. 52, 1804–1864.

at the Munich Academy of Sciences, two gymnasium teachers with good reputations as physicists, a private teacher, and a city clerk and magistrate.[27] About the latter two, the faculty reported that the first, a "son of a . . . government councillor, originally studied medicine, but physics and chemistry very soon became his favorite sciences, which he then cultivated with good success, too," and which he had been teaching for two years; the second, the city clerk and magistrate, had studied both physics and law and now wanted the Heidelberg physics chair, even though he had never taught before and had "not yet distinguished himself through any writings."

University professors could be called on to teach a variety of subjects; Ohm taught Latin as well as mathematics in his secondary school. Subjects a university professor was appointed to teach were often unrelated to his special interests, as the history of the professorship of physics at Würzburg University shows: the first professor of experimental physics there in 1749 was a teacher of mathematics; he was succeeded in turn by a theologian, a physiologist, a teacher of philosophy, a physician, a professor of chemistry and pharmacy, and, at last, a physicist who, as luck would have it, was still not properly qualified, for he was one of the first purely theoretical physicists, Rudolph Clausius.[28] Würzburg was typical in this respect.[29] Even the new universities made appointments without regard for specialized preparation: the first professor of physics at Bonn University in 1818 had previously been an apothecary and a chemist; the first professor of physics at the newly founded Breslau University was a nature philosopher, who kept on teaching nature philosophy, anthropology, physiology, and mineralogy in addition to physics; and as late as 1835 two of the professors of physics at Berlin University were by training chemists. A recommendation for a university position might then look like this: "[L. F.] Kämtz is a very good calculator and loves calculating with formulas and numbers very much. I believe that he would also make himself into a good astronomer, namely a *practical* one; for he has already zealously studied theoretical [astronomy] with [J. F.] Pfaff. . . . Indeed, he can be recommended in good conscience for a teaching position for physics and astronomy, but as well for one for mathematics and physics, since he has very zealously studied pure (also higher) mathematics . . . [and] successfully lectured on conic sections."[30]

27. Report "Die Wiederbesetzung der Lehrstelle der Physik zu Heidelberg betr.," 7 Dec. 1816, Bad. GLA, 235/3135.

28. Maria Reindl, *Lehre und Forschung in Mathematik und Naturwissenschaften, insbesondere Astronomie, an der Universität Würzburg von der Gründung bis zum Beginn des 20. Jahrhunderts* (Neustadt an der Aisch: Degener, 1966), 98–102. The physician, F. A. Sorg, was considered qualified for the "mathematical section" by his prizewinning paper on the breathing of insects. See report by Count von Thürheim to Elector of Bavaria, Bay. HSTA, Abt. I, MInn 23590.

29. Another example is Marburg University: there C. L. Gerling, professor of physics from 1817 to 1864, devoted the years before his appointment to making himself an astronomer. In 1816 he was still preparing himself for his "future astronomical profession." Gerling to Gauss, 17 Feb. 1816; see also Gerling to Gauss, 24 May 1814, 1 Mar. 1815, 28 Dec. 1815, and 25 Sept. 1816, all in Gauss Papers, Göttingen UB, Ms. Dept.

30. J. S. C. Schweigger's recommendation of L. F. Kämtz to J. W. Döbereiner, in *Neue Mittheilungen aus Johann Wolfgang von Goethe's handschriftlichem Nachlasse*, vols. 1–2, *Goethe's Naturwissenschaftliche Correspondenz (1812–1832)*, ed. F. T. Bratranek (Leipzig, 1874), 1:110–11 (hereafter cited as *Goethe's Naturw. Corr.*).

Once in a while a physics chair was filled by someone who was fully prepared for it. It happened in Göttingen in 1831, though it almost did not. Against the newer, specific qualifications for a university appointment that some now considered desirable, such as research experience, the traditional qualifications almost won out, especially as they were advocated by Göttingen University's most influential scientist, Carl Friedrich Gauss. Asked his opinion on candidates for the professorship of physics there, Gauss listed the qualifications the candidates ought to have.[31] First, it was an "essential requirement" that the professor of physics could give lectures suited to the preparations and needs of a "somewhat mixed audience" who wanted to acquaint themselves with physics "to a certain degree" without making a deeper study of it; he would also have to be able to illustrate his lectures with well-chosen and skillfully executed experiments. Second, since the professor of physics would, as a member of the Göttingen Society of Sciences, be expected to help continue the local tradition of excellence in scholarship, it was no less important that he know all parts of his science, even beyond that which is necessary for teaching, and that his publications meet the standards of the *Transactions* of the society. The measure of excellence in a physicist, according to Gauss, was a thorough knowledge of mathematics. Yet he did not want a physicist who was at the same time a mathematician of the "first rank," since such a man would not be able and perhaps would not want to find the "right measure" in his lectures for the mixed audience he had to teach. When scientific excellence was weighed against the teaching needs at the university, even at a university that owed its "unique rank of a world institution" to excellence in scholarship, Gauss might put teaching needs and other considerations ahead of scholarship.

Gauss named and ranked five physicists.[32] Of the five, Brandes was not among his first choices, but it did not bother him that Brandes's writings had been "directed more toward presenting the achievements of others, in part in popular form, than to advances of his own"; it was enough that he did not "embarrass" the Göttingen Society.[33] C. L. Gerling, whom Gauss knew best, received his strongest recommendation. Gerling was a good experimenter; at least, Gauss had never had a better

31. Gauss to Göttingen U. Curator Arnswaldt, 27 Feb. 1831, Weber Personalakte, Göttingen UA, 4/V b/95a.

32. J. G. F. von Bohnenberger, ordinary professor of mathematics and astronomy at Tübingen University; Brandes, Gerling, and Seeber, the ordinary professors teaching physics at Leipzig, Marburg, and Freiburg, respectively; and Weber, extraordinary professor at Halle.

33. Brandes's publications—listed here to show what Gauss considered a respectable body of work outside of original research—were on astronomy, mathematics, physics, and meteorology. As a student at Göttingen, Brandes had published some observations and calculations of comets with J. F. Benzenberg. During his early career in hydraulic engineering, he continued his mathematical studies (he published a translation of Euler's *The Laws of Equilibrium*) and also carried out but did not complete observations on refraction, which he published. After he had entered his academic career—as professor of mathematics at Breslau in 1811, a position he exchanged for the professorship of physics at Leipzig in 1826—he published original research only in astronomy and meteorology. Most of his writings were textbooks on geometry, mechanics, astronomy, and physics and translations of works by J. Leslie and by J. B. Biot and, with L. W. Gilbert, of Laplace's theory of capillarity. In addition, he was one of the co-editors of a new edition of *Johann Samuel Traugott Gehler's Physikalisches Wörterbuch*, and from 1827 he was editor of the *Leipziger Literaturzeitung. Neuer Nekrolog der Deutschen*, vol. 12, 1834 (Weimar, 1836), 1: 396–98; Karl Bruhns, "Brandes, Heinrich Wilhelm," *ADB* 3:242–43.

student in practical astronomy. He was skilled at such tasks as turning, filing, soldering, and working on clocks and barometers. His physical cabinet in Marburg was in good order, and he assured Gauss that he had presented many experiments in his physics lectures, which rarely failed him. Moreover, Gerling usually had forty students in his lectures, which was more, if one considered the ratio of students at Marburg and Göttingen, than Mayer used to get at Göttingen, proof that Gerling's lectures did not frighten off a mixed audience. Gerling had done some research on earth-magnetic instruments, but he had not written much on experimental physics. That was explained by his double appointment at Marburg as professor of mathematics as well as physics; most of his writings had been on mathematics. In other words, to paraphrase Gauss, Gerling was a good teacher, and he had a number of skills that would be useful to Gauss in pursuing his own interests.[34] Ludwig Seeber, who did mainly mathematical work, and Weber were treated almost as afterthoughts. The book that Weber had written with his brother was, as far as Gauss knew of it from reviews, proof that he had a mind for research and talent for experimenting. Gauss did not emphasize, however that Weber was the only one of the five candidates who had demonstrated uncommon ability in physics research. When he selected three of the five to make up the usual triad of faculty recommendations, he selected Weber along with J. G. F. von Bohnenberger, who had shown "immense skill as a practical astronomer," but it was clear to the curator of the university, the intermediary between the faculty and the government in Hannover, that Gauss wanted Gerling, who would strengthen the faculty and senate. Of Weber, Gauss had remarked on the "perhaps greater genius in the work to be expected for the Society," in light of which the curator saw in Weber "greater depth and originality" and, young though he was, a "level of scientific development that offers more than just hope" (which was what Gauss had for Gerling); he offered as well an advancement of physics. That, the curator wrote, "would be for me a decisive moment in the selection to be made." Weber got the appointment.[35]

The tasks related to teaching placed a greater burden on teachers of the natural sciences than on their colleagues in the philosophical faculty who taught the humanities. As their sciences were observational and experimental, they did not believe that they could limit their teaching effectively to the reading of a text. They required apparatus, collections of specimens, botanical gardens, and rooms in which the instruments could be stored and used and the collections displayed, all of which required large amounts of money. At some universities, especially in Prussia, the money was available for the then observational sciences—mineralogy, botany, and zoology—but not for the experimental sciences. At Berlin University, for example, from 1810 to 1840 the Prussian government spent close to 200,000 thaler, if not

34. Gauss wrote of his preference for Gerling to the astronomer Wilhelm Olbers on 24 Dec. 1830; in Wilhelm Olbers, sein Leben und seine Werke, vol. 2, Briefwechsel zwischen Olbers und Gauss, pt. 2, ed. C. Schilling (Berlin: J. Springer, 1909), 564.

35. The Hannover government had its own reasons for preferring Weber such as Weber's relative cheapness and Gerling's unwelcome politics.

more, on zoology and mineralogy, but only 3500 thaler on physics (or, to be precise, nothing until 1833 and then 500 annually) and as little on chemistry. The uneven distribution of funds did not arise from any marked discrepancy in needs—instruments for physics and chemistry, not to mention proper physical and chemical laboratories, were expensive too—but from the scorn for the experimental sciences expressed by education officials such as Karl vom Altenstein and his university advisors as well as from their desire to enhance the state through ostentatious displays of natural history collections. In the poorer German states, the observational and the experimental sciences both struggled for funds.[36]

When we look at physics instruction being offered at German universities in the early nineteeth century, we find both "experimental" and "theoretical" lectures. Physics teachers who had apparatus for demonstrating the phenomena gave "experimental" lectures, which they generally preferred. When they lacked apparatus and had to explain the phenomena solely with words and drawings, they gave "theoretical" lectures.[37] According to Kastner, who was charged with teaching physics at several German universities in the course of his career, the "theoretical" physicist drew on "historically reported observations and experiments" in presenting the laws of nature, whereas the "experimental" physicist presented those laws directly through experiments.[38] Kastner himself taught the experimental physics course as well as an "encyclopedia on all natural sciences as an introduction to the individual branches," which was a survey course like that of "theoretical" physics except that it covered more sciences.[39] The Tübingen physics curriculum was similar: C. F. von

36. Ludwig von Rönne, *Das Unterrichts-Wesen des Preussischen Staates* (Berlin, 1855), 2:430–62. The Prussian university institutes and collections for the *natural sciences* received 27,146 thaler annually; in addition, the universities had the unlimited use of some state institutes for the natural sciences with a budget totaling 16,610 thaler. Of these funds for the natural sciences, only about eight percent were allotted to the *experimental sciences:* 2156 thaler to physics (that is, physics at *all* six Prussian universities together received only slightly more than Hegel's salary of 2000 thaler) and 1372 thaler to chemistry. By contrast, botany—which the Minister of Culture Altenstein had once studied and in which he maintained an amateurish interest—received 21,732 thaler annually; in other words, botany could command ten times as much money as physics for its *annual* expenses, not including extraordinary acquisitions. Rudolf Köpke, *Die Gründung der Königlichen Friedrich-Wilhelms-Universität zu Berlin* (Berlin, 1860), 274–85, provides further evidence of the Prussian government's favoring of the observational sciences: the Prussian government spent 47,557 thaler on buying zoological collections for Berlin University in these years, 1810–40; it financed scientific expeditions to collect specimens at a cost that the zoologist Wilhelm Peters, compiler of these figures for Köpke in 1860, could no longer determine but judged "very considerable"; from 1820, it gave the zoological collections a fixed annual budget amounting to a total of 57,084 thaler for the first twenty years; and, during the same period, it enriched the mineralogical collection at a cost of 48,030 thaler and gave it an annual budget which from 1816 to 1837 grew from 1000 to 1520 thaler. The annual budgets of the observational sciences, unlike those of physics, did not have to pay for most of the scientific acquisitions of these collections or for their housing, since the collections were given space in the university. For an example of a small university in this connection, see *Die Universität Freiburg seit dem Regierungsantritt Seiner Königlichen Hoheit des Grossherzogs Friedrich von Baden* (Freiburg i. Br. and Tübingen, 1881), 48–51, 91–96.

37. Georg Wilhelm Muncke, "Physik," in *Johann Samuel Traugott Gehler's Physikalisches Wörterbuch,* vol. 7, pt. 1, ed. Heinrich Wilhelm Brandes, L. Gmelin, J. C. Horner, Georg Wilhelm Muncke, and C. H. Pfaff (Leipzig, 1833), 493–573, on 505.

38. Kastner, *Grundriss* (1810), 1:57. In the 1820–21 edition of the textbook, Kastner left out the word "historically" (1:47).

39. *Vorlesungen auf der Königlich Preussischen Rhein-Universität Bonn,* 1819–20, Bonn UA.

Pfleiderer regularly offered "theoretical physics" in his so-called public lecture for a general audience, the traditional one-hour a week lecture every professor was obliged to give every semester free of charge; in addition, he alternately lectured on "experimental physics" and on elementary mathematics in his second, so-called private lecture, which was the longer, more important, and better attended of the two and the professor's main source of student fees.[40] According to Fischer, who was more mathematically inclined, in the experimental lectures the physicist presents, in historical fashion, results that have been discovered by "mathematical acumen" and uses the lecture experiments as a sort of proof; rigorous mathematical developments were too difficult for beginners, and the complete development of mathematical-physical theories, such as those of mechanics and optics, was left to lectures on "applied mathematics."[41] These lectures too—although they were usually taught by professors of mathematics at the German universities, for example, by J. G. Tralles at Berlin from 1811 to 1822, by B. F. Thibaut at Göttingen, and by J. F. Pfaff at Halle until 1825—sometimes involved experiments. Pfaff's son described his father's lectures: "He presented . . . the main theories of physics and managed to illustrate them with experiments and to make them visible to his audience."[42]

By the first decades of the nineteenth century, it was generally accepted that classroom demonstrations were essential for proper teaching. "The most convenient way of teaching others physics seems to be to connect experience and conclusions with one another and to illustrate the different theories by experiments," Mayer wrote in 1805.[43] The Leipzig philosophical faculty, explaining why the physics professor's living quarters ought to be near his instrument collection, wrote in 1811 that physics "is largely experimental and hence presupposes the constant use of the apparatus" in lectures.[44] Physics professors usually did not get any or enough money from the university or the state to purchase and maintain apparatus and instruments, so they had to provide them themselves—and in fact were expected to do so—out of their own income and at the cost of time and money they might otherwise have spent on research. They constructed their own demonstration instruments, transported them to and from lecture halls, sometimes across town, and set them up and dismantled them for every lecture because they had to share facilities with other professors (if they had access to university lecture rooms at all).[45]

At the same time, physics was rapidly developing in a direction that made self-reliance in procuring experimental equipment in most cases merely a stopgap. The

40. HSTA, Stuttgart, E 31, Bü. 372, pp. 116, 123, 125, 737.
41. Fischer, *Lehrbuch* 1:4.
42. Pfaff, *Sammlung von Briefen*, 28.
43. Mayer, *Anfangsgründe* (1805), 18.
44. Draft letter by Leipzig Philosophical Faculty, 23 Mar. 1811, Gilbert Personalakte, Leipzig UA, Nr. 503.
45. Wagner, "Schriften über Universitäten, Dritter Artikel," col. 1016. The few physics professors who had a good collection of apparatus profited from their troubles, however, for they became more desirable to universities because of it and could set their own terms. For example, Gilbert threatened to turn down a call from Leipzig University if he was not given quarters for his collection and his lectures, a laboratory, and living quarters. He got what he wanted and moved to Leipzig. Gilbert Personalakte, Leipzig UA, Nr. 503.

materials needed had multiplied to a point where even wealthy persons could rarely acquire them with their private means, as Muncke at Heidelberg University explained to the Baden government in 1817. For that reason, he said, government officials had started to equip public educational institutions with the required apparatus and allowed them to continue supplementing the apparatus out of a specially designated fund.[46] Governments, as Muncke was to learn, yielded only in small steps to entreaties, but if physicists wanted to keep up with the developments in their field, they had no choice but to persist. Those universities that acquired instrument collections early and built them up most assiduously became the most important centers for theoretical as well as experimental physics in the middle of the century. Their chairs attracted—and, if possible, were reserved for[47]—the best of the next generation of physicists.

When Muncke became professor of physics at Heidelberg in 1817, he found a collection containing many "rather beautiful, rare, and sometimes valuable" instruments, but also "important gaps." To fill the gaps, he needed in addition to the usual barometers and thermometers a "usable electrical machine, Bohnenberger's electrometer, Coulomb's scale, Zamboni's pile, Volta's pile, Mayer's light polarization machine, Marcet's lamp, Wollaston's Chryophorus, Pictet's mirror, Rumford's cube, Leslie's photometer etc." Muncke was asking for apparatus for studying and demonstrating the latest physics. He got three quarters of the annual fund he requested, which he reserved for buying apparatus and making urgent repairs. (If a physicist was not careful, his budget could only too easily be encroached on by expenses for heating and lighting, building repairs, furnishings, and salaries for servants and mechanics. In Muncke's case, the fourth quarter of the amount he had requested did in fact go toward the salary of an institute servant.) He had also requested extra funds so that he could soon complete the physics institute in a way that measured up to the "splendor and fame" of Heidelberg University; although he was promised these funds, he did not receive them. After eleven years, he still held to his original estimate of the amount he needed to improve the institute, reminding the government that the institute was now way behind what it should be; most of the "great cabinets in Germany," he complained, had annual funds more than three times the amount of his. To allow Heidelberg to "take part in the frequent simultaneous measurements made over most of Europe," he had supplied the institute with his own astronomical clock, and he had bought a good microscope for the fine observations that were now expected, but he could do no more with his private means.[48]

While Muncke slowly built up the instrument collection, he took every opportunity for shaming the government into more support at Heidelburg. In 1828, for example, he anticipated a chance to get extra funds because of the annual meeting of the German Association of Natural Scientists and Physicians at Heidelberg the following year, when "in a sense all institutes will be subjected to a public evalua-

46. Muncke to Baden Ministry of the Interior, 1 June 1817, Bad. GLA, 235/3057.
47. As Weber thought should be done with the Heidelberg physics chair for Gustav Kirchhoff in 1854. See below, p. 289.
48. Muncke to Baden Ministry of the Interior, 1 June 1817, and to Heidelberg U. Curator, 25 Dec. 1828, Bad. GLA, 235/3057.

tion."[49] In 1836, when Muncke received an invitation from Gauss to participate in the earth-magnetic observations Gauss had organized internationally, he asked the government for money for the magnetic apparatus so that Heidelberg University and "in fact even the state of Baden, according to a remark by Gauss, should not fall behind others through any fault of mine." He had done his share, he pointed out: he had built up the good reputation of the physical sciences at Heidelberg and earned Gauss's invitation; he was now supplying suitable rooms, good student observers, and some precious instruments of his own for the earth-magnetic observations. He could not, however, use the institute funds for the work that "Gauss and the learned public in general probably expected . . . of the state of Baden."[50] Instead he had to use the funds for instruments to teach "thermomagnetism, light polarization, and magnetoelectrism," the new subjects that were then receiving "general attention." After nearly twenty years of teaching, he was still keeping the physical collection up to date, eventually enabling his successor, Philipp Jolly, to begin his teaching by setting up a student laboratory instead of starting at the bottom with the task of accumulating instruments; even important universities such as Berlin had to begin at the bottom in the 1830s.

Being at one of the preferentially treated universities such as Berlin did not necessarily give physics professors an advantage over colleagues at poorer institutions, as the position of physics at Berlin University from its founding in 1810 to the 1830s shows. Before Paul Erman became the ordinary professor of physics at Berlin in 1810, he had been a teacher in Berlin at the French gymnasium and, at the same time, at one of the Berlin military schools, and he continued in these positions even after his appointment at the university.[51] The Prussian state spent little on physics: it paid Erman as university professor a salary of 500 thaler, which was 300 thaler less than his salary as a secondary school teacher. (By comparison, when Mayer was called to the physics chair at Göttingen in 1799, he was offered a salary of 900 thaler and 100 thaler for the maintenance of the physical apparatus at the university; he asked for and got a larger salary which, in 1800, added up to 1160 thaler, on top of which came student fees.[52] As Ohm was advised in 1828, there were better places to apply the "lever" to get scientific employment than Berlin.[53]) One of the arguments favoring Erman's appointment to the Berlin chair of physics was that, because of his other jobs, he would not have to be paid so much. He was not given any physical apparatus or the 500 thaler in annual funds that had initially been designated for a physical cabinet.[54] His courses were supplemented at no expense to the state: Fischer and Karl Daniel Turte taught physics at Berlin University

49. Muncke to Heidelberg U. Curator, 25 Dec. 1828, Bad. GLA, 235/3057.

50. Muncke to "Staats-Rath," 13 Oct. 1836, and Muncke to Baden Ministry of the Interior, 9 Jan. 1837 (the letter is mistakenly dated 1836), Bad. GLA, 235/3057.

51. Erman, "Paul Erman," 54, 122–23.

52. Letters dated 8 May 1799, 23 May 1799, 4 July 1800, and 8 Sept. 1800, J. T. Mayer Personal-akte, Göttingen UA, 4/V b/67.

53. Schweigger to Ohm, 15 Dec. 1828, Ms. Coll., DM, 693.

54. Köpke, Berlin, 284–85; Albert Guttstadt, ed., Die naturwissenschaftlichen und medicinischen Staats-anstalten Berlins (Berlin, 1886), 139–40.

as extraordinary professors, appointments that did not pay any salary.

For the first ten years, Erman gave one lecture course on physics at the university each semester—in the first year, he had given two courses—while he tried to get the necessary aids. In 1814 the rector and senate of the university requested a complete and appropriate physical apparatus.[55] They were asked to submit specific suggestions, after which Erman worked out a detailed list of instruments necessary for a larger collection of apparatus for lecture demonstrations. The Prussian minister of religious affairs and education (the minister of "culture") Altenstein agreed in principle that these instruments ought to be acquired, but he did not make specific annual amounts available for the purpose and the money continued to be used elsewhere. Even a general order from the Prussian prime minister, State Chancellor Karl von Hardenberg, to Altenstein in 1818 to the effect that "each university required a complete theoretical and practical course of physics and chemistry, also a small public physical cabinet . . . not a dusty lumber-room"[56] brought no change to the University of Berlin. Altenstein seemed to have had other ideas on how to improve physics in Berlin, for in that same year he brought the physicist Thomas Seebeck to the Berlin Academy; it caused him some "work" because Seebeck was known as an adherent, at least to some extent, of Goethe's theory of color, an association that would not have recommended him to the Berlin physicists.[57] Meanwhile Erman struggled to keep physics alive at the university. He used instruments from his collection, which he transported from his home in the military school to the university and back again for each lecture. He had to share the lecture hall with others, and he was not even given enough time to dismantle his apparatus after a lecture before the beginning of the next class, which, as if to add insult to injury, was given by one of the nature philosophers whom the physicists despised. Only after Erman decided to give up his professorship in 1819, because he was overburdened with work and the position paid too little, did Altenstein improve his conditions at the university. He was also promised an institute, but he did not get it.

Freed to double his physics teaching at the university, Erman now gave two three-hour lecture courses each semester, which added up to a complete cycle of lectures covering all parts of physics every year. He began with a lecture course on general physics, followed it by one on magnetism, electricity, and galvanism, then by one on heat and light, and finally by a fourth on meteorology. Max Planck, in his account of theoretical physics at Berlin University, called Erman's lectures the earliest theoretical lectures by a professor of physics at Berlin;[58] Erman's biographer said that Erman's physics lectures constituted a "thorough" treatment of physics, set apart from the "more superficial orientation lectures" for medical and pharmaceutical

55. Max Lenz, Geschichte der Königlichen Friedrich-Wilhelms-Universität zu Berlin, vol. 1, Gründung und Ausbau (Halle an der Saale: Buchhandlung des Waisenhauses, 1910), 529.

56. Erman, "Paul Erman," 161.

57. Kuno Fischer, Erinnerungen an Moritz Seebeck wirkl. Geheimerath und Curator der Universität Jena, nebst einem Anhange: Goethe und Thomas Seebeck (Heidelberg, 1886), 11; L. Stieda, "Seebeck: Thomas Johann," ADB 33:564–65.

58. Max Planck, "Das Institut für theoretische Physik," in Lenz, Berlin, vol. 3, Wissenschaftliche Anstalten. Spruchkollegium. Statistik (1910), 276–78, on 276.

students and candidates for secondary school teaching that were offered by junior faculty.[59] These latter lectures were only surveys, "theoretical" or "historical" presentations "supplemented now and then by showing experiments." Other physics and mechanics courses taught at the university included Fischer's on mathematical physics[60] and Martin Ohm's and E. H. Dirksen's on, for example, analytical statics, dynamics, and hydrodynamics.[61]

As a member of the Prussian Academy of Sciences, Thomas Seebeck was entitled to lecture at the university, but his influence on physics in the early 1820s was through his research, not his teaching. His salary and the expenses of his experimental research on thermoelectricity at the academy had to affect physics at the university by making fewer funds available for teaching there. In 1821 a second drain on Berlin resources for physics arose when Leopold von Henning, a student of G. W. F. Hegel, took up Goethe's theory of colors. After studying the theory and with Goethe's support, Henning began to give public lectures on it at the university.[62] The government supported his experiments on Goethe's theory by giving him funds for optical instruments[63] and by promoting him to professor. As he repeated his lectures for the tenth time in 1831, he reported to Goethe that on the average he had been getting forty serious students for each course; they included students from all faculties and also artists, secondary school teachers, officers, and "other friends of natural science."[64] Soon after he had begun his lectures, a Berlin Hegelian wrote to Goethe that Henning had even more auditors than in the previous year, over sixty, and that there was a "lively interest in the theory of colors."[65] He also reported that there had been no lack of "malicious obstacles" from "several sides" against the lectures, perhaps raised by the "stubborn mathematical Newtonians" whom Henning claimed to be among his auditors.

In 1826 Fischer answered this outbreak of bad physics and Hegelian muscle-flexing in the Berlin ministry of culture with a new edition of his 1805 textbook *Lehrbuch der mechanischen Naturlehre*. Formerly he had aimed it at secondary schools, but now he rewrote it for universities. One of the reasons he did so was to emphasize the need in physics to separate fact from fiction: there were now "even men of intellect [*Geist*] who talk themselves and the world into believing that science can be outwardly expanded through all kinds of dark concepts and mystical views and

59. Erman, "Paul Erman," 123.

60. According to Ohm, in *Ohms . . . Nachlass*, 145.

61. From 1822 to 1826 the physicist Wilhelm Vollmer lectured at Berlin University with Altenstein's encouragement on "different branches of physics, on heat and light, on electricity and magnetism, on statics and mechanics, on physical geography, and physical astronomy." Altenstein, according to Vollmer, had become interested in him because of his "mechanical skill," for Vollmer was making all his own physical apparatus for his lectures except for instruments lent to him by his former teachers, Fischer, Erman, the chemist S. F. Hermbstädt, and Thomas Seebeck. He also made apparatus for their cabinets and for the Berlin military and trade schools. He left Berlin in 1826. Vollmer to King of Hannover, 25 Mar. 1838, Listing Personalakte, Göttingen UA, 4/V b/108. Vollmer's situation in Berlin resembled Magnus's ten years later, which eventually resulted in a physics institute for Berlin University.

62. *Goethe's Naturw. Corr.* 1:178–79, 185.

63. Erman, "Paul Erman," 175.

64. Leopold von Henning to Goethe, 9 Aug. 1831, in *Goethe's Naturw. Corr.* 1:185.

65. C. L. F. Schultz to Goethe, 24 May 1823, in *Goethe's Naturw. Corr.* 2:294–96, on 295.

can inwardly gain [through them] a higher and more dignified character."[66] Fischer
was not even going to mention the "fantasies very fraught with [dangerous] consequences of the so-called nature philosophy"; he was troubled more by Goethe's attempt to reestablish optics on "dark, unclear, and mystical concepts." He said that
no thoughtful scientist had ever doubted "that all natural phenomena are based on
something infinitely deep, something mysterious," but the goal of science was to
discover what could be understood, what could be known, and to collect and arrange
it in a system.

The popularity of Henning's lectures was not matched by any new attraction in
the regular physics lectures during the first half of the 1820s. The established physicists Erman and Seebeck, who had put some distance between himself and Goethe
since joining the Berlin Academy as a full-time researcher,[67] devoted themselves to
research, Erman in his private laboratory, Seebeck at the academy. The prospects
for university physics generally improved when Alexander von Humboldt came to
Berlin in 1827 and began to make his bid in government circles for support for the
experimental sciences. The university was also, for the first time, making room for
new people in physics; in 1826 it acquired its first Privatdocent for physics, Moritz
Frankenheim, whose researches showed that he took his orientation from the established Berlin physicists. Frankenheim worked in Seebeck's field of thermoelectricity
and also (later mainly) in crystallography,[68] a field which Fischer considered of
"great importance."[69] A few years later, in 1829, Berlin University acquired two
new extraordinary professors of physics, Heinrich Wilhem Dove and Georg Friedrich
Pohl. In 1831, the year Fischer died and Ohm tried to get a position at the university, two more physicists, August Seebeck and Gustav Magnus, became Privatdocenten there. August Seebeck took over mathematical physics,[70] Fischer's field, and
Magnus at first taught technology,[71] but he soon set up a private physical laboratory,
which was the beginning of the Berlin physics institute.

Even after 1827 young physicists were drawn to Berlin or remained there after
completing their studies not primarily because of superior institutional or scientific
offerings, but because Berlin, as a large city with a corresponding number of secondary schools and as a royal residence with the attendant military and technical
schools, offered physicists more opportunities to earn a living than a university town
without these advantages. Young physicists there such as Dove, August Seebeck,
and Clausius continued in Erman's footsteps, sometimes with such financial success
that to accept a university professorship elsewhere might have meant a financial
setback for them. Dove, for example, who was not happy in Berlin during the early
years of his career, nevertheless turned down calls to university chairs at Dorpat,

66. Fischer, Lehrbuch 1:xii–xiii.
67. Moritz Seebeck to Goethe, 20 Dec. 1831, in Goethe's Naturw. Corr. 2:332.
68. Otto Lummer, "Physik," in Festschrift zur Feier des hundertjährigen Bestehens der Universität Breslau, pt. 2, Geschichte der Fächer, Institute und Ämter der Universität Breslau 1811–1911, ed. Georg Kaufmann (Breslau: F. Hirt, 1911), 440–48, on 442.
69. Fischer, Lehrbuch 1:74.
70. Planck, "Das Institut für theoretische Physik," 276.
71. A. W. Hofmann, "Magnus: Heinrich Gustav," ADB 20:77–90, on 79.

Jena, Bonn, and Freiburg.[72] In his refusal of the Freiburg chair, he took pains not to appear to be acting "meanly," to be weighing "the more and the less": despite scientific "deprivations of all kinds," "often despairing of ever succeeding," and despite sixteen years as a university teacher at the humiliating low salary of 200 thaler, he could not give up the large salary of 2000 thaler that he was able to accumulate from the several teaching positions he held in Berlin; he could not have received that much as an ordinary professor at a university elsewhere. It was an "illusory advantage" in certain respects, but since Dove had to support a family, it decided him in the end.

Though there were disadvantages to university physics teaching, for a physicist interested in research but lacking the means to finance it out of his own pocket, a chair of physics held at least the prospect of a laboratory and of research in physics at some level. Letters by applicants for the vacant chair of physics at Göttingen University in 1831 show what young physicists hoped for then. Weber, for example, mentioned the "many aids for scientific activity" that Göttingen had always offered its teachers and students and the "gain for my scientific endeavors that would come more easily through cooperation on related work—in Göttingen primarily through the influence of . . . Gauss . . .—than in an isolated position."[73] Seeber, already ordinary professor at Freiburg University, applied for the Göttingen chair for similar reasons: he wanted better physical apparatus than he had at Freiburg, and he wanted to be closer to other scientists. His colleagues at Freiburg, he said, not only neglected their science because of their involvements in "politics and matters of the state," but by meddling in politics they antagonized the government so that it refused to do anything to improve the university, including his conditions there. He, too, longed for a colleague who was "thoroughly trained in the natural sciences" with whom he "could talk over scientific subjects of a higher kind, which is of such great value for scientific work." Unlike Weber, Seeber was already familiar with the people and circumstances at Göttingen, for he had been Gauss's student.[74] His expectations of the Göttingen physics institute were more realistic than Weber's, but he knew that, because of the peculiar link between Göttingen University and the Göttingen Society of Sciences, research would be supported there.

For the first three decades of the nineteenth century, Mayer had the relatively enviable physics chair at Göttingen and was the first professor of physics there to be provided with physical apparatus. His predecessor, Georg Christoph Lichtenberg, as so many other physicists then and later, had acquired his own nearly complete physical apparatus consisting of the best instruments, which he had used in his lectures in the "auditorium" in his home. Lichtenberg sold his apparatus to the state for use

72. Dove to "Regierungs-Director," 31 Jan. 1844, Bad. GLA, 235/7525.

73. Weber to "Staats-Minister," 8 Feb. 1831, Weber Personalakte, Göttingen UA, 4/V b/95a.

74. Seeber to Göttingen U. Curator, 10 Jan. 1831 (mistakenly dated 1830), Weber Personalakte, Göttingen UA, 4/V b/95a. Weber wrote in 1837: "When I was entrusted with the direction of this institute 6 years ago, without having seen it before and without having been able to receive detailed information about it from an eyewitness, I trusted the generally recognized and highly praised generosity with which the institutes of the Georgia Augusta are equipped and cared for more than those of most other universities." Weber to Göttingen U. Curator, 20 Oct. 1837, Göttingen UA, 4/V h/16.

at Göttingen University, and after his death it was moved there, where Mayer set it up near the auditorium in which he gave his lectures. In addition to instruments and rooms, Mayer also received 100 thaler in annual funds to maintain and enlarge the collection, an amount he found adequate even for "those instruments and needs . . . caused by recent discoveries."[75]

Mayer used the apparatus for his two main lectures every semester, "experimental physics" and "physical astronomy, meteorology, and theory of the earth."[76] The range of his teaching with demonstrations is apparent from the catalogue of the university instrument collection that Mayer compiled in 1813: extending to 222 pages, it lists instruments not only under the headings expected for physics, such as "optics," "electricity," and "statics and mechanics," but also under, for example, "chemistry," "arithmetic," "geometry," "astronomy," and "physical geography."[77] Mayer added "considerably" to the collection after he had taken it over and proudly spoke of the latest beautiful additions: "an excellent large electrical cylinder machine made of blue glass and a large voltaic pile consisting of 300 five-inch pairs of plates of copper and zinc" that, under favorable conditions, could give "15 inch sparks."[78]

Through his control of this fine instrument collection, Mayer could dominate the teaching of experimental physics at Göttingen in a way that amounted to a limitation of the teaching freedom (Lehrfreiheit) of his colleagues. Even before Mayer came to Göttingen, J. C. D. Wildt, an extraordinary professor of mathematics who was encouraged by both Lichtenberg and Abraham Gotthelf Kästner, professor of mathematics, to devote himself to physics in the hope of succeeding one or the other of them, was struggling to accumulate and then to keep from his creditors his own physical apparatus for teaching experimental physics.[79] Wildt learned that attempts to force the ordinary professor of physics to share the physical apparatus were more disastrous than simply competing with him for students.[80] He announced lectures on "experimental physics" alongside Mayer's (adding that they were the "first half of his nature philosophy") and at the same time applied to the university curator for permission to use the physical apparatus. But that only resulted in hardening attitudes into rules and making enemies. Mayer protested to the government that if Wildt were to use the apparatus, it—and with it Mayer's health—would be ruined. "At all universities it has now been established that the professor of physics alone has the use of the instruments" necessary for lectures on experimental physics, Mayer de-

75. J. C. D. Wildt to Hannover government, 3 Apr. 1799, Göttingen UA, 4/V h/6. Hannover government to Christian Gottlob Heyne, 8 May 1799; Heyne to Hannover government, 23 May 1799; J. T. Mayer Personalakte, Göttingen UA, 4/V b/67. J. T. Mayer, untitled article about the Göttingen physical cabinet, Göttingische gelehrte Anzeigen, 1812, vol. 2, 1417–22.

76. Details of lectures offered at Göttingen University are taken from the Göttingische gelehrte Anzeigen, of which several volumes appeared every year; the lectures for the summer semesters can be found in the volume containing the March issues, usually the first, and the lectures for the winter semester were published in September, in the second or third volume.

77. "Catalog des physicalischen Apparates verfertigt von Johann Tobias Mayer im Jahre 1813," copied in 1831 by Weber, Göttingen UA, 4/V h/9a.

78. Mayer, untitled article about the Göttingen physical cabinet, 1419–20.

79. J. C. D. Wildt Personalakte, Göttingen UA, 4/V b/64.

80. Wildt's correspondence with Hannover government, Summer 1815, Göttingen UA, 4/V h/6.

clared in support of his contention that he had been assured sole access to and use of the apparatus. He prevailed.[81]

What was true for Göttingen in Mayer's time was or would soon be generally true for the German universities that could supply their professors of physics with state-owned physical apparatus and facilities.[82] If the professor of physics had exclusive right to the use of the instruments, then his colleagues who also wanted to teach experimental physics could only do so if they had a considerable fortune; that is what it took to acquire a collection of instruments sufficient to illustrate all parts of physics and to provide a place both to display them and to teach with them.

Mayer's objection to Wildt's request concerned the use of the instruments for lectures only. The problem came up again—to look ahead—when professors of physics employed their first scientific assistants, and then it concerned the use of the instruments for both teaching and research by young physicists who had official access to the institute. When the Göttingen Privatdocent for physics Gustav von Quintus Icilius talked his way into Weber's institute as his first scientific assistant in 1852, Weber employed him under the condition that he "not be permitted to use the institute with the collections and the auditorium for his independent lectures as Privatdocent or for his special private research, which would lead to the most unpleasant collisions and would be absolutely impossible to reconcile with the order of the physical institute."[83]

Physics instruction at Göttingen—classified there with the "natural sciences" and apart from the "mathematical sciences," which included astronomy—then consisted primarily of the "big show" lectures on "experimental physics" taught by the ordinary professor of physics. At Göttingen, as elsewhere, in these lectures the professor gave a qualitative account of the various theories of physics and at appropriate points in the lecture, or when his apparatus allowed it, proved the theories by experiments. The more frequent and the more splendid the experiments, the more attractive were the lectures. Even Weber, who was not given to a prodigious use of experiments in lectures, reminded the university curator in 1837 that it was time to improve the lecture apparatus in the interest of the "glamour" of the experimental physics lectures.[84]

Mayer added lectures on the latest researches in the theory of light in 1813 and repeated them every two or three years until 1829. They grew out of his interest in Étienne Louis Malus's experiments, which he had confirmed and extended by his

81. Mayer to Hannover government, 2 Aug. 1815, and drafts of replies, Göttingen UA, 4/V h/6. When not pushed, Mayer might even offer to let a colleague use part of his collection. Mayer to Göttingen U. Curator, 13 July 1829, Göttingen UA, 4/V h/8.

82. For example, at Heidelberg, Jakob Friedrich Fries had obtained the "indispensable" sole and "unlimited" use of the physical cabinet in 1813. Fries to Rector of Heidelberg U., 25 Mar. 1813; granting of request by Baden Ministry of the Interior, 17 Apr. 1813, Bad. GLA, 235/3057.

83. Weber to Göttingen U. Curator, 14 Feb. 1852, Göttingen UA, 4/V h/21. Gustav von Quintus Icilius took on all the tasks of an institute assistant that were to become standard: assisting in laboratory courses, helping in research, taking care of the instruments, and so on. But he did not get paid for this work. His recompense was the opportunity to gain otherwise unavailable experience in handling physical apparatus for teaching and research. He was not allowed to use the apparatus for his own work.

84. Weber to Göttingen U. Curator, 20 Oct. 1837, Göttingen UA, 4/V h/16.

own experiments.[85] He lectured on the new experiments on light separately, dividing his audience into small groups so that everyone could see, which was impossible in the big experimental physics lectures.[86] When these specialized lectures on light were taken over by the Privatdocent for mathematics, Moritz Stern, he was limited to teaching the "theory" of the subject.

All during Mayer's tenure, and during Weber's first period at Göttingen, 1831–37, there were no extraordinary professors or Privatdocenten for physics, but there were a good many for mathematics. With only a few exceptions, the Göttingen mathematicians offered courses on "applied mathematics," especially mechanics and optics. Like Stern, mathematical students at Göttingen, well aware of Mayer's seventy-eight years and declining health, qualified to become Privatdocenten ("habilitated") and offered a flurry of lectures on "theoretical" physics.[87] One of them, C. F. Eichhorn, offered a "mathematical practicum," which was to deal with "pure mathematical physics, to be presented in written treatises by the auditors." After Weber had succeeded Mayer, these Privatdocenten either took jobs elsewhere or returned strictly to mathematics.

With Weber's arrival in Göttingen, physics teaching underwent two important changes. Even in his first comprehensive report to the university curator on the physical cabinet, Weber mentioned the apparatus that could be used "for the purpose of practical exercises and instruction in experimenting."[88] He thought that "after a general survey of the whole area of physics it would be useful for those who want to dedicate themselves exclusively to the natural sciences, such as physicians, chemists, pharmacists, and also for gymnasium teachers in the subject of mathematics, to find opportunity to practice experimenting and making reliable observations." By his fourth semester of teaching he had arranged for the necessary space, and he offered "practical-physical exercises in the academic laboratory" for the first time.[89] Thereafter it was a standard course along with the big "experimental physics" lectures. The second change had to do with Gauss, who from 1817 had regularly lectured on the use of the theory of probability in "applied mathematics" and on the

85. J. T. Mayer, untitled article about a paper he read at a meeting of the Göttingen Society on 21 Nov. 1812, "Über die Polarität des Lichtes," *Göttingische gelehrte Anzeigen*, 1812, vol. 2, 1977–88, on 1978.
86. Review of the fourth edition of J. T. Mayer's *Anfangsgründe der Naturlehre* (1820), by Mayer himself, in *Göttingische gelehrte Anzeigen*, 1820, vol. 3, 1619–20.
87. "Theoretical" physics here means, first of all, physics lectures in which no experiments are shown.
88. Weber to Göttingen U. Curator, 24 Apr. 1832, Göttingen UA, 4/V h/15.
89. Weber's financial report for 1833–34, dated 12 Sept. 1834, Göttingen UA, 4/V h/8: Weber said that he was making progress in his plan to use the physics institute "not only . . . as a collection for viewing, but as a workshop in which uninterrupted scientific work will be carried on." It is important to note that as yet and for some time to come only the professor's own research would be done there. The comparison with Justus Liebig's use of the chemical laboratory—Weber himself spoke of his "workshop" as being like a chemical laboratory in the sense that it should be continuously used for scientific work—shows that physics still lacked the counterpart of simple methods of analysis that allowed chemistry professors to use students in scientific investigations. Weber soon found comparable employment for some of his students in earth-magnetic observations, so that the development of earth magnetism can be seen as one of the ways of introducing the practice of student research in the German physical institutes. Weber to Göttingen U. Curator, 16 Oct. 1835, Göttingen UA, 4/V h/16.

theory and use of geodesic instruments, subjects valuable to physicists. But only after Weber's arrival did Gauss begin to lecture on theoretical physics proper, specifically on the subjects he worked on with Weber: the theory of magnetism in 1832 and 1834, and the theory and methods of earth-magnetic observations in 1835 (and, that year, on the related subject of the applications of the method of least squares).

Introduction to the World of Physics through Early Textbooks

A student consulting a lecture catalog in the early nineteenth century would, as a rule, find entries of the following kind: "*Experimental Physics* presented by Hr. Hofr. Mayer, *according to the sixth edition of his textbook*, at 4 o'clock." (The latter italics are ours.) Most of the university physicists still "read" their lectures according to a textbook, usually their own, especially after they had a professorship. Textbooks tended to be their first long publications.

In the early nineteenth century, textbooks were counted among the "literary," creative works of their authors, and as such they counted when physicists were considered for promotions or calls to other universities. But to be given favorable notice, they had to be distinguished in some way from the many other textbooks on the same subject produced by all the other university teachers (and secondary school teachers, who could also hope for university appointments), who were also working for promotion or for enhanced reputations, which might earn them larger salaries and more favorable working conditions. So textbooks might express an author's particular view of his field[90] or criticize methods and interpretations of physics by other authors,[91] or they might place the author's own research within his field of physics, thereby associating himself with physicists of greater, even great, renown.[92] The textbooks also had to claim that they made up the deficiencies of existing textbooks.[93] Since the authors expected to make money with their textbooks, when they asked for raises in salary, they sometimes explained that one thing or another had prevented them from adding to their income by writing a textbook.

The earliest textbooks we discuss here were written when Immanuel Kant was still alive. Almost to a man, the German university physicists declared themselves

90. Some textbook authors announced their particular approach to the field even in the titles of their works; for example, Muncke's *System der atomistischen Physik nach den neuesten Erfahrungen und Versuchen* (Hannover, 1809); Fries's *Entwurf des Systems der theoretischen Physik; zum Gebrauche bei seinen Vorlesungen* (Heidelberg, 1813); or Parrot's *Grundriss der theoretischen Physik*; Fischer's *Lehrbuch der mechanischen Naturlehre*; Andreas von Baumgartner and Andreas von Ettingshausen's *Die Naturlehre nach ihrem gegenwärtigen Zustande mit Rücksicht auf mathematische Begründung*, 6th ed. (Vienna, 1839); and Friedrich Hildebrandt's *Anfangsgründe der dynamischen Naturlehre* (n.p. [Erlangen], 1807).

91. Fischer wanted to produce a textbook "in as rigorously scientific a form . . . as the nature of the subject permits" (*Lehrbuch* 1:vi). He thought that the existing textbooks lacked clarity.

92. Mayer discussed his experiments on heat—"done with the greatest possible precision"—alongside the work of Pictet, Aimé-Lair, Socquet, Saussure, Dalton, Gay-Lussac, Deluc, Lambert, Smeaton, and others, as well as Rumford later. Mayer, *Anfangsgründe* (1805), 239, 263–64, 269. In the fourth edition (1820) of this work, he discussed his work on atmospheric pressure in gases alongside contemporary work on the problem by Gay-Lussac and Dalton.

93. Fischer, *Lehrbuch* 1:vi–xii; Kastner, *Grundriss* (1810), 2:vi–vii.

influenced by his work.[94] The move away from Aristotelian textbooks, which had occurred not long before,[95] to textbooks that stressed experience had been followed by renewed attention to the nature of objective knowledge and particularly to the process by which experience becomes scientific knowledge. Jakob Friedrich Fries not only wrote full-length epistemological treatises, but he also dealt with the "relationship of the natural scientist to nature" in his textbook outline of theoretical physics. Kastner opened his textbook with a discussion of the "general condition of investigating man." Mayer gave a full discussion of epistemology in his *Anfangsgründe der Naturlehre*.[96] In later textbooks, discussions of this subject were much shorter, eventually taking up no more than a paragraph or even a sentence, but they still appeared.[97]

Mayer—to begin with his textbook—traces the path to scientific knowledge from sense perceptions to the concepts formed of things and their relationships and then to the action of the mind on these concepts.[98] Natural science is limited by what is accessible to the senses; any parts of it that are the product of thought have to be verified in experience. Natural science generalizes subjective, individual understanding and experience, which is possible because the sense organs of all human beings are constituted alike and because the nature of thought is the same for everyone. Our intellectual constitution, our mind, influences this generalization of experience. The mind has developed the laws of motion entirely out of itself; these laws have been successfully applied to the objects of sensual experience in so many ways that natural science is largely pure or applied theory of motion.

On the main epistemological points and their implications for science, Kastner's treatment is much like Mayer's.[99] He differs mainly in that he introduces the idea of God or the "highest idea of being," in which the regularities of natural phenomena and through them our empirical knowledge of nature have their origin; once having introduced the idea, he immediately banishes it to the realm of philosophy. Epistemology is another matter, and Kastner believes that its importance for natural science is not fully appreciated. The philosopher and the physicist will only succeed in showing the true correspondence between mind and nature when the philosopher becomes more interested in exhibiting nature than his systems and when the exper-

94. They demonstrated their acceptance of Kant's work in their professional activities as well as in their publications. Erman, for example, was an enthusiastic follower of Kant, teaching his philosophy from the 1790s on, even when his preference for Kant drew the criticism of his superiors. Erman, "Paul Erman," 46–51. C. H. Pfaff, at Kiel University from 1797, occupied himself eagerly with Kant's philosophy in 1794. J. F. Pfaff, *Sammlung von Briefen*, 78.

95. In 1752, Freiburg University had been ordered by its government "to close the gate in experimental physics through which enter all ridiculous questions that are not appropriate for a philosopher," for which purpose it was "absolutely prohibited" to include in physics "the unfounded teachings (which cannot be confirmed by experience)" of Aristotle. *Aus der Geschichte der Naturwissenschaften an der Universität Freiburg i. Br.*, ed. E. Zentgraf (Freiburg i. Br.: Albert, 1957). The government decree is quoted on p. 11.

96. Fries, *Entwurf*, 15. Kastner, *Grundriss* (1810), 1:1–29; in the 1820 edition he revised this discussion, 1:1–22. Mayer, *Anfangsgründe* (1805), 1–18.

97. Gustav von Quintus Icilius, *Experimental-Physik. Ein Leitfaden bei Vorträgen* (Hannover, 1855), 1.

98. Mayer, *Anfangsgründe* (1805), 1–8.

99. Kastner, *Grundriss* (1810), 1:2, 6–7.

imenter accepts the view that one must start from the idea of oneself in studying the phenomena. The scientist has to realize that what he investigates in nature is always something that corresponds to his own nature; he studies heat or color, for example, because his senses produce these properties of bodies.

In Fries's *Die mathematische Naturphilosophie*—the title must be understood as referring to Newtonian natural philosophy—we see a philosophically sophisticated physicist link Kantian ideas to empirical science and to its highest development in Newtonian mathematical physics.[100] For Fries, natural knowledge is the product of our experience and of the mathematical laws we acquire through our a priori understanding, the faculty that Kant was first to posit and make the subject of critical investigation: in brief, scientific knowledge incorporates experience, mathematics, and philosophy. Fries imagines the creation of a physical theory to proceed as follows. With his senses, the physicist perceives properties of bodies such as heat, pressure, color, or sound, which require an explanation that is not found in experience. To arrive at the explanation, the physicist has to use "pure" mechanics; that is, general concepts such as space, motion, or force, and the laws relating them to one another, all of which are a priori concepts, according to Kant (and Fries). Pure mechanical theory is not itself an explanation of physical phenomena; it states which laws of motion the hypothetical explanations necessarily obey, which motions and forces are possible, which are simplest. The assumptions of the hypothetical explanations now become the basis for mathematical constructions that will, if successful, constitute the desired theory. The physicist must as a last, essential step verify the theory by comparing it with experimental results. Fries makes it clear that empirical, "scientific" physics must never allow "pure theory" to strike out on its own.[101]

Early nineteenth-century physics textbooks took up another philosophical issue. Kant's dynamical view of nature evidently provoked physicists sufficiently that they could not leave out of their textbooks discussions of philosophical world views. Muncke said that "soon after its founding by the immortal Kant, the system of dynamical physics has almost acquired such an authority" that nobody dared to defend the "atomistic system" any more.[102] That was an exaggeration, but textbook writers directed less attention to the atomists than they did to Kant and Schelling, and to Kant they devoted more positive comment than to Schelling. Schmidt discussed both the atomistic and the dynamical world views with reserve but also without ridicule, even though in the preface he claimed that he left out of his lectures and his text all "philosophical speculations on physical subjects."[103] Mayer discussed

100. Jakob Friedrich Fries, *Die mathematische Naturphilosophie nach philosophischer Methode bearbeitet. Ein Versuch* (Heidelberg, 1822).

101. Fries, *Die mathematische Naturphilosophie*, 9–11, 29–32, 610–11.

102. Muncke, *System*, v.

103. Schmidt, *Handbuch*, iv. To give an example of Schmidt's attitude: he looked at gravity first from the point of view of Lesage's atomism and concluded that atomism does not explain gravity since it refers it to another inexplicable force; then he noted that the dynamical point of view of a physical attractive force is at least "as admissible, especially if one does not, as it were, carry this force into the bodies that are already assumed to be given but, like the dynamical system [of thought], seeks to derive

the "dynamical nature philosophy" of Kant and Schelling and the "atomistic nature philosophy" of G. L. Lesage, Pierre Prévost, and Jean-Baptiste de Lamarck, and he pointed to the extended discussion he would give in his lectures on Kant's *Metaphysische Anfangsgründe der Naturwissenschaft* and Schelling's *Ideen zu einer Philosophie der Natur*.[104] Some authors even made these views the basis of their textbooks. Kastner organized his textbook for experimental physics and Fries his for theoretical physics on the basis of the dynamical view of nature. Muncke, in his alarm at what he saw as the growing dominance of Kant's dynamical physics, wrote his textbook to "show that the atomistic view," namely, the view that in physics one deals with matter made up of material particles and not of forces, "can also be applied to the newest investigations."[105]

It was appropriate for a physicist to discuss philosophical views of nature, provided he did not make improper use of them in his practical work in physics and did not introduce ideas negating the objectivity of nature. The views the physicists discussed were not at all like the "false nature-philosophical dreams," to quote Fries.[106] In a lecture on attraction and cohesion, Mayer pointed out, with reference to the dynamical interpretation of nature, that whether or not matter is the product of the interaction of forces, the physicist has to distinguish force from matter, in which and on which it acts, if he is not to fall into useless dreaming or leave common uses of language too far behind.[107] When the speculations about nature touched on a field of particular interest to Mayer, he could show impatience; "playing with forces in the dynamical nature philosophies" and playing with atoms in the "corpuscular system,"[108] he said, created "arbitrary fictions," and neither view set limits where the mind has to stop in explaining natural phenomena "if it is not to lose itself in incalculable labyrinths."[109] Parrot, in his textbook on theoretical physics, wrote that "everything reasonable and logical that can be said about a dynamical system, Boscovich, Priestley, [and] Kant have said, and it can serve to compose for oneself at best a meaningful fiction beyond experience. But to want to deduce the laws of nature from this fiction, to tell nature a priori how it should behave—that would be to make a satire of the human mind."[110]

As with epistemological discussions, discussions of philosophical views of nature underwent changes in physics textbooks. In their use of the dynamical view of nature, physicists found themselves too near German nature philosophy in language

the phenomena of matter themselves from forces, whose nature will of course always remain inexplicable for us" (pp. 76–77).

104. Mayer, *Anfangsgründe* (1805), 9–12.

105. Muncke, *System*, v.

106. Fries asserted that the unacceptable nature philosophy "most often" originates not in philosophy but in the improper use of the methods of the experimental physicist, [the improper use] of inductions and hypotheses, which "seduces" those who do not know the rules for using these methods into "false nature-philosophical dreams." Fries, *Entwurf*, 8.

107. Mayer, *Anfangsgründe* (1805), 36.

108. Mayer, *Anfangsgründe* (1805), 232.

109. Mayer, *Anfangsgründe* (1805), 12, 13, 231, passim. Quote on p. 13.

110. Parrot, *Grundriss* 1:iii–iv.

not to have to dissociate themselves from it. Whereas Kastner had repeatedly used the word "attractions" in section headings in his textbook of 1810, in the 1820 edition he left out section headings and clarified his view of nature as the interaction of forces: nature, he wrote, acts out of necessity, not because of some inner striving, which could only be willed. Explanations of natural phenomena involving such a striving were "reprehensible" to him.[111] Similarly, Fries insisted on a strict separation of the laws of physical existence from considerations of the mind.[112] Brandes, who mentioned philosophical views only briefly in his textbook of 1830, thought that the dynamical view, when taken beyond statements about the extension and density of matter to the definition of matter as nothing but the conflict of forces, led to "indissolvable darkness." The physicist does not dare enter into such questions, especially since the "gain resulting from them, either with respect to complete reliability or with respect to practical fruitfulness, has not quite shown itself to be valuable."[113]

Except for matters of emphasis, the physicists' quarrel was not with philosophy as a whole but only with a part of it, *Naturphilosophie*, which they often did not even dignify with the name of philosophy. The heated campaign of the physicists against the nature philosophers did not stop with denunciations in their textbooks. These were faint echoes of what they said in private letters, reviews, addresses, periodicals, and elsewhere. Experimental physicists such as Erman and Mayer with important academic publications at their disposal, L. W. Gilbert as editor of the *Annalen der Physik*, and even Goethe struggled against the injury to German physics and to German science in general that, as they believed, nature philosophy had done. Praising E. F. F. Chladni's *Acoustics*, Goethe wrote to Friederich Schiller that Chladni "belongs . . . among the blessed who don't have the faintest notion that there is such a thing as nature philosophy."[114] Struggling for research support in Berlin and therefore closest to the seat of conflict with nature philosophy, Erman looked in anger on attempts to vindicate Prussia's military defeat by Napoleon through intellectual renewal by means of idealistic philosophy: "Twenty lost battles do not bring us as much disgrace as this business of deceptions and lies in science," he told his students.[115] Nature philosophy had made inroads in the Prussian Academy of Sciences, and Erman was bent on discrediting it. In 1811 he proposed as a prize question of the academy that the nature philosophers' concept of polarity be tested by an investigation that "is to be conducted *purely empirically* and *independently of all speculative opinions* about the fundamental nature and the absolute existence of matter."[116] Erman continued his struggle into the late 1820s, when he still had to endure Hegel's open contempt for the exact natural sciences and the consequences for Berlin physics of Hegel's influence with the Prussian ministry of culture.[117] When

111. Kastner, *Grundriss* (1820–21), 1:2.
112. Fries, *Entwurf*, 7.
113. Brandes, *Vorlesungen* (1830), 1:13.
114. Goethe to Schiller, 26 Jan. 1803, in *Goethes Werke*, pt. 4, vol. 16 (Weimar, 1894), 170.
115. Erman, "Paul Erman," 140.
116. Erman, "Paul Erman," 141. Italics added.
117. Erman, "Paul Erman," 240.

Pohl, one of the few physicists who espoused nature philosophy, criticized Ohm's work in 1828, Schweigger wrote to Ohm that he was loath to give Pohl the satisfaction of having his opinions acknowledged by scientists.[118] Another adherent of nature philosophy, Henrik Steffens, having moved in 1832 from his position as professor of physics and nature philosophy at Breslau University to Hegel's philosophy chair in Berlin, recorded the scientists' view of his philosophical direction without bitterness: "The natural scientists [at Berlin] expected little of me, and although they began to see that I possess some scientific knowledge and received me in a friendly manner, they were nevertheless firm opponents of nature philosophy. The great discoveries in physics on the one hand, then in geology, and finally in comparative physiology had throttled every germ of speculative views, and nature philosophy was considered an arbitrary, fantastic game, which perhaps here and there could stimulate poetic but never scientific interest."[119] The full vocabulary of contempt for nature philosophy entered the obituary that the *Annalen der Physik* published for its editor Gilbert in 1824:

> Nothing embittered him [Gilbert] more than the shallow, superficial treatment of the sciences, the endless hypothesizing, the mystical point of view, and the poetry that had entered science. As little opposed as he was to the latter [i.e., poetry] in everyday life, as hostile he was to it when, leaving its domain, it wanted to carry the dreams of the imagination into science. And who could blame him? What true admirer of the . . . exact sciences must not agree with him on this with all his soul? This mixing of fiction and truth, of poetry and science, this playing with empty, half-true analogies, this guessing and suggesting instead of knowing and understanding has ruined our good name for us Germans abroad, has led us away from thorough science, and has brought us to believing that we know everything, while we have fallen behind in real knowledge.[120]

The main purpose of physics textbooks was to present contemporary physics, not to educate future physicists. Often intended for the self-instruction of "friends of science," they gave detailed accounts of important new experiments that the

118. *Ohms . . . Nachlass*, 90. For his part, as it happened, Schweigger was criticized for his ideas. Anxious to keep the experimental sciences uncontaminated by "mysticism," natural scientists even scorned ideas that originated in historical interest rather than in nature philosophy. In 1828, Schweigger's interest in research combining philology and natural science was received with derision. He believed that the combination of the modern scientist's knowledge of nature and the philologist's research tools would facilitate the study of the ancient mysteries, the depositories, in his view, of the ancients' knowledge of nature, and thus would be helpful in discovering how much the ancients had known about nature. Schweigger proposed to lecture on the subject before the annual meeting of the German Association, where following French academic custom, he intended to request a commission made up of classical scholars and of physicists to examine the matter. "They found this idea . . . *arrogant even* (whereas in France one has exactly the opposite view when someone wants to submit something for examination)," he wrote to Ohm, "and Leopold von Buch (who had *heard* of it only *by chance*) was, as is his manner, terribly rude." Schweigger to Ohm, 15 Dec. 1828, Ms. Coll., DM, 693.
119. *Idee und Wirklichkeit einer Universität. Dokumente zur Geschichte der Friedrich-Wilhelms-Universität zu Berlin*, ed. Wilhelm Weischedel (Berlin: Walter de Gruyter, 1960), 333.
120. *Ann.* 76 (1824): 468–69.

readers might want to try. The more "scientific" textbooks contained in addition, and to the same end, extensive descriptions of the latest barometers, thermometers, and other measuring instruments and physical apparatus. The largest part of a physics textbook was given over to the many new theories of the so-called imponderables: heat, light, electricity, galvanism, and magnetism.

The new work in physics that Mayer added to his textbook from the second edition in 1805 to the last editions in the 1820s introduced, among other names, those of P. S. Laplace, C. L. Berthollet, John Dalton, J. J. Berzelius, Chladni, L. J. Gay-Lussac, Count Rumford, A. M. Ampère, H. C. Oersted, and Malus[121]— names that conjured up great physical and chemical advances. Textbook writers conveyed to their readers the sense of living in a time of rapid change in the understanding of physical nature. Decade by decade that understanding was "so much expanded through the zealousness of the natural scientists," Schmidt wrote, "that it was often difficult for me to connect the new with the old in such a way that the whole need not be recast."[122] Kastner's second edition of his *Grundriss der Experimentalphysik* reveals how current advances could affect the writing of a physics textbook. The first volume was published in 1820, but the second volume, which began with galvanism, was delayed until 1821. Meanwhile, the news of Oersted's discovery of electromagnetism had reached Kastner, who immediately set about to include it in his already completed but not yet printed chapter on galvanism. This led him to work on electromagnetism himself as well as learn everything he could about it from the writings of others. When he sent the hastily reworked manuscript to the publisher, he included along with the discussion of electromagnetism the proposal of a new name for the new phenomenon, "Siderismus" ("electromagnetism" being awkward and "Oersted" not going well with "ismus").[123] In 1837 C. H. Pfaff summed up his whole career in terms of the great advances in physical understanding between Alessandro Volta and Oersted:

> Only a few years are lacking from the *half century* within which one of the greatest discoveries in the natural sciences [Volta's] expanded from its first small beginning to such a [great] extent, within which the whole of chemistry has found its own theory, the bond that was long sought in vain between electricity and magnetism has been tied, and the pulsing of the great life of nature as well as of the microcosm has become more understandable.
>
> The dawn of my studies dedicated to nature coincided with the dawn of that new theory; with enthusiasm I then greeted the new light, and my inaugural dissertation, which announced it, I brought as the firstborn of my muse to the alter of science. I think of myself as having lived to see the bright day that that dawn promised, even though meanwhile the evening of my own life has fallen.[124]

121. Mayer, *Anfangsgründe* (1820), 22–23, 76, 81–82, 148, 277; (1823), 516, 541, 546, 551, 555.
122. Schmidt, *Handbuch*, iii.
123. Kastner, *Grundriss* (1820–21), 2: x–xi.
124. C. H. Pfaff, *Revision der Lehre vom Galvano-Voltaismus mit besonderer Rücksicht auf Faraday's, de la Rive's, Becquerels, Karstens u.a. neueste Arbeiten über diesen Gegenstand* (Altona, 1837), ix–x.

The "theories" that textbooks such as Mayer's, Kastner's, and Schmidt's, the main German textbooks, presented side by side for each of the phenomena of current interest were hypothetical explanations of the *nature* of the phenomena. To discover the "nature" of heat, light, electricity, magnetism, galvanism, and even of phenomena that already had a different, mathematical theory, such as elasticity,[125] was the general problem on which many of the German experimental physicists worked. The task of the physicist, according to Kastner, even though it involves observations and experiments, is to gain "insight into the nature of things"; "experiences seen as an end in themselves, without having conclusions derived from them about the nature of the observed object, are of no use to science."[126] Some statements from other textbooks bear out this concern. Schmidt, remarking on the nature of heat, observed that physicists "are still arguing whether one is to think of the unknown cause of the . . . phenomena [of heat] as a substance of a particular kind, a *heat substance,* or a mere modification of the bodies, which according to some is to be sought in the motion of the particles of the body, according to others in the motion of a generally distributed fluid (the ether), or finally (as some recent dynamicists would have it) in the changed relations of the fundamental forces of matter."[127] Mayer wrote similarly that the "opinions of scientists are still very divided on what actually constitutes the principle that excites heat."[128]

In their accounts of the theories of physics, textbook writers were wary of claiming too much for them. "Theories of heat are nothing but hypotheses," Schmidt wrote, "whose inner value may only be judged by [their] degree of probability and by their usefulness to the experimenting natural scientist in unveiling the truth."[129] On the nature of magnetism, Kastner could only discuss "a forerunner to a future theory instead of a complete theory," which he thought was not yet possible.[130] In electricity, optics, and elsewhere in physics, Mayer simply acknowledged that scientists were still very much in the dark.[131] "You will, I hope, not scold me that I have not stated a decisive view about the nature of light," Brandes wrote in 1831.[132]

To a large extent, it was possible to ignore the confusion of contradictory hypothetical explanations and to take a different route in physics. In connection with recent work on electromagnetism, especially Ampère's, Fischer said that what is important is not to decide between qualitative explanations of the phenomena, but to find the "*laws of the phenomena* with mathematical certainty."[133] Again, in con-

---

125. Kastner, *Grundriss* (1820–21), 1:126–27. Kastner was the physicist who saw the need to find the "nature" of elasticity.

126. Kastner, *Grundriss* (1810), 1:19; (1820–21), 1:24.

127. Schmidt, *Handbuch,* 257.

128. Mayer, *Anfangsgründe* (1805), 228.

129. Schmidt, *Handbuch,* 257.

130. Kastner, *Grundriss* (1820–21), 1:448. Kastner's equanimity may have been based on his understanding that natural science does not, strictly speaking, *explain* the phenomena, that it does not reduce them to their essence. He said that since science is never complete and is always being added to, "every theory is useful only for a time" (p. 29 in 1810 ed.; p. 22 in 1820–21 ed.).

131. Mayer, *Anfangsgründe* (1805), 483, passim.

132. Brandes, *Vorlesungen* 2:356.

133. Fischer, *Lehrbuch* 2:113.

nection with the various explanations of light, he said that what is important is not that any one of these is true but that *"we know the laws* that govern the phenomena." He added that "in this, the human intellect has succeeded almost as perfectly as [it has] with regard to the laws of gravitation."[134] Although the intellect can know only the laws of natural forces and not their "inner nature," Fischer said, we can find "pictures" that connect the laws. But we must not confuse the pictures with the nature of the thing itself, and if we find more than one picture we must be free to use the one or the other without believing that we have solved the "puzzle."[135] Fischer was not the only textbook writer to identify physics with the study of laws in this way.[136]

Fischer's approach to physics was signaled by the title he gave to his textbook, *Lehrbuch der mechanischen Naturlehre.* He wrote it, he said, because existing texbooks of physics had defined their subject carelessly, including chapters on chemistry, for example, on the grounds that the dividing line between physics and chemistry could not be clearly defined. His fellow textbook writers had blamed on their subject what was due to their inability to make distinctions between concepts. Subjects such as electricity could indeed be discussed in both chemistry and physics because certain aspects of electrical phenomena were chemical in nature and others physical; but if concepts were properly defined, there could be no question about which aspects of electricity belonged where. What belonged to physics proper were investigations of natural phenomena on the basis of the laws of mechanics. These included not only the observable motions of bodies, but also the unobservable motions within bodies—even though we have no clear idea of what it is that moves—of heat, light, electricity, and so on.[137]

Not all early textbook writers extended mechanics throughout physics as Fischer did, but all of them admired, for example, Laplace's mechanical theory of capillarity, which they presented without its mathematical development. By the mid-1820s, the fields of the "imponderables" had been made the subject of mathematical, largely mechanical theories, obtaining, in Ohm's words, the "right of citizenship in physics [although] not without objection from individuals with the right to vote."[138] These theories—the work of the great French physicists A. J. Fresnel, Ampère, S. D. Poisson, and others—were then being introduced to German physicists by Gilbert in the *Annalen der Physik,* by G. T. Fechner in his translation of J. B. Biot's textbook on experimental physics and in his own book on electromagnetism,[139] and by

134. Fischer, *Lehrbuch* 2:123. Also see Brandes, *Vorlesungen* 3:516: he defended Ampère by pointing out that his mathematical presentation is what is important. To the objections having to do with the nature of the circular currents in Ampère's theory, he replied that "one can probably not say anything except that wherever we want to investigate the inner nature of bodies, we encounter similar darkness."

135. Fischer, *Lehrbuch* 2:259–60.

136. Parrot, *Grundriss* 1:4–7. "We know nothing of the causes of phenomena," Parrot said. "The purpose of all physics is to discover the special and general laws of nature . . . and to reduce the natural phenomena to them; the latter is called: to explain the phenomena" (pp. 6–7).

137. Fischer, *Lehrbuch* 1:vii–viii, 4–5.

138. Georg Simon Ohm, *Beiträge zur Molecular-Physik,* vol. 1, *Grundriss der analytischen Geometrie im Raume am schiefwinkligen Coordinatensysteme* (Nuremberg, 1849), vii.

139. Jean Baptiste Biot, *Lehrbuch der Experimental-Physik, oder Erfahrungs-Naturlehre,* translation of

several others in their treatises on special areas of physics, such as C. H. Pfaff's on electromagnetism, and they had to be included in German textbooks on physics.

An extremely competent presentation of the recent kind of physical theory appeared, though still without advanced mathematics, in the textbook by the Austrian physicists Andreas von Baumgartner and Andreas von Ettingshausen in 1839.[140] Ettingshausen wrote the "actual mathematical part," which was the start of his use of physics textbooks to teach the methods of mathematical physics; five years later he published his *Anfangsgründe der Physik,* in which he presented all areas of physics founded on mathematics.[141] He had already contributed to mathematical physics by reporting on it and by inviting others to write about it for the journal he edited with Baumgartner, *Zeitschrift für Physik und Mathematik.*

In the textbook with Baumgartner, Ettingshausen used the section on optics to show how a mathematical physical theory is made. After discussing the phenomena of light, he treated light in such a way as to give "insight into the causes of the phenomena, that is, an explanation of the phenomena." The theory of light, "more than any other part of physics, offers an opportunity to get to know the development of research." From an ignored, if not despised, hypothesis, the wave interpretation of light had become a "model of a physical theory" and now occupied "one of the highest places in science."[142] To develop the theory, Ettingshausen did not begin with the phenomena of light, but with an assumption about the medium in which light waves are propagated, the ether. Assuming that the ether is a system of material particles, he applied analytical mechanics to study their vibrations. He showed that the vibrations could all be reduced to simple vibrations "in which . . . the ether particles describe either straight lines or circular or elliptical orbits." He then explained how such motions are expressed in mathematical terms.[143] Only after this long detour through the mechanics of the ether did he return to the discussion of light: "The application of the theoretical definitions to the phenomena of light is as simple as it is satisfactory"; each aspect of light corresponds to some theoretical property of the ether.[144] Ettingshausen looked to theory for further progress in optics: "Since the wave theory of light-phenomena is based only on the laws of oscillating motion, it is understandable that its further development depends not on new experiences but on advances of theoretical mechanics, which in turn are determined in part by those of mathematical analysis."[145]

Upon reading Ettingshausen, a student of physics who had been exposed to traditional textbooks and lectures would have been struck by the shift in emphasis from the direct study of phenomena to an abstract theoretical approach drawing on

---

3d French ed. by G. T. Fechner, 4 vols. (Leipzig, 1824–25). Gustav Theodor Fechner, *Elementar-Lehrbuch des Elektromagnetismus, nebst Beschreibung der hauptsächlichsten elektromagnetischen Apparate* (Leipzig, 1830).

140. They collaborated on the sixth edition of Baumgartner's *Naturlehre.*
141. Andreas von Ettingshausen, *Anfangsgründe der Physik* (Vienna, 1844).
142. Baumgartner and Ettingshausen, *Naturlehre,* 373.
143. Baumgartner and Ettingshausen, *Naturlehre,* 382.
144. Baumgartner and Ettingshausen, *Naturlehre,* 387.
145. Baumgartner and Ettingshausen, *Naturlehre,* 410.

a system of laws and mathematical deductions. To the "friend of science," Ettings-hausen's treatment of physics did not promise the fluent reading, or probably the enjoyment, he was used to. But it made clearer than earlier treatments had that at least part of the purpose of textbooks—whatever else it might be—was to instruct students in the methods of building physical theories.

2

German Physicists before 1830

Research in Physics

While textbooks were still being used to publish original research, another form of publication had been developing that shared the task of bringing out new research results, the journal. The most important physics journal in Germany was the *Annalen der Physik und Chemie*, which was long established by the time Ohm began publishing in it. Founded in 1790, and already having had three editors and four titles, it was now entering a period of relative stability. Neither editor nor title would change over the next half century. During this time the *Annalen*, as no other journal,[1] would come to "unite in itself the entire physical life in Germany"[2] and give a "true and complete picture of the advances and transformations of the physical disciplines represented in it."[3] Since we use the contents of the *Annalen* extensively for our portrayal of these advances and transformations and of the physical life in Germany, we introduce this important source here.

The founder of the journal, F. A. C. Gren, professor of physics and chemistry at Halle University, wanted to make German readers familiar with recent discoveries in the "mathematical and chemical parts of natural philosophy [*Naturlehre*]." He called for serious originial work rather than entertaining lectures, for which, he said, there already existed a crowd of journals; he set the tone in the first volume by publishing an original work of his own, an "examination of the new theories of fire, heat, fuel, and air."[4] Most of the rest of the volume was taken up by Gren's abstracts

1. While Ohm distributed his papers among several journals including the *Annalen*, physicists from his time on tended to publish or republish most of their articles in the *Annalen*.
2. Karl Scheel, "Die literarischen Hilfsmittel der Physik," *Naturwiss.* 16 (1925): 45–48, on 46.
3. Gustav Wiedemann, "Vorwort," *Ann.* 39 (1890), first four unnumbered pages.
4. F. A. C. Gren's foreword to the first volume (1790) of *Journal der Physik*, his original title for the *Annalen*. His paper was "Prüfung der neuern Theorien über Feuer, Wärme, Brennstoff und Luft," 3–44, 189–201. In this paper Gren disputed Adair Crawford's theory of heat and combustion, which he called a "lazy philosophy" (vol. 1, 1790, p. 30). Gren was critical of theories based on too few experiments, which only revealed the experimenters' narrowness of view and ignorance of the many already established laws of nature (pp. 26–27). Gren recognized the importance of theories: the mind, he wrote, requires "theories of natural phenomena that bring unity and cohesion to our conceptions of them" (p.

from other independent periodicals and from society and academy transactions. These journals were beyond the means, if not beyond the linguistic and technical capacities, of the doctors, apothecaries, and even the handful of professors who made up much of the initial list of subscribers to Gren's journal.[5]

After Gren's death in 1798, his journal—with his understanding of its demanding labor and with the new title he had intended for it, the *Annalen der Physik*—along with his teaching assignments passed to Gilbert, a young colleague of his at Halle. Recognizing that the richest source of material for the journal would continue to be foreign journals,[6] Gilbert undertook an enormous work of translating, for which he was well prepared. Being of Huguenot descent, he spoke excellent French, so that on his obligatory scientific pilgrimage to Paris he was received in an especially friendly way by Laplace, Biot, and other scientists. Since he spoke English, Dutch, and Italian as well, he could also read the physics publications in those languages.[7] In addition, German researches by the "best physicists" would stand honorably in the *Annalen* beside the best foreign work such as Henry Cavendish's experiments on the density of the earth with their wonderful "exactness."[8]

Gilbert's editorship of the *Annalen* established his fame, but it left him little time for anything else. After twenty-five years of it, he said that the *Annalen* had swallowed up all of his other plans. Apart from his translations there, his physical writings were limited to a few original papers. If, as they say, he lacked mechanical skills, feared explosions in his laboratory, and in general failed as an original experimenter, he was still a good teacher, and for this reason he was a good editor.[9] In effect, through his journal, he taught physics throughout Germany,[10] giving shape to his subject by grouping researches on like themes, by selecting from current work the most significant, by translating—and more than translating, rewriting—foreign

---

208). He used his journal to uphold the phlogiston theory of chemistry against Lavoisier's new chemistry, defending his own theory of the negative gravity of phlogiston against the criticism of J. T. Mayer, then the professor of mathematics and natural philosophy at Erlangen University. Gren claimed that his theory of negative gravity was more comprehensive and simpler than the antiphlogistic explanations. Mayer, whose work and criticism always hinged on the question of whether or not a theory or hypothesis was in conflict with the laws of mechanics, soon persuaded Gren on mechanical grounds to retract his theory of negative gravity (p. 200), but Gren continued to defend phlogiston until his conversion to the new chemistry in 1794 (vol. 8, 1794, p. 14). The decision between the old and the new chemistry was the central theme of Gren's journal at first. It began to be displaced by the theme of animal electricity after Galvani's experiments were reported in the journal in 1792. Throughout the *Journal der Physik*—in the articles, extracts, book reviews, letters to the editor, and annotations by the editor—rival theories in physics, chemistry, and physiology were compared in light of the results of experiments. Both theories and experiments were needed to achieve what Gren said was the "goal" of the natural philosopher: the establishment of the general laws of nature (vol. 1, 1790, p. 25).

5. From the subscription list at the beginning of the first volume, we see that there were fewer than a hundred subscribers, among them fourteen professors.

6. L. W. Gilbert, "Vorrede," *Ann.* 1 (1799), first three pages.

7. Obituary of Gilbert, *Neuer Nekrolog*, vol. 2, 1824 (Ilmenau, 1825): 491, 493.

8. Gilbert, "Vorrede."

9. *Neuer Nekrolog* 2:484, 488.

10. Gilbert's colleagues who wrote texts to teach physics sent their readers to Gilbert's accounts of recent physics. See, for example, Fischer, *Lehrbuch* 2:81–82, 120. Mayer referred the reader to the "excellent annals of physics of Prof. Gilbert" in his announcement of the third edition of his *Anfangsgründe* in the *Göttingische gelehrte Anzeigen*, 1812, vol. 2, 1273–74.

work, by commenting on it extensively in footnotes, and in general by constantly guiding his readers, as a proper teacher does, through the demanding material. He was concerned that his readers could follow the papers, so although he himself was mathematically proficient, he omitted most mathematical discussion from the journal.[11]

German "friends of physics" were presented with a good deal of contemporary French physical theory through Gilbert's "free adaptation" of it. A particular French theory that was to stimulate much interest in Germany, Laplace's capillarity theory of 1806 and 1807, Gilbert promptly included in the form of Biot's treatment of it. He and Brandes followed this up two years later with a complete account of Laplace's original papers.[12] The electrodynamic theory that Ampère presented to the Paris Academy in late 1820 Gilbert brought out in translation in two long sections in the *Annalen* early the next year—without a single mathematical formula.[13] Gilbert's version contained the physical laws along with his summary of the contents and his advice to the reader not to be deflected from this "great and important" work by the author's overly general "obscure discourse" at the beginning.[14] Later that same year, Gilbert included excerpts from two more papers by Ampère, exhorting the reader not to "skip" them, for they were "as interesting as important." He responded to the complaint of several readers that they could not get any further with this subject because they had no overview of it: "That at least may not be the result of studying these 'Annalen,' in which I have not only adapted the papers of foreigners myself but have also been at pains to bring the greatest possible clarity to the presentations and for each issue to find such a selection that the . . . papers interlock to a certain degree and each promotes the understanding and interest of the others."[15] That was Gilbert's accurate description of the personal stamp he put on the *Annalen* during the twenty-five years he was its editor.

After Gilbert's death in 1824, as expected, a number of German physics professors wanted to take over the editorship,[16] but none of them got it. Instead it went to a Berlin student who had published only one paper several years before. The student, Johann Christian Poggendorff, persuaded the publisher of the *Annalen* that he was the man to continue it by telling of his earlier plan to launch a new "physi-

11. Obituary of Gilbert, *Ann.* 76 (1824): 468–69.

12. Ferdinand Rosenberger, *Die Geschichte der Physik*, vol. 3, *Geschichte der Physik in den letzten hundert Jahren* (Hildesheim: G. Olms, 1965), 99.

13. A. M. Ampère, "Ueber die gegenseitigen Wirkungen, welche auf einander ausüben zwei electrische Ströme, ein electrischer Strom und ein Magnet oder die Erdkugel, und zwei Magnete," *Ann.* 67 (1821): 113–63, 225–58.

14. Gilbert's annotations, *Ann.* 67 (1821): 113–14, 225–26.

15. Gilbert's remarks, *Ann.* 69 (1821): 65.

16. Gilbert had become ordinary professor of physics at Leipzig University in 1811 and moved the *Annalen* with him. He was succeeded in his chair by Brandes, who, according to Poggendorff, wanted to become editor of the *Annalen* as well, as did Kastner in Erlangen and Muncke in Heidelberg. Emil Frommel, *Johann Christian Poggendorff* (Berlin, 1877), 70. All three of these prospective editors were authors of several textbooks, some of them major ones. In the same year that Poggendorff succeeded in taking over the *Annalen*, Kastner began editing the *Archiv für gesammte Naturlehre*, and in the following year Brandes along with others began bringing out a new edition of *Gehler's Physikalisches Wörterbuch*. The editing of the *Annalen* was a type of literary activity that commonly extended a professor's work.

cal-chemical" journal, which he now wanted to "unite" with the *Annalen* and that way avoid harming science by needlessly multiplying its journals. As he envisioned it, his journal was to cover principally physics and chemistry, "in their entire scientific compass," and mathematics, "which can never be given enough consideration"; it was also to cover the fields that touch on these three, by which Poggendorff meant most of the other physical sciences and their applications, which taken all together constituted a "whole" whose borders "cannot be marked off precisely."[17]

Poggendorff's actual, more realistic journal came out as the *Annalen der Physik und Chemie*. In announcing it, he explained that physics and chemistry in their present state cannot be separated. This view, he said, reflected a direction of research that was strong in France and Sweden and that was recently introduced in Germany. The German chemists Heinrich Rose and Eilhard Mitscherlich, who were associated with it, were original influential supporters of Poggendorff's venture. In the years to come, much of the experimental work appearing in the *Annalen* belonged to this chemical-physical direction.[18]

The *Annalen* excluded pure mathematics and accepted mathematics in any other form only insofar as it made experiments more precise or linked experimental facts through the principles of mechanics.[19] Poggendorff's initial thought of including mathematics expressed an association with physics parallel to that of chemistry; that there was a felt need for a journal for mathematical work in physics at just this time is shown by the founding of two journals almost immediately after Poggendorff began editing the *Annalen*. In 1826, the Austrians Baumgartner and Ettingshausen brought out the *Zeitschrift für Physik und Mathematik*, through which they hoped to build mathematical and physical interest, as Gren, Gilbert, Schweigger, and A. F. Gehlen had built physical and chemical interest through their journals.[20] The *Journal für die reine und angewandte Mathematik*, begun the same year by the Berlin mathematician A. L. Crelle, included mechanics under "pure mathematics" and mathematical physics under "applied mathematics." With Crelle's *Journal*, Germany now had its own journal for mathematics, one of the last areas of learning to be without one.[21]

Although Poggendorff's *Annalen* was not as close to mathematics as these two contemporary journals were, it contained a fair amount of mathematical physics, some of it highly mathematical. From the start of Poggendorff's editorship, the mathematically most capable physicists in Germany—among them Ohm, Weber, Franz Neumann, and, soon, August Seebeck—published their work in the *Annalen*, in most cases almost exclusively. Their choice of journal agreed with Schweigger's opinion that mathematical physics should be reserved for the *Annalen* (for Poggen-

17. J. C. Poggendorff to J. A. Barth, 16 Mar. 1824 and 3 Apr. 1824. Quoted in Frommel, *Poggendorff*, 25–26, 31–35, on 32.

18. Wiedemann, "Vorwort."

19. J. C. Poggendorff's foreword to the first volume of *Annalen der Physik und Chemie* (1824), v–viii.

20. Andreas von Baumgartner and Andreas von Ettingshausen, "Vorrede," *Zs. f. Phys. u. Math.* 1 (1826): 1–4. At first, the journal's quarterly issues were divided into "physical" and "mathematical" departments, the latter containing both pure mathematics and mathematical physics and mechanics.

21. A. L. Crelle's foreword to the first volume of *Journal für die reine und angewandte Mathematik* (1826), 1–4.

dorff's as it had been for Gilbert's) or for the new *Zeitschrift für Physik und Mathematik*.[22]

Schweigger explained to Ohm, who had submitted a rebuttal of Pohl's criticism to Schweigger's *Journal für Chemie und Physik*, how scientific journals expected mathematics to be used. Schweigger gently criticized Ohm's "qualitative" style, which he did not find suitable for a science journal, even a "qualitative," primarily chemical one like his. In his opinion, any paper on physics containing mathematical considerations, wherever published, could be expected to be as clear as possible on the mathematics; it might give examples of calculations, if possible, and it should certainly give the formulas used in the calculations or at least a reference to them if they were published elsewhere. If the paper withheld the information about the mathematics, the reader might well believe that the author did not intend to inform him at all but only wanted to tease him, as a "qualities-man" (*Qualitätler*) would. To reassure Ohm, he added that the only opinion of Ohm's work that mattered was that of the French "mathematicians." (The important German physicists were then only just beginning their publishing careers, so Schweigger had no mathematical physicists to point to but the French.)[23] The suggestion was that journals such as the *Annalen* should help define the field.

Schweigger's *Journal* was a natural place for Ohm's galvanic studies, since they belonged equally to chemical and physical interests. Ohm published there and also in Kastner's *Archiv*. The *Journal* and the *Archiv* were two of the three rivals of the *Annalen* that "fell silent" during the first years of Poggendorff's editorship; the third was the *Zeitschrift für Physik und Mathematik*. Crelle's *Journal* continued, but its strongly mathematical direction largely removed it from any serious rivalry, and with satisfaction Poggendorff could say on the fiftieth anniversary of his editorship that the *Annalen* had become the "only organ of physics for Germany, which, thank God, it has remained until the present day."[24]

For Poggendorff, as for Gren and Gilbert before him, the task of editing the *Annalen* was onerous. He continued their practice of including extensive translations of foreign research; at the start, he had told his publisher that his qualifications as editor included a knowledge of languages as well as a knowledge of the physical sciences.[25] He occasionally gave summaries of work on particular subjects, and he also annotated, though he did less of it than his predecessor Gilbert. He rigorously excluded all "personal elements,"[26] restricting polemics between researchers to a minimum. In passing from Gilbert to Poggendorff, the *Annalen* became the severely scientific journal it remained, as detached from personality as can be expected of a journal in which complete control is invested in one man.

People who knew Poggendorff were impressed by the sense of order that filled his whole being.[27] It equipped him for editing, and in time it also allowed him to

22. Schweigger to Ohm, 15 Dec. 1828, Ms. Coll., DM, 693.
23. Schweigger to Ohm, 15 Dec. 1828.
24. From Poggendorff's talk at the fiftieth anniversary of his editorship on 28 Feb. 1874, reprinted in Frommel, *Poggendorff*, 68–72, on 71.
25. Poggendorff to J. A. Barth, 3 Apr. 1824, quoted in Frommel, *Poggendorff*, 31–35, on 33.
26. Wiedemann, "Vorwort."
27. W. Baretin, "Johann Christian Poggendorff," *Ann.* 160 (1877): v–xxiv, on ix.

become one of the most prolific authors of original research to appear in his journal. His editing always came first, and from early on he foresaw, correctly, that his editing was to be his greatest contribution to physics in Germany. After ten years of editing the *Annalen,* he wrote to Oersted:

> From my own experience I know only too well the circumstances that keep one from scientific investigations, although in my case they are of a different kind than in yours. I have often regretted that I am only the archivist of science; but just as often I have felt the necessity of devoting all my energy to this office if I want to discharge it with complete success, which in my opinion I have not yet succeeded in doing. The only thing that compensates me for the chance of being able to contribute something directly to the advance of science is the knowledge of the recognition of my journalistic efforts by men like you; and this knowledge helps me greatly in keeping from tiring in my efforts, which otherwise would be understandable even if not justified, given the excessive abundance of materials that flows in daily from all sides.[28]

Soon after this, Poggendorff became a regular member of the Prussian Academy of Sciences. He was already an extraordinary professor at Berlin University, but unlike his predecessors he did not seek an academic career, and he later turned down many offers from universities. He was financially able to pursue his editing of the *Annalen* and his researches undisturbed by the demanding official duties of an ordinary professor.[29]

The German researchers who published their work in the *Annalen,* and sometimes elsewhere, were frequently employed as teachers. About half of those who published on physics there in 1800–1830 were professors at universities. The rest were independent researchers, academicians, or physicists just beginning their teaching careers. The university professors included Schweigger, Erman, Mayer, Pfaff at Kiel, and Schmidt at Giessen. Representing the last of the eighteenth-century tradition, the prominent independent researchers included Chladni, Thomas Seebeck in the early years of his career, Johann Wilhelm Ritter for a time, Peter Riess who went on working independently in Berlin long after 1830, and the universal giants Goethe and Humboldt. Julius Konrad Yelin and Ritter worked at the Munich Academy; Poggendorff and, in his last years, Thomas Seebeck, worked at the Berlin Academy. Carl Wilhelm Boeckmann taught at the polytechnic school in Karlsruhe. The young university researchers who had not yet reached chairs before 1830 included Weber, Ohm, and Fechner.[30]

We distinguish between independent and university researchers, but the dearth

28. Poggendorff to H. C. Oersted, 5 Mar. 1834, in *Correspondance de H. C. Örsted avec divers savants,* ed. M. C. Harding (Copenhagen: H. Aschehoug, 1920), 2:487.

29. Baretin, "Poggendorff," ix; Frommel, *Poggendorff,* 36.

30. A contemporary, Brandes, included in his *Vorlesungen* (1830–32) an account of the researches of the Germans Fechner, Ohm, Thomas Seebeck, Paul Erman, C. H. Pfaff, Bohnenberger (who was known for his instruments), Weber, Chladni, G. G. Schmidt, Muncke, Schweigger, Humboldt, Ritter,

of research facilities and of financial support for research at the universities during this period made the university physicists all but "independent" with respect to their resources, too. The main benefit they derived from their positions was an income; to do significant research in addition to their teaching, they had to have private means[31] along with uncommon interest and initiative.[32]

Independent or not, physics researchers pursued a calling for which there was then no set course of training or regular career. Usually they started out by preparing for one of the traditional fields: Chladni and Goethe in law, Erman in theology, Pfaff, Seebeck, and Fechner in medicine, Schweigger in philology, Humboldt in mining, and Poggendorff in pharmacy. Later they were drawn to physical research, often by the example of other scientists; some of the researchers we discuss here served as examples to some of the others. Chladni's exclusive devotion to physical research—to "a purely scientific life," as a contemporary called it—influenced Weber, for example; and Humboldt drew young men such as Ritter and Riess to physics through his enthusiasm and often practical support.[33] Others were drawn to physical research by a great discovery announced while they were preparing for another field;

---

and in a negative remark Pohl. But he gave much more space to the researches of French physicists than to those of the Germans.

Earlier textbooks on physics also regularly mentioned Goethe's physical researches, both to criticize and to praise, but after Goethe's death the long accounts of his theory of color, sometimes extending to several pages, stopped appearing.

31. As research materials became more elaborate and more expensive, fewer and fewer private fortunes sufficed: "The necessary aids" for the scientific investigations "have gradually increased extraordinarily," Muncke wrote in 1817, "and rarely even prosperous private persons can afford to buy them with their own means." Muncke to Baden Ministry of the Interior, 1 June 1817, Bad. GLA, 235/3057.

32. One prominent physicist who did not have his own research equipment and yet could expect to be furnished with it never attained a university professorship as a result: he was too eminent in his state of Baden. The physicist was Carl Wilhelm Boeckmann, teacher at the gymnasium in Karlsruhe from 1802 to 1821 and director of the ducal collection of physics instruments, with which he also gave public lectures. Boeckmann befriended Rumford, who invited him to take part in his investigations in Munich and stimulated him to do research on heat theory on his own. Later, following the discoveries by Oersted, D. F. J. Arago, Ampère, and others, Boeckmann studied the Voltaic pile and the magnetic and electrodynamic effects of currents. Rumford got Boeckmann offers of positions, for example, at the University of Landshut (soon to be the University of Munich), which strengthened Boeckmann's financial situation at Karlsruhe. Also, in 1805 and again in 1816, Heidelberg University considered Boeckmann for its chair of physics, aware that Boeckmann was inclined to accept a call. They considered him by far the best candidate for the Heidelberg chair, describing him as a "known, very skilled physicist with a beautiful, lively lecturing [style], recognized and praised by the scholarly world." Indeed, in 1816 Boeckmann had just received a prize from the academy at Harlem for his researches, which was seen as a further recommendation. Both times, however, Boeckmann's "circumstances" at Karlsruhe stood in the way of an appointment at Heidelberg; he was too well paid there and had a well-housed and well-supported instrument collection at his disposal. In addition, in 1805, the government seized the opportunity to save a salary at Heidelberg, when Fries offered to take on physics without pay in addition to his previous appointment. In 1816 Boeckmann was already getting the salary at Karlsruhe that Heidelberg could offer under the best of circumstances. As expert adviser to the Baden government, Boeckmann could influence the career of a university physics professor such as Wucherer. Document regarding the appointment of a successor to Georg Adolph Succow (Suckow), 7 Dec. 1816, Bad. GLA, 235/3135. Lehmann, "Karlsruhe," pp. 230–34.

33. C. G. Carus, Lebenserinnerungen und Denkwürdigkeiten, nach der zweibändigen Originalausgabe von 1865/66, ed. E. Jansen (Weimar: Kiepenheuer, 1966), 1:264; K., "Riess: Peter Theophil," ADB 28:584–86; Robert J. McRae, "Ritter, Johann Wilhelm," DSB 11:473–75, on 473.

C. H. Pfaff, for example, was drawn by Volta's discoveries, Thomas Seebeck by Volta's and Malus's.[34]

Just as there was no prescribed plan of study, there was no prescribed access to the means to do research. Whether the young physicist pursued a university career in the hope of rising some day to the directorship of a physical cabinet or whether he derived his income from some other source, to begin with he had to provide for his space, apparatus, books and periodicals (which were expensive), and perhaps even assistants. With a beginning university teacher's small income from student fees and an occasional extraordinary stipend of 100 thaler, the researcher's "laboratory" was likely to be his room and his research equipment was certain to be modest. There was always the chance that the senior physicist might invite him to work in his laboratory or lend him some instruments, but it rarely worked that way. The other principal opportunity for a beginning physics researcher to earn a living and, perhaps, at the same time to be near instruments was to teach at one of the secondary or technical schools that had such equipment; Schweigger, Erman, and Ohm tried this combination with varying degrees of success. Then there was always the possibility of pooling resources. C. H. Pfaff, for example, at the beginning of his scientific pursuits, "felt a great want, the want to be able to ask nature herself for advice"; carried away by the experimental work he saw in the great laboratories in Paris on a visit there in 1801, he together with five other young men rented a laboratory of their own.[35]

Materials and facilities for research remained a problem even after a university physicist had been given access to a physical cabinet, for he was not encouraged to view the purpose of the instrument collection as the furthering of his private research.[36] He might use what instruments he had, but new acquisitions had to be justified first of all by teaching needs. Since the institute budget was small and the instrument collection was expected to have roughly equal strength in all parts of physics for lecture demonstrations, it was difficult for the director to acquire the apparatus he needed for research on a particular subject. Often the best he could do was to follow the latest developments in physics no matter what the subject. That helped him in his teaching, but it also meant that his researches were usually diverse.

For the independent researcher, too, after he had used what private means he could spare—an inheritance or dowry as in Ritter's, Humboldt's, Chladni's, and Seebeck's cases, or family wealth as in Goethe's and Riess's—the problem of materials and facilities remained. Thomas Seebeck, for example, speaks in his letters of

34. Kuno Fischer, *Seebeck,* 9; C. H. Pfaff to his brother, the mathematician J. F. Pfaff, Stuttgart, 1792, in J. F. Pfaff, *Sammlung von Briefen,* 105, also 78.

35. C. H. Pfaff to J. F. Pfaff, Paris, 1801, in J. F. Pfaff, *Sammlung von Briefen,* 159–60.

36. In Baden, the government told Heidelberg University "that we consider *discovery* in science as the *business* of the *scholar,* but not as that of the *teacher,*" which is what university professors were. Lehmann, "Karlsruhe," 257. Lehmann assumed that the resistance offered by the physics professor at the Karlsruhe Polytechnic to having the state's physics cabinet, which was under his direction, be made the polytechnic's was due to his understanding that he would no longer be able to use the cabinet for research once it belonged to a *teaching institution,* whereas research was the declared purpose of the *state* cabinet.

years of idleness owing to lack of laboratory facilities. To earn money, Chladni made frequent lecture tours to all parts of Europe, taking time away from his researches. Weber deplored Chladni's independence when he reflected on what Chladni might have accomplished under better conditions.[37] What the independent researchers could and usually did do that distinguished them from most university physicists was to specialize in their research: Chaldni specialized in acoustics and meteorites, Seebeck in optics and thermoelectricity, Ritter in electricity, and Riess in electromagnetism.

Erman, who as a university professor was tied down by teaching but who still gained a reputation for research, illustrates the difficulties of the researcher in Germany in the early nineteenth century. From the beginning of his teaching career, Erman collected materials for research and carried out experiments in his home at the military school, trying all the while to keep up with foreign research despite the growing burdens of his several teaching jobs. For his research, the Institut National in Paris awarded him its "galvanic" prize of 3000 francs in 1807; he was the first of four scientists to receive it (the others being Davy, Gay-Lussac, and Thénard). Erman, according to Humboldt, was regarded by Laplace and other leading French scientists as the "first physicist of Germany,"[38] but none of this recognition earned him any support in Prussia for his research, which he continued to carry out under the same conditions as before. Understandably, he saw nothing desirable in combining a university position with research: "Most often fate is stingy with the invaluable gift of independence," he said. His ideal was a "life dedicated solely to knowledge . . . alien to all drives of passion, free from all ordered (by others) business, insatiable only with regard to knowledge, inexhaustible only in research."[39] He advised scientists to reduce their personal material needs as much as possible to achieve that precious independence. Not having had it himself, he thought he had not produced the important scientific results he might have if he had had better working conditions. When the London Royal Society elected him Fellow in 1827, he wrote to his son of his feeling of shame at being honored undeservedly: "This for me! And yet signed Davy, Brown, Everard, Home, Herschel, Wollaston, Kater, in short the whole Olympus! Perhaps these magnates have the *scientia media* of the theologians and know what I *could* have achieved under favorable circumstances, but as it was, this was without exception the unhappiest moment of my life; it was just as if I had been stealing!"[40]

Always aware of the important new physics, particularly new foreign physics, Erman wrote to Oersted in 1835 that, still burdened with his various duties, as "a conscientious teacher of physics" he had his hands full just keeping up with the advances following upon the work of giants such as Oersted, Faraday, and Fresnel.

37. Thomas Seebeck to Goethe, 25 Apr. 1812 and 11 Dec. 1819, in *Goethe's Naturw. Corr.* 2:317, 331; Wilhelm Bernhardt, *Dr. Ernst Chladni, der Akustiker* (Wittenberg, 1856); Eugen Lommel, "Chladni: Ernst Florens Friedrich," *ADB* 4:124–26; Wilhelm Weber, "Lebensbild E. F. F. Chladni's," in *Wilhelm Weber's Werke*, vol. 1, *Akustik, Mechanik, Optik und Wärmelehre*, ed. Woldemar Voigt (Berlin, 1892), 168–97, on 172.
38. Erman, "Paul Erman," 114, 181.
39. Erman, "Paul Erman," 198.
40. Erman, "Paul Erman," 251.

And a year later: "I have never left off thanking God that he let me live at the same time as Volta, Oersted, and Faraday, and now Melloni, too."[41]

Like Erman's efforts to keep up with the new work, most German physics research consisted of confirming, varying, and extending experiments reported from abroad. It dealt for the most part with subjects that were then receiving the most attention from physicists generally: electricity above all, but also magnetism and heat. We can get an idea of the character of their work by looking at one subject they cultivated intensively, electromagnetism. Our main source is the account C. H. Pfaff wrote four years after Oersted's discovery, describing the work that followed.[42]

One problem German researchers took up in connection with electromagnetism was to determine the effects of their instruments or apparatus on the observed phenomena: Schweigger, Schmidt, and Yelin worked on the influence of the Voltaic apparatus on the motions of the magnetic needle; Yelin, Poggendorff, and Boeckmann worked on the influence of the composition of the solid conductors, and C. H. Pfaff and Poggendorff on that of the composition of the fluid conductors.[43] A second, related problem they worked on was the effects of multiplying the electromagnetic action by coiling the wire, the principle of a new instrument, the multiplicator. Schweigger, an inventor of the multiplicator, used it to show the effect of the direction of the electric current on the motions of the magnetic needle; Poggendorff, a co-inventor, studied the effect of different numbers of coils on the strength of the electromagnetic action; Pfaff considered theoretically the action of the multiplicator, which depends on the spatial relations of the electric current and magnetic needle rather than on the electrical properties of the conductor.[44]

German researchers studied the problem of the relationship between the chemical process in Voltaic apparatus and the magnetic motions it gives rise to. This problem appealed to those who wanted to show a connection between "chemism" and magnetism, for they thought the magnetic needle might prove to be a more sensitive reagent than all previous ones. It also appealed to those who, conversely, wanted to show that there is no connection between chemism and magnetism; for as Pfaff pointed out, not just galvanism, which always involves a chemical process, but other electricity too produces magnetic reactions.[45]

Generally speaking, the problem of the connections between the parts of physical science interested German researchers. Erman, Thomas Seebeck, C. H. Pfaff, and Yelin all tried to determine if galvanism and electricity are the same.[46] Erman, who was the first to observe electroscopic tension in a moist conductor closing a Voltaic pile,[47] provided the "main foundation" of Ohm's work a quarter century later, as Ohm acknowledged.[48] Independently of Ampère, Erman worked on another

41. Erman to Oersted, 1 Aug. 1835 and 2 Apr. 1836, in Oersted, *Correspondance* 2:318–19.

42. C. H. Pfaff, *Der Elektro-Magnetismus, eine historisch-kritische Darstellung der bisherigen Entdeckungen auf dem Gebiete desselben, nebst eigenthümlichen Versuchen* (Hamburg, 1824).

43. Pfaff, *Elektro-Magnetismus,* 71–77, 91, 95.

44. Pfaff, *Elektro-Magnetismus,* 71, 102, 108, 115.

45. Pfaff, *Elektro-Magnetismus,* 71, 78–79.

46. Pfaff, *Elektro-Magnetismus,* 182–83.

47. Eugen Lommel, "Erman: Paul," *ADB* 6:229–30.

48. Erman, "Paul Erman," 60.

problem suggested by Oersted's discovery, which was to determine the effect of magnetism on the motion of an electric conductor, furthering the link between electricity and magnetism.[49] Thomas Seebeck established thermoelectricity, connecting electricity with yet another part of physics.[50]

Although in the first decades of the nineteenth century experimental methods of research were sometimes opposed to mathematical methods, German researchers did not, on the whole, take sides, and they admired work that used both methods successfully. They were, however, wary of a mathematical physics that acquired a life of its own, independent of experience, one that claimed secure knowledge of nature in advance of experiment and observation. In short, research "guided by theory" was commended,[51] while research relying on the "magic power of analysis in solving all problems" was not.[52] Muncke cautioned readers of *Gehler's Physikalisches Wörterbuch* that there is no such thing as a mathematical physics in which the mathematics is in itself sufficient to discover the laws of nature: the laws are always found "through observations and experiments that must be given first." In recent times, French physicists—or, as many Germans preferred to call them, mathematicians—had valued mathematics in physics "to an exaggerated degree." (He acknowledged that many German physicists did, too, because they did not want to be accused of not knowing any mathematics.) It was true, he said, that mathematical physicists had given certain areas of physics excellent mathematical treatments that would forever stand as masterpieces in the mathematical literature, for example, Leonhard Euler's and J. L. Lagrange's treatments of sound and J. B. J. Fourier's of heat, but they had not explained the "nature and behavior" of these physical phenomena.[53]

German researchers were wary of highly mathematical work in physics for another reason: its abstractness, its lack of *Anschaulichkeit*. As it seemed not to allow for any kind of image, its results could not be grasped by any of the senses, and so it could not be empirically verified. Lagrange was criticized most often in this regard as the "calculator" who had eliminated images. "What good is a mechanics without figures, such as Lagrange's?" Kästner asked J. F. Pfaff in 1798: "I have not found any application of Lagrange's *Mechanics* yet."[54]

C. H. Pfaff's attitude toward theory, specifically electromagnetic theory, was that of the practicing physicist: he was interested in methods that worked. First, he expected a theory to establish a "principle of unity" for all phenomena belonging to the same class. Second, he cautioned that all theories dealing with phenomena that are not directly observable should be regarded as only "similes"; to understand the actions of the imponderable substances, for instance, the physicist has to compare them to the actions of directly observable substances. Without giving up one for the

49. Pfaff, *Elektro-Magnetismus*, 135.
50. For example, Kuno Fischer, *Seebeck*, 9.
51. In 1803 Gilbert criticized experimental work that had been "done blindly," and he commended Erman's because it was "experimenting guided by theory." Erman, "Paul Erman," 108.
52. In this remark to J. F. Pfaff, Parrot had in mind especially the French physicists and especially Laplace. J. F. Pfaff, *Sammlung von Briefen*, 180–81.
53. Muncke, "Physik," 508–12.
54. J. F. Pfaff, *Sammlung von Briefen*, 222, 216, respectively.

other, Pfaff distinguished mathematical theories of physical phenomena from physical theories.[55] Mathematical theories ignore the nature of the phenomena, the proper subject of physical theories. The mathematician conceives of electromagnetic phenomena, for example, only as "various modifications of motions," which he seeks to describe by a fundamental equation. If he is a "deeply inquiring mathematician who is practiced in calculations," he may find the equation but not the "secret source" of the phenomena. By contrast, the physicist probes deeply with his physical theory, seeking to present the phenomena in their "large, general connection with all of nature." The "true physical explanation" is, for Pfaff, at the same time a mathematical one: "it may not stop at showing only *in general* the inner nature of the phenomena and their mutual dependency, but it must derive the influence of all circumstances and their variations on the quantitative [aspects] of the phenomena from the nature of the forces themselves. In fact, from a certain point of view of physics, all of nature becomes simplified to form and motion, and from that point of view every physical explanation becomes necessarily—the further it advances—a more and more purely mathematical one."[56]

At the turn of the nineteenth century, Mayer foresaw that as the parts of physics became subject to mathematical treatment, they would be handed over to the mathematicians.[57] Some thirty-odd years later, Brandes foresaw much the same progression: if the work of such scientists as Fourier, Ampère, and Poisson were any indication, he said, then one would probably soon have to consider the theories of heat, electricity, and magnetism as "branches of applied mathematics," just as mechanics and optics already were.[58] In between Mayer's and Brandes's predictions, German physicists had begun to carry out researches that would bear them out. The work and careers of Ohm and Weber, who differed from their fellow researchers mainly in ability, introduce our theme: theoretical physics.

Careers and Theories in Physics

In 1831, at the close of the period we treat in this chapter, Wilhelm Weber became ordinary professor of physics. In his late twenties then, he had already given good evidence of his talent for research; his earliest work represented measuring and mathematical physics at its most exacting. We discuss here his researches on wave phenomena, which led to his recognition and rapid advancement.

Weber received his original impetus to work in science from home. For a time his family lived in the house of the Wittenberg professor of medicine and natural history, whose cabinet was well known in scientific circles.[59] Living in the same

55. C. H. Pfaff, *Elektro-Magnetismus*, 199, 200–201.

56. Pfaff, *Elektro-Magnetismus*, 201.

57. Mayer, *Anfangsgründe* (1805), 17.

58. Heinrich Wilhelm Brandes, "Mathematik," in *Johann Samuel Traugott Gehler's Physikalisches Wörterbuch*, vol. 6, pt. 2 (1836): 1473–85, on 1477.

59. Christian August Langguth's cabinet contained instruments useful for instruction in physics and mathematics as well as in natural history and medicine. *Göttingische gelehrte Anzeigen*, 1811, vol. 2, 1240.

house was the independent researcher Chladni, who became a close friend of the Webers.[60] Most important, Wilhelm's older brother Ernst Heinrich was drawn to science and was, in Wilhelm's words, "my only tutor."[61] The same year, 1821, that Ernst Heinrich became professor of anatomy at Leipzig University, he and the seventeen-year-old Wilhelm began their exhaustive experimental research into the mechanics of waves.

The Webers' immediate stimulus to study waves was an observation Ernst Heinrich made when pouring mercury between bottles: the mercury's surface resembled the "sound figures" that Chladni had observed in fine sand strewn on vibrating plates of glass or bronze. The Webers' more general stimulus was the new interest in waves prompted by Fresnel's work from 1815 on the wave theory of light. In response to this work, which the Webers followed closely,[62] the wave theory was cultivated in optics, but there was little parallel new work on wave phenomena in other parts of physics such as acoustics and hydrodynamics. Propagating and standing waves had long been studied mathematically, but the simplified assumptions of the theories did not always correspond to the complex physical facts of waves.[63] Euler, Daniel Bernoulli, and other early mathematicians had studied the simplest type of standing waves, which, the Webers pointed out, was hardly ever observed in nature. Existing theories of waves had little empirical foundation; acoustics, for example, had been almost the exclusive domain of mathematical studies before Chladni, and the experimental study of waves in water had only just been touched on.[64] Nicolas T. Bremontier's experiments, for example, were carried out in the ocean under conditions that could not be controlled. To improve on this, the Webers set up a 190-foot trough for the controlled study of water waves. Their intention was to give the wave theory a new direction by supplying it with proper empirical foundations.

The treatise containing the Webers' researches on the wave theory, *Wellenlehre auf Experimente gegründet*, came out in 1825 and was immediately praised as a "classic work" by the German physicist best qualified to judge, Chladni.[65] Wilhelm, now

60. It should be pointed out that the Webers no longer lived in the same house with Chladni and Langguth's cabinet after Wilhelm was nine. The biographical facts on Weber are taken mainly from Heinrich Weber, *Wilhelm Weber. Eine Lebensskizze* (Breslau, 1893), but also from Eduard Riecke, "Wilhelm Weber," *Abh. Ges. Wiss. Göttingen* 38 (1892): 1–44, and K. H. Wiederkehr, *Wilhelm Eduard Weber. Erforscher der Wellenbewegung und der Elektrizität 1804–1891* (Stuttgart: Wissenschaftliche Verlagsgesellschaft, 1967).

61. Riecke, "Weber," 4–5.

62. A. J. Fresnel submitted his first treatise to the Paris Academy in 1815. He submitted the completed work *Mémoire sur la diffraction de la lumière* to the academy in 1818, and he published some papers on the subject in the *Annales de chimie et de physique* around this time. He also published a popular account of it in 1822, which was translated in the *Annalen* in 1824. By 1825, when their treatise came out, the Webers knew these articles and cited them. Rosenberger, *Geschichte der Physik*, 178–79; E. H. Weber and Wilhelm Weber, *Wellenlehre auf Experimente gegründet oder über die Wellen tropfbarer Flüssigkeiten mit Anwendung auf die Schall- und Lichtwellen* (Leipzig, 1825), reprinted as vol. 5 of Weber's *Werke*, ed. Eduard Riecke (Berlin, 1893).

63. Rosenberger, *Geschichte der Physik*, 256.

64. Introductory remarks by the Webers in their *Wellenlehre*, 1–18, especially 4–6, 12–13.

65. The Webers dedicated the *Wellenlehre* to Chladni, which was the occasion of Chladni's letter on 20 Aug. 1825 to Wilhelm Weber. Chladni said that the Webers had presented wave motion "more clearly and coherently" than anyone before them and had treated the "really existing" nature rather than the "idealistic webs" of the nature philosophers. Wiederkehr, *Weber*, quotes from this letter on 25.

twenty-one and a university student, had already immersed himself in the most difficult mathematical physics. He and his brother had examined wave theories from Newton and Euler through their own contemporaries, Laplace, A. L. Cauchy, and Poisson. They had also become practiced in exact measurement and observation. By using water from the local river, they followed the motion of the impurities in it, observing the detailed behavior of waves. They measured the velocity, width, and height of waves and the time a particle of water takes to complete its cyclical path. They produced patterns on the surface analogous to sound figures; they passed water through horizontal tubes with vertical glass tubes regularly inserted into them; they stretched ropes across the river and observed in them waves analogous to water waves; they set membranes and other sounding bodies into vibration. They repeated others' experiments, compared others' theories, and, in general, discussed the whole gamut of problems of the forces and motions of particles responsible for waves. In this collaboration, Wilhelm acquired an admirable education in physics, which he could not have gotten by any formal course of study at that time.

In these first researches, Weber displayed a characteristic that was to reappear in his later, more famous researches on electricity. It was to work experimentally, mathematically, and critically over a large field of phenomena, guided by a theoretically unifying conception. Here the field was waves: waves in rope, water, air, and ether, waves as a universal phenomenon. He and his brother observed: "Just as the surface of the ocean . . . , the air [and] all solid bodies are in a manifold, never completely ceasing wave motion. As a body that has fallen into the water excites waves . . . , so every, even the minutest, impulse on a solid, fluid, or gaseous body excites waves. . . . Above all, by means of the rapid propagation of waves, nature appears to have made it possible for us to receive, for example, through light and heat, sense impressions of bodies separated from us by enormous distances and to be able to be in contact with other people over shorter distances by means of sound."[66]

The Webers did their research in Halle, where the family had moved. They were encouraged by the local professor of physics and chemistry, Schweigger, who let them use apparatus from the university's physical cabinet.[67] While working with his brother on the *Wellenlehre*, Wilhelm studied physics with Schweigger, and in 1826, the year following its publication, he graduated with an acoustical dissertation that originated in his wave studies.[68]

After graduation at Halle, Weber wanted to widen his scientific knowledge. To this end, he hopefully applied to the Prussian ministry of culture, which had come to his and his brother's aid in their researches on waves. He asked to spend a year at Göttingen to study mathematics and exact research with Gauss,[69] pointing to his

66. Wilhelm Weber and E. H. Weber, "Allgemein fassliche Darstellung des Vorganges, durch welchen Saiten und Pfeifen dazu gebracht werden, einfache Töne und Flageolettöne hervorzubringen," *Allgemeine musikalische Zeitung* 28 (1826): 186–99, 206–13, 222–35, reprinted in Weber, *Werke* 1:134–67, on 135–36.
67. Wilhelm Weber refers to Schweigger's apparatus in his paper: "Auszug aus den die Theorie des Schalles und Klanges betreffenden Aufsätzen von Felix Savart," *Jahrb. d. Chem. u. Phys.* 14 (1825): 385–428, reprinted in Weber, *Werke* 1:3–28, on 3.
68. Wiederkehr, *Weber*, 27–28.
69. Heinrich Weber, *Weber*, 9–10.

understanding of the mathematical competence required of a physicist in the 1820s
and of Göttingen University as the place to acquire it in Germany. The ministry
saw no need for him to go there, arguing that it would be less expensive if he
corresponded with Gauss; but if he liked, he could go see him on his own during
vacation. Weber had also asked the ministry to be sent to Paris for a year after
Göttingen. Paris was, above all, where the kind of physics was done that Weber
wanted to do. With his brother he had studied much recent French physical work
and had used Poisson's theory extensively to check their experimental results. They
had written a summary of the *Wellenlehre* in French to ensure that the competent
audience in Paris would notice it. But the ministry saw no need to send Weber to
Paris either. So Weber settled in as Privatdocent and then as extraordinary professor
at Halle. There he continued has acoustical researches in his "Habilitationsschrift,"
the research paper qualifying a candidate for university teaching, and in a series of
papers he published in Schweigger's and Poggendorff's journals in 1825–31.
Schweigger was impressed by his precocious student and junior colleague, whose
special interest was "mathematical physics" and who at the same time was experienced with instruments.[70]

Weber's researches on sound waves in his Halle years led him to physics of exact
measurements in general. He thought that our sense of hearing would allow us to
measure smaller distances than our sense of sight, so that with perfected acoustical
measurements he expected to gain a more exact knowledge of the physical processes
within bodies:

> If it were posible to make as exact determinations with the sense of
> hearing as measurements of space with the visual sense, then we would
> get to know more precisely some properties and forces of bodies such as
> cohesion, compressibility, dilatability, [or] expansion through heat,
> which are not well suited for investigations by spatial measurements with
> the visual sense. How small, for example, the elongation of a metal rod
> is when it expands through heat and how difficult it is to measure pre-
> cisely this small elongation! How large, on the other hand, the change
> is in the height of a tone of a transversally vibrating metal string when
> it undergoes even the slightest elongation while it is fastened at its ends
> to two invariable points and stretched.[71]

The great difficulty in using sound for exact measurements does not lie in any insen-
sitivity of the ear but in the lack of a reliable standard for the height of tones. Weber
devised an arrangement of organ pipes to produce a standard tone, for which purpose
he performed a series of experiments to learn the laws of reed pipes (musical-like
instruments consisting of oscillating plates and columns of air). Through another of
his acoustical inventions, the "monochord" for comparing tones, Weber acquired an
instrument for measuring the shortest times then attainable; with it he intended to
measure the velocity of impulses within bodies, which would reveal their physical

70. *Goethe's Naturw. Corr.* 2:310; Wiederkehr, *Weber*, 32.
71. Wilhelm Weber, "Compensation der Orgelpfeifen," *Ann.* 14 (1828): 397–408, on 397.

properties.[72] This early concern with precise measurements typified Weber's entire career.

Essential as they were to his work, however, precise measurements could not of themselves give Weber the full understanding he asked from physics. As a measuring physicist, he could follow up the numbers he recorded with his instruments by fitting empirical interpolation formulas to them, and within the limits of accuracy of the measurements he could then regard these formulas as "*true* laws" of nature, but they were not the same as a "*true* theory." Weber wanted to establish the true theory, because once he had it he could deduce *all* of the laws, as he showed with his theory of reed pipes.[73]

In physics in general and in acoustics in particular, Weber's theoretical concerns included physiology. As the physicist is part of the nature he observes, his physical theory cannot omit consideration of the observer if he desires a full understanding of the phenomena. The physicist studies light waves that "are too small and propagate too quickly for us to be able to distinguish and follow them with our eyes," and he studies sound waves that are inaudible for the same reason.[74] But waves that are too small and too fast to be perceived individually can combine to become sensible, the explanation of which brings physiological facts to the attention of the physicist:

> Several waves make a single, common, confused total impression on the specially organized sense organs of our body, and they become the cause of peculiar sensations, which provide us with no idea of the small and fast oscillations giving rise to the sensations. Thus, the fast waves of matter cause the sensation of sound and its modification, tones, and the soul is so little conscious of the true process in the perception of tones that one can take pleasure in music for a long time without knowing that it is the vibrations of bodies that give us this pleasure. Even faster waves of matter become the cause of the sensation of light and its modifications, colors.[75]

Weber published these physiological observations in the *Wellenlehre* in 1825. After ten years of subsequent work on sound, he elaborated on them in a discussion of the nature of acoustics, the science of sound. If acoustics is defined as the theory

72. Weber, "Compensation," 400–401, 404. Wilhelm Weber, "Über die zweckmässige Einrichtung eines Monochords oder Tonmessers und den Gebrauch desselben, zum Nutzen der Physik und Musik," *Ann.* 15 (1829): 1–19, on 1–2, 14.
73. Wilhelm Weber, "Versuche mit Zungenpfeifen," *Ann.* 16 (1829): 415–38, on 433. Weber was highly critical of the use of empirical laws where theoretically deduced ones were to be had. The former, he said, are relatively imprecise, require skill for their use in contrast with the "automatic" use of deduced laws, give nonuniform results, and probably arise from imperfect experimental arrangements. In "Vergleichung der Theorie der Saiten, Stäbe und Blaseinstrumente," *Ann.* 28 (1833): 1–17, reprinted in Weber, *Werke* 1:365–76, on 367. He demonstrated that the laws can be deduced from a true theory in "Theorie der Zungenpfeifen," *Ann.* 17 (1829): 193–246.
74. Wilhelm Weber and E. H. Weber, "Allgemein fassliche Darstellung," 135. Wilhelm Weber, "Über Savart's Klangversuche," *Jahrb. d. Chem. u. Phys.* 15 (1825): 257–310, reprinted in Weber, *Werke* 1:29–59, on 51.
75. E. H. Weber and Wilhelm Weber, *Wellenlehre*, 17.

of strings, rods, and sound—the "classical" subject, as Weber called it—it could be said to be complete in its principles, allowing only further mathematical elaboration and application. For this reason, Weber thought, physicists tended to ignore acoustics and instead to explore electric, magnetic, and galvanic forces, which offered them new phenomena to compare with theory. But to Weber, acoustics was not yet complete in its principles; for in addition to exploring the fundamental forces, physicists must "advance further and seek to determine what is even more interesting for us, namely, according to what laws the motions produced by the fundamental forces act on us ourselves, on our sense organs." The goal of understanding the action of the sense organs was within reach: "Since we only go back to the fundamental forces of nature to go forward again to our sense organs, it is a matter of course that as soon as we have reached some completeness in the first endeavor (which goal is perhaps not far off any longer), all efforts will be turned toward this second goal."[76] We learn about sound in two ways, Weber explained: by our sense of hearing and by physical observations of bodies that produce sound. By its nature, acoustics must include the organs of the human body; moreover, it must subject them to the same dynamical principles, since they are made of the same matter as bodies outside us. Beyond that, sensation itself must enter acoustics, since "we are not only dealing with motions (whether of our organ of hearing itself or of the bodies surrounding it) but also with sensations, and it is just the relations between the two that we want to understand."[77]

According to Weber, this comprehensive science of acoustics is supposed to uncover the forces responsible for the quality and articulation of tones. He urged physicists to ignore their physical cabinets and study actual, if suitably modified, musical instruments. Existing acoustical theory was inadequate: "It is notorious and beyond doubt that the theory deserts us in the calculation of the magnitude and usually even the duration of the motions of musical instruments as they are really used." Weber thought that after working out a provisional theory for a few instruments, he could readily make similar theories for all other instruments. He promised to reveal a new acoustical principle that governed these theories, the "principle of conservation of tones," in a forthcoming study of wind instruments.[78] But he did not publish this study; he left Halle, and he left the acoustical apparatus behind him.[79] His acoustical theory remained incomplete; he could only hope that others who had "fine acoustical measuring devices" might continue his work.[80]

In the physics section at the 1828 meeting in Berlin of the German Association of Natural Scientists, Weber gave a lecture on organ pipes and their use in precision measurements in physics. It impressed his audience, which included Gauss and Humboldt, and Weber was told that there was "some hope" that he would be invited

76. Weber, "Vergleichung der Theorie der Saiten," 366, 374.
77. Wilhelm Weber, "Akustik," in *Universallexikon der Tonkunst* (1835), 1:99–119, reprinted in Weber, *Werke* 1:377–402, on 379.
78. Weber, "Vergleichung der Theorie der Saiten," 375, 376.
79. Weber to Göttingen U. Curator, 15 Dec. 1832, and Curator's reply, 17 Jan. 1833, both in Göttingen UA, 4/V h/16.
80. Weber to F. G. K. Zamminer in Giessen, 8 Apr. 1855, A Schweiz. Sch., Zurich.

to Göttingen when the physics chair there fell vacant.[81] He had been working in the right field, at least with respect to the purely physical parts of acoustics. For after he had sent Gauss one of his papers, Gauss wrote to him: "I have always been of the opinion that acoustics belongs to those parts of mathematical physics where the most brilliant advances are still to be made. In fact, it is only a matter of spatial and temporal relations and it should be possible to make it completely subject to mathematics; and yet, how little, how extremely little do we know so far!" Gauss was "convinced that the human mind . . . will produce the same clarity here as has been given to the optical sciences."[82] In his application to the Hannover government for the Göttingen chair after Mayer's death, Weber proposed Gauss and Humboldt—and Oersted and Berzelius, too—as the scientists to ask for recommendations concerning his work and ability.[83] No other young physicist in Germany then could have offered a more imposing list of references.

When Weber finally moved to Göttingen in 1831, it was as Gauss's colleague and not, as he had proposed only five years earlier, as his student. He told Gauss that he came to make use of the "favorable conditions" in Göttingen for "scientific investigations."[84] In Göttingen, with his younger brother Eduard, Wilhelm soon undertook a mechanical study of the human anatomy, employing exact methods of physical research and the calculus in setting out the equations of motion for walking and running.[85] He also undertook, as he had observed his colleagues do, to explore in collaboration with Gauss the fundamental forces of nature and the new phenomena associated with them. From now on, magnetic and electric forces were to be his principal subjects, to which he brought the wide mathematical and measuring experience he had acquired during his study of wave phenomena.

Georg Simon Ohm was another German researcher who did advanced theoretical work in connection with experimental research in physics before 1830. Like Weber, Ohm worked extensively in acoustics and electricity (though in reverse order). His early research dealt with the new fundamental force of galvanism, which in time established him as a leader of German physics.

As with Weber, Ohm's original impulse to study science came from home. His father, a master locksmith in Erlangen, on his own had studied mathematics, education, and philosophy, particularly Kant's. He befriended the mathematicians at Erlangen University, and with his sons Georg and Martin he studied Euler's books on analysis, including his integral calculus in Latin.[86] His example was lasting, as is seen by his sons' careers: Martin became a university professor of mathematics, and Georg began his career as a mathematics teacher and author with strong interests in education and philosophy.

After leaving the gymnasium, Ohm entered the local university in Erlangen,

81. Wiederkehr, Weber, 34.
82. Gauss to Weber, 2 Apr. 1830, Gauss Papers, Göttingen UB, Ms. Dept. .
83. Weber to "Staats-Minister," 8 Feb. 1831, Weber Personalakte, Göttingen UA, 4/V b/95a.
84. Wiederkehr, Weber, 37.
85. Wilhelm Weber and Eduard Weber, Mechanik der menschlichen Gehwerkzeuge (Göttingen, 1836).
86. Füchtbauer, Ohm, 39–40.

where he took up the subjects that would most interest him for the rest of his life: mathematics, philosophy, and physics, all of which appealed to him because of their "important influences on absolute *Menschenbildung.*" Although Ohm began his university studies in 1805, he did not finish them until 1811. His father did not have enough money to support him, which required him to go to work for a time. He taught privately and at a secondary school, while at the same time on his own he studied Euler, Laplace, and S. F. Lacroix on the recommendation of the Erlangen mathematicians. In addition, he sought practical training with instruments and machines and even considered working in a mine for that reason.[87] His self-education took him beyond the requirements of the doctoral examination, just as it took him beyond what he needed to teach mathematics and physics at private, secondary, and technical schools and, eventually, at the university. It was, however, essential preparation for the theoretical and experimental researches he would carry out in what free time he had during and in between his various teaching jobs.

As a researcher, Ohm began as an experimental physicist. In 1825 and 1826, he carried out "innumerable" experiments, leading to his first publications in Schweigger's and Poggendorff's journals. He chose to work on the galvanic current mainly because he thought that with it he would meet with less competition from other researchers than he would with other topics.[88] To determine the "law" by which metals conduct galvanic current, he carried out three sets of experiments: the goal of the first was to find the relation of the length of wires to their conductivity, of the second to find the relative conductivities of wires of different metals, and of the third to establish the law. In the first two sets of experiments his procedure was to insert lengths of wire between the terminals of a copper-zinc wet cell and then to measure the galvanic current by a Coulomb torsion balance; with this instrument a magnetic needle, suspended over the current by a fine wire, is turned by the magnetic action of the current, and the torsion of the suspension wire is a measure of that action. It was known that the magnetic action of a current in a wire decreases as the conductivity of the wire decreases, and Ohm correlated the "loss of force" of the current with the length and kind of wire it passed through. In the third set of experiments, he exchanged the wet cell for Thomas Seebeck's recently invented "thermoelement," a combination of copper and bismuth that gave a steadier current. Ohm's measurements supported a law, which he stated as an equation: $X = a/(b + x)$, where X is the strength of the magnetic action of the current, x is the length of the conductor, a is a constant proportional to the temperature difference of the thermocouple junctions and is a measure of the electromotive, or "exciting," force, and b is the "equivalent length," or internal resistance, of the rest of the circuit. The "unity" that his simple formula brought to previous experience with galvanic currents persuaded him that he had come upon a "pure law of nature."[89]

87. Füchtbauer, *Ohm*, 82–101; quotation on 82.
88. Füchtbauer, *Ohm*, 142.
89. In other words, $b + x$ measures the total resistance of the circuit, which today we write as R; a measures the electromotive force of the battery, or E; and if the magnetic action is proportional to the current I, the formula Ohm wrote in 1826 is, in appropriate units, the formula we write today, $I = E/R$. Ohm's experiments are analyzed in Morton L. Schagrin, "Resistance to Ohm's Law," *Am. J. Phys.* 31 (1963): 536–47, especially 544. The quotation is from Ohm, "Bestimmung des Gesetzes, nach welchem

In 1830 Ohm remarked that if he had had more success than others in explain-ing certain phenomena, it was because he was constantly guided by "theory."[90] He made the remark in connection with unipolar conduction, but it applied as well to his other researches, including his research on the law of metallic conduction. Al-though in his first publications he presented the law as a summary of his experimen-tal results, the laboratory notebooks of his researches in 1825 and 1826 suggest that it came from theoretical considerations as well as from experiment; it would appear that he was guided to the mathematical form of the law by an analogy between resisted galvanic current and the resisted flow of fluids, as it is understood in hydro-dynamics.[91] He tested the mathematical law by more experiments, and he designed new experiments to give physical meaning to the constants that enter it. In 1826 Ohm published a second, "electroscopic" or "tension," law, leading up to his major work the following year, The Galvanic Circuit Investigated Mathematically (Die galva-nische Kette, mathematisch bearbeitet).[92]

More than talent and desire are needed to produce major works in physics. Time and money are needed as well. Feeling increasingly burdened by his teaching job in a secondary school in Cologne, Ohm took his brother's advice and asked the Prus-sian minister of culture for a year off. To the minister he explained that for a long time he had divided his attention between mathematics and physics, though for practical reasons he had emphasized physics. By taking up physics he did not have to give up mathematics, he said, since the two were closely connected. His appeal to the minister contained an element of calculation: he regretted that the French had recently dominated physics, and he had been studying the mathematical works by Laplace, Fourier, Poisson, Fresnel, and other French masters to see what they had left for him to do. He had been doing purely experimental work on the whole, but he had in hand a mathematical theory of galvanic current; all he needed was time off to complete it and, he added, to work out a theory of light as well. On the recommendation of Erman, the minister approved Ohm's request. With half salary, Ohm went off to Berlin in 1826 to live in his brother's house, where he had a small apartment with space for doing experiments. With these improved working condi-tions, he developed the mathematical theory of the galvanic current, perhaps with his brother's help with the calculations.[93] The result was the Galvanic Circuit.

The expression "investigated mathematically" in the title of Ohm's book de-

Metalle die Contactelektricität leiten, nebst einem Entwurfe zu einer Theorie des Voltaischen Apparates und des Schweigger'schen Multiplicators," Journ. f. Chem. u. Phys. 46 (1826): 137–66, reprinted in G. S. Ohm, Gesammelte Abhandlungen, ed. Eugen Lommel (Leipzig, 1892), 14–36, on 15 (hereafter cited as Ges. Abh.).

90. G. S. Ohm, "Versuche zu einer näheren Bestimmung der Natur unipolarer Leiter," Journ. f. Chem. u. Phys. 59 (1830): 385–435, 60 (1830): 32–59, reprinted in Ges. Abh., 344–401, on 344.

91. The interplay of theory and experiment is analyzed in John L. McKnight, "Laboratory Note-books of G. S. Ohm: A Case Study in Experimental Method," Am. J. Phys. 35 (1967): 110–14. Also Joseph Heinrichs, "Ohm im mathematisch-naturwissenschaftlichen Gedankenkreis seiner Zeit," in Georg Simon Ohm als Lehrer und Forscher in Köln 1817 bis 1826. Festschrift zur 150. Wiederkehr seines Geburtstages, ed. Kölnischer Geschichtsverein (Cologne: J. P. Bachem, n. d. [1939]), 254–70, on 259.

92. G. S. Ohm, Die galvanische Kette, mathematisch bearbeitet (Berlin, 1827), reprinted in Ges. Abh., 61–186.

93. Füchtbauer, Ohm, 151–56; Ohms . . . Nachlass, 70–74.

scribed his objective: to deduce the properties of the galvanic circuit from a set of "fundamental laws." The first of these laws states that electricity passes only between adjacent particles of the conductor and that the quantity passed is proportional to the difference in electroscopic force at the two particles. Here Ohm drew on an analogy to Fourier's heat theory, in which the quantity of caloric passed between two particles is proportional to the difference of their temperatures. Ohm's second law, supported by Coulomb's experiments, states that the loss of electricity in unit time from the conductor to the air is proportional to the electroscopic force of the electricity, to the amount of surface exposed, and to a coefficient that depends on the air; acknowledging that this second law has little bearing on the phenomena of galvanic currents, Ohm included it to make the theory complete and parallel to Fourier's theory of heat. The third and last law states that two bodies in contact maintain the same difference of electroscopic force at their common surface, which is the basic tenet of the contact theory of the battery. From these three laws, Ohm derived differential equations for electric currents analogous to Fourier's and Poisson's for heat, which indicated to him an "intimate connection" between the two phenomena.[94]

The mathematical expression of Ohm's physical analogy between the conduction of electricity and the conduction of heat is an equation identical in form to Fourier's. The only difference is in the physical significance of the symbols entering the equation: in Fourier's the independent variable is temperature; in Ohm's it is the electroscopic force, which is the force with which an electroscope, a body of constant electrical condition, is attracted to or repelled from a body it is brought into contact with. Following an approach Fourier had made familiar, Ohm mathematically divided the conductor into infinitely thin disks and calculated the quantity of electricity transferred per unit time across the parallel surfaces and outward through the edges of the disks. The result was the fundamental, second-order, partial differential equation of Ohm's theory. The electroscopic force u at each point of a conductor carrying a current is:

$$\gamma \frac{du}{dt} = \chi \frac{d^2u}{dx^2} - \frac{bc}{\omega} u,$$

where the several constants refer to electrical and geometrical properties of the conductor. Having formulated the physical problem as a differential equation, Ohm then solved it to obtain relations between directly measurable quantities. Manipulating the solution written as an infinite series of sine and cosine functions with damping coefficients, Ohm arrived at the simple formula of his earlier work, his law relating electric current, resistance, and tension.[95]

The "torch of mathematics," Ohm wrote, shines through physics, illuminating

94. Ohm, *Die galvanische Kette,* 62–64.
95. Ohm wrote the law as $S = A/L$, where A is the sum of all "tensions" in the circuit, L is the "reduced length" of the circuit and proportional to its resistance, and S is the "electric current." *Die galvanische Kette,* 80.

its dark places.[96] With his *Galvanic Circuit*, he could claim that mathematics had "incontrovertibly" possessed a "new field of physics, from which it had hitherto remained almost totally excluded."[97] By means of mathematical deductions from a few experimental "principles," galvanic phenomena had been brought together in "closed connection" and presented as a "unity of thought."[98] The deductions showed that the seemingly disparate phenomena of electric tension and current are really connected in nature, partially realizing Ohm's goal of fashioning the theory of electricity into a "whole."[99]

To Ohm a physical theory was incomplete unless it was capable of mathematical development, as he had shown his to be. To complete his theory of the galvanic circuit, he had looked to recent French mathematical work, above all to Fourier's. No comparable mathematical physics existed in Germany, though there was a good deal of experimental physics.[100] Ohm's choice was not between German and French approaches but between Fourier's and Laplace's.[101]

Ohm regarded his work on the galvanic circuit as belonging to the "most difficult in mathematics."[102] But his approach was not that of a mathematician; he did not, for example, examine the convergence of infinite Fourier series but treated them as if they were finite polynomials, a standard practice of physicists in his day. (It remained for Dirichlet, one of Ohm's students at the Cologne gymnasium, to construct an adequate theory of Fourier series.) Again with the physicists of his day, Ohm did not question the existence of solutions to differential equations, as mathematicians did, but solved the equations as they arose in physical problems.[103] Critical of mathematical theories, such as Laplace's, that were insufficiently concerned with real bodies,[104] Ohm believed that mathematical physics may be done separately from, but not independently of, experimental physics and that it must always return to experiment again. The "chief merit of mathematical analysis," Ohm wrote in the *Galvanic Circuit*, is that "it calls forth, by its never-vacillating expressions, a generality of ideas, which continually demands renewed experiments, and thus leads to a more profound knowledge of nature."[105]

When the *Galvanic Circuit* appeared, few physicists in Germany knew mathematical physics sufficiently to understand it. Journal editors were afraid their readers could not understand papers containing the simplest mathematics, as Ohm complained.[106] For reviewing, Ohm sent a copy of his book to Schweigger at Halle, who

96. *Ohms . . . Nachlass,* 71.
97. Ohm, *Die galvanische Kette,* 64–65.
98. Ohm, *Die galvanische Kette,* 62.
99. Ohm, *Die galvanische Kette,* 61.
100. Fourier's *Analytical Theory of Heat* was published only five years before. Ohm remarked on French mathematical physics, in *Ohms . . . Nachlass,* 71. Ohm cited experimental work by Erman, Ritter, and other German physicists in *Die galvanische Kette,* 87.
101. Actually, Ohm thought that his mathematical treatment of "molecular actions" reconciled Fourier's and Laplace's approaches. *Die galvanische Kette,* 114.
102. Ohm, *Die galvanische Kette,* 64.
103. Heinrichs, "Ohm," 260–61.
104. Ohm, *Die galvanische Kette,* 114.
105. Ohm, *Die galvanische Kette,* 106.
106. Füchtbauer, *Ohm,* 157–58. Ohm tried to make his book accessible by giving a simple geometrical presentation of the theory at the beginning, with doubtful effect.

did not see the point of a mathematical treatment. To have it evaluated, the Prussian minister of culture sent a copy to Kämtz, Schweigger's colleague at Halle, who could not follow the mathematical derivation, as is clear from his cautious review of it. In Berlin, which desperately needed a "mathematical physicist,"[107] Ohm's work received its most famous and, to Ohm, irritating review from Pohl, who was neither a mathematical nor a typical Berlin physicist. Pohl belonged to an association formed "especially under Hegel's auspices," which published a journal for scientific criticism.[108] As a reviewer of works on physics and chemistry for this journal, Pohl followed the policy—which was apparently a general policy of the association—to make the work reviewed the starting point for an essay on the reviewer's own theories and general views. The reviewer was to judge scientific works from a "higher point of view," such as a "simple and dignified view of nature." This policy Pohl applied to Ohm's *Galvanic Circuit*. Having only recently completed a work of his own on the subject, "The Process of the Galvanic Circuit," which Helgel was eager to see reviewed in their journal, and enjoying Hegel's "especially good intentions" toward him, Pohl had understandable reasons for rejecting Ohm's work. To this circumstance, it should be added that Ohm's theory with its violation of the common distinction between current and tension electricity was not easy for everyone to understand or accept.[109]

The tone of Pohl's criticism was shrill and belittling, and Ohm answered it despite friendly advice by Schweigger to ignore it.[110] More than most German physicists, Pohl adopted the language of nature philosophy. He complained that Ohm had not paid attention to the "essence" of the circuit and had merely expressed some properties of electricity in formulas. That was no achievement but only a replication of Fourier's and Poisson's work in another part of physics. Pohl likened Ohm's mathematical theory to a report of a trip that enumerates the traveler's stops and his velocity between them but nothing more.[111]

In general, the response to Ohm's book reflected a paucity of physicists with good mathematical knowledge in Germany in the late 1820s. But one German review of Ohm's book showed complete comprehension. Ohm sent his book to Kastner in Erlangen to be reviewed in his journal. Kastner asked the mathematician Wilhelm Pfaff to write the review, but Pfaff did not know the literature and did not know how "Laplace and consorts" would proceed in this instance. The review that appeared under Pfaff's name was apparently written by Ohm himself, after his brother had interceded. The review was, of course, favorable, but a favorable review does not necessarily make a successful book. Sales of the *Galvanic Circuit* were unimpressive, and Ohm paid friends to order the book from out of town to make a better impression on his publisher. The book was in print for eight years, then not again for sixty years, though in the meantime it had come out in several transla-

107. According to Martin Ohm. Füchtbauer, *Ohm*, 157, 167–68.
108. G. F. Pohl to Franz Neumann, 1 Jan. 1828 (the letter is dated 1827 in error), Neumann Papers, Göttingen UB, Ms. Dept.
109. Pohl to Neumann, 1 Jan. 1828. Also, Schagrin, "Resistance," 545–46.
110. Füchtbauer, *Ohm*, 171; *Ohms . . . Nachlass*, 90.
111. Füchtbauer, *Ohm*, 168.

tions.[112] Ohm sent free copies to everyone who might help him, as he did not want to return to his teaching in Cologne.

To continue his "pure scientific works," Ohm looked for a position with access to literature in the field and, above all, to ample physical apparatus. But his hopes were damped by repeated rejections, which he attributed to his insistance on the need for apparatus.[113] When he was offered a small salary for conducting private practice sessions at a military school, the Allgemeine Kriegsschule, in Berlin, he was offended and protested. But he was advised to accept for the time being, and he formally withdrew from his Cologne job in 1828.[114] Over the next five years, while he taught at the miliary school (and also briefly at another Berlin military school, the Vereinigte Artillerie- und Ingenieurschule), he regularly sent off job applications.

During his search for a job, Ohm wrote repeatedly to the king of Bavaria, who received his own copy of the *Galvanic Circuit* and Ohm's assurance that the book was opposed by only one person (clearly Pohl), who adhered to the "Hegelian principles."[115] The government forwarded Ohm's application to the Bavarian Academy of Sciences, to which Ohm had alread sent a copy of his book. The academy in turn referred it to the physicists Thaddaeus Siber and K. D. M. Stahl, who gave a "very favorable" opinion of it. Stahl said that Ohm showed great mathematical skill in expressing the laws of the galvanic circuit in "mathematical-analytical formulas"; Siber said that it is useful to apply mathematics to physics, as Ohm had done, since general formulas for phenomena point the way for experimenters' future work. Moreover, Ohm was the "first German analyst" to work in electricity. Despite their appreciation of Ohm's work, however, Stahl and Siber did not want Ohm to teach physics at Munich University because of the "inevitable collisions" over the apparatus and auditorium, nor did they want him to interfere with the apparatus if he were hired by the academy. As if to personify Ohm's worry over the influence of nature philosophers on his life, it was from the nature philosopher F. W. J. Schelling, then president of the Bavarian Academy, that he learned that the academy did not know what to do with him and at best could offer him an extraordinary position without salary.[116] Ohm, who needed an income, applied for the physics position at the Munich polytechnic school; he wanted to combine that job with an appointment at the university. He could now point to the recognition of his work on the galvanic circuit by Schweigger, Fechner, Kastner, Pfaff, and some other German physicists. The philosophical faculty of the university reported favorably on Ohm's application, but nothing came of it or of any of his other applications in these years.

112. Füchtbauer, *Ohm*, 156–57, 163–64.

113. *Ohms . . . Nachlass*, 118–19, 129, 148. His competitor Pohl may have stood in his way, too. Pohl saw the realization of his protectors' good intentions: he was appointed extraordinary professor at Berlin in 1830 and ordinary professor at Breslau University in 1832. Lenz, *Berlin*, vol. 2, pt. 1, *Ministerium Altenstein* (1910), 380–81.

114. Füchtbauer, *Ohm*, 161. Also *Ohms . . . Nachlass*, 94–97.

115. Ohm to King Ludwig I of Bavaria, 30 Mar. 1829, in *Ohms . . . Nachlass*, 115–19, on 118.

116. Stahl's and Siber's evaluations, 7 and 5 May 1829, respectively, in *Ohms . . . Nachlass*, 121–24; Schelling to King of Bavaria, 10 May 1829, on 125–26.

At one stage Berlin University looked like a prospect; Ohm told the Prussian ministry of culture that the death of the extraordinary professor of physics Fischer, who preferred to teach "mathematical physics," left a gap at the university, which he was qualified to fill. The ministry informed him that physics was well looked after in Berlin with two ordinary and three extraordinary professors and several Privatdocenten.[117] In 1833, Ohm at last received a new appointment as physics professor at the Nuremberg polytechnic. As Ohm's practical difficulties show, research was not a decisive consideration in the hiring of a physics teacher around 1830.

After the *Galvanic Circuit*, Ohm carried out important researches on tones and on crystal optics, and he undertook a comprehensive theory of physics. In the year the *Galvanic Circuit* was published, he began to speak of a greater work to come, one that would treat the whole of molecular physics. Apparently he wanted to derive all physical phenomena from analytical mechanics and molecular hypotheses. Ohm published the first volume containing the mathematical preliminaries. In the second volume he intended to treat dynamics and in the third and fourth its application to physical phenomena. But Ohm's late call to Munich University interfered with his plan, and the volumes never appeared.[118] The existence of the plan, however, pointed to the confidence of the author of the *Galvanic Circuit* in the power of mathematical physics to complete the understanding of nature that Newton had begun.

Ohm's contemporaries were more inclined to trust his electromotive law because it had been experimentally confirmed than because it had been given a mathematical derivation. Ohm's own experiments on it were less persuasive than others', especially Fechner's.

Gustav Theodor Fechner is known as a psychophysicst, philosopher, and creator of world views. He is not often remembered as a physicist, yet he was the ordinary professor of physics at Leipzig University from 1834 until 1843, and early in his life he did a good deal of first-rate experimental research in physics. His reputation as a precise investigator of physical nature stemmed largely from his response to Ohm's work on the galvanic circuit. Some fifty years later his biographer would claim that his experiments were still the most important proof of Ohm's law.[119]

Fechner was drawn to Ohm's work for a number of reasons. He found the "mathematical theory" of galvanism largely satisfactory, even if Ohm's theoretical

---

117. Ohm to King of Bavaria, 1 Sept. 1831, *Ohms . . . Nachlass*, 151–54; Ohm to Bavarian Minister of the Interior Ludwig Prince Öttingen-Wallerstein, 23 Feb. 1833, on 157–59; Ohm to Prussian Ministry of Education, 29 Jan. 1831, on 143–45; the ministry's reply, 10 Mar. 1831, on 145–46.

118. Eugen Lommel, "Vorrede und Einleitung," in Ohm, *Ges. Abh.*, v–xviii, on xiv–xv.

119. Wilhelm Wundt, "Zur Erinnerung an Gustav Theodor Fechner," *Philosophische Studien* 4 (1888): 471–78. Historically, Fechner's experimental work was the most important foundation, though Ohm's electromotive law continued to be tested with ever greater exactness under varying conditions. Ohm's second, or electroscopic, law, which expresses the intensity of electricity in a cross section of the galvanic wire as a function of the electric state and the dimensions of the conductor, was not experimentally founded until some twenty years later by Rudolph Kohlrausch in Marburg. The reason for the delay was the lack of an electrometer capable of measuring the small difference in tension at two points of a closed circuit. Karl Max Bauernfeind, "Ohm: Georg Simon," *ADB* 24 (1970); 187–203, on 195.

derivation could have been "much more elementary." The theory lacked only "supporting experiments."[120] What is necessary in a theory, in Fechner's view, is for the phenomena it explains to be expressed in numbers and for the theory to agree with the numbers (which was the experimenter Fechner's task to show). The discovery of Ohm's law confirmed the observation that "measuring and weighing are the two great secrets of chemistry and physics," the "foundations of all discoveries with which these two sciences have enriched themselves in recent times."[121] Fechner admired Ohm's theory for another reason: it covered and connected an entire field of phenomena,[122] as Fechner never tired of pointing out. It was "only through your theory," Fechner wrote to Ohm, "that I obtained clarity about the conditions of the circuit, which were apparently so complicated and are now so simply resolved because of it"; the law that it contains, with its "simple formula," connects a "great area of phenomena, which previously remained unconnected in a chaotic and puzzling way";[123] it sheds "great light over many very general relationships of the galvanic circuit,"[124] offering a "beautiful linking of facts."[125]

In his work on Ohm's law, Fechner showed himself to be a meticulous experimenter, making measurement after measurement, methodically eliminating secondary influences and errors, and selecting his measuring methods with the greatest care.[126] He gave his readers every last detail of his experiments, so they could reproduce them from his exact description and confirm the truth of the "fundamental law of the galvanic circuit": the "force" of the circuit is proportional to the total electromotive force divided by the total resistance.[127] Ohm welcomed Fechner's experiments, for his own were done "only on a microscopic scale" owing to a lack of means (and, it would seem, a lack of comparable experimental patience).[128]

In experimentally confirming Ohm's mathematical theory, Fechner worked with a sense of original purpose. The accuracy he demanded of his work was not to be taken for granted in physics at this time. He thought it was necessary to tell his readers that the agreement between his results and Ohm's theory was not "artificially" produced by adjusting observations to calculations; wherever he found a seeming disagreement, he analyzed it.[129] Yet despite his conscientious experimental work, he lacked—in his own estimation—the full complement of abilities expected of a properly equipped physicist. His doubts about his abilities reflected in part his scientific personality and in part the changing character of physical research in Germany and the inadequacies of physics teaching there.

Fechner began his scientific studies at Leipzig University in 1817. The standard, undifferentiated education in science he received did not prepare him for his later

120. Gustav Theodor Fechner, *Massbestimmungen über die galvanische Kette* (Leipzig, 1831), iii; Fechner to Schweigger, 17 Nov. 1828, Ms. Coll., DM, 690.
121. Fechner's translation of Biot, *Lehrbuch der Experimental-Physik* 1:151, 2:196.
122. Fechner, *Elementar-Lehrbuch des Elektromagnetismus*, v–vi.
123. Fechner to Ohm, 14 Nov. 1828, Ms. Coll., DM, 692. Fechner, *Massbestimmungen*, iii.
124. Fechner to Schweigger, 17 Nov. 1828.
125. Fechner to Ohm, 14 Nov. 1828.
126. Fechner, *Massbestimmungen*, viii–x, 6.
127. Fechner, *Massbestimmungen*, 5, 225.
128. Füchtbauer, *Ohm*, 173.
129. Fechner, *Massbestimmungen*, v.

work in physics.[130] The general studies that preceded his professional studies in medicine were the same for all students of science and were, in fact, the only science
courses offered. They included logic, botany, zoology, chemistry, and mathematics,
in addition to physics; Fechner enrolled in them all. He studied physics with the
Annalen editor, the respected physics professor Gilbert, but the material presented
was so elementary that Fechner soon started to educate himself from physics books.
By and large, his other science courses were no better. The mathematics lectures did
not extend beyond algebra, since, as the professor said, more advanced mathematics
would require "far too much writing on the blackboard." With this attitude toward
teaching, the mathematics professor could use any student to help him, as he used
the medical student Fechner, who had completed the course of elementary mathematics. Fechner studied the most difficult writings of Cauchy on his own, regretting
his lack of mathematical competence, which he considered indispensable for theoretical work in the sciences: "I understood after all that without it [mathematics]
nothing could be accomplished in my subjects."[131]

After deciding against becoming a physician, Fechner looked toward an academic life, though still without a clear goal. He earned his living by writing, in part
on physics, especially French physics. The way he came to French physics and its
tangled relationship with his work on Ohm's law and with his uncertain means of
subsistence are best told by Fechner himself:

> On 13 February 1823 I became Master of Arts and I habilitated on 6
> September of the same year to lecture on ideas of nature philosophy in
> the spirit of Schelling and Oken which then still held me imprisoned;
> but that came to nothing. Instead, after the death of Prof. Gilbert in
> 1824 and until the appointment of Prof. Brandes, I took over the lec-
> tures of physics (for half a year), after the translation of the Biot [text-
> book on physics on which he was working] had introduced me a little to
> it, without being otherwise especially prepared for it. Following this I
> began little by little to make my own experimental investigations in the
> area of electricity and galvanism, also to give weekly two-hour public
> (i.e., unpaid) lectures on it, for which I purchased the necessary appa-
> ratus from my savings from my literary jobs.

Fechner went on to explain the place of Ohm's law in his early research and academic advancement. His experimental investigations were mainly directed

> toward a thorough proof of Ohm's law, which had received no attention
> until then; besides my literary work they kept me busy for two whole
> years and appeared in 1830 under the title "Maassbestimmungen über die
> galvanische Kette"; other [investigations] treated different electrical
> themes in Kastner's Archiv, Schweigger's Journal, and later in Poggen-

130. See the discussion of Fechner in Jungnickel, *Saxon Society*, 30–31.
131. Johannes Emil Kuntze, *Gustav Theodor Fechner, Dr. Mises; ein deutsches Gelehrtenleben* (Leipzig,
1892), 107.

dorff's Annalen. More on the basis of this scientific-experimental activity than on the basis of my insignificant academic teaching, I received an extraordinary professorship without salary in 1831 or 1832, after I had made a trip to Paris in 1827 with the support of a stipend of 300 thaler to get to know Biot, Thénard, and Ampère in person.[132]

Fechner's voluminous "literary work" consisted of writing scientific satires and other humorous essays, editing an eight-volume encyclopedia and a pharmaceutical journal, and translating a medical work, Thénard's six-volume textbook on theoretical and practical chemistry, and Biot's four-volume textbook on physics. In his "translations" he incorporated the latest research, and the updated works appeared under the names of the French scientists rather than under his own only because they sold better that way. His Leipzig colleagues considered his work on Biot's textbook sufficient proof of his ability as a physicist to consider him for Gilbert's chair in 1824.[133] (They did not seek his appointment because he was too young for a chair, and, although they did not mention it, he was completely inexperienced as a teacher of physics.) With Fechner's combination of activities—making ends meet by writing and, at the same time, advancing science and his reputation—it is not surprising that in the same letter to Ohm in which he spoke of the care with which he did his experiments on Ohm's law, he also spoke of having to interrupt them to earn his living with other work.[134]

As an additional source of income, Fechner published reports on experimental physics and on difficult mathematical-physical investigations. The overwhelming contribution of the French can be seen in his report in 1832 on the literature in mathematical physics and mechanics: the authors most heavily represented there were, in order, Poisson, Cauchy, and Laplace.[135] These names stood for proficiencies that Fechner knew were immeasurably beyond his own. Although he could not do advanced mathematical physics himself, he contributed to it by his accounts of French work in it—as well as by his experimental confirmation of part of Ohm's theory.

When in 1834 the Leipzig chair of physics became available, Fechner hesitated over whether or not to make an effort to secure it. In the eyes of the Leipzig faculty, he qualified as a skilled experimentalist and as an "excellent physicist" respected by German and foreign physicists for his "ingenious" insights. Fechner himself, however, was depressed by his lack of talent for mathematics to the point of considering giving up the professorship soon after he had been appointed to it. He found it especially difficult to give lectures, and he completely avoided all mathematical considerations in them, which meant that they had to be of a popular nature. After a

132. Quoted in Kuntze, Fechner, 68.
133. Report from Leipzig U. Philosophical Faculty to Ministry of Culture and Public Education, 29 June 1834, Fechner Personalakte, Leipzig UA, Nr. 451.
134. Fechner to Ohm, 8 Dec. 1829, Ms. Coll., DM, 702.
135. Poisson by sixty-two papers, Cauchy by fifty-five, and Laplace by twenty-two. The source is the bibliography in Gustav Theodor Fechner, Repertorium der Experimentalphysik, enthaltend eine vollständige Zusammenstellung der neuen Fortschritte dieser Wissenschaft, vol. 3 (Leipzig, 1832).

while he began to occupy himself with experimental investigations again, partly, he said, "because my position demanded it, and partly because I had to use my head less for them than for theoretical investigations."[136] Psychosomatic illness finally freed Fechner from having to do physics at all;[137] in 1843 he resigned his chair in favor of Wilhem Weber.[138]

More examples of early nineteenth-century physicists in Germany would not greatly change the picture we have drawn here. Their impulse toward study and research in physics came partly from within and partly from without, from the father or brother or uncle, from the friend or boarder or neighbor, from the secondary school teacher or university professor who kept abreast of physics and perhaps did research in it, and from self-study. If they had an unusual mathematical ability that enabled them to understand mathematical theories of physics, and if they were doubly endowed with an ability for experimental manipulation, and if in one way or another, from home or school or elsewhere, they gained access to recent treatises on mathematical physics and costly instruments, acquiring the research skills that it was no purpose of regular education to provide, they might become a Weber or an Ohm.

136. Leipzig U. Philosophical Faculty Report, 29 June 1834. Kuntze, *Fechner*, 107.
137. Dean of Leipzig U. Philosophical Faculty A. Westermann to Rector and Leipzig U. Faculty, 29 July 1841, and the response of the faculty, Fechner Personalakte, Leipzig UA, Nr. 451.
138. During the next three years, Fechner gradually recovered. He started lecturing on philosohy at the university in 1846, and he published one more—important—physics paper. However, after his complete recovery in 1849, he turned definitely from physics to philosophy, accepted an appointment to the chair of natural philosophy and anthropology at Leipzig, and began his famous work on psychophysics.

3

Promoting a New Physics: Earth Magnetism at Göttingen

By the middle decades of the nineteenth century, a life in physics in Germany usually meant the life of a university physics professor or of a physics teacher at a higher technical school. Developments in physical research led to changes in physics instruction, which in turn led to changes in institutional arrangements; these changes benefited research by raising physics instruction to the level of professional training. Within German institutions of higher education, opportunities for doing research in physics increased; outside, independent physics research had become nearly impossible, and industrial physics laboratories had not yet taken its place. Meanwhile, all aspects of physics became more demanding as researchers confronted the new mathematical and experimental methods then being introduced. Eventually, university physics professors could claim that it was not only desirable but necessary for their teaching that they be researchers as well as teachers and that they were therefore entitled to be furnished by the state with means for research. To reach that stage, however, took most of the forty years the present volume covers.

More than any other development around 1830, research in earth magnetism set physics on a new course. This was the first major research in physics that successfully commanded support at the universities from the German states. It did so largely because of its association with astronomy, the one physical science that had long been supported by the state. Like astronomy, earth magnetism promised to benefit the state.[1]

Astronomers were used to being called upon for surveying and triangulation projects. For military purposes (at first those of the French during their occupation of parts of Germany), for the assimilation of newly acquired territories, and for re-

---

1. Gauss mentioned the practical uses of earth magnetism in his "Einleitung" to the *Resultate aus den Beobachtungen des magnetischen Vereins im Jahre 1836*, 3–12, reprinted in Carl Friedrich Gauss, *Werke*, ed. Königliche Gesellschaft der Wissenschaften zu Göttingen, vol. 5 (n.p., 1877), 345–51, on 350, to give one example.

forms of taxation based on land ownership, the German states required new topographical maps, a job they gave to their astronomers.[2] Gauss, for example, as the
astronomer at Göttingen University in the service of the state of Hannover, spent
much of his early career on work of this sort. To support practical astronomy, the
states refurbished existing or built new observatories; by 1830 Berlin, Munich, and
Göttingen had all recently acquired new astronomical observatories. The observatories and surveying work required, in turn, optical and measuring instruments at a
time when Napoleon's continental blockade had cut off the supply from England of
the best instruments then available. German technologists such as Georg Reichenbach and Joseph Fraunhofer soon advanced the art of instrument making to a new
level, giving astronomers reason to request money from their states for the new
German instruments even when they were already equipped with earlier English
ones.[3] The availability of such instruments in German astronomical observatories
proved valuable for research in earth magnetism.

Since the states that were interested in undertaking earth-magnetic observations
already had the necessary telescopes, theodolites, and astronomical clocks at their
observatories, the observations became the responsibility of the resident astronomers. They not only already had the necessary instruments, except for magnetometers, they also had the necessary skill: "The most precise observations" now possible
in earth-magnetic research, Gauss pointed out, "can be expected only of those mathematicians who are familiar with the finest means of observation, namely, the practical astronomers."[4] Of these practical astronomers, it was Gauss himself, according
to Humboldt, who brought about the "revolution" in research in earth magnetism.[5]

2. A. Galle, "Über die geodätischen Arbeiten von Gauss," in Gauss, Werke, vol. 11, pt. 2, 1st
treatise (Berlin and Göttingen: Springer, 1924), 16, 27, 38, 47–48, to cite only a few references to the
interests of the different German states in the surveying and triangulation projects. The participating
astronomers frequently referred to in this connection were, aside from Gauss, F. W. Bessel, Bohnenberger, Johann Franz Encke, Bernhard August von Lindenau, Wilhelm Olbers, Johann Georg Soldner, and
Franz Xaver von Zach.
    E. Weis, "Bayerns Beitrag zur Wissenschaftsentwicklung im 19. und 20. Jahrhundert," in Handbuch
der bayerischen Geschichte, vol. 4, Das neue Bayern 1800–1970, ed. Max Spindler, pt. 2 (Munich: C. H.
Beck, 1975), 1034–88, on 1043; Günter D. Roth, Joseph von Fraunhofer, Handwerker — Forscher —
Akademiemitglied 1787–1826 (Stuttgart: Wissenschaftliche Verlagsgesellschaft, 1976), 31–37, 65, 70.
    3. Roth, Fraunhofer, 31–32, 45–46, 71–73; Weis, "Bayerns Beitrag," 1042. An inventory of the old
astronomical observatory in Göttingen dating from 1788 lists eight instruments from English instrument
makers among a total of eleven, including a "Newtonian reflecting telescope by Herschel" and two telescopes by Dollond. Gauss used Dollond's instruments, but his main work in practical astronomy at Göttingen did not begin until after he had acquired from Reichenbach the new instruments that he would
have liked to have bought from the English instrument maker Ramsden, if that had been possible, but
which he was now getting from Ramsden's student. Martin Brendel, "Über die astronomischen Arbeiten
von Gauss," in Gauss, Werke, vol. 11, pt. 2, 3d treatise (Berlin and Göttingen: Springer, 1929), 46–49,
55–56. Reichenbach was sent to study in England at the expense of the Bavarian government. Weis,
"Bayerns Beitrag," 1037–38.
    4. Gauss to Göttingen U. Curator, 29 Jan. 1833, Göttingen UA, 4/V f/48.
    5. Briefe zwischen A. v. Humboldt und Gauss. Zum hundertjährigen Geburtstage von Gauss am 30. April
1877, ed. K. Bruhns (Leipzig, 1877), 24. Humboldt's letter to Gauss containing the remark is dated 17
Feb. 1833.

Gauss's Interest in Earth-Magnetic Research

Organized earth-magnetic research in Germany was initiated by Alexander von Humboldt, who built himself a small magnetic observatory in Berlin in 1828 and coordinated observations by researchers at various locations at prearranged times.[6] Apparently from the start he tried to interest Gauss in participating, for during the annual meeting of the Association of German Natural Scientists in Berlin in 1828, which Gauss attended at Humboldt's personal invitation, he showed Gauss his magnetic apparatus and let him experiment with it.[7] Gauss was not impressed. Humboldt and his fellow investigators were using the expensive Gambey dip magnetometer, the shortcomings of which Poisson and, following him, Riess and Ludwig Moser in Germany worked to overcome in the next years.[8] It was not until 1831 that Gauss felt ready to join in the work, and in the following decade he and his co-worker Weber gave both scientific and organizational form to earth-magnetic research.

As a practical astronomer, Gauss had given "very thorough descriptions" of the basic instruments he had acquired over the years and also accounts of the methods of observation he used with them. His observations were never extensive, never a complete series; they served mainly "to create new methods and to reach greatest precision." Together with the astronomer at Königsberg, F. W. Bessel, whose concerns were similar to his, Gauss worked on the theoretical foundations of observations and instruments, which would enable astronomers to "determine more precisely such quantities as the constants of precession, nutation, and aberration."[9]

The contrast between the precise work of the astronomers and the indifferent work on earth magnetism up to then was striking to Gauss. Existing accounts of magnetic theory, to begin with, contained "so much that is vague, meaningless, illogical . . . that one must start building from the ground up again," Gauss complained to Encke in the summer of 1832.[10] Expensive French apparatus then in

6. Gauss to Göttingen U. Curator, 29 Jan. 1833. A general account of the various investigations of earth magnetism in the late eighteenth and early nineteenth centuries, including Humboldt's, may be found in John Cawood, "Terrestrial Magnetism and the Development of International Collaboration in the Early Nineteenth Century," *Annals of Science* 34 (1977): 551–87.

7. Clemens Schaefer, "Über Gauss' physikalische Arbeiten (Magnetismus, Elektrodynamik, Optik)," in Gauss, *Werke*, vol. 11, pt. 2, 2d treatise (Berlin and Göttingen: Springer, 1929), 9. Schaefer's book-length treatise of Gauss's development of his physical ideas draws on correspondence and unpublished manuscripts as well as on the published papers and so is an accurate, very useful source for the chronology of Gauss's work.

8. Schaefer, "Über Gauss' physikalische Arbeiten," 25–26. One shortcoming was that Gambey's magnetometer used a microscope to observe and measure the smallest changes in the direction of the magnetic needle. Gauss substituted a telescope for the microscope to be able to observe the needle from a distance so that he could avoid disturbing the needle with extraneous occurrences such as air currents caused by the body heat of the observer and sudden motions caused by the observer. F. W. Bessel, "Ueber den Magnetismus der Erde," in *Populäre Vorlesungen über wissenschaftliche Gegenstände*, ed. H. C. Schumacher (Hamburg, 1848), 326–86, on 333–43.

9. Brendel, "Über die astronomischen Arbeiten von Gauss," 3, 4. As it turned out, Bessel did most of the theoretical work, but Gauss's early participation revealed his general approach to a scientific problem involving observation.

10. Schaefer, "Über Gauss' physikalische Arbeiten," 13.

use displeased Gauss, too: "It has always seemed to me that the apparatus that one uses for magnetic determinations is very incomplete and in flagrant disparity with the precision of our astronomical and geodetic measurements."[11] Finally, the measuring methods that were commonly used gave results of only limited usefulness. They could not exclude the effects of variations in the magnetic state of the instrument, for example, and therefore were useless for any investigations of earth-magnetic variations at a location over a long period.[12] And because they gave only relative measures, they allowed different standard units of intensity for different locations, which had obvious disadvantages.[13]

Gauss had long been interested in magnetism, but not until after Weber's arrival in Göttingen as professor physics did he feel that he could "do something about this bad state of affairs" in magnetic research.[14] As he told Humboldt, he could occupy himself with a subject "really eagerly only when I have at my disposal the means of thoroughly entering" into it; those means had been lacking in earth magnetism up to then. Now Weber, who was interested in the subject, too, could offer Gauss the apparatus of the Göttingen physical cabinet and, more important, his friendship, scientific cooperation, and "wealth of practical ideas."[15]

In the months following September 1831, Gauss occupied himself almost exclusively with the general problem of earth magnetism; starting "right from the beginning from ideas I have already had for many years," he told Olbers, he came up "with something new almost every week."[16]

Gauss's Physical Principle in Earth Magnetism

Among the "means" Gauss needed for entering into earth-magnetic research was a physical principle. He believed that, in general, the first step in developing a mathematical theory for a group of phenomena was to discover a physical principle, using if necessary experimental observations.[17] In search of a guiding physical principle, Gauss first considered the magnetic distribution in a body. Like others working in the subject, he speculated on the source of the earth's magnetism. To H. C. Schumacher, astronomer at Copenhagen, he wrote in March 1832:

---

11. Gauss to Olbers, 2 Aug. 1832, in *Briefwechsel zwischen Olbers und Gauss*, 586–91, on 587.

12. Carl Friedrich Gauss, "Intensitas vis magneticae terrestris ad mensuram absolutam revocata," *Göttingische gelehrte Anzeigen*, 24 Dec. 1832, 2041–58, reprinted in Gauss, *Werke* 5:293–304, on 294–95. The article is Gauss's German announcement of the Latin paper he presented to the Göttingen Scientific Society on 15 Dec. 1832, published under the same title and reprinted in Gauss, *Werke* 5:79–118.

13. Cawood, "Terrestrial Magnetism," 577.

14. Gauss to Olbers, 2 Aug. 1832 (p. 587).

15. Since Weber's institute lacked basic measuring instruments and electromagnetic apparatus, the apparatus Weber made available to Gauss would not have been the main reason for his turn to earth-magnetic research. Weber to Göttingen U. Curator, 15 Dec. 1832, Göttingen UA, 4/V h/16. Gauss to Humboldt, 13 July 1833, in Schaefer, "Über Gauss' physikalische Arbeiten," 9.

16. Gauss to Olbers, 2 Aug. 1832 (p. 587).

17. See, for example, the advice Gauss gave to Weber in 1844, in Schaefer, "Über Gauss' physikalische Arbeiten," 118–19.

I have always considered these immense changes [in earth magnetism] as
something highly remarkable. Without doubt, the magnetic force of the
earth is not the result of a pair of large magnets near the center of the
earth, which gradually move many miles from their places, but the result
of all the polarized iron particles contained in the earth, and in fact more
of those that lie closer to the surface than of those that lie closer to the
center. But what is one to think of the immense changes that have taken
place in the last centuries? For me, this phenomenon has always seemed
to favor especially the hypothesis . . . according to which the solid crust
of the earth is, comparatively speaking, thin. Naturally, in that case, the
magnetic forces can be located only in it, and the gradual thickening of
this crust through the solidification of formerly liquid layers explains the
great variation occurring in earth magnetism in the most natural way,
which otherwise remains a great puzzle.[18]

The problem of the distribution of magnetism in a body led Gauss, as a first
step, to consult Biot's *Traité de physique* and to read Poisson's memoir of 1812 on
the distribution of electricity on the surface of conductors. He was bothered by the
discrepancy he found in Biot between the assumption that every magnetic body,
even the smallest part of it, contains equal amounts of "northern" and "southern"
magnetism and the observation that the poles of a magnetic body act as if they
contain only the one or the other magnetic fluid. Poisson's paper contained a statement—"new, as far as I know," Gauss remarked to Bessel in December 1831—that
suggested a way out of the difficulty.[19] The principle Gauss arrived at he stated
without proof in 1832: "however the distribution of free magnetism may behave
within a body, one can always put in its place, as a result of a general theorem in
accordance with a certain law, another distribution only for the surface of the body,
which to the outside acts entirely with the same forces as the former [that is, the
distribution inside the body]; so that an element of magnetic fluid placed anywhere
outside [the body] experiences exactly the same attraction and repulsion from the
real distribution of magnetism within the body as from that imagined to be on the
surface."[20]

In his "general theory" of earth magnetism in 1839, Gauss likened the task of
earth-magnetic researchers to that of astronomers: to subject magnetic observations
to "one principle" analogous to Newton's gravitational law and from it to predict
other phenomena. Earlier researchers had calculated magnetic phenomena from one,

18. Gauss to H. C. Schumacher, 3 Mar. 1832, in Schaefer, "Über Gauss' physikalische Arbeiten," 30.

19. In S. D. Poisson, "Mémoire sur la distribution de l'électricité à la surface des corps conducteurs,"
Mémoires de l'Institut, année 1811 (Paris, 1812), 1: "It is not sufficient for maintaining a constant electric
state in an electrified conducting body that the internal border surface of the free electricity at the surface
of the conductor be an equilibrium surface, but it is also required that this electricity does not exert any
attraction or repulsion at any point in the internal space." Gauss now pointed out that the second
condition, namely, that the resultant force at every point in the internal enclosed space be zero, is already
contained in the first, if the attraction and repulsion take place according to the inverse-square force law.
Quoted in Schaefer, "Über Gauss' physikalische Arbeiten," 99–100. Schaefer also quotes Gauss's letter
to Encke, 18 Aug. 1832 (pp. 13–14), and to Bessel, 31 Dec. 1831 (p. 100), on this work.

20. Schaefer, "Über Gauss' physikalische Arbeiten," 14.

two, or more infinitesimal magnets in the earth's interior, which reminded Gauss of the accumulation of epicycles in pregravitational astronomy. By contrast, Gauss offered a theory independent of "particular hypotheses about the distribution of the magnetic fluids in the body of the earth" and even of the hypothesis of magnetic fluids itself. Although he presented the theory in terms of the usual two magnetic fluids, nothing would have changed if instead he had viewed magnetism as originating in galvanic currents. The physical assumptions essential to his theory went back to his work of 1832. They were, first, that the "earth-magnetic force is the total action of the magnetized parts of the earth" and, second, that the magnetic fluids act according to an inverse-square force, a "proven physical truth."[21] These two assumptions allowed him to introduce the potential—although he did not call it that yet—into his magnetic theory.

In imagination, Gauss divided the earth into infinitely small volume elements, each containing a quantity of magnetic fluid $d\mu$. He then wrote the potential of the magnetized elements of the whole earth as $V = \int d\mu/\rho$, where ρ is the distance of the element from the point where the potential is evaluated. From this expression he derived components of the magnetic force parallel and normal to the earth's surface; the components are given by infinite converging series of spherical functions, and Gauss retained only their first few terms as approximations. To determine the coefficients of the terms, he referred to empirical maps of the intensity, declination, and inclination of the earth's magnetic force. He then calculated the magnetic elements for ninety-one magnetic stations all over the earth, finding satisfactory agreement between observations made at these places and his calculations. (The predictive power of the theory was shown two years later when Charles Wilkes found the south magnetic pole close to where Gauss had calculated it would be.)

The method that Gauss developed within his theory of earth magnetism was applicable throughout theoretical physics. Helmholtz, who as a young man was "stimulated by Gauss's magnetic investigations" to study mathematical physics, later extolled the method that Gauss's theory exemplified. Gauss, along with Neumann and several British physicists, had demonstrated the empirical character of mathematical physics, Helmholtz said, by their method of dividing bodies, as Gauss had divided the earth, into elementary volumes whose properties are determined through experimental physics like those of any large body in our experience.[22]

A year after the publication of his general theory of earth magnetism, Gauss published a systematic presentation of the mathematical tool he had used in that work, the potential. Here Gauss formally introduced the term "potential" to desig-

    21. Carl Friedrich Gauss, "Allgemeine Theorie des Erdmagnetismus," *Resultate* . . . *1838*, reprinted in Gauss, *Werke* 5:119–75, on 122–25, 126.
    22. Hermann von Helmholtz, "Gustav Magnus. In Memoriam," in *Popular Lectures on Scientific Subjects*, trans. E. Atkinson (London, 1881), 1–25, on 17–19; Leo Koenigsberger, *Hermann von Helmholtz*, 3 vols. (Braunschweig: F. Vieweg, 1902–3), 2:194–96.

nate the function from which the components of forces varying as the inverse square of the distance can be derived. He wrote the function as $V = \Sigma\mu/r$, which expresses the action at any point of a collection of point "masses" or, in general, "agents," and he developed a collection of theorems concerning the behavior of this function. The significance of V is that its properties are the "key to the theory of the attracting or repelling forces" of nature.[23] Potential theory applies to the phenomena of nature described by inverse-square forces between particles, to the phenomena of gravitation, electricity, and magnetism. Gauss even considered its application to electrodynamic phenomena, since Ampère's force between current elements depends on the inverse square of the distance; but the action of this force is complicated by the directionality of currents, and Gauss did not treat it here and only spoke of discussing it in a later paper, which he never did.[24]

Gauss showed that despite the striking differences of the observed phenomena of gravitation, electricity, and magnetism, their mathematical description draws on a common body of theorems. Potential theory provided mathematical methods of impressive generality: by studying the behavior of one function, abstracted from any one domain of phenomena, physicists could learn at once the mathematical structures relating the phenomena belonging to several domains. The conservation of energy principle, enunciated soon after Gauss's potential theory, made the potential an even more important aid in developing physical laws.

23. For the case in which the agents are continuously distributed, Gauss replaced the sum by an integral. He derived the standard equations for the potential in the absence of, and in the presence of, sources k:

$$\frac{ddV}{dx^2} + \frac{ddV}{dy^2} + \frac{ddV}{dz^2} = 0$$

and

$$\frac{ddV}{dx^2} + \frac{ddV}{dy^2} + \frac{ddV}{dz^2} = -4\pi k.$$

Gauss, "Allgemeine Lehrsätze in Beziehung auf die im verkehrten Verhältnisse des Quadrats der Entfernung wirkenden Anziehungs- und Abstossungs-Kräfte," *Resultate . . . 1839*, reprinted in Gauss, *Werke* 5:195–242, on 199–200. Gauss read the paper on 9 Mar. 1840.
   Limited uses of the potential long antedated Gauss's general, rigorous theory of the potential. In the late eighteenth century, Lagrange and Laplace wrote the components of gravitational attraction as the partial differential quotients of a certain function. In the early nineteenth century, this way of expressing forces was extended by Poisson and others to electricity and magnetism. Morris Kline, *Mathematical Thought from Ancient to Modern Times* (New York: Oxford University Press, 1972), 681–82. Before Gauss, some of the theorems on the potential had already been derived by George Green in 1828, but Green's work remained unnoticed until after Gauss's had attracted wide interest in the subject. Green's work was resurrected in 1846 by William Thomson, and it was only made readily accessible to a German audience through its publication in Crelle's *Journal* in 1850–1854. For this reason it was largely on the basis of Gauss's work that potential theory was developed in Germany into an "independent mathematical discipline" of importance to mathematicians and physicists alike. Albert Wangerin's "Anmerkungen" to the reprint of Gauss's "Allgemeine Lehrsätze," ed. Albert Wangerin as vol. 2 of Ostwald's Klassiker der exakten Wissenschaften (Leipzig, 1889), 51–60, on 52.
   24. Gauss, "Allgemeine Lehrsätze," 197–98.

Development of Mathematical and Instrumental Techniques

The experimental, as opposed to the theoretical, investigation of earth magnetism depended on overcoming two obstacles. First, a way had to be found to obtain observations that were more useful than the "relative" observations gathered before 1832. Gauss solved that problem by his introduction of "absolute" measuring units into the study of magnetism. Second, instruments had to be developed that would allow observations precise enough for the use of absolute units.[25] Gauss was excited by these problems not only because magnetism was one of the most interesting subjects, especially owing to discoveries of its connections to electricity; it was "almost even more important" to him that magnetic "experiments are becoming capable of a precision that far surpasses everything that went before, and its fundamental laws can have a truly mathematical precision, so that the separation between actual so-called physics and applied mathematics here, too (as in the theory of motion and optics long ago), begins to disappear, and the more thorough treatment begins to fall to the mathematician."[26]

Throughout 1832 Gauss worked to develop and test a method for reducing measures of the earth's magnetic force to the fundamental units of length, time, and mass. In February he informed Olbers that he was working on earth magnetism, "in particular [on] an absolute determination of its intensity. Friend Weber is doing experiments according to my specification."[27] From then until August, when he wrote to Olbers again, he had worked, "one might almost say, exclusively" on magnetism. The experimental results had not only met his expectations "but far surpassed" them: "At present I have completed two apparatus (completely alike) with which absolute declination and its variations, duration of oscillation, etc., can be measured with a precision that leaves nothing to be desired, except for a more suitable location where there is no iron nearby and every current of air is kept away." Gauss intended to devote a separate publication to the project, but not immediately, since he hated to hurry immature work. For the time being, he told Olbers, he would read to the Göttingen Society of Sciences a paper on the "most important" application; namely, the determination of the absolute intensity of earth magnetism.[28] The paper, which he read in December 1832, became his first publication on earth magnetism.

To establish absolute units for magnetic research, the precondition for experimental progress, Gauss proceeded from the assumption of northern and southern magnetic fluids, any two elements of which mutually repel if they belong to the same fluid and mutually attract if they belong to opposite fluids. Magnetic phenomena arise when the fluids, which are bound in equal amounts to the particles of ponderable bodies, are displaced relative to one another. Since the action between the magnetic fluids tends to set in motion the ponderable bodies to which they are

25. Gauss, "Intensitas vis magneticae terrestris," 298.
26. Gauss to Göttingen U. Curator, 29 Jan. 1833.
27. Gauss to Olbers, 18 Feb. 1832, in Briefwechsel zwischen Olbers und Gauss, 584–85.
28. Gauss to Olbers, 2 Aug. 1832 (p. 587).

bound, the measure of magnetic quantities and forces can be expressed in the same units used to express the interaction of ponderable bodies; namely, the familiar units of length, time, and mass. Force, mechanically measured, determines the unit of magnetic quantity; this is the key to Gauss's system of absolute units.[29]

Gauss's introduction of absolute units had "extraordinary significance for physics"; the fundamental units of mechanics were now seen to apply to another branch of physics, magnetism, and Gauss suggested their extension to still another branch, electricity. Weber soon established absolute units in electrodynamics, and they were extended to other forces and promised to create a common measure throughout physics.[30]

It was not enough to give the theory of the methods for reducing earth-magnetic intensity to absolute units, since it was impossible to use them in practice as long as magnetic observations remained as imprecise as they had been in the past. So Gauss set out to construct the necessary apparatus, having the "certain expectation that magnetic observations can be brought to a precision that is nearly, if not completely, as great as the finest astronomical [observations]."[31] The first magnetometer Gauss constructed in 1832 used prismatic rods nearly a foot long and weighing nearly a pound. He suspended these magnetic "needles" by a strong, untwisted silk thread, which could be rotated at its upper end. At one end of the needle he attached a plane mirror, set perpendicular to the magnetic axis of the needle. The freely suspended magnetic needle was then encased so that it could be observed even as it was protected from disturbing influences such as air currents. To obtain the precise measurements he wanted, Gauss had to construct his instruments for observing the magnet as carefully as he arranged the magnet itself. Opposite the mirror on the magnetic needle, he set up a theodolite so that its vertical axis and the suspension thread were in the same magnetic meridian, separated from one another by about sixteen feet. The optical axis of the telescope on the theodolite was a little higher than the needle and tilted downward in the vertical plane of the magnetic meridian so that it was aimed at the middle of the mirror on the needle. To the stand of the theodolite Gauss attached a four-foot-long horizontal scale (divided into millimeters)

29. The unit of magnetic quantity is that which acts on another unit of magnetic quantity at unit distance with unit moving force. Poisson had expressed the intensity of earth magnetism by the force with which a unit of magnetic quantity acts on a second unit, but he did not have an absolute system because his unit of magnetic quantity was arbitrary. E. Dorn's "Anmerkungen" to Gauss's "Intensitas vis magneticae terrestris," translated and reprinted as *Die Intensität der erdmagnetischen Kraft auf absolutes Maass zurückgeführt* (1832), ed. Ernst Dorn, vol. 53 of Ostwald's Klassiker der exakten Wissenschaften (Leipzig, 1894), 50–62, on 54. Schaefer has noted that Poisson did not have an absolute system in Gauss's sense and as it has come to be defined following Gauss, but that in the sense that his method did produce values for earth-magnetic force that are independent of the magnetic state of the needles used, he, too, got "absolute measures." Schaefer, "Über Gauss' physikalische Arbeiten," 25.

30. Dorn, "Anmerkungen," 50. Rosenberger, *Geschichte der Physik*, 302. In the course of the nineteenth century, opinions on the possibility of expressing all physical laws in absolute units varied. The early promise of the universal applicability of absolute units led to their overvaluation, as physicists later recognized: chemistry, heat, radiation, and even electricity and magnetism required a fourth fundamental unit (Dorn, 52).

31. Gauss, "Intensitas vis magneticae terrestris," 298. In this announcement of his paper of the same title on absolute measures, Gauss described the first magnetometer.

at right angles to the magnetic meridian. He called the point on the scale that lay in the same vertical plane as the optical axis of the telescope "point zero" and marked it with a weighted fine gold thread hanging from the middle of the objective lens. The scale was at such a level that an image of a part of it could be seen in the mirror through the telescope. With this instrumental arrangement, Gauss could determine the direction of the needle and its variation precisely. He could also measure the variation as frequently as every minute, because he did not have to wait until the needle had come to rest. His distance measurements were of "microscopic precision."[32]

Gauss's apparatus was immediately useful for measuring magnetic declination. Before he tackled the problem of making it equally useful for measuring magnetic intensity, he further refined its precision. For this purpose, he needed heavier magnets and an iron-free building, a special earth-magnetic observatory.[33]

On the day Gauss read his paper on absolute magnetic measures to the Göttingen Society, Weber, who had already been "extremely helpful"[34] in the experiments to test the new apparatus, requested materials for a large magnet from the Hannover government. He explained that Gauss's researches that year on earth magnetism showed how to produce an immensely powerful magnet, which would have the greatest importance for research. All that was needed was sufficient iron and steel, which should not be too costly. Weber more or less promised that Gauss would supervise its production, and the Göttingen University curator, assuming that Gauss would direct the research with the magnet, granted funds for buying five hundred pounds of steel, noting the "interesting investigations on earth magnetism that Hofrath Gauss has recently made."[35] Weber spent several days at the royal ironworks in Sollingen to make sure that the large steel rods, which weighed 25 pounds each and were 4½ feet long, and some of the smaller 4-pound steel rods were properly tempered "according to my instructions and under my eyes." (He cleverly pointed out to the curator that not only had he saved money by supervising the job at the ironworks, but he was also now bringing business to the state, since as a result of his work other universities had asked him to order similar steel rods for them.) The rest of the smaller steel rods Weber tempered at the physics institute, and he, Gauss, and "some of our friends and students who are especially interested in these investigations" did the remaining work.[36]

In 1833 the Göttingen earth-magnetic observatory was built on the grounds of the astronomical observatory, where Gauss worked and lived. Gauss had successfully argued for it by indirectly pointing to his researches of the previous year. He would be neglecting his duty toward Göttingen University, he wrote to the curator, if he

32. Gauss to Olbers, 2 Aug. 1832 (p. 588).

33. Gauss to Göttingen U. Curator, 29 Jan. 1833. Also Gauss to Olbers, 2 Aug. 1832 (p. 587); Schaefer, "Über Gauss' physikalische Arbeiten," 28; and Gauss to Encke, 18 Aug. and 25 Dec. 1832, in Schaefer, 31.

34. Gauss to Olbers, 2 Aug. 1832 (p. 588).

35. Weber to Göttingen U. Curator, 15 Dec. 1832, and Göttingen U. Curator to Weber, 17 Jan. 1833, Göttingen UA, 4/V h/16.

36. Weber to Göttingen U. Curator, 12 Aug. 1834, Göttingen UA, 4/V h/16.

did not call the government's attention to an opportunity for Göttingen not only to join the increasing number of institutions with magnetic observatories, but also to light the way for them with its new methods.[37] At the new magnetic observatory, Gauss's fellow astronomer at Göttingen, Carl Ludwig Harding, would observe the variation of magnetic declination several times a day at fixed times, and Gauss would determine the absolute magnetic intensity from time to time. In addition, they would make observations every quarter hour or at least every hour for two days and one night; they would do this eight times a year, on days fixed in advance to allow for simultaneous observations at all the magnetic observatories around the world. That, at least, was Humboldt's program for coordinating magnetic observations.

Organization of Earth-Magnetic Observations

But the new apparatus Gauss had created forced him to change Humboldt's program. To achieve greatest precision, it was desirable to make observations as frequently as the apparatus allowed, which was once per minute, or at least as frequently as could be expected of a large number of observers with varying skill, which Gauss decided was once every five minutes. But to observe at such close intervals for as long as forty-four hours would have been asking too much of the observers, so Gauss reduced the hours to twenty-four, starting at noon, and the number of prearranged observation dates in a year from eight to six. Observers elsewhere quickly followed suit, as they acquired apparatus modeled on Gauss's. From mid-1834, the old Gambey magnetometer was no longer used in these observations anywhere, and scientists such as Encke who wanted to set up the new magnetometer received an urgent appeal from Gauss to come to Göttingen to look at the prototype before doing anything.[38] Muncke visited Göttingen in 1836 to acquaint himself with the "grand magnetic installations there." In 1838 Gauss reported that "several excellent physicists, among them Herschel, will visit Göttingen, I am told, especially because of the magnetic institutions."[39] The center of earth-magnetic observations was Göttingen.

From all over Europe and beyond, earth-magnetic observatories joined in an informal organization, the Magnetic Union.[40] Their public forum was a journal begun by Gauss and Weber, the *Resultate aus den Beobachtungen des magnetischen Vereins*. Its six volumes covering 1836 to 1841 contained mainly Gauss's and Weber's own theoretical and observational results and descriptions of the magnetometers and other precision instruments in use.

Observatories of the Magnetic Union first measured variations in magnetic declination only. The preference for measuring declination, Gauss said, was not due to the practical advantages of knowing its variations but to the "present state of the

37. Gauss to Göttingen U. Curator, 29 Jan. 1833.
38. Gauss, "Einleitung," 347–49; Schaefer, "Über Gauss' physikalische Arbeiten," 37.
39. G. W. Muncke to government official, 13 Oct. 1836, Bad. GLA, 235/3057. G. W. Müller to Göttingen U. Curator Hoppenstedt, 17 May 1838, Listing Personalakte, Göttingen UA, 4/V b/108. Müller quoted Gauss's letter in this letter.
40. Gauss, "Einleitung," 349.

aids," the instruments available. "Seeking the laws of natural phenomena has, for the natural scientist, its purpose and its value in itself alone," he wrote in the introduction to the *Resultate*, "and a special enchantment surrounds the discovery of measure and harmony in what seems to be completely irregular. In following the wonderful play of the always changing variations of declination, the presently used apparatus leaves nothing to be desired with respect to certainty, precision, and ease of observing; but one cannot say the same of the means of observation [available] so far for the two other elements [inclination and intensity]."[41] As soon as the apparatus for these elements was perfected, the Magnetic Union would study them, too. Gauss did not expect that time to be far off.

Gauss's original, single-thread magnetometer was not well suited for precise observations of magnetic intensity. It measured the oscillations of the needle, which gave the average value of the intensity over a period of time, within which the intensity might change. In 1837 Gauss announced a new instrument "to fill the gap," the bifilar magnetometer.[42] As its name suggests, this magnetometer is suspended from two "threads" (actually a continuous loop of steel wire) instead of from one thread as in the case of the earlier instrument. The "conflict" between the magnetic force acting on the needle and the restoring force of the apparatus when it has been displaced from equilibrium results in an "intermediate," or equilibrium, position of the apparatus.[43] Every change in the intensity of the earth-magnetic force affects the position of the needle directly and can be easily, quickly, and precisely measured. The calculable mechanical restoring force gives an absolute measure of the intensity of the magnetic force; with the bifilar magnetometer the horizontal part of the earth's magnetism could now be "as precisely observed as the stars in the sky."[44]

Gauss had reached an end of sorts.[45] He believed that the vertical part of the earth's magnetism would never allow for similar precision, and he was not going to pursue it. The magnetometers he had invented had not required excessively fine and expensive mechanical work, but to measure the vertical part of the earth's magnetic force expensive instruments were needed. An inclination apparatus of a type then available, which Gauss considered "very far from what was desirable," already cost

41. Gauss, "Einleitung," 350–51. Carl Friedrich Gauss, "Ein neues Hülfsmittel für die magnetischen Beobachtungen," *Göttingische gelehrte Anzeigen*, 30 Oct. 1837, 1721–28, reprinted in *Werke* 5:352–56, on 352.

42. Gauss, "Ein neues Hülfsmittel," 353. Carl Friedrich Gauss, "Über ein neues, zunächst zur unmittelbaren Beobachtung der Veränderungen in der Intensität des horizontalen Theils des Erdmagnetismus bestimmtes Instrument," *Resultate . . . 1837*, 1–19, reprinted in *Werke* 5:357–73, on 358. The lecture to the Göttingen Scientific Society on which this paper is based was given on 19 Sept. 1837. The subject of these papers is the "bifilar" magnetometer.

43. Gauss, "Über ein neues . . . Instrument," 361.

44. Gauss to Olbers, 2 Sept. 1837, in *Briefwechsel zwischen Olbers und Gauss*, 649–50, on 649.

45. Gauss preferred to limit his observations of intensity to the horizontal component of the earth-magnetic force from the beginning. Oscillations in the horizontal plane could be made more easily and more precisely than in the plane of the magnetic meridian, and observations of the horizontal component were just as useful, he said, since the relation of the total earth-magnetic force to its horizontal component depends in a known way on the magnetic inclination. Carl Friedrich Gauss, "Erdmagnetismus und Magnetometer," *Schumachers Jahrbuch für 1836*, 1–47, reprinted in *Werke* 5:315–44, on 324.

considerably more than Gauss had to spend in a year on the astronomical and magnetic observatories together.[46]

Then the Göttingen physics institute became unavailable to Gauss to help with
the acquisition of apparatus. For to Gauss's grief, in the middle of his collaboration
with Weber, Weber was dismissed from his professorship for political reasons. Gauss
wondered whether to "bid the public farewell and announce the destruction of our
association" or to continue: "The arrangement of the new intensity apparatus lets us
look into a new world of wonders. But now that the way has been paved into it,
the gate is to be slammed shut in our faces."[47]

Extension of Techniques to Electricity

Gauss's frustration at being stopped in his collaboration with Weber at a promising
point referred mainly to their work on electromagnetism. Electricity was for Gauss a
"still almost completely new field," which like earth magnetism he set out to explore
in the measuring spirit in the early 1830s.[48] In 1832, for example, he applied a
magnetometer to galvanic as well as magnetic measurements; the magnetometer
proved to be a "most precise" galvonometer "for the strongest as well as the weakest
forces of a galvanic current," and he expected no difficulty in reducing galvanic
measurements to absolute measures, too.[49] At about the same time, Weber brought
him news of Fechner's recent measurements confirming Ohm's law, which were the
"finest made so far." To Gauss they already seemed only "rough approximations."[50]

The year 1832 also brought German physicists the translation in the *Annalen
der Physik* of Faraday's first publication on electromagnetic induction, which had
appeared in Britain at the end of 1831. Faraday's work naturally attracted Gauss's
and Weber's interest. Weber requested the large magnet in December of that year
"especially now in following up Faraday's discoveries on producing the phenomena
of the galvanic pile by strong magnets."[51] A few weeks later, Gauss justified his
request for a magnetic observatory not only by the needs of earth magnetism but
also by its use in "almost innumerable other magnetic, galvano-magnetic, and electromagnetic observations and measurements," which would help in clarifying "many
as yet dark parts in these theories." Over the next months, Gauss used his apparatus

---

46. Gauss to Olbers, 2 Sept. 1837 (p. 649–50).

47. G. W. Müller to Hoppenstedt, 17 May 1838.

48. Gauss to Gerling, 28 Oct. 1832, quoted in Schaefer, "Über Gauss' physikalische Arbeiten,"
104.

49. Gauss, "Intensitas vis magneticae terrestris," 301.

50. Schaefer, "Über Gauss' physikalische Arbeiten," 104. Later Gauss did most exacting galvanic
measurements. By coiling a great length of wire around the magnetic bar and passing a current through
it, he converted the bifilar magnetometer into a sensitive galvanometer. With it, the weakest galvanic
force deflected a twenty-five pound bar significantly. With it, he also measured frictional and thermoelectric currents as well as battery currents. Christoph Stähelin, "Wilhelm Weber in seiner allgemeinen
Bedeutung für die Entwicklung und die Fortschritte der messenden und experimentirenden Naturforschung," in J. C. F. Zöllner, *Principien einer elektrodynamischen Theorie der Materie*, vol. 1, *Abhandlungen
zur atomistischen Theorie der Elektrodynamik* (Leipzig, 1876), xcix–cxxiv, on c–ci, cxi.

51. Weber to Göttingen U. Curator, 15 Dec. 1832.

"mainly for experiments on the so-called induction, which is one of the most inter-esting phenomena of nature and which I can make much more strongly visible."[52]

Gauss and Weber's continuous expansion of the magnetic facilities at Göttingen and their "development and perfection" of magnetic observations allowed them "to subject *galvanic* observations to analogous principles" in a number of electromagnetic investigations.[53] In 1834 Gauss gave his first magnetometer to the physical cabinet, so that there were now three observations points in Göttingen: one in the magnetic observatory, used "when great precision is required," one in the astronomical obser-vatory, and the one in Weber's institute, all linked together by a wire circuit.[54] One use to which Gauss and Weber put this arrangement was to study the velocity of electric current. They found the velocity to be so great that it was impossible to measure the time it took for the current to pass through a half mile of wire; the three magnets in the three locations seemed to move simultaneously when the cur-rent was turned on. Gauss and Weber also studied the intensity of electric current in their circuit; they measured induction; and they improved on Fechner's work by giving their own experimental proof of Ohm's law. They perfected their instruments with one purpose in mind: to aid in the "investigation of the *mathematical laws* governing the production and action of the magneto-electric induction discovered by Faraday and its reduction to absolute measures."[55] The magnetometer was the necessary complement, Gauss said, to "Oersted's and Faraday's brilliant discoveries," which "have opened a new world to scientific research, the enchanted gardens of which fill us with admiration; we can subject these rich fields to our domination only under the guidance of the art of measuring."[56] On these "rich fields," Weber's dismissal from Göttingen slammed the gate, at least for Gauss.

As an independent researcher, Weber continued to collaborate with Gauss for a time. Beyond that, he saw his work with Gauss on earth magnetism as the begin-ning of a new way of organizing research and education in physics. "It happens to be my conviction that the way in which physics has been treated so far is outdated and needs to be changed," he wrote in 1841, "and that our treatment of the mag-netic problem is a first test. It goes against many deep-rooted practices and arouses in many the wish that something like this had not been started; but if it is carried out, it will soon develop further and affect beneficially all parts of science."[57] To Edward Sabine he wrote in 1845 that magnetic observations had already become important for *"many other physical investigations."* Weber also described to Sabine the

52. Gauss to Göttingen U. Curator, 29 Jan. 1833. Gauss to Schumacher, 21 Mar. 1833, in Schae-fer, "Über Gauss' physikalische Arbeiten," 127.

53. Weber to Edward Sabine, 20 Feb. 1845, in Wilhelm Weber, *Werke*, vol. 2, *Magnetismus*, ed. Eduard Riecke (Berlin, 1892), 274–76.

54. Göttingen U. Curator to Gauss (with a copy of the letter to Weber), 5 May 1834, authorizing the transfer, Göttingen UA, 4/V h/16. Carl Friedrich Gauss, "Eine Fortsetzung der am 9. August 1834 gegebenen Nachricht," *Göttingische gelehrte Anzeigen*, 7 Mar. 1835, 345–57, reprinted in *Werke* 5:528–36, on 529–30.

55. Gauss, "Fortsetzung," 531–32.

56. Gauss, "Erdmagnetismus und Magnetometer," 336.

57. Weber to Karl von Richthofen, 9 Apr. 1841, Göttingen UB, Ms. Dept., Phil. 182.

simultaneous influence that the earth-magnetic investigations had had on the organization and teaching of physics:

> In Germany . . . until now there existed only collections of physical instruments without permanent facilities for their use; there were no physical *laboratories* and *observatories*. Such laboratories and observatories, which have become indispensable for the advances of science, are now beginning to come into being, and the grants given for magnetic observations provide solid and reliable *support* in this, as I can attest from my own experience. . . . At our universities one finally increasingly recognizes the importance that the education of *exact observers of nature* has for science and for practical life. So far only astronomy has offered an opportunity, very one-sided, for the education of exact observers, which could be used by only a few. Experience has shown that magnetic observatories can serve as excellent *educational institutions* for observers.[58]

The slow realization of ideas like Weber's, our subject in chapter 4, came about through the efforts of a few physicists whose physical researches were done in the "Gaussian" spirit,[59] using the new mathematical and measuring techniques. It took them several decades to reach their goal of providing proper training for physicists, since physics was not highly valued in government quarters. "It is of course sad to apply one's energy to things on which no value is placed as yet in the world or at least in Germany, especially in Berlin," Weber complained to a Berlin friend in 1841; but "with perseverance, one will make truth triumph in the end after all."[60]

58. Weber to Sabine, 20 Feb. 1845.
59. The term "Gaussian" was applied to Kirchhoff's work, for example.
60. Weber to Richthofen, 9 Apr. 1841.

4

Reforms in Teaching University Physics: Development of the Seminar and the Laboratory in the 1830s and 1840s

During the middle decades of the nineteenth century, the universities in Germany added a function to physics instruction: they now not only provided general education in physics for medical and other students of the professions but also physics training for those—still few—who chose a career in physics. Instead of having to depend solely on chance encouragement and self-study, university students attracted to physics were offered a grounding in research methods by physics teachers who were themselves good researchers.

In the physics laboratory, students handled apparatus not only to learn about nature but also to learn methods of investigating nature. Likewise, they solved mathematical problems in physics in part to learn methods of investigating nature mathematically. A new spirit of teaching physics, a wish to stimulate students to independent thought, as Ohm had urged, entered the universities where the better physicists taught. The new teaching found its place in new institutions within the university such as the physics seminar, the teaching laboratory, and the physics colloquium.

Seminars for Physics

Improved secondary school education in the early nineteenth century made greater demands on the training of secondary school teachers. Because of the emphasis on the classical languages in the gymnasiums, these demands were first felt—and met—by the philologists in the philosophical faculties. In the past, it had been the practice to allow theology students or preachers waiting for an appointment to a parish to teach classical languages in the secondary schools. Now these classes began to be taught by philologists properly trained in university philology seminars. When mathematicians and natural scientists in turn needed to train secondary school teachers, they looked to the philology seminars as a "finished model." The success of these

seminars together with a reminder of the recent developments in scientific knowledge was an argument that persuaded most German ministries of education to establish seminars for the teaching of science and mathematics beginning in the 1830s.
The "influence" of the philological seminars "on the development of humanistic
education is undoubted and they are therefore seen as an integrating part of every
university," Stern, by then an extraordinary professor of mathematics at Göttingen,
wrote in 1849: "The philological seminars came into being in an intellectual epoch
[*Bildungsepoche*] extending into our own time in which the knowledge of antiquity
was seen as the almost exclusive foundation of all scientific knowledge. But the
louder the so-called realistic direction demands its right, the greater the need becomes for all educated people to understand the foundations on which rest the mechanical and physical discoveries and inventions that affect our conditions so might-
ily, and the more it also becomes necessary that future teachers of mathematics and
physics be offered an academic institute that has their further training as its special
purpose."[1]

Unless they were privately arranged, university seminars were regulated by
printed statutes, were announced along with the university lectures, and were given
a little money for books, a few instruments, and stipends or prizes to inspire and
then reward student effort. Professors of the fields covered in the seminar were appointed directors of the seminar by the ministry of education, and they took turns
administrating it. Although they were in charge, they had to send yearly reports,
sometimes together with student work, to the ministry of education, where their
work might be reviewed by an official concerned with secondary school education.

The idea of a seminar for mathematics and the natural sciences was first referred
to in official documents and in the writings of individual scientists around the mid-
1820s. In 1824, for example, the curator of Heidelberg University, at the instigation
of the professor of mathematics, proposed to the Baden ministry of the interior the
establishment of a "mathematical seminarium," pointing out that such a step would
reserve for their state the "fame" of having been the first in Germany to create such
as institution.[2] The following year, Bonn University began a seminar for all the
natural sciences, excluding mathematics. By the late 1820s Halle University had a
"physical seminar" directed by Schweigger and a private "mathematical society,"
which was announced alongside the historical and theological seminars.[3] Weber, an

1. Moritz Stern to "Ministerial-Vorstand" Braun, 10 Oct. 1849, Göttingen UA, 4/V h/20.
2. Heidelberg U. Curator Froehlich to Baden Ministry of the Interior, 23 Feb. 1824, Bad. GLA,
235/3228. The Heidelberg classical philologists were not quite ready yet to give up their monopoly of
secondary school education and concede the usefulness of seminars in other fields, even mathematics.
One member of the faculty suggested, sarcastically, that seminars for Arabic, Persian, or physics might
be next. Their dominance did not come to an end until 1863. Riese, *Hochschule*, 194, 196.
3. Bonn U. Curator Beseler to Prussian Minister of Culture von Mühler, 14 Sept. 1864, in "Acta
betreffend den mathematischen Apparat der U. Bonn," N.-W. HSTA, NW5 Nr. 558. Prussian Ministry
of Culture, "Acta betreffend: das naturwissenschaftliche Seminarium der Universität zu Bonn," especially
the report by the directors of the seminar to Bonn U. Curator Beseler, 20 Mar. 1867, N.-W. HSTA,
NW5 Nr. 483. The Halle seminar was mentioned by Weber, who identified himself as a "member" in
"Auszug aus dem die Theorie des Schalles und Klanges betreffenden Aufsätzen von Felix Savart," *Jahrb.
d. Chem. u. Phys.* 14 (1825): 385–428, reprinted in *Werke* 1:3–28, on 3. Also in Heinrich Weber, *Weber,*
7. From 1839, mathematics was part of the Halle seminar: *Vorläufiges Reglement für das Seminar für Ma-*

early member of the Halle seminar, brought the idea with him when he became professor of physics at Göttingen in 1831; he soon began a laboratory practice course for physics that included training secondary school teachers,[4] but he did not call it a seminar until he established it anew in 1850 as part of a mathematical-physical seminar. Giessen University expressed the wish for a seminar for mathematics and the natural sciences at least as early as 1832, but the Hessen ministry of the interior ignored it and later requests until the early 1860s.[5]

Following Bonn's example, in 1828 the physicists Franz Neumann and Heinrich Wilhelm Dove with two of their colleagues proposed a natural sciences seminar at Königsberg University; the Prussian government approved the seminar but did not provide any money, so it did not get under way until 1835, and then it lasted for only four years.[6] In 1834 Neumann and the Königsberg mathematicians set up a mathematical-physical seminar[7] as a parallel institution to the planned seminar for the natural sciences which included experimental physics and its professor, Moser. At Berlin in 1834, the mathematician Gustav Lejeune Dirichlet began a private mathematical seminar in his house that offered gifted students a chance to solve problems and to practice lecturing.[8] The same year, a "mathematical society" founded at Greifswald took on as one of its functions the training of secondary school teachers.[9] Freiburg established a seminar for mathematics and the natural sciences in 1846; Göttingen, Munich, Breslau, Heidelberg, and Tübingen all acquired mathematical-physical seminars in the 1850s and 1860s.[10] Between 1825 and 1870, half of the German universities established seminars of this sort.

---

thematik und die gesammten Naturwissenschaften auf der Universität Halle-Wittenberg (Halle, 1840), dated 27 Nov. 1839, in Göttingen UA, 4/V h/20. On the Halle mathematical society: Lorey, Das Studium der Mathematik, 113. Its announcement did not mention the training of secondary school teachers, however.

4. In his first comprehensive report on the Göttingen physical cabinet to the university curator, Weber mentioned his intention of giving "physicians, chemists, pharmacists, and also . . . gymnasium teachers in the subject of mathematics" the chance to practice experimenting and making reliable observations. Weber to Göttingen U. Curator, 24 Apr. 1832, Göttingen UA, 4/V h/15.

5. H. Kopp to Giessen Philosophical Faculty, 20 Jan. 1861, Giessen UA, Phil H Nr. 36.

6. Albert Wangerin, Franz Neumann und sein Wirken als Forscher und Lehrer (Braunschweig: F. Vieweg, 1907), 148–49. Lorey, Das Studium der Mathematik, 114.

7. "Statuten des mathematisch-physikalischen Seminars an der Königsberger Universität," Feb. 1834, Göttingen UA, 4/V h/20. Also Wangerin, Neumann, 150.

8. Kurt-R. Biermann, Die Mathematik und ihre Dozenten an der Berliner Universität 1810–1920. Stationen auf dem Wege eines mathematischen Zentrums von Weltgeltung (Berlin: Akademie-Verlag, 1973), 31. Dirichlet's seminar does not seem to have been intended for training teachers.

9. Lorey, Das Studium der Mathematik, 116–17. One of the departments of the "society" studied the parts of mathematics that were taught in Prussian gymnasiums according to existing ordinances; the other department studied more difficult parts, including the applications of mathematics to the natural sciences, and it was intended for those who specialized in mathematics and wished to become mathematicians.

10. Freiburg: Statuten des Seminars für Mathematik und Naturwissenschaften an der Universität zu Freiburg im Breisgau (Freiburg i. Br., 1846); also Freiburg U. Senate to Baden Ministry of the Interior, 7 Sept. 1846, Bad. GLA, 235/7766. Göttingen: "Statuten des mathematisch-physikalischen Seminars zu Göttingen," 11 Feb. 1850, Göttingen UA, 4/V h/20. Munich: "Statuten für das mathematisch-physikalische Seminar an der kgl. Universität München" and official decree establishing the seminar, 12 June 1856, Munich UA, Sen. 209, Nr. 5213. Breslau: Festschrift . . . Breslau, 440. Heidelberg: Kirchhoff and Leo Koenigsberger to Baden Ministry of the Interior, 14 Apr. 1869, including "Statut für das mathematisch-physikalische Seminar in Heidelberg," Bad. GLA, 235/3228. Tübingen: Minister of Church and School Affairs to King of Württemberg, "Anbringen . . . betreffend das mathematisch-physikalische

Stern's call for the founding of mathematical-physical seminars implied that the traditional ways of teaching mathematics and natural sciences at universities had been inadequate to train good secondary school teachers in these subjects. The complaint appeared as early as 1824 in the proposal of a mathematical seminar at Heidelberg: "The importance and usefulness" of a seminar is clear, the proposal stated, "when one considers how superficially and in what sloppy manner mathematics is taught and practiced at the majority of our secondary schools."[11] The science seminars established at Bonn and Königsberg in the late 1820s also claimed that their purpose was to train good teachers for the natural sciences, as did most later seminars.

The seminars offered future gymnasium teachers of mathematics and the natural sciences the opportunity to learn how to present their subject, handle basic instruments, and conduct observations and simple experiments in the most important natural sciences. The wider the students' exposure to different natural sciences in the seminar, the better gymnasium directors and officials in charge of secondary education liked it. Seminars covering all of the natural sciences were accordingly the first science seminars to be financially supported by the Prussian government. In 1834 it gave money to the Königsberg seminar for the natural sciences but not to the specialized mathematical-physical seminar proposed that year.[12] At Bonn it established a seminar for physics, chemistry, mineralogy, botany, and zoology; in it students had to work in all the fields, and as late as 1867 the seminar directors could still report that gymnasium directors requested students from the seminar to teach at their gymnasiums because of their thorough education and versatility.[13] The government of Hannover, at the suggestion of the spokesmen for its secondary schools, tried to include other natural sciences in the mathematical-physical seminar being planned for Göttingen in 1849, but it settled for a compromise.[14]

With respect to the numbers of students the seminars trained for teaching at secondary schools, the seminars soon did their work too well: many more students qualified than there were open positions. For example, in its first thirty-six years,

---

Seminar in Tübingen," 25 July 1887, HSTA, Stuttgart, B14, B1475; also Karl Klüpfel, *Die Universität Tübingen in ihrer Vergangenheit und Gegenwart dargestellt* (Leipzig, 1877), 128; Württemberg, Statistisches Landesamt, *Statistik der Universität Tübingen*, ed. K. Statistisch-Topographisches Bureau (Stuttgart, 1877), 65; *Festgabe zum 25. Regierungs-Jubiläum seiner Majestät des Königs Karl von Württemberg* (Tübingen, 1889), 14.

11. Heidelberg U. Curator Froehlich to Baden Ministry of the Interior, 23 Feb. 1824.

12. Wangerin, *Neumann*, 149, 151.

13. Directors of the Bonn science seminar to Bonn U. Curator Beseler, 20 Mar. 1867, N.-W. HSTA, NW5 Nr. 483.

14. Weber, Listing, and the mathematicians and other natural scientists at Göttingen U., "Bericht die Gründung eines mathematisch-physicalischen Seminars an der Universität Göttingen betreffend," 19–31 Jan. 1850, Göttingen UA, 4/V h/20. The mathematicians and scientists at Göttingen felt that a seminar representing all of the natural sciences and mathematics was unrealistic, mainly because it demanded too much of the students. As a compromise, they arranged with the professors of the other sciences that members of the seminar could attend regular practice courses in these extra fields without having to do as much work in them as the regular students. Further, they arranged that if the need should arise, the representatives of the other sciences would teach sections in the seminar. But the need never arose.

1834–70, Neumann's section of the mathematical-physical seminar trained 138 students; of these, fewer than half, 59, are known to have become teachers at secondary schools, and in the crucial early years before 1860 as few as 19 did. Of the latter, 16 found positions in Prussia; the other 3 were Swiss and returned home to teach.[15] The Göttingen mathematical-physical seminar trained 129 students in its first *five* years, 1850–55. That number alarmed the officials, since there were only 29 secondary schools with a total of 31 positions for the natural sciences and mathematics in the state of Hannover. The secondary schools pointed to the growing list of candidates waiting in vain for teaching positions and suggested that the Göttingen seminar had completed its task.[16] The small demand for mathematics and physics teachers at Bavarian secondary schools was the reason why the professor of physics at Munich University Siber in 1832 opposed the formal establishment of a seminar for training teachers of mathematics and physics, even though he recognized the value of seminar training and provided it himself on an informal basis. He acknowledged that physicists received poor training; unlike mathematicians who can educate themselves, "experimenting" physicists could not. But he also pointed out that Bavaria needed only about one new mathematics teacher a year and a new physics teacher only every five or six years, and with so few openings at secondary schools most of the graduates of such a seminar would not find jobs.[17]

The small demand for science teachers reflected the small part of the gymnasium curriculum given over to the natural sciences. Even after several reforms, gymnasiums required few teachers for these fields, two at most.[18] Moreover, the reforms were as likely to decrease as to increase science instruction in the schools. As one university professor observed, despite the existence of excellent mathematical-physical seminars, such as Königsberg's, much of the fate of secondary school instruction in these subjects depended on the "attitudes" of government officials and educators in charge of the schools.[19] In Prussia, for example, the few hours devoted to physics were further reduced in 1837 and could even be filled in part by natural history.[20]

15. Information on Neumann's students appears in Neumann's seminar reports (drafts) for the academic years 1847–67 and beyond, with the exception of the academic years 1849/50, 1851/52, and 1853/54, for which reports are missing, Neumann Papers, Göttingen UB, Ms. Dept.; Wangerin, *Neumann*, 152–56; Paul Volkmann, *Franz Neumann. 11. September 1798, 23. Mai 1895* (Leipzig, 1896), 55–68; and Kathryn Mary Olesko, "The Emergence of Theoretical Physics in Germany: Franz Neumann and the Königsberg School of Physics, 1830–1890" (Ph.D. diss., Cornell University, 1980), 504–23.

16. "Bericht des Ober-Schulcollegii" to Hannover Ministry of Religious and Educational Affairs, 27 July 1855, Göttingen UA, 4/V h/20.

17. Siber was opposing the proposal made in 1832 by the Berlin mathematician Martin Ohm for the establishment of a "Bavarian Institute for the Training of Future Professors of Mathematics and Physics." Having presented his arguments to a meeting of the Bavarian Academy, he, along with a committee of the academy, concluded that the training teachers now received was adequate. If it should prove not to be, Siber added, future teachers could always be sent to Martin Ohm in Berlin, who should then found a German Central Institute for the purpose. Karl Neuerer, *Das höhere Lehramt in Bayern*, 106–7.

18. "Bericht des Ober-Schulcollegii" to Hannover Ministry of Religious and Educational Affairs, 27 July 1855.

19. Plücker to Bonn U. Curator Beseler, n.d., received 13 Sept. 1864, N.-W. HSTA, NW5 Nr. 558.

20. Wilhelm Lexis, ed., *Die Reform des höheren Schulwesens in Preussen* (Halle a. d. S.: Buchhandlung des Waisenhauses, 1902), 274.

Gymnasiums were required to offer one hour of physics a week in the sixth and seventh years and two hours in the eighth and ninth, which roughly equated physics with drawing, singing, and philosophy in the time it received. Most of the class hours were allotted to Latin, Greek, and mathematics, in that order, followed by history, German, French, and the "most essential and most important," though not the most time-consuming, subject, religion. With another new Prussian curriculum in 1856, the hours devoted to physics did not change, but its importance was further diminished.[21] Physics together with natural history, the other natural science in the secondary curriculum that was also taught in the lower classes, was removed from the final examination. "For the young tree of natural science instruction," the historian of Prussian education Wilhelm Lexis lamented, "the raw winter time had come."[22]

Only at the new type of secondary school known as the Realschule was science given an important place. This school, like the gymnasium, offered a complete nine-year general education, but it was directed to occupations that did not require university study. The prominence the Realschulen gave to the natural sciences earned them the tag "natural science gymnasiums": preliminary directions for the Realschulen in Prussia in 1832 called for a final oral and written examination on theories in all branches of physics; when the Realschulen were formally subsumed under government regulations in 1859, their curriculum allotted more time to the natural sciences in the last four years than to any other subject.[23] But there were fewer Realschulen than gymnasiums, and their needs remained largely outside university interests in the period we are considering.

Although the training of teachers was a justification for establishing a seminar, it was not a sufficient reason for it to survive and flourish. When in 1855 the directors of the Göttingen seminar were confronted with the charge that they were producing too many gymnasium teachers, they replied that even though the "immediate" purpose of the seminar was the training of teachers, this training was not the "primary" purpose. They explained that the seminar was meant to improve university studies in the mathematical-physical sciences, to promote scientific endeavors, and to contribute to the training of researchers.[24] At other universities, seminar directors, such as Neumann at Königsberg and Kirchhoff at Heidelberg, expected their mathematical-physical seminars to promote a "more serious study of physics" and to train students to "undertake independent scientific work."[25] The seminar acquired more purposes than the one first put forward by its founders; university

21. Giese, Quellen, 125, 127–28, 157.

22. Lexis, Reform, 274.

23. Lexis, Reform, 275–77; Giese, Quellen, 33–34, 160–62.

24. "Bericht des Seminars," 19 Nov. 1855, Göttingen UA, 4/V h/20. In the first annual seminar report in 1851, Weber had already said that many members of the seminar did not intend to become secondary school teachers; the students were coming to the seminar for other reasons. "Jahresbericht des Vorstandes des mathematisch physikalischen Seminars, den Zustand des Seminars von Ostern 1850 bis dahin 1851 betreffend" to Göttingen U. Curator, 31 Mar. 1851, Göttingen UA, 4/V h/20.

25. Wangerin, Neumann, 153; Kirchhoff and Koenigsberger to Baden Ministry of the Interior, 14 Apr. 1869, Bad. GLA, 235/3228.

physicists used it in ways that only incidentally contributed to the training of secondary school teachers. In developing this point, we draw mainly on the experiences
of Neumann and Weber.

Uses of the Seminar

One way of improving university physics was to improve its material means, and to
this end the seminars proved helpful. By allowing physicists to claim that their
teaching was valuable for the state, the seminars provided them with an argument
for increased financial support. For the physicists more money meant more apparatus
and instruments, not only for teaching but also for research. In turn, their research
advanced their reputations as scholars, improving their chances for further support
for their work. Franz Neumann at Königsberg is an example of a physicist who
sought to use the seminar for this purpose.

Neumann's desire to improve mathematics and physics education at every level
owed, no doubt, in part to the deprivations he had experienced in his own education. From early on, he had a keen interest in mathematics; as a gymnasium student
in Berlin, he was called "Mathematicus" for excelling in both his own assignments
and those of other, less gifted students. He had a stern mathematics teacher who
refused to cater to students who could not follow him, who included almost every-
body but Neumann, who was already studying Legendre. He befriended booksellers
who let him sit on the floor of their shops and read mathematics books he could not
buy. When he left the gymnasium, his certificate noted his advanced knowledge of
mathematics, which exceeded the requirements of the school, and it also noted his
good work in physics. Neumann's interest and accomplishments in mathematics and
physics led him to hope for a career in these fields, but his father, a farmer, advised
him to study for a profession that would guarantee a job.[26] So when Neumann
entered Berlin University in 1817, he gave theology as his field. After a year, he
moved to Jena University, where he heard lectures on nature philosophy by Lorenz
Oken; the other natural history professors at Jena disappointed him, and he returned
to Berlin. He now completely gave up the practical course his father had urged on
him and took up natural sciences, especially mineralogy, under the decisive influence then, and for some time after, of the Berlin mineralogy professor Ernst Christian Weiss. A second formative influence on Neumann during these years was Fourier's treatise on the analytical theory of heat; it probably being beyond his means,
he copied it out in its entirety. With the exception of Weiss, he said, no one had
taught him as much as this French mathematical physicist; later he often called
Fourier his greatest teacher and ranked him almost alongside Newton.[27] His self-
study of Fourier and of other French writers gave him a solid grounding in the
methods of mathematical physics.

26. Luise Neumann, *Franz Neumann, Erinnerungsblätter von seiner Tochter*, 2d ed. (Tübingen:
J. C. B. Mohr [P. Siebeck], 1907), 67, 79–80.

27. Luise Neumann, *Neumann*, 84–85, 110–11, 244–45. Also Voigt, "Neumann," 252; Volkmann,
Neumann, 7.

By the time Neumann applied to the Prussian minister of culture for a teaching position, he had already defined his interests as the "mathematical-physical" parts of mineralogy and, beyond that, those parts of "physics in general" that have received or are now capable of receiving a "higher mathematical" development. Appointed Privatdocent of Königsberg University in 1826, he accepted the position with reluctance. He was worried, first, that at Königsberg he might not be allowed to teach physics and, second, that he might not have access to physical apparatus or a mineralogical collection.[28] He was soon reassured on the first point, for his ability moved Bessel, the Königsberg astronomer, to recommend him for promotion on the grounds that he would soon be among the first "mathematical physicists."[29] He was promoted to extraordinary professor in 1828 and ordinary professor for mineralogy and physics the following year. His second worry concerning apparatus, however, occupied him for the rest of his career at Königsberg and had much to do with the development of his seminar there.

Throughout most of his career, Neumann based his pleas for the improvement of physics at Königsberg on the needs of the mathematical-physical seminar.[30] Little as that argument gained him in the end, it was still more than he would have gained in any other way. As ordinary professor, he received an annual budget of 150 thaler for material needs such as instruments, and he was put in charge of the small existing collection of apparatus, which he found inadequate for his needs. So he began his work virtually without equipment and with a budget that was approximately a tenth of the amount he would have needed for a good collection of basic measuring instruments and apparatus.[31] His participation in the plans for a state-financed seminar began at about the same time, and indeed when the mathematical-physical seminar was established in 1834, he received some money for physical apparatus.[32]

In 1831 a second physicist, Ludwig Moser, began to teach at Königsberg, adding to the demands on the small physical collection. Neumann invited Moser to select what he needed for lectures from the collection, which was still under his supervision. They then stored the instruments in the physics lecture hall, so that Moser as well as Neumann could have free access to them. The new instruments Neumann bought with his annual budget he reserved for his own research, unwilling to let Moser use them because of the time and work it would require of him constantly to readjust them.[33] Moser must have been as little satisfied with the apparatus Neumann permitted him to use (in fact he never did use it) as Neumann had been, and

28. Luise Neumann, Neumann, 226, 231, 233–34.

29. Volkmann, Neumann, 7.

30. Luise Neumann, Neumann, 364, 371–72; Wangerin, Neumann, 155, 181–83. Wangerin's claim here that Neumann saw the need for a teaching laboratory "at a time [1837] when at least in Germany nobody thought of such facilities for physics" is, of course, nonsense. For their own reasons, Neumann's disciples routinely made such sweeping and incorrect claims and must be read with greater skepticism than most authors of obituaries and encomiums.

31. Olesko, "Emergence," 284–86.

32. Olesko, "Emergence," 314. Wangerin, Neumann, 155. The two accounts disagree on the details concerning the appropriations, however.

33. Neumann to the Königsberg U. Curator, draft, 1833, Neumann Papers, Göttingen UB, Ms. Dept.

in 1833 and again in 1835 he requested instruments of his own. Neumann at first responded to what he thought was unjust criticism of himself, but in the end he saw the matter from Moser's point of view and requested that Moser be given at least 100 thaler annually for instruments for his own use.[34] Eventually Moser was given an annual budget of 200 thaler.[35] Moser also joined the seminar for the natural sciences that began in 1835, which for the next five years received state support while the mathematical-physical seminar did not. In 1839 he was appointed ordinary professor for experimental physics and was then of the same rank as Neumann. His annual budget was larger than Neumann's, but Neumann had more money at his disposal since the seminar for the natural sciences of which Moser was a part was discontinued, while the mathematical-physical seminar of which Neumann was a part now regularly got 350 thaler a year.[36]

From the founding of his seminar, Neumann argued that for it to achieve its purpose, he would have to train his students in observational and experimental techniques. That training required student participation and practice, "the opportunity [to learn] physical methods and [to awaken] their imagination through their own . . . experimental work." So a suitably equipped laboratory was necessary. He petitioned for space and money in 1834 when the university put up a new building, again in 1840 when the Prussian king visited Königsberg and condescended to hear Neumann and even to promise him a laboratory, again in 1844 when the university put up another new building, and again and again, and always in vain.[37] In 1846, he described the space he needed: an instrument room, an auditorium, two general workrooms, a workroom for large galvanic apparatus, a long narrow room with a heliostat and a theodolite, and a proper laboratory that is bright, dry, and solid. If he had rented this space outside the university, it would have cost him more than his entire annual budget.[38]

In the mid-1840s, when Neumann was doing his most influential research, the number of students in his lectures was dropping off: from between twelve and seventeen in the early 1840s to four in his public lectures in the summer of 1846, and the attendance in his seminar was decreasing, too.[39] Moreover, the government evaluation of the seminar in the fall of 1845 had charged the seminar with not doing what it was supposed to do; namely, train school teachers. The report implied that

34. Neumann to Königsberg U. Curator Reusch, draft, 21 May 1835, Neumann Papers, Göttingen UB, Ms. Dept.
35. Moser's account of his finances in the letter dated 26 Apr. 1844, Bad. GLA, 235/7525.
36. Wangerin, Neumann, 148–80; Volkmann, Neumann, 50.
37. "Statuten des mathematisch-physikalischen Seminars an der Königsberger Universität." Also Volkmann, Neumann, 52–53, and Luise Neumann, Neumann, 347–48, 364. Quotation in Olesko, "Emergence," 304.
38. Franz Neumann, "Andeutungen über die Erfordernisse eines physikalischen Laboratoriums," 1846, in Luise Neumann, Neumann, 445.
39. Volkmann, Neumann, 56–58; Olesko, "Emergence," 504–23. We have been careful to distinguish between attendance in the seminar as a whole and attendance in Neumann's section of the seminar only, particularly for the 1840s. During the 1840s, twenty-five individuals attended the Königsberg seminar, but only eleven attended Neumann's section. For the seminar as a whole, attendance during those years was an average of six per semester (Olesko, 308), while Neumann had only one or two students or none at all during most of these same years.

the work of the members of the seminar did not show that they were learning to "instruct . . . by speaking," as teachers must, but were writing up their research.[40] The student work in question must have included Kirchhoff's, in which case the government's evaluation was confirmed by the best research ever produced in Neumann's seminar: Kirchhoff's papers on the distribution of electric currents in metal disks, which contain the principles for calculating the distribution of electric currents in any system of linear conductors, and his dissertation on the constants that determine the intensity of induced currents.[41] Neumann reported with pleasure that the work justified his "great expectations of [Kirchhoff's] future scientific achievement," but it may be questioned if his student's excellent research worked in Neumann's favor.[42]

As Neumann's pleas for a laboratory went unheeded, he used a small inheritance his wife received to provide for himself by buying a house in 1847 and enlarging it to accommodate a laboratory, a place for woodworking and glassblowing, rooms for a telescope, air pumps, and other instruments belonging to him and to the university, and living quarters for his family.[43] From 1852 on, his seminar and his teaching in general again attracted students in larger numbers, but that did not affect his mood of resignation toward the government. To an inquiry about his needs in 1857, he replied that for too long he had had to fit his academic work and particularly his teaching in the seminar to the limited means and rooms at his disposal; he no longer wanted anything for himself. But as for the university, there was no hope for "truly fruitful" physics teaching unless it had a physics laboratory.[44] In the early 1860s, the Prussian government at last responded by giving Moser money for a physical cabinet.[45]

When Neumann retired in 1876, he made a plea for better conditions for his successor by restating his view of the close connections between material resources, teaching, research, and scholarly reputation: "The necessity of a physical laboratory for this university follows from these two facts. First, one cannot give as much phys-

40. Quoted in Olesko, "Emergence," 347. None of the students in Neumann's section of the seminar in the 1840s did, in fact, become a secondary school teacher, as far as is known.

41. Kirchhoff's first two publications were "Ueber den Durchgang eines elektrischen Stromes durch eine Ebene, insbesondere durch eine kreisförmige," Ann. 64 (1845): 497–514; and "Nachtrag zu dem Aufsatz 'Über den Durchgang etc.,' " Ann. 67 (1846): 344–49. According to Volkmann, Neumann, Kirchhoff's dissertation, "De valore constante experimentis determinato, a quo electricitatis motae pendet intensitas inductione effectae," was published in translation in Ann. 76 (1849): 412–26, as "Bestimmung der Constanten, von welcher die Intensität inducirter elektrischer Ströme abhängt." See also Friedrich Pockels, "Gustav Robert Kirchhoff," in Heidelberger Professoren aus dem 19. Jahrhundert. Festschrift der Universität zur Zentenarfeier ihrer Erneuerung durch Karl Friedrich, vol. 2 (Heidelberg: C. Winter, 1903), 243–63, on 246–47; Emil Warburg, "Zur Erinnerung an Gustav Kirchhoff," Naturwiss. 13 (1925): 205–12, on 206; Volkmann, Neumann, 25, 47; Wangerin, Neumann, 176–77.

42. Volkmann, Neumann, 47. Although Neumann "greatly emphasized" Kirchhoff's papers in his seminar report to the ministry and even sent a reprint, the minister, to Neumann's disappointment, in his reply did not comment on that part of the report. Neumann to C. G. J. Jacobi, 13 Jan. 1846, quoted in Leo Koenigsberger, Carl Gustav Jacob Jacobi (Leipzig: B. G. Teubner, 1904), 360–61.

43. Luise Neumann, Neumann, 373; Wangerin, Neumann, 183.

44. Neumann to Dean of the Königsberg Philosophical Faculty, undated draft, ca. 1857, Neumann Papers, Göttingen UB, Ms. Dept.

45. Olesko, "Emergence," 292.

ical instruction here as the needs of higher institutions of learning demand, given the present state of physics, and second, the teachers of physics do not have the means to enable them to take part in the development of this science as much as one rightly expects of academic teachers." After this brief summary of the problem, in which he properly put teaching first, Neumann discussed the problem that was most important to him:

> The academic teacher who is conscious of his calling knows that he is called not only for instruction in his discipline but that he is also supposed to take part in its development and advancement; he also knows that his effectiveness is fruitful and secured only to the extent to which he feels himself to be an independent researcher in that science. If he is denied the means for his own scientific work, as he is if he is not granted a laboratory, then he will take the first opportunity to leave the university. . . . Think of the position of a scientist who must stand aside from great . . . important investigations and observations of his contemporaries because he does not have the means and the rooms to test them and to form an independent opinion about the value and the limits of reliability of their results. Think of how with every scientific problem he approaches, before he starts to investigate it, he must always first ask himself the question, do his means permit it. Such a man sees himself limited to a small area of independent investigations for which the means and rooms at his disposal happen to suffice; he soon feels isolated and outside the community of those who are charged with the cultivation and advancement of science.[46]

In making explicit the link between the physicist's material resources and his scholarly reputation, Neumann spoke from personal experience. He had published twenty-nine papers between 1823 and 1848, after which he stopped publishing his research.[47] He had given up hope for a university laboratory and settled for the limited one he could provide for himself. Having started his career with the idea that the state would reward research, he appears to have taken the state's refusal to give him a laboratory as a judgment on the value of his work.[48] He chose a kind of

46. Luise Neumann, Neumann, 455.

47. Neumann's papers are listed in Volkmann, Neumann, 39–43. He published three papers after 1848, which we leave out of consideration: they were a four-page paper published in a French journal in 1862, a paper done with one of his students in 1865, and a paper published by his son in 1878 containing his resarch from 1834.

48. In 1825 Neumann wrote to the Prussian minister of culture that it would make him unhappy to give up his purely scientific work and do nothing but teaching. Luise Neumann, Neumann, 226. In 1829 he wrote to Weiss that he had gone to Königsberg in 1826 in the vain hope of finding the means for experimental research there. Two undated drafts of his letter to Weiss in copies by Luise Neumann entitled "Aus F. N.s erster Königsberger Zeit" in Neumann Papers, Göttingen UB, Ms. Dept. He and Jacobi encouraged students to publish research by making publishing part of the plan for the mathematical-physical seminar. We note Neumann's fervor for belonging to the world of scientific scholarship, because neither it nor his remarks from 1876 agree with the reasons Neumann himself is supposed to have given for ceasing to publish, as reported by Voigt: these were that the "great happiness is the discovery of a new truth [and that] the recognition connected with it can add little or nothing"; and that teaching is so closely connected with research that, for Neumann, research results are satisfactorily used if they enrich lectures and seminars and stimulate students. Voigt, "Neumann," 248–49.

scientific exile for himself in Königsberg, and reports of his continuing research reached the outside world largely through a few disciples he created as a teacher. Among his colleagues his reputation as a researcher remained high; for example, they counted him among the five physicists—Magnus, Dove, Weber, and Ettingshausen being the others—who were out of reach for Heidelberg University in 1854, when the physics chair there had to be filled again.[49]

Only after discussing his successor's needs for research did Neumann discuss his need for a laboratory for physics instruction, specifically for instruction in the seminar:

> Concerning instruction in physics, it must be remarked that it has to satisfy a two-fold requirement. It must, to begin with, provide the knowledge and views that belong to the general education of those who want to devote themselves to one of the different natural sciences, chemistry, mineralogy, botany, etc., or to study medicine. The first requirement is satisfied by the lectures on experimental physics. These lectures are at the same time the foundation for any deeper study of physics, but they are not enough for those who want to become teachers of physics at higher institutions of learning or physicists by profession. For them, the lectures on theoretical physics are intended, which develop the exact mathematical connection between phenomena that experimental physics had to leave more or less unconnected. . . .
>
> With this experimental and theoretical instruction, our university as a rule concludes the training in physics, and for that reason it remains incomplete. It still lacks an essential aspect, practical training. The art of observation, the handling of apparatus, the methods for determining time and length, the methods by which the elements that are to be determined are derived from the phenomena, etc., can only be acquired in practical work in a laboratory; only here the teacher can give the necessary guidance and instruction.[50]

In the early years, Neumann had also intended practical work to be part of the subject of the seminar; to make "measuring observations" for the purpose of determining physical phenomena, he had written in 1849, was the "ultimate purpose and the real goal" of the seminar.[51] But in this last report he no longer tied the seminar to practical training, perhaps because by 1876 the laboratory had become a place for physics instruction in its own right.

Wilhelm Weber, too, learned that research by itself (except perhaps when it was done in collaboration with Gauss, who could make government officials tremble) was not the most effective argument for requesting money for apparatus. When he went to Göttingen as professor of physics in 1831, the university did not yet have its seminar for physics. But he offered "practical exercises" for students of physics

49. Robert Bunsen, as Dean of the Heidelberg U. Philosophical Faculty, to Baden Ministry of the Interior, 26 July 1854, Bad. GLA, 235/3135.

50. Luise Neumann, *Neumann*, 456: quotation from Neumann's report of 1876.

51. Luise Neumann, 372: quotation from Neumann's 1849 report to the ministry.

who wanted to become secondary school teachers or else enter the applied sciences, such as medicine or pharmacy. He found the physical cabinet sufficiently equipped for these exercises, even if it lacked the finer measuring instruments and apparatus he required for his own research. In early 1832 he requested funds from the Hannover government for instruments "for the purpose of *special* lectures (which cover only individual parts of physics) and for the purpose of *scientific investigations* (which are both to be closely connected with one another). . . . The more deeply penetrating lectures on individual parts of physics gain scientific rigor when the methods by which one gives the required precision to experiments and measurements . . . can be thoroughly discussed and demonstrated on one's measuring instruments."[52] These new measuring instruments would also round out the apparatus at hand for scientific research.

Weber's request moved the government to ask him what he needed. In reply he listed parts of a precision measuring apparatus costing 400 thaler (the complete apparatus would have cost 1000 thaler), acoustical apparatus costing 250 thaler, and electromagnetic apparatus costing 120 thaler. This time he mentioned only their importance for research, but he received money only for what he had mentioned earlier as being important for teaching; namely, the parts of the measuring apparatus.[53] After that, Weber did not again forget to mention that the instruments he wanted were also needed for teaching. He informed the curator a year later that he had spent 99 thaler for new instruments "that seemed indispensable for the lectures on experimental physics, namely, a few organ pipes, which the cabinet lacked altogether, a few sounding plates, and a monochord that I constructed myself."[54] These were some of the items he had been denied when he asked for them for his research the year before; now although he was criticized for spending money without authorization, he was reimbursed. To his accounting records he added a new category: "Needs in lectures and experiments."[55]

Weber's successor in 1839, J. B. Listing, continued Weber's "exercises" when he had interested students, but he lacked Weber's skill in exploiting his teaching to add to the instrument collection.[56] For example, in the early 1840s he bought an excellent chronometer costing over 400 thaler with his own money in the hope that he would be reimbursed. But his erratic bookkeeping for the physics institute so incensed the Hannover government that he was not reimbursed for the chronometer until 1854, and then it was only because Weber interceded with his proven argument: "Measurements of time, measurements of space, and weighings constitute the fundamental operations in all work in physics, and it is the main purpose of the practical exercises of the students, for whom the mathematical-physical seminar has been established, to impart practical dexterity in the execution, combination, and

52. Weber to Göttingen U. Curator, 24 Apr. 1832, Göttingen UA, 4/V h/15.

53. Göttingen U. Curator to Weber, 9 June 1832, Göttingen UA, 4/V h/15; Weber to Curator, 15 Dec. 1832, and Curator to Weber, 17 Jan. 1833, Göttingen UA, 4/V h/16. Weber's modest annual salary—for the sake of comparison—was 800 thaler.

54. Weber to Göttingen U. Curator, 10 July 1833, Göttingen UA, 4/V h/8.

55. Weber to Göttingen U. Curator, 12 July 1833, Göttingen UA, 4/V h/8.

56. Listing Personalakte, Göttingen UA, 4/V b/108.

application of these three fundamental operations, which is not possible without the aid of good instruments."[57] In one respect, Listing had a small measure of success; between 1837 and 1848, his institute was enlarged to encompass space for the instrument collection, a large laboratory, a room for "chemical-physical" work, a workroom for himself, a mechanical workshop, and living quarters for an employee.[58]

In 1849, Weber was reappointed at Göttingen. We discuss the circumstances of his return in chapter 6; for our present purposes it is sufficient to note that Göttingen now had two physics professors, Weber for experimental physics and Listing for mathematical physics. Weber gave the "demonstrative survey of the phenomena that chemists, pharmacists, physicians, etc., above all require," while Listing dealt "mainly with the theoretical and practical education of observers of nature through introducing them to observing and measuring physics, which must be tied more or less to mathematical discussions."[59] They were free to teach subjects belonging to one another's domain as well. In addition, they both participated in the mathematical-physical seminar that was founded soon after Weber's return. Since Weber got the lion's share of the apparatus and of the rooms in the original institute along with a larger budget than Listing's, his section offered the students of the seminar most of their practice in "observing and measuring physics." Weber did not reinstate his former "practical exercises" as a separate course but now taught it in the seminar.[60]

Like Königsberg's mathematical-physical seminar, Göttingen's was used in arguments for more financial support for physics,[61] and seminar funds were used on occasion to buy equipment which was incorporated into the instrument collections of Göttingen's two physics institutes; for example, twenty-five kilograms of thick conduction wire and two microscope micrometers "for the purpose of more extended work on galvanism, induction, etc." for Weber's section in 1851–53, and a "fine scale" for Listing's section in 1853.[62] Most of the time Weber used the seminar indirectly, arguing for improvements for his institute, insofar as it "is used for the physical section of the seminar" so that he could meet his obligation to the semi-

57. Listing to Göttingen U. Curator, 2 Jan. 1853, Listing Personalakte, Göttingen UA, 4/V b/108; Göttingen U. Curator Adolph von Warnstedt to Rudolf Wagner [1854?], Rudolf Wagner Correspondence, vol. 11, Göttingen UB, Ms. Dept. Weber, "Unterthäniger Antrag des Professor Weber, die Anschaffung eines Chronometers für das physikalische Institut betreffend," 8 July 1854, Göttingen UA, 4/V h/16.

58. Report by Listing to Hannover government, 21 Jan. 1848, Göttingen UA, 4/V h/10.

59. According to Weber's description of the jobs: Weber to Göttingen U. Curator, 22 May 1848, Weber Personalakte, Göttingen UA, 4/V b/95a.

60. Listing to Göttingen U. Curator, 2 Jan. 1853. "Statuten des mathematisch-physikalischen Seminars zu Göttingen, 11 Feb. 1850, Göttingen UA, 4/V h/20.

61. But in other respects, the Göttingen seminar was unlike Königsberg's. Weber and Listing did not try to enhance their seminar, as Neumann did his, as an institution by acquiring material resources for it. The level of support for Göttingen's seminar was not equal to that of Königsberg's: even though it had four professors—Weber, Listing, and two mathematicians—instead of just one physics and one mathematics professor as Königsberg's seminar came to have, its annual 160 thaler for student prizes and 60 thaler for running expenses amounted to considerably less than Königsberg's annual 350 thaler. Again unlike Königsberg's arrangements, Göttingen's seminar directors were not paid and could not collect student fees. "Statuten . . . Göttingen." Also Listing to Göttingen U. Curator, 2 Jan. 1853.

62. "Bericht des Vorstandes des mathematisch-physikalischen Seminars," 1853–54, Göttingen UA, 4/V h/20.

nar.[63] "The practical exercises that are to be conducted in [the seminar] unavoidably cause some expenses," he explained to the Göttingen curator, "which I try to cover as well as I can with the annual funds" received for the institute, or 300 thaler. "Although in general these funds are somewhat short, I would nevertheless hope to make do with them, if aside from this the institute were up to date in its instrumental equipment." Weber believed that the institute needed a complete renovation of its instrument collection, costing 4000 thaler by his calculation. He asked for occasional installments of 1000 thaler, and he got 500 from time to time.[64]

Listing, who taught as many students in his section of the seminar as Weber did in his but had to make do with smaller quarters and with less equipment, did not improve his institute through the seminar. At the time the Göttingen physics chair was divided, he received an annual budget of 200 thaler for his institute for mathematical physics, which consisted of two large rooms that were impractically located some distance apart, a few small rooms, and the part of the instrument collection he needed for his specialty, optics. One of the two large rooms had to serve as both "auditorium and laboratory for seminar exercises." Although his institute was worse off than Weber's in every respect, Listing usually did not, as Weber did, request specific improvements for his institute (which could be claimed to serve both teaching and research) but limited himself to requests for raises, which he justified by his disadvantageous position and the circumstances of his institute that prevented him from earning as much with his teaching as he otherwise might.[65]

In his reports on his institute, Listing almost never mentioned his teaching. He apparently attributed his disfavor with the curator to insufficient research, writing in 1848 that he had been too busy setting up the physical cabinet to keep up his "scientific endeavors" as the curator had wished; he hoped to regain official good will as soon as no new difficulties stopped him from doing research. In an attempt to get a raise in 1864, Listing again pointed to the obstacles standing in the way of his research and cited praise by "authorities" such as Helmholtz for the limited research he had managed to accomplish, despite everything.[66] The curator's attention to the number of Listing's students and his unfavorable comparison of it with the number of Weber's were not affected by his arguments. The curator granted that Listing had "fine intelligence," "talent," and "sagacity," but he found that Listing lacked the "necessary intellectual energy, a zeal that overcomes all difficulty, without which even the scholar cannot achieve anything great in literature." Finally, even though Listing had taught two hundred students in the preceding six years, the curator concluded that he was not a success as a teacher.[67] (Later he would cite

63. Weber to Göttingen U. Curator, 4 Apr. 1851, Göttingen UA, 4/V h/10.
64. Copy of a report by Weber to Göttingen U. Curator, "Bericht über das die Errichtung einer Assistentenstelle am physikalischen Institute betreffende Gesuch des Dr. von Quintus Icilius," 10 May 1851, Göttingen UA, 4/V h/21; "Bericht des Professors Wilhelm Weber, die Instrumenten-Sammlung des physikalischen Instituts betreffend," 13 Aug. 1849, to Göttingen U. Curator, and Curator to Weber, 22 Aug. 1849, Göttingen UA, 4/V h/19; Listing to Göttingen U. Curator, 2 Jan. 1853.
65. Listing to Göttingen U. Curator, 2 Jan. 1853.
66. Listing to Göttingen U. Curator, 8 Aug. 1848 and 7 Dec. 1864, Listing Personalakte, Göttingen UA, 4/V b/108.
67. Report by Curator von Warnstedt to King of Hannover, 30 Mar. 1859, Listing Personalakte,

Weber's thousand or more students to make the point.) So nothing was done to improve substantially Listing's working conditions, his institute budget, or his personal income.

University physicists lacked not only facilities and scientific apparatus (for which lack they sometimes found a partial remedy through seminars), but they also lacked students for all but the general physics lectures. The seminar was of use in that regard, guaranteeing them at least some students for the special or advanced subjects that interested them as researchers and that often went unattended when offered as a lecture.

That physicists planned to use their seminars in this way is clear from the statutes and from the requirements for enrolling in them. The first paragraph of the statutes of the Göttingen seminar stated: "The mathematical-physical seminar . . . is to give students who dedicate themselves primarily to mathematics and physics the opportunity to acquaint themselves with such parts of these sciences that are treated briefly or not at all in the usual academic lectures."[68] The statutes of the Munich mathematical-physical seminar also provided for "theoretical discussions of such themes that are taken up either not at all or only incidentally in the public lectures."[69] At Königsberg, where Neumann gave lectures on advanced areas of physics, the seminar was coordinated with the lectures and did not incorporate them. The prerequisites of the Königsberg seminar exceeded those of the later seminars at Göttingen and Munich; Königsberg admitted as ordinary members of the seminar only students majoring in mathematics or physics who knew the differential calculus, the beginnings of the integral calculus, and the main subjects treated in Fischer's physics textbook.[70] Elsewhere in Prussia, at Halle, where the seminar treated all the natural sciences and mathematics, students admitted to the seminar also had to be science or mathematics majors or candidates for teaching positions involving mathematics or the natural sciences.[71] The Heidelberg mathematical-physical seminar, which was not Prussian but was co-founded by Kirchhoff who had been educated in the Königsberg seminar, was similarly limited to mathematics and physics majors.[72] (A comment on this practice from a less bureaucratic university than the Prussian was that such requirements were superfluous, since students who were not sufficiently prepared for the work of the seminar would not stay long in any case; besides, the requirements might keep out desirable students, since young people often begin in a field that turns out not to be their true calling. Somewhat unfairly, the commentator pointed out that the Prussian seminar statutes would not

---

Göttingen UA, 4/V b/108. The number of Listing's students is taken from records in Listing's Personalakte.

68. "Statuten . . . Göttingen."

69. "Statuten . . . München."

70. For example, Neumann's seminar report for 1873–75, quoted in Luise Neumann, *Neumann*, 443. For the requirements for the Königsberg seminar, "Statuten . . . Königsberger Universität."

71. *Vorläufiges Reglement . . . Halle.*

72. "Statut . . . Heidelberg."

have admitted either the student of theology Johannes Kepler or the student of medicine Wilhelm Olbers.[73])

The seminars guaranteed students for the university physicists because seminar training was the surest way to a teaching position. Seminars either certified students as acceptable candidates for teaching positions[74] or guaranteed that they would be considered for such positions before other candidates who had not been members of a seminar.[75] The seminars also attracted students because membership in them could bring students to the attention of the respective ministries for other types of appointments: they could ease the way into a university career or to appointments at state astronomical observatories or technical institutions, where several of Neumann's seminar students went, for example.

For whatever reasons students may have joined the seminars, they provided physics professors with an audience: directors of seminars could insist on regular attendance, an advantage that no lecturer enjoyed; seminar rules generally demanded that members attend all of the exercises and meetings, usually in all sections of the seminar. Moreover, to receive credit for the seminar, members had to attend the whole course of it, which sometimes extended over several years. Where the requirement was not explicitly stated at the beginning, as at Göttingen, it was made clear at the first drop in attendance in any part of the seminar.[76] By 1874 students in the mathematical-physical seminar at Munich would be asked to spend five hours each week in seminar classes, even though, as the directors of the seminar acknowledged, they already spent most of their time in preparation for the seminar and in the past they sometimes had not had enough time for the required work.[77] Neumann tried to coerce even disinterested students into the seminar by asking the ministry to require future secondary school teachers to submit a "substantial written work" as part of their qualifying examination.[78]

The mathematics and natural science seminars enriched the working lives of university physicists in yet another way. They gave official expression to the scien-

73. Stern to "Ministerial-Vorstand" Braun, 10 Oct. 1849.

74. Bonn's did from 1831. Later that right was revoked, after which the number of students in the seminar dropped so far that its directors were afraid it might not survive. Prussian Minister of Culture von Mühler to Bonn U. Curator Beseler, 19 Feb. 1867; the directors of the Bonn U. science seminar to Beseler, 20 Mar. 1867; "Antrag des Vorstandes des Seminars für die gesammten Naturwissenschaften wegen Erhöhung des Dotations-Fonds," 20 May 1867; and Beseler to von Mühler, "Den Jahresbericht der Vorsteher des Seminars für die gesammten Naturwissenschaften für das Studienjahr 1866–67 betreffend," 12 Dec. 1867; all in N.-W. HSTA, NW5 Nr. 483.

75. The annual reports on the activites of the seminars to the different ministries of education usually listed by name at least those students who had won money awards with independent work or who had been assistants to the directors. Having one's name brought to the attention of the ministry in this way gained one an advantage over fellow candidates for secondary school teaching, as Kirchhoff and Leo Koenigsberger pointed out in 1869. Letter to Baden government, 14 Apr. 1869, Bad. GLA, 235/3228.

76. In 1853 the directors of the mathematical-physical seminar reported that one of the mathematics sections of the seminar had to be canceled because only one student registered for it. This would never happen again, they assured the curator, because they had now made it obligatory for all members of the seminar to attend all sections of it. Annual seminar report for 1853–54, Göttingen UA, 4/V h/20.

77. Ludwig Seidel, "Pro memoria," 28 Feb. 1874, Munich UA, Sen. 209.

78. Wangerin, *Neumann*, 153.

tists' methods of acquiring knowledge, a sign of increasing recognition of the kind of *Bildung* that Ohm argued for. At about the time of the founding of the Freiburg seminar, the director of its physics section, Johann Müller, described the objective of this new way of teaching the natural sciences in a textbook: "Physical truths must not be delivered to the student in a dogmatic manner as finished results, but throughout, the derivation of laws must be made clear to him; he must become familiar with the connection between facts and—arising from a logical combination of the facts—ideas about the causes and the connection of the phenomena; in short, even in elementary instruction the student must be introduced to the way of physical thought and inference and be made familiar with the nature of the inductive method."[79] The difference between Müller's teaching, which imparted a way of reasoning about the physical world, and that which was common not long before can be appreciated by comparing his textbook with, for example, Brandes's. The latter presented physical theories dogmatically and associated them with practical applications and ordinary experiences of the world around us.[80]

The Marburg physicist Gerling wrote in 1848 what it meant in practical terms for students to be no longer satisfied with merely "listening to and practicing what they have heard." Students in his time were "stimulated and satisfied only where they found themselves invited to take part in the progress of science." For that reason all institutes had to be set up to offer them the opportunity to carry out physical investigations.[81] All of the natural science seminars represented the new way of teaching their subjects, but some of them went even futher, taking on aspects of research institutions as well.

In 1868 the Bonn mathematician Rudolf Lipschitz wrote that scientific and mathematical education at the universities was then in transition from an earlier encyclopedic training in the main branches of the natural sciences and in some parts of mathematics to the present specialized training; it took the form of concentration on the individual sciences, which were to be studied in depth.[82] Where the older encyclopedic view of science education still prevailed, as at Bonn or among some science professors at Königsberg and Freiburg, the scientists established seminars for the several natural sciences that were important to future secondary school teachers. The different sciences entered the seminar as autonomous fields; they made equal claim on the students' attention, so that the students could not pursue any science in depth in the short time given to each. How studies in physics fared in such a program can be illustrated by the examples of Bonn and Freiburg.

In the Bonn seminar for the natural sciences, with its aim of preparing "thoroughly trained and well-rounded teachers," the members of the physics section, particularly the senior students, spent most of their time giving talks on whatever sub-

79. Johann Müller, *Grundriss der Physik und Meteorologie. Für Lyceen, Gymnasien, Gewerbe- und Realschulen, sowie zum Selbstunterrichte*, 5th rev. ed. (Braunschweig, 1856), vii.

80. Brandes, *Vorlesungen* 1:iii–vi.

81. Christian Ludwig Gerling, *Nachricht von dem mathematisch-physicalischen Institut der Universität Marburg* (Marburg, 1848), 2.

82. Rudolf Lipschitz, "Separatvotum eingeliefert in der Sitzung der philosophischen Facultät vom 13. Juli 1868," Plücker Personalakte, Bonn UA.

jects they chose. What deeper knowledge of physics the students acquired, they did
so in the laboratory exercises, which in some semesters were all taken from one
particular area of physics.[83] It was not much at best. The Freiburg seminar for mathematics and the natural sciences, founded in 1846 by the physicist Müller and his
colleagues, was like the early Bonn seminar in that, in keeping with its main purpose
of training teachers, it also engaged its students in diverse scientific activities, letting
them handle apparatus, animals, plants, and minerals. In addition, the directors
required their students to attend certain lecture courses, including mathematics
courses. Again as at Bonn, the work of the Freiburg seminar was elementary; for
example, even students who wanted to become mathematics teachers were required
to hear lectures on mathematics only through the calculus.[84] The statutes of the
seminar contained an extraordinary provision that allowed a student who produced
publishable research in the seminar to earn a doctorate with it, which indicates that
the directors of the seminar did not expect research as a rule.

Where the second, or more specialized, view of science education prevailed,
physicists established mathematical-physical seminars in collaboration with their
mathematical colleagues. The union of mathematics and physics in one seminar
differed from the combination of several autonomous sciences in the more general
seminar; the former had a "*scientific* purpose" and the latter did not, as the mathematician Stern pointed out in his program for the Göttingen mathematical-physical
seminar. Because, by definition, a "thorough" education in physics is based on mathematics, Stern wrote, the "separate training of mathematicians and physicists is no
longer thinkable."[85]

Physicists and mathematicians who founded mathematical-physical seminars
were seen to be introducing a new element into scientific education; namely, the
systematic preparation of students for research. They were sometimes resisted for this
reason. For example, when Neumann and the mathematician C. G. J. Jacobi established the Königsberg mathematical-physical seminar in 1834 (an act that could be
construed as criticism of the natural sciences seminar established there at about the
same time, especially since Neumann had at one time wanted to join the latter),
certain other Königsberg scientists made the inclusion of mathematics and of student
research in physics in the curriculum of a science seminar an issue of contention.[86]
The Bonn philosophical faculty was wary of mathematics in science seminars, too.
It supported Plücker in 1841 when he unsuccessfully proposed a separate "full course
for the purpose of practical exercise in experimenting and for discussion of the phenomena and the apparatus," but when, in 1864, he addressed the other main requirement for training physicists, namely, mathematical instruction, by proposing a
mathematical seminar that would also teach mathematical physics, the directors of

83. Annual reports of the seminar, especially for 1857–58 and 1862–63, N.-W. HSTA, NW5 Nr.
483.
84. *Statuten . . . Freiburg.* The mathematical lectures required of all ordinary members were on
algebra, geometry, trigonometry, "analysis," and analytic geometry. Those who planned to teach mathematics also heard lectures on differential and integral calculus.
85. Stern to "Ministerial-Vorstand" Braun, 10 Oct. 1849.
86. This example is in Olesko, "Emergence," 320–21.

the seminar for the natural sciences opposed him. They did not want any union of mathematics and physics, which they saw as tantamount to research, whether in a new seminar or in the existing one.[87]

The better German physicists such as Neumann and Weber agreed on the need to prepare students for research, that is, to teach them to use the new measuring and mathematical tools. From the time he became professor of physics at Göttingen in 1831, Weber planned to offer "instruction in experimenting" and "reliable observation," and, as we have seen, he began student "exercises." He was still in the process of completing the measuring apparatus for "higher scientific training" when, in 1837, he was dismissed from his professorship; the idea of physics institutes as "workshops" for teachers and students alike, of which he was fond, and the idea of linking workshops and advanced physics lectures could not be realized until after his return to Göttingen in 1849.[88] Neumann also began with the idea of a workshop in which his students could acquire through practice the experimental, measuring, and mathematical techniques of physics. In the statutes of the Königsberg mathematical-physical seminar of 1834, he and Jacobi declared that student participation in the physical section was to consist of independent work, which was to be either pure theory or observations and measurements on the basis of mathematical theory, and lectures on the branches of mathematical physics. Like Weber, Neumann encountered obstacles in carrying out the idea. Because of the lack of an adequate laboratory, independent work proved to be possible only for the more experienced student who could be trusted to use seminar apparatus for experiments in his living quarters without damaging it.[89] For the rest of the students, Neumann developed the seminar program we discuss below, which accomplished his aim of teaching the methods of physical research with limited experimental means. Weber's solution to the problem, which we discuss after Neumann's, resulted in an important regular feature of physics education in German universities.

Running of the Seminar

Although the Königsberg mathematical-physical seminar had been set up with statutes to guide its organization and its work, Neumann ran his section as circumstances and student progress dictated, not by the book.[90] Instead of the prescribed

87. "Eingabe des Herrn Prof. Plücker an E. H. M., betr. die Vorlesungen über Physik," 8 Dec. 1841, Plücker Personalakte, Bonn UA. Bonn U. Curator Beseler to Prussian Minister of Culture von Mühler, 14 Sept. 1864, and Plücker's proposal of a mathematical seminar to Beseler, 13 Sept. 1864, both in N.-W. HSTA, NW5 Nr. 558.

88. Weber's report of 24 Apr. 1832 to Göttingen U. Curator. Weber to Göttingen U. Curator, 20 Oct. 1837, Göttingen UA, 4/V h/16. Also, for example, in a report by Weber, 16 Oct. 1835: "Every physical cabinet, [or] at least one at so great an institute of learning as our university, where a greater interest for . . . [science] is to be propagated through the advancement of science, should be a workshop in which work goes on all the time as in a chemical laboratory." Weber was asking for money for equipment and assistance, which would allow him to let more of his students take part in the work. Göttingen UA, 4/V h/16.

89. Wangerin, Neumann, 183.

90. The following discussion of Neumann's seminar is based primarily on Neumann's seminar re-

two sections of advanced and beginning students, he had sometimes only advanced, sometimes only beginning, students, often both and often working together in some fashion. Students stayed in the seminar for a single semester or for as long as five years; most stayed one to three years.

A reasonable regularity in the work of the physical section was assured by the order of Neumann's private lectures: from 1838 until about 1860, he devoted his four hours of weekly lectures to three subjects, "theoretical physics," "theory of light," and "mineralogy," each taught for a semester, the whole taught as a regular cycle, which he rarely varied.[91] The cycle affected his seminar teaching: the proper beginning of seminar work was the part of its instruction that was correlated with his "theoretical physics" course. Beginning students were expected to take the two together or to postpone the seminar part until after they had completed the lecture course.

Neumann's lectures affected the seminar in another way, too: in the seminar discussions and homework assignments, Neumann either prepared his students for his lectures or he deepened their understanding of what he had covered in his lectures, tested their understanding by letting them apply what they had learned, and augmented the lectures he had been unable to complete in class or to treat thoroughly enough. His description of the seminar for the years 1847–49 gives an example of several of these uses of the seminar. In the summer of 1847, Neumann taught the seminar in two sections; he had beginning students whom he had to keep occupied until the second semester, when his "theoretical physics" lectures were scheduled. So he used the first semester to make the beginners, who had only recently come from the gymnasium, "aware of gaps in their knowledge," as he reported to the ministry of culture. He had found in past lectures on optics a "great ignorance" on the part of his students of the "fundamental concepts ordinary optics," which were a prerequisite for his lectures. Since he was going to give the lecture course on the theory of light again in 1848, he used the seminar in the summer of 1847 to prepare its seven beginning members, his so-called second section, for the lecture course by making them work on questions from optics. He used the subject not only to make them familiar with the funadmental concepts but also to let them "apply mathematical treatment to physics problems in these simplest cases." His lecture course on the theory of light in the summer of 1848 was disrupted by the political upheavals of the year and by his illness, and to make up the missed course

ports, the drafts of which are in the Neumann Papers in the Manuscript Department of the Göttingen University Library. Neumann's details there on student attendance are supplemented by Volkmann's and Olesko's cited in note 15. Neumann's lectures are listed in Volkmann, 55–58.

91. Neumann taught "Mineralogy" from 1827, "Theory of Light" from 1830, and "Introduction to Theoretical Physics," a course on the mechanical foundations of physics, from 1838. From 1861 on, he extended that series to five semesters by adding lecture courses on the theory of electric currents and the theory of elasticity. The five courses covered the major areas of Neumann's researches. Almost from the start, according to Voigt, Neumann's lectures on mineralogy included all areas of theoretical physics. "Neumann," 254–55. In time, he also gave separate two-hour public lectures on the parts of theoretical physics. The complete list of the lectures Neumann actually held—as opposed to the lectures he announced—complete with the numbers of students who attended is given by Volkmann, Neumann, 56–58. Neumann's lectures were published by some of his students in the 1880s.

work he used the seminar in the winter of 1848–49 to complete and complement his lecture course. In the seminar they "discussed problems from the theory of interference, polarization, and the theory of light phenomena at the surface of noncrystalline media, extended to the reflection of crystalline surfaces."

Only in the case of advanced students did seminar work become independent of Neumann's lectures; once his students had embarked on independent investigations, they continued with their particular subject over several semesters, regardless of what Neumann was covering in his lectures. He adapted his teaching of advanced students to their needs. In a few cases of unusually talented students, he allowed them to carry out independent investigations of scientific merit.

In the 1850s Neumann came closer than ever before to making the seminar what he thought it should be. One reason for the improvement was that he had acquired a laboratory in his house;[92] another was that the number of students he had was large enough for a seminar but not yet too large for his limited facilities.

From his reports to the ministry for these years, we get an idea of how Neumann ran his seminar under reasonably favorable conditions. The report for 1850–51 tells that the physics seminar was attended only by new members who were also attending Neumann's "theoretical physics" lectures. The seminar and the lecture course were taught in "close conjunction," Neumann reported: the mechanical and physical concepts he presented in the lectures he clarified further in the seminar, and by making the students use the concepts, he gave them a "certain ease" in handling them. After the seminar discussions, he gave the students questions in the form of written assignments, and their solutions showed him the points they were still unclear about. He followed the same procedure whenever he taught this part of the seminar. Once the students had learned to determine the theoretical means required to solve a problem, they were given practical exercises, principally measuring observations, in addition to theoretical ones. In connection with the practical exercises, the students analyzed the data they obtained from their observations, making calculations and determining the reliability of their end result.

Neumann chose only a few subjects for exercises each time, for his goals were thoroughness and exactness rather than versatility. In the early 1850s, he started his students off with topics drawn from mechanics, such as the development of the concepts of mass and force, the influence of the distribution of mass on motion, and the derivation of the principles of the equilibrium of forces. He then assigned them practical exercises, such as measuring observations on pendulums to determine the circumstances that influence their amplitude and period. In the seminar section that accompanied his "theoretical physics" lectures in the winter of 1854–55, for example, his topics from mechanics included a treatment of Atwood's machine, the theory of collisions for rigid and elastic bodies and its application to Newton's law of resistance, the theory of the pendulum and its application to observations of the velocity of missiles, and the influence of the rotation of the earth on the deflection of falling bodies. Neumann justified the treatment of these topics by the difficulties

92. Luise Neumann, *Neumann*, 373.

his students had in applying the fundamental laws of mechanics. The following year, when most of the same students were still in the seminar, he took up "purely theoretical investigations," beginning with the theory of the motion of a system of separate mass particles. As he reported to the ministry in 1851, making his students "receptive and well prepared" for the study of mechanics was one of the rewards of teaching the seminar. This work had the further purpose, as he described it in 1858, of giving "directions as to how physical phenomena are brought into the domain of rigorous concepts and the calculus." It was also the methodical preparation for treating other areas of physics, as his curriculum for the seminar showed.

How Neumann followed up this first part of the seminar work depended on whether or not his students returned for more instruction. In the early 1850s he frequently had only two or three students who had been in his seminar before and had completed the elementary phase. He called them his first section and tended to assign them independent work. His principal objective was to teach them to make exact observations and measurements, to evaluate the resulting data, and to bridge the "chasm," as he put it, "between theoretical understanding and practical execution." "The opportunity to practice measuring observations" was what, in 1852–53, he gave to his son Carl Neumann and to Alfred Clebsch, both of whom later became mathematicians: "written work was demanded of them only occasionally, when their experimental results and the discussion of these gave cause for them." They observed electric-current and optical phenomena, from which they derived "subjective gain," but hardly publishable results. In 1854 a change occurred; in that year, Neumann had eight new students in his seminar, six of whom stayed for a second year (another, Georg Quincke, skipped that year to return later), four for a third year, and two even for a fourth. As they left, they were replaced by new students, who also stayed in the seminar beyond the first year. Into the early 1860s, each year Neumann had ten to twelve students in the seminar of whom about half were continuing students. The existence of groups of equally prepared students over longer periods allowed him to engage them in series of related investigations in particular areas of physics.

When the first large group entered the seminar, Neumann assigned to the two advanced students in it independent measurements of induced dielectric currents and the determination of the elements required for that work. When most of the group returned in the summer of 1855, Neumann continued the work already begun with them. Observations from the year before on the effect of induced electric currents on horizontally suspended, movable magnets had had the purpose of developing the theory of the motion of the pendulum to apply to unusual circumstances. That work presupposed an ideal magnetic state, and now the seminar members were told to discover what could be derived reliably from the observed data with regard to the actual existing magnetic state. They were to derive certain magnetic concepts, develop theoretical methods for magnetic work, and apply to magnetic problems the principles of potential theory, which Neumann had taught them. Neumann followed up the theoretical investigations by observations, particularly observations of earth-magnetic forces, for which the students had to use and compare various methods.

These observations also led to smaller theoretical investigations on, for example, the influence of the properties of the mirrors used in the observations or the influence of the thread in bifilar suspensions. Neumann justified these secondary investigations by his general aim of getting students to pay attention to every fact that might influence the outcome and to include it in their calculations.

From earth magnetism Neumann moved the seminar topic to electric current the following semester. He considered the work continuous because the students were to apply the same methods as before to their observations. The students discussed methods of determining constants and then applied them, and they developed further the theory and methods of measuring instruments, here especially of the differential multiplicator. In the summer of 1857 Neumann directed three of the students from the previous year to apply their knowledge of electric currents to heat conduction. They were led to Fourier's analytical theory of heat and its methods, which they then applied, especially to problems in which heat and electricity interact. In the winter semester of that year, a new group of students was ready to join the remaining members of the old; they, too, worked on heat, the topic Neumann stayed with for the next two years, always with an orientation toward the methods of physics.

Neumann's task, as he saw it, was to give his students methods for discovering which aspects of any given physics problem would allow them to obtain a solution. The methods included those for doing research in physics, but Neumann's official seminar reports do not indicate that the students, with rare exceptions, actually did research. What the reports of the 1850s and 1860s do show is a falling off of any independent work, particularly sustained work on experimental problems.[93] The work by advanced students who did get independent assignments was an extension and refinement of the work of the seminar. As much as possible, Neumann moved his students through the seminar in coordinated groups, to which he assigned common tasks; with the limited facilities at his disposal, he could not allow them to do as much research as he had once hoped.

The mathematical-physical seminar at Göttingen opened in the summer of 1850 with twenty-two students, who were committed to attending both the mathematics section directed by two professors of mathematics and the physics section directed

---

93. Neumann, in fact, over his entire teaching career, had a remarkably small number of dissertation students. These were his "students" under the then customary meaning of the term. Of Neumann's sixteen or seventeen students, in this sense, only two or three achieved any eminence as physics researchers; at most three made careers of gymnasium teaching; and about the same number became university physics professors. The direct influence of his teaching on physics researchers was far more limited than members of the "Königsberg school" such as Volkmann and Wangerin have claimed.

The looser meaning of "students," invoked to establish the influence of the school, was applied by Volkmann to all who signed up for Neumann's private lectures, which were coupled with the seminar. Since students usually studied at more than one university, many of "Neumann's students" could by the same definition be counted among the "students" of Weber, Magnus, and so on. In fact, several of "Neumann's students," among them O. E. Meyer, Pape, Von der Mühll, and Heinrich Weber, inscribed their names on the list of sixty-eight of "Weber's students" who honored him in this way in 1876. Only an analysis of individual students' histories could decide in which cases this looser meaning of "students" is appropriate.

by Weber and Listing. The plan of instruction for the physics section was that meetings would be held in the physics laboratory for "two to four" hours each week, where the directors, each in his own part of the laboratory, would lecture on "individual subjects of theoretical physics, connected with exercises in observations and measurements." The students had to keep records of all observations and experiments, and if the results were suitable, they were to work them out in a paper and submit it. In addition, they had to report on the contents of certain physics treatises and papers in academic publications and physics journals, which the directors had chosen as guidelines for the physical exercises. In the physics section students were freed from having to give practice lectures, as the mathematics section took over the job of coaching students in lecturing.[94]

As in Neumann's seminar, student exercises in observing and measuring were the most important part of the work at Göttingen. The seminar statutes required that all students first be made acquainted with the instruments in the physical collection. After seeing to that, Weber began immediately to train them in observation "to prepare them for participation in the regular magnetic observations," which was the "best opportunity for practical training of the members of the mathematical-physical seminar." As early as 1850, he had some students take part, and with their help he was able to cover more kinds of magnetic observations than he had been able to before.[95] To his instruction in measuring techniques, which were of all kinds, not just magnetic, he linked discussions of the details of precision instruments and their theories. He also lectured on physical theories, for example, on electromagnetic theory, elasticity theory, and potential theory. Finally, he gave his students the opportunity to combine their experience in measuring with theoretical insight by involving them in experiments that were part of his researches and with which he was developing fundamental laws.[96]

Listing, whose small institute was equipped primarily for optics, also had his seminar students do "elementary exercises, such as measurements, weighings, determining specific weights, etc.," and other exercises to prepare them for making magnetic observations.[97] But beyond that, he devoted most of the work in his section to optics, specifically to optical measurements, for which his institute was well equipped. He had his students determine the rotation of the plane of polarization of light, for example, and obtain diffraction data and data from the human eye. This work went hand in hand with the study of instruments: his students determined the elements of complex optical instruments such as systems of lenses; they measured indices of refraction using a microscope and then discussed the theory of the instrument; they derived the wavelength of light by various methods and combined that work with the study of diffraction apparatus. For example, in 1861 (when Ernst Abbe was his student) Listing reported that "extensive measurements and determi-

94. "Statuten . . . Göttingen."
95. Annual seminar report 1850–51, and Weber to Göttingen U. Curator, 16 Dec. 1851, Göttingen UA, 4/V h/20 and 4/V h/19, respectively.
96. Our discussion of the Göttingen seminar is based mainly on the annual seminar reports for 1850–70 to the Göttingen U. Curator, Göttingen UA, 4/V h/20.
97. Annual report of 1851–52.

nations of wavelength for Fraunhofer lines have been made on the spectrometer by means of diffraction using two Nobert interference gratings."[98]

The intention of the directors of the physics section of the Göttingen seminar was to draw on subjects from contemporary research, as they stated in the statutes of the seminar. Most of the subjects were taken from the directors' own research, mainly because their institutes were better equipped with instruments and apparatus for the parts of physics they cultivated than for other parts. In the second year of the seminar, 1851–52, for example, Weber chose several topics from his own researches: "the theory of the bifilar magnetometer together with the determination of its elements," "the theory of the induction inclinatorium together with an inclination measurement," and "experiments with the electrodynamometer." Other topics that year were not a part of his work at the moment, but they were topics of current discussion in physics and mathematics journals. For example, Weber treated "acoustical experiments with the monochord to determine the elasticity module together with the development of the theory of oscillations of elastic bodies" soon after the *Journal für die reine und angewandte Mathematik* had devoted most of the section on mechanics in the 1850 volume to two articles on almost the same subject. Also in 1851–52, Weber treated "Foucault's experiments on the influence of the rotation of the earth on the oscillations of a pendulum," which had just been published in France and reported on in the *Annalen der Physik;* it was the most exciting subject in science at the moment.[99]

Although the aims of Neumann and the Göttingen physicists for their respective seminars were similar, the results were not. Because he lacked adequate laboratory facilities, Neumann regarded his teaching of "mathematical physics" at Königsberg as only a "shadow" of what it could have been.[100] But the resulting theoretical emphasis in his seminar teaching, which was enhanced by the coordination of the seminar with his theoretical physics lectures, was imitated elsewhere. Theoretical physics became associated with the idea of a physics seminar at Würzburg, for example, where the founders of the mathematical seminar in 1872 recommended that the establishment of the physics section of a mathematical-physical seminar be postponed until the "recently begun lectures on mathematical physics have been successfully attended for several semesters."[101] By contrast, the Göttingen seminar gave

98. Annual report of 1860–61.

99. Annual report of 1851–52. The papers were von Heim's (professor of physics and chemistry at the military academy in Stuttgart) on the theory of oscillations of elastic solid bodies and Kirchhoff's on the equilibrium and motion of an elastic disk. The latter paper included a mathematical treatment of Chladni's oscillating disks and therefore touched on Weber's old interest in acoustics. That year Weber also treated experiments on cooling through heat radiation, a topic on which the physicist Ludwig Wilhelmy, then Privatdocent at Heidelberg University, had just published a paper in the *Annalen.* About Foucault's experiments, one physicist at the time noted that they received much attention in "newspapers and journals." Karl Marx (professor of physics and general chemistry at the Collegium Carolinum in Braunschweig from 1824 to 1847), "Über einen neuen experimentellen Beweis von der Umdrehung der Erde," *Ann.* 83 (1851): 302.

100. Paul Volkmann, "Franz Neumann als Experimentator," *Phys. Zs.* 11 (1910): 932–37, on 936.

101. "Gehorsamster Bericht der philosophischen Fakultät, hier, das mathematische Seminar betr.," 9 Dec. 1872, in Reindl, *Würzburg,* 214–15.

rise to the counterpart of Neumann's, an institution devoted entirely to laboratory training.

Weber had always believed that practical training in laboratory methods was desirable for all students of physics, including medical students and other science students who attended his general lectures. Various regulations governing examinations and curricula stood in his way in 1837 and again in 1849, when he inquired into these matters in an attempt to realize his idea.[102] More important, an insufficiency of institute funds, instruments, and personnel for large laboratory classes prevented him during most of his career from doing more than introducing laboratory training gradually, whenever an opportunity presented itself, as it did in the mathematical-physical seminar from 1849 to the late 1860s. He and Listing wrote into the statutes of the seminar the first important condition for such training; namely, that for the instruction of beginners, there should be an assistant, chosen from the older students in the seminar and given a small salary. In 1852 Weber obtained some help, though not exactly in this form, when he acquired an unpaid assistant for his institute (due to the man's enthusiastic pursuit of the Hannover government to create such a position) and promptly charged him with, among other tasks, assisting "in the practical exercises of the members of the seminar."[103] There were usually a dozen or more students in the Göttingen seminar, so that setting up laboratory equipment for the exercises of so many students would have taken more of Weber's time than he was willing to give. By 1866 Weber reported that larger numbers of students in the seminar—the largest had been nineteen in 1864—greatly limited "practical physical exercises" and made them difficult to carry out; the many students got in the way of the "purpose of the institute," which was for teachers and students to do "scientific work" in it "as they have always done."[104] The position of a salaried assistant at the physics institute was now properly established as an item in the university budget; the position was filled by Friedrich Kohlrausch, the son of Weber's former collaborator in Marburg, Rudolph Kohlrausch. In the official description of the position, Weber said that the assistant was to take part in directing the practical physical exercises in the mathematical-physical seminar, "especially directing the students in making observations and experiments."[105]

102. At Göttingen, only the medical faculty had the right to examine medical students, even in the subjects outside its competence, such as physics. In an effort to change that regulation, Weber collected information on science requirements and examinations in other states such as Prussia and Saxony in 1837; his dismissal at Göttingen interrupted this inquiry. Weber to Göttingen U. Curator, 14 June 1837, Göttingen UA, 4/V h/15. In his negotiations for his return to Göttingen in 1848, he immediately brought up the issue, making his participation in the examinations of medical students a condition for his return. However, since the matter also involved the medical faculty, the curator could only promise Weber to pursue it—which he did—and Weber declared himself satisfied with his good intentions. The medical faculty opposed Weber's proposal. Weber to Göttingen U. Curator, 8 July 1848; Curator to Göttingen U. Medical Faculty, 31 July 1848; report by the Medical Faculty to Curator, 22 Aug. 1848; Curator to Weber, 28 Aug. 1848; Weber to Curator, 14 Sept. 1848; all in Weber Personalakte, Göttingen UA, 4/V b/95a.
    103. Weber to Göttingen U. Curator, 14 Feb. 1852, Göttingen UA, 4/V h/21.
    104. The numbers of students in the seminar are given for each semester in the annual seminar reports. Also, Weber to Göttingen U. Curator, 29 Dec. 1866, Göttingen UA, 4/V h/10.
    105. Weber to Göttingen U. Curator, 18 Oct. 1866, Göttingen UA, 4/V h/21.

In the preceding decades, Weber had often spoken of the need to reorganize completely the physics curriculum at Göttingen, particularly the laboratory work;[106] he had put it off because he lacked the necessary material aids. In the 1860s, when chemistry and pharmacy students were required under a new ruling to take part in the physics laboratory course, Kohlrausch was assigned the task of organizing a new laboratory course for them *within* the seminar. For a short time the two institutions that were soon to exist side by side at every German university, the beginners' laboratory and the seminar, were still one at Göttingen. In 1870 Weber resigned from the directorship of his section of the seminar because Kohlrausch had now organized the "practical exercises in the physics institute for physicists, chemists, and pharmacists (which include the physical exercises of the seminar members)." Weber felt that it was in the interest of the seminar that the person who directed the exercises should also be one of the directors of the seminar.[107]

The two aspects of physics teaching initially embraced by the seminar, mathematical physics and laboratory practice, were carefully coordinated in the physical seminar established by Heinrich Buff at Giessen in 1862, our last example.[108] Buff used all the best features worked out by the earlier seminars, but he did not want a seminar for mathematics *and* physics. He wanted a seminar that "treated equally the two main directions of physics, the experimental-inductive and the mathematical-deductive"; in short, a "physical" seminar.[109] He took the statutes of the philological seminar as his model,[110] particularly the division of members of the seminar into a small group of "ordinary" members who would receive special attention such as instruction in laboratory practice, and a group of "extraordinary" members who would be admitted as auditors only. For the eight ordinary members of the seminar, the most he would admit, he planned two kinds of exercises: they would examine the branches of physics and mechanics either through written exercises or, where necessary, through experimental exercises or studies of apparatus; and they would work through physical papers and lectures. The teachers of the seminar would have two tasks: to present the areas of physics and mechanics in such a way that the students would have an opportunity to test and enlarge their knowledge, and to stimulate and guide the ordinary members to independent work on problems or lectures. Corresponding to his plan, Buff set up two sections in the seminar, an experimental-physical section, which he taught, and a mathematical-physical section, which the extraordinary professor for mathematical physics, Johann Konrad Bohn, taught. The

106. For example, in a report dated 10 May 1851 and again in a letter to the Curator dated 12 Aug. 1865, Göttingen UA, 4/V h/21 and 4/V h/8, respectively.

107. Weber to Göttingen U. Curator, 2 Jan. 1870, and Göttingen U. Curator von Warnstedt to Prussian Minister of Culture von Mühler, 10 Jan. 1870, both in Göttingen UA, 4/V h/20.

108. Correspondence dealing with the founding of the seminar and the statutes, 1861–62, Giessen UA, Phil H Nr. 36. Wilhelm Lorey, "Die Physik an der Universität Giessen im 19. Jahrhundert," *Nachrichten der Giessener Hochschulgesellschaft* 15 (1941): 80–132, on 90–95.

109. "Vortrag des Facultäts-Referenten Dr. Kopp," 20 Jan. 1861, Giessen UA, Phil H Nr. 36.

110. "Antrag des Grossh. Professors Dr. Buff," 5 Jan. 1861, Giessen UA, Phil H Nr. 36. Lorey was wrong when he guessed that the statutes of the Giessen seminar were modeled on those of the Königsberg seminar. "Physik . . . Giessen," 92.

professor of mathematics pointed out to the ministry that the physics seminar would offer the first opportunity at Giessen University to study mathematical physics.[111]

The development of physics instruction into a theoretical branch and an experimental branch took only part of its course through the mathematical-physical seminar. Theoretical physics as a subject of university instruction benefited at least as much, and probably more, from Neumann's lectures as from his seminar. His lectures were important because they attracted twice as many students as the seminar in the crucial early years before 1860.[112] They were important, too, because even though Neumann was the second physics professor at his university and charged with teaching the specialized lectures that nobody was required to attend (and that at other universities almost never attracted enough students), he nevertheless managed to cover all the areas of physical theory in a sequence of courses and to keep them going for over forty years. He established the first complete university lecture program in theoretical physics at a German university.

Neumann worked against great odds. The numbers of students he had in the early years, although impressive given his subject, were in the range that marked university teachers as failures in the eyes of government officials. We lack the comments of the Prussian government officials on Neumann's performance, other than the indirect comment of not supporting him financially; but we have their response to Weber's request to be retired in 1873, which shows their thinking. The Göttingen curator wrote to the Prussian minister (Göttingen was Prussian by then): "In view of . . . Weber's extended and successful 2nd teaching—his students numbered 936 from Michaelmas 1862 to Easter 1873 while those of Professor Listing in the same period were limited to 78—I submit this request with painful feelings, considering the flowering of physical instruction at our university." What made Weber a great and successful teacher was his mastery in explaining his material to students and in stimulating them to "intellectual collaboration"; the government was provided with numbers of students to document this success year by year: "50, 36, 40, 27, 27, 24, 55, 52, 67."[113] During the decade after the Göttingen seminar had been established, 1850–60, Listing had 113 students and Neumann 135 (counting total attendance, not individuals) in the lectures unrelated to their seminars; Weber had 889. In the seminar and in lectures related to the seminar, Listing and Weber had 232 students, Neumann around 150.[114] The physicists knew, of course, that the difference be-

111. "Vortrag des Coreferenten Dr. H. Umpfenbach," 28 Jan. 1861, Giessen UA, Phil H Nr. 36.

112. In 1834–39, 41 individuals attended Neumann's private lectures, but only 18 attended his seminar. In 1840–49, 56 individuals attended his private lectures, 11 his seminar. For 1850–59, 52 attended his private lectures, 34 his seminar. After 1860, the seminar became stronger: in 1860–69, 84 attended the private lectures, 61 his seminar.

113. Warnstedt to Prussian Minister of Culture Falk, 29 Oct. 1873, Weber Personalakte, Göttingen UA, 4/V b/95a.

114. The figures for Neumann here and above are compiled from Volkmann's and Olesko's lists of students and lecture attendances. We have had to estimate the number of students in the Königsberg seminar, since Olesko usually lists academic years during which a student was a member of the Königsberg seminar rather than semesters; we have assumed in our count that if the academic year is given, the student spent both semesters in the seminar. The figures for Listing and Weber are from their Personalakten in the Göttingen University Archive and from the seminar reports there.

tween Listing's and Neumann's numbers of students on the one hand and Weber's on the other was due to the difficulty and specialization of the formers' courses. Both Gauss and Weber pointed out to their government that mathematical physics never attracted many students and that a small number of students was "no good measure of the achievements of the lecturer."[115] Government officials ignored them on this point, as they ignored the needs of physicists such as Listing and Neumann, who should have at least been exonerated by it, if not admired for their achievements.

A mathematical-physical seminar could almost destroy the lectures of the ordinary professor of mathematical physics by depriving him of students. Weber's general lectures on experimental physics were a prerequisite for the seminar, so the seminar did not affect their attendance, but Listing's specialized courses were not required. Since the Göttingen seminar was free and Listing's lectures on his subject, optics, were not, most of Listing's students attended the seminar, saving themselves the lecture fees. That left Listing without the proof of successful teaching he needed to improve his working conditions.

Experimental physics instruction benefited greatly from the Göttingen seminar. Kohlrausch's organization of it, disseminated in part through his laboratory manual, became a model for laboratory courses at other German universities.[116] Simultaneously with its development in Göttingen, experimental physics instruction was nourished by Magnus in Berlin.

Other New Institutions for Physics

Gustav Magnus reorganized physics instruction at Berlin University with an advantage that neither Weber nor Neumann enjoyed—wealth. He was able to advance to Prussia the means for setting up a university laboratory; starting with that, he, as they, introduced new ways of teaching physics.

Although Magnus had shown an early talent for mathematics, he worked exclusively as an experimentalist. As a student in Berlin in the 1820s, he was encouraged and aided by experimentalists such as Heinrich Rose and Mitscherlich. Upon graduating in 1827, he extended his experimental training by going to Stockholm to work in Berzelius's laboratory and then to Paris to learn from the experimentalists there. Gay-Lussac received him especially warmly, we are told by Gay-Lussac's laboratory assistant Buff, who, like Magnus, moved from chemistry to experimental physics after his return to Germany.[117]

In 1831 Magnus began teaching technology at Berlin University, but he soon

115. Weber to Göttingen U. Curator, 22 May 1848, Weber Personalakte, Göttingen UA, 4/V b/ 95a. Gauss wrote to Weber on 26 June 1848 that "lectures on mathematical physics can bring only insignificant material yield." Gauss Papers, Göttingen UB, Ms. Dept.

116. Otto Wiener, "Das neue physikalische Institut der Universität Leipzig und Geschichtliches," *Phys. Zs.* 7 (1906): 1–14, on 4.

117. Hofmann, "Magnus," 78–79. A. Oppenheim, "Heinrich Gustav Magnus," *Nature* 2 (1870): 143–45, on 144. Magnus went to Stockholm as well as to Paris in pursuit of his chemical interests. Hofmann, "Magnus," 78.

added physics to his teaching, advancing to extraordinary professor for the two subjects in 1834. The university then had almost no physics instruments, even though from the founding of the university, the budget had included 500 thaler annually for the maintenance and growth of a physical collection. Erman had discovered that the 500 thaler were not available for this purpose, and Magnus now found a way to make it available: he agreed to buy the most important apparatus himself and to turn it over to the state gradually as he was reimbursed; in this way he built the Berlin physical cabinet and at the same time recovered the yearly 500 thaler for physics. The cabinet became respectable: by 1860 it contained over four hundred pieces of apparatus, by 1870 over five hundred. (A half century later, Magnus's apparatus was still used at Berlin for lecture demonstrations, distinguished from recent acquisitions by their elegant and polished wooden parts and Biedermeier style.)[118]

For the first ten years, while Erman was still the ordinary professor of physics at Berlin, Magnus supplied a place to keep and use the university's apparatus. He lectured in his house and, lacking a university laboratory such as Göttingen's and Heidelberg's, he also allowed advanced students to do research in the laboratory in his house and to use his and the university's instruments and his library. He returned the university's instruments to the university in 1844 so that the other two extraordinary professors of physics, Adolph Erman and Dove, could also use them. Magnus was given two rooms at the university, one for the apparatus and one for lectures, but this accommodation "left much to be desired." There was no space for any kind of physical investigation, so he continued to use the laboratory in his house for student research, from 1863 designating it as the official Berlin "physical laboratory." In 1867 he proposed a proper physics institute, which was to have two lecture halls, a preparation room, workrooms, and living quarters for himself. It was approved, but the problem of getting the right building for it delayed the institute until after Magnus's death in 1870.[119]

The quantity of published research from Magnus's laboratory was impressive,[120] as was its variety: Magnus did not follow what was later to become the common practice of laboratory directors of setting his students research themes from his own work. He preferred to wait for them to come to him with proposals of their own.[121] Young physicists from all over Germany and from abroad came to Berlin to work in his laboratory. In 1860, wishing to demonstrate the inadequacy of the space and apparatus available to physics students at the university, Magnus listed the published work of four young researchers—Carl Brunner, Jr., Christian Langberg, J. C. Heusser, and Adolph Wüllner—that could not have been done but for the availability of

118. Heinrich Rubens, "Das physikalische Institut," in Lenz, Berlin 3:278–96, on 278–80; Guttstadt, Staatsanstalten, 140; Peter Pringsheim, "Gustav Magnus," Naturwiss. 13 (1925): 49–52, on 49–50.

119. Rubens, "Das physikalische Institut," 279–82; Guttstadt, Staatsanstalten, 140.

120. In the twenty years from 1843 to 1862, twenty-nine published researches were carried out in Magnus's private laboratory. In only eight years, from 1863 to 1870, forty-eight more were carried out. Rubens, "Das physikalische Institut," 280–81.

121. Gustav Wiedemann, Ein Erinnerungsblatt (Leipzig, 1893), 7.

his private laboratory.[122] Their work covered a wide range of topics. Brunner, a Swiss, wrote his dissertation on capillarity in 1846, and the year before he published a paper on the expansion, density, and specific gravity of ice at different temperatures; he acknowledged that Magnus let him use his laboratory and his instruments. About the same time, Magnus's laboratory attracted Langberg, a Norwegian scientist in his thirties who had already published a number of papers in Scandinavian journals; he was interested in developing a precise measuring technique to prove the new mathematical theories of heat phenomena such as Fourier's and Poisson's; Magnus not only furnished him with the necessary apparatus but directed the delicate work. Heusser, a student of Heinrich and Gustav Rose, followed his dissertation on crystallography with physical measurements in Magnus's laboratory designed to confirm Fresnel's theory of light for previously unexamined classes of crystals; Magnus supported him through the whole work and set up a suitable place for him "that got sun from early in the morning until the afternoon and could easily be darkened." Wüllner, Jolly's student in Munich, came to Berlin after settling on a technique developed by Magnus as the best way to do experiments on the surface tension of steam from salt solutions; in Magnus's laboratory he did the experiments for both his dissertation at Munich and his qualifying research to become Privatdocent at Marburg.[123] A good many other physicists got early experience doing experimental research in Magnus's laboratory: Helmholtz and Wiedemann, for example, and later on August Kundt and Emil Warburg. At times the *Annalen der Physik* was dominated by Magnus's present and former students.[124]

As he did in the laboratory, Magnus brought teaching and research together in the weekly "physical colloquium," which he began holding in his house in 1843. "One of the most important means of physical instruction," the colloquium directed young researchers to recent literature and gave them practice in the art of lecturing. It also directed them to "new scientific thoughts and problems" and "improved experimental methods."[125] Magnus encouraged unbiased criticism of the physics literature by welcoming polemics against his own work; publications that members reported on were "horribly dismembered and picked to pieces," which helped them learn to go to the heart of the matter and recognize which problems were already worked over and which it would pay to take up.[126] The physics colloquium was

122. Guttstadt, *Staatsanstalten*, 140.

123. Carl Brunner, Jr., "Über Dichte des Eises bei verschiedenen Temperaturen," *Ann.* 64 (1845): 115. C. Langberg, "Ueber die Bestimmung der Temperatur und Wärmeleitung fester Körper," *Ann.* 66 (1845): 1–5. J. C. Heusser, "Untersuchung über die Brechung des farbigen Lichts in einigen krystallinischen Medien," *Ann.* 87 (1852): 454–55. Wüllner's "Versuche über die Spannkraft des Wasserdampfes aus wässerigen Salzlösungen" were published in the *Annalen*, in volumes 103 and 105 (1858) and 106 (1859).

124. In a single volume of the *Annalen* in 1858, six of the nine university physicists publishing in it were Magnus's present or former students; another was at Berlin University.

125. Originally the colloquium had ten participants. The included the experimental physicists Wilhelm Beetz, Gustav Karsten, and Ottokar von Feilitzsch and the theoretical physicist Clausius. Rubens, "Das physikalische Institut," 281.

126. Observations by two participants in Magnus's colloquium: Wiedemann, *Ein Erinnerungsblatt*, 7; Adolph Paalzow, "Stiftungsfeier am 4. Januar 1896," *Verh. phys. Ges.* 15 (1896): 36–37.

adopted by other German universities, becoming, like the laboratory and the seminar, a standard institution.

Through his colloquium, Magnus's teaching gave rise indirectly to another major institution of German physics. From time to time, some younger members of the colloquium met separately in one another's rooms to continue their discussions over tea, and in 1845 they formally organized as the Berlin Physical Society. Five of the six founding members worked in Magnus's laboratory; the sixth had a laboratory of his own.[127] They were not all physicists, but all wanted to be familiar with physical approaches in science; the physiologists among them looked to physics to rid their science of the notion of a special life force with its overtones of nature philosophy.[128]

Although the established Berlin scientists, including Magnus, kept aloof, by the end of the first year the society had fifty-three members. They included a half dozen mechanics and as many army officers and a good many more who, like Helmholtz, wrote "Dr." in front of their names.[129] Membership fluctuated, but on the average it grew, doubling over the first fifteen years. Most members were from Berlin, but a scattering were from Bonn, Heidelberg, and even farther away.[130] Although the Berlin society was by no means the only or the first physical society in Germany,[131] it was the most important. Toward the end of the century, its predominance was expressed by its new name: the *German* Physical Society.

Members of the society met every two weeks to report on their own or others' work. At first the reports were given mainly by the founders of the society, but soon increasingly by new members; Kirchhoff began presenting papers in 1847, the same year in which Helmholtz presented his memoir on the conservation of force. Clausius joined not long after.[132] The work discussed in the early meetings was often

127. Gustav Karsten's foreword in *Fortschritte der Physik im Jahre 1845* (Berlin, 1847), vi. H. Ebert, "Die Gründer der Physikalischen Gesellschaft zu Berlin," *Phys. Bl.* 6 (1971): 247–54, on 248–49. The six were the physicists Beetz, Gustav Karsten, and Hermann Knoblauch, the physiologists Emil du Bois-Reymond and Ernst Brücke, and the chemist Wilhelm Heintz.

128. Gustav Wiedemann, "Stiftungsfeier am 4. Januar 1896," *Verh. phys. Ges.* 15 (1896): 32–36, on 33.

129. Wilhelm von Bezold's address given on 4 Jan. 1896, reprinted in "Zur Vollendung des 50. Jahrganges der 'Fortschritte,' " *Fortschritte* 50, pt. 2 (1894), ii–vii, on iv. Membership list in *Fortschritte . . . 1845*, vii–viii.

130. Membership had fallen to forty-eight in 1848, but it recovered the following year. In 1851 it was seventy, in 1854 eighty-seven, in 1859 ninety-seven (*Fortschritte* for these years). Of the ninety-four members in 1857, for example, thirty-six lived outside Berlin and a good many of these lived outside Germany (*Fortschritte* for 1857).

131. For example, the Physical Society of Stettin came into existence in 1835 and had a long life. Its founder and first president was Justus Günther Grassmann, a Stettin gymnasium teacher whose physics lectures led a number of men to desire a society for following the progress of the physical sciences. His son, the mathematician Hermann Grassmann, was later president of the society. Friedrich Engel, *Grassmanns Leben* (Leipzig: B. G. Teubner, 1911), 63. This is vol. 3, pt. 2 of *Hermann Grassmanns gesammelte mathematische und physikalische Werke*, ed. F. Engel, 3 vols. in 6 (Leipzig: B. G. Teubner, 1894–1911).

132. From the volumes of the *Fortschritte* for these years. Clausius joined only in 1851; Helmholtz thought that Clausius held back out of personal regard for Magnus, believing that Magnus did not welcome this offspring of his colloquium. Helmholtz, "Zur Erinnerung an Rudolf Clausius," *Verh. phys. Ges.* 8 (1889): 1–7, on 1–2.

important because of the talent of its members and because the society was founded at a time of extraordinary research in Germany.[133]

The main work of the society was the compilation of an annual report, the *Fortschritte der Physik*, edited by one or more of the members. It included the proceedings of the society, but its main purpose was to survey the past year's research, calling on members of the society to contribute critical reports on publications in their specialties. The *Fortschritte* was a systematic response to the problem that Magnus's colloquium had addressed; in fact, Magnus himself had considered bringing out a "yearly physical report."[134]

As the first volume explains, the *Fortschritte* was part of the original plan of the society. With the proliferation of journals, the physics literature threatened to engulf physicists, a problem which had given rise to various solutions, such as physical dictionaries and "repertoriums" by Fechner and others. Although these literary aids were improvements over the compilations of earlier textbooks, they were necessarily incomplete and out of date. Physics literature sometimes entered yearly reports in chemistry, but physics needed its own, and it now had a society with enough willing members to compile a large yearly report.[135]

Despite the ample and competent help, the editors had taken on an almost overwhelming task. By the second year, 1846, the *Fortschritte* surveyed over a hundred journals in several languages and reported on hundreds of articles by hundreds of authors.[136] The literature it reviewed was often not the last word on the subject by the time it came out: the 1845 volume appeared in 1847, the 1848 volume in 1852, and eventually the volumes fell behind by as many as seven years, which gave rise to other bibliographic efforts.[137] But in the middle years of the century, for German physicists the *Fortschritte* was the indispensable guide through the world's physics literature, selecting, describing, evaluating, and organizing it by the large and the small divisions of physics.[138]

Of all the physicists to teach in Berlin, Magnus, the "organizer," accomplished most.[139] His colloquium was continued by others after him, and the physical society furthered its objective of reviewing new research. Although Magnus did not live to see the new physics institute building—his successor, Helmholtz, received it—he had

133. E. Brüche, "Aus der Vergangenheit der Physikalischen Gesellschaft," *Phys. Bl.* 16 (1960): 499–505, 616–21, on 616–21.

134. Emil Warburg, "Zur Geschichte der Physikalischen Gesellschaft," *Naturwiss.* 13 (1925): 35–39, on 35. The first editor was Gustav Karsten, who was also the first president of the society. Bezold's 1896 address, iii; Wiedemann, "Stiftungsfeier," 35.

135. Karsten's foreword in *Fortschritte . . . 1845*, iii–v.

136. To be exact, there were 726 articles by 365 authors in 1846. During the first fifteen years of the *Fortschritte*, the annual number of articles reported varied roughly between 500 and 900 and the number of their authors between 300 and 800.

137. Scheel, "Die literarischen Hilfsmittel der Physik," 47.

138. The reports were grouped in the large divisions by which physics was organized in the standard textbooks.

139. Rubens, "Das physikalische Institut," 282. Magnus's organizational talent was not limited to the physical arrangements we discuss here; he applied it generally in the affairs of the university, in the Prussian Academy, and in government commissions. Helmholtz, "Magnus," 8–9.

planned it and had implanted laboratory teaching and research within Berlin University. With a fine collection of physical instruments, he conducted the physics program during the long transition in Berlin from the professor's home laboratory to the state-owned university physics institute. In his will, he left his remaining instruments and his library to the university, completing the transition.

5

Physics Research in "Poggendorff's *Annalen*" in the 1840s

Foreign Recognition of German Physicists

Poggendorff's *Annalen der Physik* in the middle of the nineteenth century was in an important respect a different journal than the one he began editing twenty-five years before. New foreign physics, in translations and reports, still had a prominent place in it, but the German physics appearing there was no longer in its shadow. The *Annalen* now regularly published work by German physicists that equalled, and occasionally surpassed, the best work by foreign physicists.

At the same time, German work was gaining recognition abroad. (This was a greater achievement than one might think, particularly in France. Humboldt had found in his many years abroad that the German language did not "flourish excessively in the great Babel," and that at the Institut de France "almost everything is lost that is sent in in German without excerpt and explanation."[1] Even a paper by Gauss might get lost, which was why Humboldt translated Gauss's paper on absolute measures before submitting it.) In the 1830s in France, the *Comptes rendus* and the *Annales de chimie et physique* together published only about a dozen papers on German physics. These were by Gauss, Magnus, Riess, Poggendorff, Ferdinand Reich, Muncke, C. H. Pfaff, and one of the Karstens, a sampling of German experimental physics. The *Journal de mathématiques pures et appliquées* published no German mathematical physics at all in the early years following its founding by Joseph Liouville in 1836. In the 1840s these journals added nearly a dozen new German names, mainly those of experimentalists but including Neumann and Kirchhoff. But it was not until the 1850s that German physics came to be published in the *Annales* as copiously as French physics had long been published in the German *Annalen*. Twenty-five German physicists and well over a hundred of their papers appeared in the *Annales* between 1850 and 1863, and German theoretical physics now received almost as much attention as German experimental physics: while experimentalists such as Magnus, Plücker, and Buff were represented by more papers than ever in the

---

1. A. v. Humboldt to Gauss, 17 Feb. 1833, in *Briefe zwischen A. v. Humboldt und Gauss*, 23.

Annales, Clausius appeared eight times and Kirchhoff thirteen. (Unlike the *Annales,* Liouville's *Journal* published very little German mathematical physics: of the new physicists, only Clausius appeared there with a single paper on the mechanical theory of heat in 1855.)[2]

In Britain in the 1830s and 1840s, German physics papers appeared very occasionally in the *Philosophical Magazine* and the *Edinburgh New Philosophical Journal* but frequently in *Taylor's Scientific Memoirs*. The *Memoirs* published the work of experimentalists such as Magnus, Dove, and Hermann Knoblauch, and they published a good many German theoretical works as well. Two volumes of the *Memoirs* were especially rich in German physics. The volume for 1841 contained a translation of Ohm's 1827 publication on the theory of the galvanic circuit as well as of ten other, more recent German physics papers, mainly by Gauss and Weber dealing with earth magnetism. (At about the same time, Ohm received the Copley medal, an honor that Poggendorff made use of to remind German physicists of the importance of Ohm's work, translating for the *Annalen* the Royal Society's citation accompanying the medal.[3]) The volume for 1853 was devoted almost entirely to German work, including Helmholtz's memoir on the conservation of force and many papers by Clausius. This was the last volume of the *Memoirs*. From then on, the *Philosophical Magazine* assumed the task of frequently publishing translations of German physics papers. By the 1850s the work of German physicists could be read in translation in Britain, as in France, about as regularly as the work of British and French physicists could be read by German physicists in the *Annalen*.

Physicists and Physics Appearing in the *Annalen*

In the 1840s, the German physicists who had gained a good reputation abroad were, by and large, the most prominent authors on physics in the *Annalen* as well. To publish in this journal became almost a necessity for any physicist hoping for a university career. With few exceptions, all of the established physicists published there, most of them regularly, as one can see by comparing the men in the physics chairs of the German universities with the authors in the *Annalen* over a few years,

2. Our account of German physics in foreign publications is based on our survey of the journals mentioned. The work by German physicists appearing in the *Comptes rendus* of the Paris Academy of Sciences constituted a minute fraction of the journal's contents. The German physicists who published there in the 1840s were Dove (2 papers), Holtzmann (1), Kirchhoff (2), G. Karsten (1), Magnus (2), J. R. Mayer (3), Moser (2), Plücker (3), Poggendorff (2), Reich (2), and Wiedemann (1). In the 1840s Liouville's *Journal* published only three papers on mathematical physics by Germans: 1 by Gauss and 2 by Neumann. In the same decade, the *Annales* published papers by Buff (1), Dove (2), Magnus (3), Moser (1), Poggendorff (4), and A. Seebeck (1). In the subsequent period, 1850–63, the *Annales* published work by many more German physicists: Beer (2 and 1 with Plücker), Beetz (2), Buff (9 and 1 with Wöhler), Clausius (8), Dove (2), Eisenlohr (2), Hankel (1), Helmholtz (8 including some on physiology), Holtzmann (1), Kirchhoff (13), Knoblauch (6), R. Kohlrausch (3), Magnus (13), J. R. Mayer (1), J. Müller (2), Neumann (1), J. F. Pfaff (2), Plücker (8), Poggendorff (4), Quincke (7), Reich (3), Riess (6), Weber (1 with Kohlrausch), Wiedemann (11), and Wüllner (3); Gauss appeared with a paper on mathematical physics.

3. J. C. Poggendorff, "Oeffentliche Anerkennung der Ohm'schen Theorie in England," *Ann.* 55 (1842): 178–80.

1840–45. The only exceptions were three or four physics professors belonging to an earlier time in physics and to earlier publication practices and a philosopher and a mathematician who happened to be charged with teaching physics.

The *Annalen* tells us a good deal about the German researchers and the nature of their interests and work in the middle of the century. In 1840–45, as before, the *Annalen* came out in issues making up three volumes per year, each volume containing about six hundred pages. Poggendorff allocated roughly forty percent of this space to physics, the rest to chemistry, his other major subject, and to related bordering sciences such as mineralogy, meteorology, and physiology. Of the space for physics, he gave over about half, or four hundred pages each year, to German physics and half to foreign physics; the foreign included a steady flow of results from the laboratories of Victor Regnault and Michael Faraday. Most of the German physics papers published in the *Annalen* came from physicists who already had or would soon have an ordinary university professorship of physics. In the volumes for 1840–45, twenty such physicists contributed over half of the work; another quarter came from Poggendorff and Riess; and the rest was made up of the occasional, usually brief, contributions by thirty or more scientists and teachers largely outside university physics. Expressed in terms of pages, the nine most productive university physicists—Fechner, Moser, Pfaff, Weber, Dove, Magnus, Ohm, Wilhelm Hankel, and August Seebeck—each published the equivalent of one twenty-page paper per year. The two Berlin Academy physicists Riess and Poggendorff published more, the equivalent of two or three such papers per year. For the rest, a five- to ten-page note every two years or so was about the rule.[4]

Three of the ordinary professors of physics—Fechner, Weber, and Neumann—published physical theories in the *Annalen* in the mid-1840s, all on electrodynamics and all dealing with Faraday's induction. If only Weber and Neumann had been publishing, theoretical work from Germany in the 1840s would still have made a difference to physics. But they were not alone, and it is clear from hindsight that the theoretical work of the greatest consequence for physics was about to appear in the first publications of several young men who had just graduated or were still students: Clausius, Helmholtz, and Kirchhoff. Ottokar von Feilitzsch, who made a strong effort at the start of his career but did not sustain it as the other three did, began at the same time. In the 1840s, all four came to be associated with the new professor of physics at Berlin, Magnus. Clausius and Feilitzsch had been two of the original ten participants in Magnus's colloquium, and through him they kept in touch with university research while working outside.

We should add to these young men in Berlin the Jena Privatdocent Ernst Erhard

4. The survey of the *Annalen* for these years, on which the figures and discussions of the research published there are based, is our own. In 1840–45, the ordinary professors of physics publishing in the *Annalen* were: Buff (1 paper, 13 pp.), Dove (8, 151), Fechner (6, 127), Magnus (4, 77), Moser (7, 143), J. Müller (1, 10), Muncke (1, 1), Neumann (1, 28), Osann (1, 25), C. H. Pfaff (4, 93), Pohl (1, 24), and Weber (5, 90). German physicists publishing there who later became ordinary professors were: Beetz (1, 18), Feilitzsch (3, 58), Hankel (6, 121), G. Karsten (2, 33), Kirchhoff (1, 18), Knoblauch (1, 12), Ohm (5, 98), and A. Seebeck (8, 169). Physicists at the Berlin Academy were: Poggendorff (18, 355) and Riess (10, 194).

Schmid, who at this time published in the *Annalen* mathematical work on the wave theory of light, derived from his dissertation. With a remarkable dedication (for this late date) to the natural sciences in their "whole compass," he pursued, in addition to physics, mathematics, meteorology, physiology, chemistry, technology, and increasingly, mineralogy and geology. His work was seen as being "very splintered," with the result that he contributed little to physics.[5]

It was not only physicists in universities who published theoretically advanced papers in the *Annalen* around the mid-1840s. The Berlin gymnasium professor Emil Wilde published there on mathematical optics, and the Stettin gymnasium professor Hermann Grassmann on mathematical electrodynamics. August Seebeck and Ohm published on mathematical acoustics while they were teachers in technical schools. Gotthilf Hagen, a building official and member of the Prussian Academy of Sciences, published on fluid problems that combined theoretical with experimental approaches. More names might be added, but not many. Work on mathematical theory added up to only a small share of the whole of German research in physics; entire volumes of the *Annalen* appeared without any mathematical theory at all. Sparse as the work was, it nonetheless testified to the presence in Germany of at least a half dozen physicists with strong ability in mathematical physics. Special teaching positions for the subject had hardly begun to be created, but the inclination and talent for doing research in it were evident.

The Common Ground of the Sciences in the *Annalen*

The *Annalen*'s authors gave evidence of a clear understanding that research is done by people identified with individual sciences, by physicists, chemists, and other more or less specialized scientists. But when they referred to their special interest, it was often to acknowledge—if not to call attention to—a mutual interest, which they did not want to lose sight of considering the "now more than ever unavoidable division of labor" in research. In the 1840s in the *Annalen*, the "mineralogist" offered "physicists" his observations; the physicist offered his advice to other "physicists" who took an "interest in meterology"; the "physicist, chemist, and mineralogist" all took an interest in the refractive power of transparent bodies; men with "practical interest" as well as those with "pure scientific" interest used the law of expansion of steam with temperature; and so forth.[6] The need to specialize was conceded, but the ideal remained of shared labor in closely related fields, which together constituted the study of a single object, nature.

Poggendorff's policy for his journal was to include works bearing on physics or chemistry from the other natural sciences. From the side of mineralogy, a topic such

5. Von Gümbel, "Schmid: Ernst Erhard," *ADB* 31:659–61, on 660.

6. Wilhelm Haidinger, "Ueber den Pleochroismus der Krystalle," *Ann.* 65 (1845): 1–30, on 1–2. Victor Regnault, "Hygrometrische Studien," *Ann.* 65 (1845): 321–60, on 360. Georg Sabler, "Neue Methode zur Bestimmung des Brechungsverhältnisses durchsichtiger Körper durch weisses farbloses Licht, ohne Hülfe des Prismas," *Ann.* 65 (1845): 80–89, on 80. Gustav Magnus, "Ueber die Ausdehnung der Gase durch die Wärme," *Ann.* 55 (1842): 1–27, on 4.

as a new mineral species belonged in the journal: a mineral has physical attributes such as internal and external structure, hardness, specific gravity, and responses to light and heat, and it also has chemical attributes such as its chemical constitution and its behavior in acids.[7] For similar reasons, the earth, the heavenly bodies, the atmosphere, and man-made objects all belonged to the circle of interests of the *Annalen*: all had their physics and chemistry.

The common ground of physics and chemistry and the other natural sciences arose in part, as Poggendorff and his authors understood it, from the common world they studied: solids, liquids, and gases entered the investigations of all scientists, whatever their special domains and methods. To them it went without saying that matter obeys physical and chemical laws whether it burns in the sun or over the chemist's flame, whether it rises in the vessels of a tree or in the physicist's capillary tube, whether it belongs to the earth's crust or to the mineral cabinet, or whether it is the free air outside or air in a cylinder.

Between physics and chemistry on the one hand and the life sciences on the other, *Annalen* authors recognized a wealth of connections. Common laws govern the chemical combinations of both the nonliving and the living worlds. Exact curves defined by the mathematicians, like those which had been found to govern the motions of heavenly bodies and the motions produced in the physics laboratory, also describe the forms of plants and animals: leaf positions obey the Archimedean spiral, mollusks the logarithmic spiral. "Hydromechanics" explains the flow of water in plants, "statics and mechanics" the flow of blood and lymph in animals; part of the study of nourishment and secretion falls well within the bounds of "inorganic physics"; "physicists and physiologists" come together over the mechanism of sight; and so on.[8] Electrical physiology, physiological optics, and physiological acoustics, the eye, the ear, and the voice, all belonged to the physical and chemical interests of the *Annalen* in the 1840s.

No subject in the *Annalen* in these years engaged the overlapping interests of physics and chemistry more persistently than galvanic current; physicists and chemists could claim galvanism with equal justice: the current deflects the physicist's galvanometer needle and dissociates the chemist's substances. Galvanism and electrical phenomena in general, when joined with the phenomena studied by several branches of physics, defined a good many of the research problems for the *Annalen* authors. They published on the connection of electricity with heat in pyroelectric crystals and on the connection with optics in Nobili's electrically deposited colored rings, which resemble Newton's interference rings. They published on the tones

7. Theodor Scheerer, "Polykras und Malakon, zwei neue Mineralspecies," *Ann.* 62 (1844): 429–43, illustrates the point.

8. Salomon Weidmann and Matthias Eduard Schweizer, "Ueber Holzgeist, Xylit, Mesit und deren Zersetzungsproducte durch Kali und Kalium," *Ann.* 49 (1840): 135–82, 293–322, on 322. Carl Friedrich Naumann, "Ueber den Quincunx, als Grundgesetz der Blattstellung im Pflanzenreiche," *Ann.* 56 (1842): 1–37, on 2, 36. Ernst Brücke, "Ueber das Bluten des Rebstockes," *Ann.* 63 (1844): 177–214, on 177, 210; "Beiträge zur Lehre von der Diffusion tropfbarflüssiger Körper durch poröse Scheidewände," *Ann.* 58 (1843): 77–94, on 77. J. C. F. Sturm, "Ueber die Theorie des Sehens," *Ann.* 65 (1845): 116–34, 374–95, on 116.

produced by interrupting the current in a wire spiral inside an iron cylinder, connecting electricity with acoustics. They published on the magnetization of steel needles by an electric spark, connecting electricity with magnetism.[9] Electrical crystal "axes" and electrical "pictures," among other technical terms they used, also pointed to the development of electricity in relation to other parts of physics.[10]

From the theoretical side, *Annalen* authors established connections between electrical and other phenomena most often by applying ideas of electrical motions of one kind or another. Although the older idea of magnetic fluids was still in use, Ampère's reduction of magnetism to aligned electric currents around molecules appealed to many physicists for its linking of the "area of electricity" to the "area of magnetism."[11] Electric resistance was explained by an *Annalen* author as electric motion that disappears in conduction and reappears as heat, light, magnetism, chemical action, and other kinds of motion, each of which is a relative measure of electric motion. K. W. Knochenhauer explained electric sparks as electric oscillations in the ether under tension; if static electricity sets up the tension and if that electricity is then set in motion, oscillations are propagated in the ether between nearby conductors.[12]

The omnipresence of oscillations and their physical understanding suggested to some *Annalen* authors the possibility of a uniform view of much, if not all, of physical nature. Since according to the "present state" of knowledge, light and radiant heat are wave motions, the remaining question for Ernst Brücke was whether or not light and radiant heat are the same wave motion, differing only by wavelength. Light and heat are both polarizable, transverse, and propagated in a medium through airless space, so the reason that radiant heat is invisible has nothing to do with its nature but only with the optical media of the eye. As there is no "mechanical understanding" of any difference between light and radiant heat, Brücke concluded, there can be no difference.[13] Light and radiant heat had only recently been established as wave motions, while in other parts of physics—in acoustics, in elastic solid theory, and in hydrodynamics, for example—waves had long been of central concern. Müller offered readers of the *Annalen* an account of his stroboscopic disk to demonstrate waves visually, which he justified by the "great importance" of the

9. Peter Riess and Gustav Rose, "Ueber die Pyroelectricität der Mineralien," *Ann.* 59 (1843): 353–90. Emil du Bois-Reymond and Wilhelm Beetz, "Zur Theorie der Nobili'schen Farbenringe," *Ann.* 71 (1847): 71–91. Anon., "Tönen beim Elektromagnetisiren," *Ann.* 63 (1844): 530. Wilhelm Hankel, "Ueber die Magnetisirung von Stahlnadeln durch den elektrischen Funken und den Nebenstrom desselben," *Ann.* 65 (1845): 537–68, especially on 549.

10. Wilhelm Hankel, "Ueber die Thermoelektricität der Krystalle," *Ann.* 50 (1840): 237–50, 471–96, 605–15, on 615. Gustav Karsten, "Ueber elektrische Abbildungen," *Ann.* 60 (1843): 1–17, on 5.

11. Richard van Rees, "Ueber die Vertheilung des Magnetismus in Stahlmagneten und Elektromagneten," *Ann.* 70 (1847): 1–24. Hankel, "Ueber die Magnetisirung von Stahlnadeln," 549.

12. F. C. Henrici, "Untersuchungen über einige anomale und normale galvanische Erscheinungen," *Ann.* 58 (1843): 61–76, 375–91, on 390. K. W. Knochenhauer, "Versuche über gebundene Elektricität," *Ann.* 58 (1843): 31–49, on 32; "Versuche über die gebundene Elektricität (Zweiter Artikel)," *Ann.* 58 (1843): 391–409, on 405–8.

13. Knochenhauer, "Versuche," 405. Ernst Brücke, "Ueber das Verhalten der optischen Medien des Auges gegen Licht- und Wärmestrahlen," *Ann.* 65 (1845): 593–607, on 604–6.

"laws of wave theory for today's physics."[14] It was a simple statement of fact in the 1840s.

The mass of connections between the parts of physics was a primary fact of experience for physicists in the middle of the nineteenth century. It made no difference that their conclusions often took the form of distinguishing between classes of phenomena rather than asserting their identity—electricity and magnetism are *distinct* natural forces,[15] light and radiant heat are *distinct* radiations[16]—for they were still concerned with the same fact. The existence of the connections prompted a good deal of speculative reasoning, which within limits Poggendorff admitted into his journal. For example, the doctrine of polarity of natural forces allowed Christian Ernst Neeff, a physician and co-founder of the Physical Society in Frankfurt am Main, to conclude that light, heat, magnetism, and chemical action are not, as others had claimed, merely the results of electric currents; the "great cosmic forces" are distinct and independent, yet interconnected. Neeff welcomed Faraday's discovery of the magnetic rotation of light as confirmation of his theory.[17]

Experimental Research

To discover the nature, if possible, the common nature, of the phenomena they studied was only one of the principal tasks of experimentalists in the 1840s. Another was to explore little-known areas of phenomena for which mathematical physics had provided few maps, perhaps not even a first reconnaissance. Looking at some work on magnetism, Ohm saw "lasting value" in experimental researches like these that resulted only in "purely empirical" laws, because the results threw "light on many dark points" and provided support where the empirical foundations were insecure. Magnus explored the differences in tension of steam at different temperatures using an empirical interpolation formula rather than the existing theoretical formulas, because the latter were based on hypotheses he did not consider sufficiently established: "If one knew the law of the dependence of the tension on temperature and on all other quantities that enter, one could give a theoretical formula that would certainly be preferable to all others. But unfortunately this law is not yet known." The "scholarly dress" of mathematical theory, as Ohm called it, was not always an advantage. Where physics for the time being was better served by the discovery of new phenomena and the empirical determination of their laws, a physicist might well "fear," as Ohm did, "the sin of robbing this [experimental] work of its original simplicity."[18]

14. Johann Müller, "Anwendung der stroboskopischen Scheibe zur Versinnlichung der Grundgesetze der Wellenlehre," *Ann.* 67 (1846): 271–72, on 271.

15. Dove's position, as argued against by Hankel, "Ueber die Magnetisirung von Stahlnadeln," 549.

16. Ludwig Moser, "Ueber die Verschiedenheit der Licht- und Wärmestrahlen," *Ann.* 58 (1843): 105–11.

17. Christian Ernst Neeff, "Ueber das Verhältniss der elektrischen Polarität zu Licht und Wärme," *Ann.* 66 (1845): 414–34, on 429, 433; "Nachträgliches über das Verhältniss der elektrischen Polarität zu Licht und Wärme," *Ann.* 69 (1846): 141–42, on 141.

18. Ohm's comment appears in a footnote to Paul Wolfgang Haecker, "Versuche über das Tragver-

Sometimes the growing body of physical measurements forced physicists to reexamine well-established laws by going over the experimental ground once again. One of the laws that came to be questioned was that of the expansion of gases with temperature. Magnus took up the problem of finding the reason for the discrepancy between Gay-Lussac's law and Fredrik Rudberg's work on air: it was "too important" for him to know if "one of the most general laws of physics is right or not" not to undertake the tedious repetition of the earlier work. He concluded that it was not right, that all gases did not expand by the same coefficient,[19] but his experimental means did not also allow him to put another simple, empirical law in the place of Gay-Lussac's.

The most impressive and abundant evidence that experimental physicists with their laboratory methods could bring to light important new knowledge came to German physicists from abroad in the 1830s and 1840s. Almost every year they read in the *Annalen* yet another of Faraday's long papers on electrical research, the German translation appearing almost immediately after its original publication in English. By the period we are considering, Faraday's early work on induction, which had stimulated Gauss and Weber along with many others in Germany, had come to pervade the German physical literature so completely that Faraday's name no longer needed to be mentioned along with the phenomenon. In 1840–45, Faraday was the third most copiously translated foreign physicist in the *Annalen*. (Faraday's long series of connected researches, entitled "Experimental Researches in Electricity," beginning with his discovery of induction in 1831, were all promptly published in the *Annalen*. Poggendorff's *Annalen* was the only journal to publish systematically in translation Faraday's electrical researches, though later on Liebig's chemical journal and some French journals published some of the papers. Over the whole of his career, Faraday was the foreign physicist who received most attention in the *Annalen*; his work filled more than twice the space given to any other foreign physicist, the equivalent of nearly three volumes.[20]) Faraday was, for now, overshadowed by Regnault and the Austrian Knochenhauer, who also offered the German physicists largely experimental work, as did the other half-dozen foreign physicists to whom Poggendorff gave the most space in 1840–45: the Swiss Auguste de La Rive, the Italian Macedonio Melloni, the Belgian J. A. F. Plateau, the Russian H. F. E. Lenz, M. H. Jacobi who was working in Russia, and the Englishman Charles Wheatstone.

The German physicists working on electricity and magnetism responded to Faraday's researches with long papers dealing with his work, either contending its valid-

---

mögen hufeisenförmiger Magnete und über die Schwingungsdauer geradliniger Magnetstäbe," *Ann.* 57 (1842): 321–45, on 321–22. Gustav Magnus, "Versuche über die Spannkräfte des Wasserdampfs," *Ann.* 61 (1844): 225–47, on 244–45.

19. Magnus, "Ueber die Ausdehnung der Gase durch die Wärme," 4, 24.

20. In 1840–45, the *Annalen* gave over 361 pages to Regnault, 229 to Knochenhauer, 214 to Faraday, 153 to Lenz, 145 to Plateau, 142 to de La Rive, 136 to Melloni, 113 to M. H. Jacobi, and 103 to Wheatstone. To look ahead, by 1874 Faraday's papers filled 1617 pages of the *Annalen*, Regnault's 696 pages, and Arago's, Becquerel's, Biot's, David Brewster's, Fresnel's, Macedonio Melloni's, Auguste de La Rive's, G. G. Stokes's, and John Tyndall's each nearly as many as Regnault's. W. Bn. [Wilhelm Barentin], "Ein Rückblick," *Ann.*, Jubelband (1874): ix–xiv, on xiii.

ity or carrying it forward or using his results or experimental arrangements for other purposes. Over one three-year period in the early 1840s, papers dealing explicitly with his work in some form or other constituted over a third of all the many German papers on electricity and magnetism published in the *Annalen*. Even though in the early 1840s Faraday was between what might be considered high points in his research—his discovery of the magnetic rotation of the plane of polarization of light came only at the end of our period, in 1845—he was important to German "electricians" then, especially for his views on the galvanic circuit. They were central to the controversy about the origin of galvanic electricity: the "chemical" theory, which Faraday's work supported, was opposed by the "contact" theory, which leading German experimental physicists such as Fechner, Poggendorff, and Pfaff held, though with a degree of caution. The "majority of contemporary physicists," by Poggendorff's count, placed such "great importance" on a decision between the two theories, "whether with justification or not," that the German physicists had to examine and reexamine Faraday's account of the galvanic process.[21]

According to advocates of the chemical theory, electricity is developed in the battery by the chemical action of the liquid on the metals. By the contact theory, first advanced by Volta, the source of galvanic current lies solely in the contact of the two metals, the liquid serving only as a conductor. By "contact," the followers of Volta—and Volta himself, in Poggendorff's view—meant a force arising on contact of the metals, analogous to capillary forces which also could not be reduced to chemical affinities.[22] There was much interest in reconciling the two theories; Buff's way of doing it, for example, was to view the attraction of the two metals in "contact" as "chemical." That, F. C. Henrici, a private researcher living in Göttingen, objected, was no solution, for even if one thought of chemical attraction as "general molecular attraction," as he did, rather than as chemical affinity, one was still not justified in using the term "chemical" for galvanic attraction; it resulted only in mechanical effects, not chemical ones.[23] Pohl's reconciliation was more elaborate, involving the recognition that although "mathematical formulas are a priceless vehicle of physics," the mathematical form into which Volta's theory had been put would not yield a solution to the galvanic controversy; that had to be settled by "concepts of another kind." His solution was to recognize that electricity is just one of the expressions of "chemism," the source of which is polarity, the fundamental law of nature.[24]

Müller discussed the theoretical grounds for the controversy in his report in 1849 on recent advances in physics. The passion for controversy dies away once the

21. J. C. Poggendorff, "Ueber die galvanischen Ketten aus zwei Flüssigkeiten und zwei einander nicht berührenden Metallen," *Ann.* 49 (1840): 31–72, on 36.

22. J. C. Poggendorff, "Zusatz vom Herausgeber," addition to W. R. Grove, "Ueber eine Volta'sche Gas-Batterie," *Ann.* 58 (1843): 202–6; Poggendorff's addition on 207–10, the remark here on 209.

23. Buff's view, as described by Henrici, "Untersuchungen über einige anomale und normale galvanische Erscheinungen," 386.

24. G. F. Pohl, "Ueber galvanische Ketten mit zwei verschiedenen Flüssigkeiten, und über einiges aus den neuesten, diesen Gegenstand betreffenden Untersuchungen," *Ann.* 54 (1841): 515–37, on 517, 519–20.

theory is well grounded, he explained, which could not yet be said for the theory of galvanism. Müller had a historical parallel in mind: just as the wave theory of light was not completed until the discovery of polarization revealed the true nature of light waves, electrical theory would not be completed until new facts revealed the true nature of electricity. Once the facts were known, the theory would then develop "easily and without being forced," and controversy would cease.[25]

Not all German physicists would have agreed with Müller on the need to know the true nature of electricity to bring the controversy to an end. Poggendorff, for one, had redefined the physical problem in such a way that it did not much matter for the time being which hypothesis about the origin of galvanism was right, as long as one could get a measure of the forces at work. "However one may imagine the origin of galvanic currents," he wrote in 1841, one could not help but think "that the electromotive force or that which is measured by it must be directly proportional to the ultimate cause of these currents, and on this assumption, which is certainly most natural, exact determinations of the electromotive force . . . seem to be best suited to throw a brighter light on the origin and variation of hydroelectric currents, which in some respects are still so puzzling."[26] The contact theory could only be established by measuring the phenomena and by mathematically formulating the results. "The nerve, the foundation" of the contact theory was the assumption of a proportionality between the electromotive forces driving the current and the difference in the tensions of the metals as measured by the electrometer when contact is made. If this proportionality did not exist or if deviations from it could not be sufficiently explained, then, Poggendorff concluded, the contact theory would have to be abandoned. In maintaining that the "true theory of voltaism" no longer meant the theory of the origin of electric currents but of their laws,[27] Poggendorff was recommending a method that produced results where the experimental search for the *nature* of the phenomena had often failed.

Weber's researches in the early 1840s touched on Poggendorff's concerns (not by accident, for Weber and Poggendorff were friends, and during the years of Weber's exile from Göttingen University he sometimes worked with Poggendorff in Berlin). Weber argued that the controversy was beside the point; starting from Faraday's "electrolytic law," he used the measure that the law offered and defined the measure physically in terms of the absolute units of electricity rather than in chemical terms, as Faraday had done. In the absence of a decision between the contact force and the "no less unknown" chemical forces of affinity as the source of electricity, Poggendorff said, the advantage lay with the theory that was developed with "measure and number, the true foundation of exact scientific research."[28] It was the type of theory that German physicists were then making their specialty.

25. Johann Müller, *Bericht über die neuesten Fortschritte der Physik. In ihrem Zusammenhange dargestellt*, 2 vols. (Braunschweig, 1849), 1:225–26.

26. J. C. Poggendorff, "Methode zur quantitativen Bestimmung der elektromotorischen Kraft inconstanter galvanischer Ketten," *Ann.* 54 (1841): 161–91, on 161–62.

27. J. C. Poggendorff, "Ueber die Volta'schen Ketten mit zwei einander berührenden Flüssigkeiten," *Ann.* 53 (1841): 436–46, on 443; "Ueber einen Versuch des Hrn. Daniell und die daraus gezogene Folgerung," *Ann.* 56 (1842): 150–56, on 152.

28. Wilhelm Weber, "Ueber das elektro-chemische Aequivalent des Wassers," *Ann.* 55 (1842): 181–89; Poggendorff's commentary on Grove, "Ueber eine Volta'sche Gas-Batterie," 209–10.

Poggendorff spoke here as one of the German experimentalists involved with tasks arising from the drive for reduction to "number and measure . . . [that] the new physics in all its parts demands."[29] These tasks put the experimentalist in touch with mathematical work at every turn. Typically, at the beginning of the experimental report, the researcher introduced some minimal mathematics by way of formulas expressing laws, which he usually took from other publications. Then he extracted from the formulas constants to measure with his apparatus, and if he also wanted to explain his measurements, he included some mathematical work at the end of the report, which constituted an original theoretical effort.

The study of instruments and their methods of use was no less a part of the work of experimentalists than the study of nature, for which the instruments were designed.[30] In their reports of experiments, they sometimes spoke of the "theory" of the instrument and of the observations,[31] which instructed them, for example, on the attainable precision of their work. The best examples of the theoretical design and discussion of instruments from around this time are in the papers by Gauss and Weber, which reappeared later in excerpts in the *Annalen*.[32] Where the theory of the instrument was not yet established, as in the quantitative relation of the intensity of current to the degree of deflection of the galvanometer needle, the experimentalist might use and discuss in his report the instrument at hand together with the best experimental method he could devise for it. It might be a simple, cheap galvanometer, for example; for as Poggendorff noted, there were still many investigations in which "precision of a half to a whole degree in the deviations of the magnetic needle suffices completely for all purposes."[33]

The instrument or apparatus that the physicist bought or built himself or, if he was fortunate, had built for him by the university mechanic was not the only kind of instrument he was concerned with in his work. The eye and the ear—corresponding to the senses the physicist relied on most heavily—were themselves instruments capable of precision if used intelligently and of imprecision if used carelessly. As they were the physicist's access to the external world he studied, their relationship to it demanded his close attention. He studied the physical components in sense perceptions,[34] and he used his physiological understanding in physical experiments.[35]

29. F. A. Nobert, "Ueber die Prüfung und Vollkommenheit unserer jetzigen Mikroskope," *Ann.* 67 (1846): 173–85, on 174.

30. The *Annalen* furnished experimentalists with studies of this kind by scientific instrument makers such as Nobert, or Ludwig Merz, "Ueber einen neuen Apparat zum Messen der Brennweite," *Ann.* 64 (1845): 321–26, or Haecker, "Versuche über das Tragvermögen hufeisenförmiger Magnete." Nobert was affiliated with Greifswald University and worked on microscopes following Joseph Fraunhofer; Merz, a teacher at Munich University, was part owner with his father and brother of the optical firm once directed by Fraunhofer; Haecker worked in constant collaboration with Ohm at Nuremberg. Ohm claimed to have verified all of Haecker's investigations with Haecker's experimental means.

31. Adolph Erman, "Bestimmung der magnetischen Inclination und Intensität für Berlin im Jahre 1846," *Ann.* 68 (1846): 519–52, on 519. J. C. Poggendorff, "Ueber Hrn. De la Rive's Hypothese vom Rückstrom in der Volta'schen Säule," *Ann.* 56 (1842): 353–69, on 356.

32. To take an excellent example: Wilhelm Weber, "Elektrodynamische Maassbestimmungen," *Ann.* 73 (1848): 193–240.

33. J. C. Poggendorff, "Von dem Gebrauch der Galvanometer als Messwerkzeuge," *Ann.* 56 (1842): 324–44, on 328.

34. For example, G. T. Fechner, "Ueber die subjectiven Nachbilder und Nebenbilder," *Ann.* 50

It was useful for the physicist to know, for example, that the ear can distinguish a difference of one oscillation in twelve hundred, since his studies of, or with, sound often depended on the discrimination of the hearing sense. By the same token, it was useful for him to know that the eye is an unreliable judge of intensities of different colors for his studies of, or with, light.[36] Moser, noting that the eye completely misses a "group of light rays," the recently discovered invisible light, argued that the time had come to abstract from the subjective sensations of light and to settle on an objective action of light that affects all bodies in the same way, so that its intensity can be measured.[37] Papers in the *Annalen* in the 1840s by Ohm and Seebeck show that physiological accoustics belonged to the more mathematical and theoretical parts of physics, and the same was true for physiological optics.[38]

The task of experimental physicists that required most measuring skill, using precision instruments, was the testing of the mathematical laws of physics and their consequences. Gauss and Weber's work on earth magnetism had shown the intimate connection between theory and measurement. The connection extended to work on specific heats, refractive indices, coefficients of expansion, and other physical quantitites.[39] It extended—bringing German physicists much satisfaction—to the experimental verification of the "*most scientific* of all recent discoveries in the area of galvanism," Ohm's law relating current intensity, electromotive force, and resistance in a conductor.[40] Poggendorff noted that the confidence of German physicists in the accuracy of Ohm's law was due to countless careful measurements carried out for all conditions under which the law applies. "Only measure and number can decide here," Poggendorff said again, and Ohm's use of measure and number undoubtedly did decide his earliest supporters, Fechner, Gauss, Lenz, Jacobi, and Poggendorff, in his favor. "This theory" taught German physicists "to apply measure and number to the phenomena."[41]

(1840): 193–221, 427–70; or August Seebeck, "Bemerkungen über Resonanz und über Helligkeit der Farben im Spectrum," *Ann.* 62 (1844): 571–76.

35. Heinrich Wilhelm Dove, "Ueber inducirte Ströme, welche bei galvanometrischer Gleichheit ungleich physiologisch wirken," *Ann.* 49 (1840): 72–98.

36. August Seebeck, "Beiträge zur Physiologie des Gehör- und Gesichtssinnes," *Ann.* 68 (1846): 449–65, on 463–64. Ludwig Moser, "Ueber die Wirkungen der farbigen Strahlen auf das Jodsilber," *Ann.* 59 (1843): 391–407, on 393.

37. Ludwig Moser, "Ueber das Latentwerden des Lichts," *Ann.* 57 (1842): 1–34, on 2–3.

38. August Seebeck, "Beobachtungen über einige Bedingungen der Entstehung von Tönen," *Ann.* 53 (1841): 417–36; "Beobachtungen über Zurückwerfung und Beugung des Schalles," *Ann.* 59 (1843): 177–203. Georg Simon Ohm, "Ueber die Definition des Tones, nebst daran geknüpfter Theorie der Sirene und ähnlicher tonbildender Vorrichtungen," *Ann.* 59 (1843): 513–65. August Seebeck, "Ueber die Sirene," *Ann.* 60 (1843): 449–81. Georg Simon Ohm, "Noch ein paar Worte über die Definition des Tones," *Ann.* 62 (1844): 1–18. August Seebeck, "Ueber die Definition des Tones," *Ann.* 63 (1844): 353–68; "Ueber die Erzeugung von Tönen durch getrennte Eindrücke, mit Beziehung auf die Definition des Tones," *Ann.* 63 (1844): 368–80.

39. Wilhelm Weber, "Ueber die Elasticität fester Körper," *Ann.* 54 (1841): 1–18, for example; or Magnus, "Ueber die Ausdehnung der Gase durch die Wärme."

40. Poggendorff referred to Ohm's law in this way in a footnote to a paper by C. F. Schönbein, "Notizen über eine Volta'sche Säule von ungewöhnlicher Kraft," *Ann.* 49 (1840): 511–14, on 514.

41. The quotation is from Poggendorff's footnote to an article by Auguste de La Rive, "Neue Untersuchungen über die Eigenschaften der discontinuirlichen elektrischen Ströme von abwechselnd entgegengesetzter Richtung," *Ann.* 54 (1841): 231–54, on 236. Poggendorff, "Oeffentliche Anerkennung

The importance that laws deduced from mathematical theories could have for an experimentalist is again clear from Poggendorff's reception of Kirchhoff's work. Kirchhoff's laws of branched currents answered Poggendorff's call for "quantitative determinations" for electrical and, especially, galvanic science.[42] The laws for the branching of linear electric currents from two points were known, a simple case for which Poggendorff had given a generalized "theory" in 1841.[43] For more complicated branching—as with four branch points—it was not clear that known principles applied. In 1844 Weber drew Poggendorff's attention to the complexity of the problem and gave him his formula for the total resistance of a branched circuit. Although the problem had a "purely theoretical interest" at the time, by the next year it had acquired a practical interest through Wheatstone's differential galvanometer, which contained a complex branched circuit. After Poggendorff had tested the galvanometer and found it in some ways preferable to Becquerel's galvanometer with its simple circuit, he decided that a "detailed theory" of complex branched circuits was desirable; he then asked Weber for his full calculation and received it immediately. About the same time, Kirchhoff published his theory of the flow of electricity in a plane, which Poggendorff followed up with a paper of his own on the subject in 1846. Poggendorff recognized in Kirchhoff's work a "real advance in theoretical galvanometry," one which suggested a method for solving the problem of linear branching in the most general way. With Weber's permission, Poggendorff published Weber's less general solution for a circuit of four branch points alongside the solution by Kirchhoff's method, which was simpler and which rendered Weber's more or less superfluous. Even though Poggendorff and Weber regarded the principles on which the solutions were based as sound, they thought it was "interesting" to compare "theory" and "experience," which each did and found the expected confirmation.[44]

---

der Ohm'schen Theorie in England," 180. Once established, Ohm's law proved so useful for experimentalists that Buff, who gladly admitted that "Ohm's theory is a highly important aid for our researches in electrical theory," complained that it was being used too often, at every "ever so insignificant opportunity." Heinrich Buff, "Bemerkungen zu einem Aufsatze von Henrici, 'zur Galvanometrie' überschrieben," Ann. 54 (1841): 408–12, on 411–12. Poggendorff answered Buff in a footnote (p. 412) that one could hardly blame the "galvanician" for frequently mentioning Ohm's law any more than one could reprove the "optician" or the "chemist" because he spoke so often of the interference formula or the atomic theory.

42. J. C. Poggendorff, "Ueber die Einrichtung und den Gebrauch einiger Werkzeuge zum Messen der Stärke elektrischer Ströme und der dieselbe bedingenden Elemente," Ann. 50 (1840): 504–9, on 504.

43. Poggendorff, "Methode zur quantitativen Bestimmung der elektromotorischen Kraft inconstanter galvanischer Ketten."

44. Gustav Kirchhoff, "Ueber den Durchgang eines elektrischen Stromes durch eine Ebene, insbesondere durch eine kreisförmige," Ann. 64 (1845): 497–514. J. C. Poggendorff, "Ueber ein Problem bei linearer Verzweigung elektrischer Ströme," Ann. 67 (1846): 273–83.

Kirchhoff's work was "of interest especially for me," Poggendorff wrote to a colleague, because it was related to a problem he and Weber had already discussed: "namely, the determination of the intensities and resistances in a wire rhombus with a wire bridge." Poggendorff encountered this "not inconsiderable" problem in a Wheatstone differential galvanometer. Weber had already developed the necessary formulas, and Poggendorff had at first meant to publish them with Kirchhoff's paper, but he did not because he thought it would be better if he, Poggendorff, could first confirm them with measurements. Poggendorff to Neumann, 20 June 1845, Neumann Papers, Göttingen UB, Ms. Dept.

When in late October 1845, Faraday announced the laws governing the rotation of the plane of polarization of light passing through a transparent body between the poles of an electromagnet, German experimentalists were immediately interested in this latest great connection in nature. The first account of Faraday's discovery to appear in the *Annalen* preceded Faraday's own there. Rudolph Boettger, a teacher of physics and chemistry at the Physical Society in Frankfurt am Main, read about this experiment of the "highest importance" in two popular journals, in the *Athenäum* on 8 November, only a week after Faraday's announcement, and in the *Rheinische Beobachter* on 7 December. He was certain that "all physicists of Germany and Europe were filled with deep joy" by it, but he realized that if they wanted to see it for themselves soon, they had to reproduce Faraday's result from "entirely unclear and confused," incomplete reports in the "political newspapers."[45] So he set to work. By 20 December he was ready to show Faraday's experiment to the members of the Physical Society, and the next day he described it in a paper for the *Annalen*. Next Poggendorff commented on Faraday's discovery, for now two reports on it had appeared in foreign scientific journals, and physicists did not have to rely on reports by journalists any longer.[46] The translation of Faraday's full paper on the magnetic rotation of light appeared in the next volume of the *Annalen*.[47] It had only seemed a long time in coming to impatient German electrical researchers, who promptly did experiments to confirm the discovery and then offered theoretical explanations of it that differed from Faraday's own.[48]

Theoretical Research

Much of the German experimental research in the *Annalen* in the 1840s explicitly invoked theory in one way or another. The purely theoretical or mathematical papers were infrequent, but in several cases they were of such quality and importance that we discuss them individually in chapter 6 after our brief summary below. By dividing German physics research into experimental and theoretical parts in our discussion, we do not mean to suggest that publications in the *Annalen* were neatly separated or that physicists at the time identified themselves with one or the other direction. University positions for physicists were rarely divided this way, and physicists only occasionally referred to one another as an "experimental physicist" or a

45. Rudolph Boettger, "Ueber Faraday's neueste Entdeckung, die Polarisationsebene eines Licht-strahls durch einen kräftigen Elektromagneten abzulenken," *Ann.* 67 (1846): 290–93. The paper is dated 21 Dec. 1845. Also, "Ueber die durch einen kräftigen Elektromagnet bewirkte, im polarisirten Lichte sich kundgebende Molecularveränderung flüssiger und fester Körper," *Ann.* 67 (1846): 350–53.

46. J. C. Poggendorff, "Faraday's neue Entdeckung und deren Zusammenhang mit Seebeck's Trans-versalmagnetismus," *Ann.* 67 (1846): 439–40.

47. Michael Faraday, "Neunzehnte Reihe von Experimental-Untersuchungen über Elektricität," *Ann.* 68 (1846): 105–36.

48. German physicists commonly thought that magnetism acted on the molecules of the transparent body and not directly on light, as Faraday thought. Plücker, for example, thought that Faraday's discovery revealed a connection between the crystal forces of the transparent body and magnetic forces, which might enable physicists to determine crystal forms by magnets. Julius Plücker, "Ueber die Abstossung der optischen Axen der Krystalle durch die Pole der Magnete," *Ann.* 72 (1847): 315–43, on 341–42.

"mathematical physicist." The designation "theoretical physicist" was not unknown, but it was still uncommon[49]—and unnecessary.

German physicists working in the 1840s did not have to contend seriously with attitudes of rejection of mathematical theory. Nevertheless, it was still possible for them to come across opinions in the *Annalen* skeptical of the use of mathematics in physics. In 1845 the elderly Parrot, who was remembered as one who doubted the place of mathematics in physical understanding, as one who severely criticized Laplace's mathematical theory of capillarity in 1819, and as the author of a textbook on "theoretical physics" in 1809–15, now after working in physics for fifty-eight years was still sending contributions to the *Annalen* from St. Petersburg. He was still concerned with establishing the priority of the eighteenth-century French electrician Nollet in experiments on endosmosis, and he was still critical of the reality of certain common mathematical assumptions, which he viewed as the doctoring of physical assumptions for the convenience of mathematical treatment. In particular, he criticized Feilitzsch for building a hydrodynamic theory on the same error that Newton and every theorist after him had made, which was to assume that liquids are inelastic, or rather that their elasticity is so insignificant that it can be ignored. If mathematical theories with that false assumption agreed with experiment, Parrot reasoned, it only showed how "easy it is to misuse noble calculation," and he presented a verbal argument for endowing liquids with elasticity.[50] Verbal theoretical arguments characterized much of the physical reasoning in the *Annalen*. Henrici, for example, liked to discuss his theoretical ideas there, and he rarely did so mathematically. Like Parrot, he criticized the mathematically simplifying assumption of the inelasticity of fluids, this time of the imponderable electric fluids, allowing at best that the assumption was a useful fiction for orienting physicists within electrical phenomena and enabling them to introduce mathematics.[51] When he wanted to, Henrici occasionally resorted to mathematics, which he did when he joined physicists such as Ohm in opposing Pohl's "polarities," as he contemptuously referred to Pohl's nature-philosophical leanings.[52]

The most significant theoretical work by German physicists in the 1840s made

49. For instance, the expression "theoretical physicst" was used in reference to Laplace and Poisson by Brunner in "Untersuchung über die Cohäsion der Flüssigkeiten," *Ann.* 70 (1847): 481–529, on 482.

50. Georg Friedrich Parrot, "Zur Geschichte der Endosmose," *Ann.* 66 (1845): 595–97; "Ueber den Ausfluss der tropfbaren Flüssigkeiten durch kleine Oeffnungen im Boden der Gefässe," *Ann.* 66 (1845): 389–414, on 389–90.

Parrot had been reproved for the "bitter, almost mocking tone" in which he had criticized "the application of mathematical analysis in physics." He replied that he had written only against the "misuse" of mathematical analysis, "which occurs when this analysis is based on physical data that are either only hypothetical or even in contradiction with precisely executed experiments." He scornfully called this misuse of mathematical analysis "mathematical *Naturphilosophie*." Parrot, "Nachtrag," *Ann.* 27 (1833): 234–38, on 234–35.

51. F. C. Henrici, "Einige die Theorie und Anwendung der Elektricität betreffende Bemerkungen," *Ann.* 64 (1845): 345–56, on 346–47.

52. F. C. Henrici, "Zur Galvanometrie," *Ann.* 53 (1841): 277–94. Henrici showed that Pouillet's laws of the galvanic circuit follow from Ohm's theory, and he furnished a mathematical explanation of phenomena that Pohl had cited as contradicting the theory of currents. He accused Pohl of "deliberately ignoring a theory that has long been confirmed in all its assertions by the most careful experiments, which were undertaken to test it" (p. 286).

extensive use of mathematical analysis, much like the French theoretical work on which the Germans continued heavily to draw. German physicists often cited Laplace, Poisson, and other French writers. If, as often as not, they cited the French mainly to criticize them, that does not detract from their importance to the Germans' work. Within a criticism of Laplace's capillarity theory, Hagen observed that Laplace's investigations provided a "model" for the way a physical phenomenon is to be subjected to rigorous calculation; within a criticism of Laplace's explanation of molecular action, Ohm praised the "immortal Laplace."[53] If the great exactness demanded of experimenters by the mathematical capillarity theories of Laplace and Poisson may have discouraged German physicists earlier, it encouraged them in the 1840s. French work was the constant point of reference for their own, the source of their assurance that they were using the most advanced methods in the construction of theories of the physical world. For the subjects Clausius treated in his papers in the 1840s, for example, the French theories were still the most directly useful: Poisson's and Cauchy's in elasticity, and Carnot's and Clapeyron's in the mechanical theory of heat.

As the French examples of mathematical theory were at the same time embraced and attacked by German physicists, a body of German examples appeared alongside them. Leading German theoretical research done around the middle of the century drew on so much of the earlier German mathematical and experimental work that it can be described as belonging in part to an emerging German tradition in the subject. Helmholtz, Weber, Clausius, Kirchhoff, and Neumann all developed their theories with the aid of the mathematical concept of potential, which Gauss had formulated. They shaped mathematical methods that had entered German work earlier to suit their own work: Ohm's work on Fourier series, for instance, became the basis of his acoustical theory, as it had been of his much earlier galvanic theory. They used each others' physical researches: Weber's wave theory served Seebeck's acoustics, and his electrodynamic theory of the 1840s rested on the measuring theory and instruments that he and Gauss had introduced into magnetism in the 1830s. Kirchhoff's early papers were directed toward extending the domain of application of Ohm's law and theoretically establishing it in agreement with Weber's electrodynamics. Ohm's law, Kirchhoff's development of it, and Weber's and Neumann's electrodynamic laws all entered Helmholtz's grand survey of contemporary physics in light of the principle of conservation of force.

---

53. Gotthilf Hagen, "Ueber die Oberfläche der Flüssigkeiten," *Ann.* 67 (1846): 1–31, 152–72, on 9. Ohm, *Die galvanische Kette*, 113.

6

Connecting Laws: Careers and Individual Theories in the 1840s

The 1820s and 1830s saw significant theoretical work by Ohm in electricity, Neumann in optics, Weber in acoustics, Gauss in magnetism, to mention only the more important names and subjects. Yet it was from the 1840s, and especially from 1845, that we see the most influential German work in theoretical physics in the first half of the nineteenth century. With substantial contributions from Germany, it was then that foundations were laid for the mathematical development of the principle of conservation of energy, the mechanical theory of heat, and electrodynamics. The second half of the century saw the elaboration and interpretation of these theories, which largely constituted "classical" physics at the beginning of the twentieth century, when the foundations of "modern" physics began to be laid. It was in the mid-1840s that Weber and Neumann published the theories that were to bear centrally on the understanding in Germany of the nature of classical physics. It was in the late 1840s that Helmholtz, Kirchhoff, and Clausius began publishing; over the next forty years, these three men were to be preeminent in Germany in theoretical physics.

By the 1840s the branches of physics were controlled by a wealth of experimentally established mathematical laws. This made possible one of the striking characteristics of theoretical work at this time: as often as not, laws, rather than new experimental findings, were the starting point for the theoretical construction of further laws. These laws, which connected other laws, often had great generality and included the foundations of entire branches of theoretical physics. Fechner, Weber, Neumann, Kirchhoff, and Helmholtz theoretically connected the laws of electrostatics, electrodynamics, and electric induction, and through the law of conservation of force, Helmholtz brought them into relation with the laws of heat; Weber founded all of electrical theory on one encompassing law, and Clausius founded all of the mechanical theory of heat on two encompassing laws. These are only several of the more notable examples of theoretical work in Germany at this time, which enlarged the connectedness of nature. A whole generation of German physical theorists was bent on following Gauss, who wrote to Schumacher in 1826: "Surely you did not mean that I would achieve more for science if I were satisfied with delivering individual building stones, tiles, etc., instead of a building, be it a temple or a hut. . . . But I don't like to erect a building in which main parts are missing, even if I place little value on external ornaments."[1]

Electrodynamic Researchers at Göttingen and Leipzig

In the course of Gauss and Weber's collaboration in the 1830s on magnetic and electromagnetic research, Gauss privately began theoretical work on a fundamental law that would unite electrical phenomena.[2] Starting from Ampère's relation between electric current and magnetism, Gauss around 1833 developed an equation relating the magnetic potential and current intensity, but he did not give a proof of it then. In the following years he developed various parts of electrodynamic theory, but he published none of this, and the mathematical treatment of the subject later came to be associated with such physicists as Neumann and Kirchhoff.[3] In 1835 Gauss worked out his fundamental law for the total electrostatic and electrodynamic action between two electric quantities, but it too remained in the form of notes to himself. Even his collaborator Weber did not learn of his work until a decade later. Gauss did not publish his law because his theory lacked the "capstone"; "namely, the *derivation* of the additional forces (that are added to the mutual action of electric particles at rest when they are in relative motion) *from the action that is not instantaneous* but (in a similar way as with light) propagated in time." He believed that before he could complete the theory he had to have an idea of the manner in which the propagation takes place.[4] It was a profound insight into the complex problem, but it was to have little if any influence on the development of electrical theory in Germany.

Taking up the problem of uniting parts of physics from the side of measurements, late in 1835 Gauss did some preliminary work on a treatise to be entitled "Reduction of the Interaction between Galvanic Currents and Magnetism to Absolute Measures." Early the next year he told Encke of his interest in working "on the fundamental laws of galvanic currents and of induction and their reduction to absolute measures." His notes contain examples of absolute measurements of currents as well as of the "internal" and "external" resistances of the galvanic elements and circuit, but the papers he began remained incomplete.[5]

1. Gauss to Schumacher, 12 Feb. 1826, in Brendel, "Über die astronomischen Arbeiten von Gauss," 141.
2. Gauss's law was the forerunner of the many fundamental laws of electrical action that physicists, especially German physicists, were to develop through the nineteenth century. His law is concerned with electrical quantities rather than with Ampère's current elements, and it modifies the law of electrostatic action by terms depending on the relative motion of the electrical quantities. Weber, the mathematician Bernhard Riemann, and probably others knew that Gauss had developed such a law, but it was only published after Gauss's death, in his collected works in 1867. Gauss, "Zur mathematischen Theorie der elektrodynamischen Wirkungen," *Werke* 5:601–26.
3. Schaefer, "Über Gauss' physikalische Arbeiten," 108–9, 136–37, 145, 147.
4. Gauss to Weber, 19 Mar. 1845, in Gauss, *Werke* 5:627–29, on 629.
5. Schaefer, "Über Gauss' physikalische Arbeiten," 115–17.

Weber began his work on electrodynamics about the same time as Gauss, but he from the start approached the subject from measuring physics, the particular strength he brought to their collaboration. By the summer of 1837, he had the first precision instrument with which to begin his electrodynamic experiments. He had overcome a crucial technical difficulty that had stood in the way of the advancement of electrodynamics since Ampère, as he explained in his first major paper on the subject nearly a decade later, in 1846.[6]

That Weber should only have begun to publish his electrodynamic researches nine years after he had mastered the technical problem was primarily a result of his dismissal from Göttingen University in December 1837 and his subsequent unemployment until 1843. Weber lost his Göttingen professorship because he along with six other Göttingen professors refused to take the loyalty oath to the person of the king, which was demanded by the new king of Hannover; Weber's reason was that he had already sworn an oath of office on the state's constitution and would not dishonor it.[7] His dismissal, which was not accompanied by exile as some of his colleagues' dismissals were, brought an immediate end to his teaching but not to his use of the physics institute. He continued to do research there for several months,[8] and he hoped that in the future, as a private person, he would still be able to work in Göttingen with Gauss. He described his vision of a life dedicated to research and to the training of researchers in a letter to Gauss in 1838: "I am not so attached to either the physical cabinet, as it is, or to the kind of lectures on experimental physics that can be given to an audience consisting mostly of medical students, that I should not greatly prefer the freer scientific position that I have in Göttingen as a member of the Society [of Sciences], by your side." He only needed the material means to go on living there.[9]

Weber had some hope that the restoration of the old political order in Hannover might eventually permit him to return to Göttingen University "as teacher of physics . . . , even if not as teacher of experimental physics." An example of how he envisioned the future arrangement for physics was offered by chemistry, a "far more limited" subject, which nevertheless already had two positions at several universities: one for the "so-called theoretical chemistry" consisting of survey courses for large audiences of beginners, and another for the "so-called analytical (measuring) chemistry" consisting of courses for students who have a serious interest in the science. Weber did not know if Göttingen University would get two professorships for physics, but he thought that it could not remain a "higher institution of learning" with regard to physics if it did not.[10]

Despite his hopes for greater freedom, Weber felt keenly the disadvantages of losing his institute. By March 1838, three months after his dismissal, he had finished

6. Wilhelm Weber, "Elektrodynamische Maassbestimmungen. Ueber ein allgemeines Grundgesetz der elektrischen Wirkung," *Abh. sächs. Ges. Wiss.* (1846), 211–378, in *Werke*, vol. 3, *Galvanismus und Elektrodynamik, erster Theil*, ed. Heinrich Weber (Berlin, 1893), 25–214, on 35.

7. Heinrich Weber, *Weber*, 44–47. This includes the text of the refusal submitted by the seven Göttingen professors to the Göttingen U. Curator on 18 Nov. 1837.

8. Weber to Gauss, 16 Mar. 1838, Gauss Papers, Göttingen UB, Ms. Dept.

9. Weber to Gauss, 31 May 1838, Gauss Papers, Göttingen UB, Ms. Dept.

10. Weber to Gauss, 31 May 1838.

the work on hand in Göttingen. He could not start anything new because he was no longer *"master"* of the physical cabinet (although he still had possession of it), and he had "neither the right nor the inclination and courage" to work in it.[11] To escape Göttingen for a while, for the "purpose of not letting myself be taken away from scientific activity by the present external circumstances," he started on his "scientific" travels through Germany and to England and France as a promoter of earth-magnetic observations.[12] In between months of travel, he stayed with his brothers in Leipzig, with Poggendorff in Berlin, and with Gauss in Göttingen, carrying out smaller researches on his own or with friends and editing the *Resultate*.[13] In Gauss's letters to him, Weber soon saw a waning of interest in physics and a renewed preoccupation with mathematics, which also put into question any further collaboration.[14]

Gauss's position at Göttingen had not been affected by the political issue. He did not hold Weber's political views (he even seems to have doubted that Weber really held them). But he treated political views in any case as irrelevant in evaluating physicists, provided they did not stray from science in their public activities. Gauss argued that Weber should be allowed to continue in his position, since he could not be of any political influence on his students through his teaching.[15] Gauss was deeply grieved, as we have seen, by the threat to their joint work, and he was determined to prevent any disruption of it. For half a year, he kept the Hannover government waiting for his cooperation in the selection and appointment of a successor to Weber, and he used his influence (independently of Weber's wishes) with the Göttingen faculty, with persons such as Alexander von Humboldt who had access to the German courts, and with the ministry to obtain a compromise under which Weber could be reinstalled without dishonor. He gave up his efforts only when Weber urged him to participate in the selection of his successor to ensure the appointment of a physicist whom they would like as collaborator and friend.[16]

Not only Gauss but the Göttingen faculty as a whole also argued repeatedly with the Hannover government that Weber must be kept at Göttingen, if not as a teacher then as a researcher. Although they were influenced by Gauss's wishes and

11. Weber to Gauss, 16 Mar. 1838.

12. Weber to Gauss, 16 Mar. 1838. Weber's letters to Gauss document his scientific activities at Berlin (18 Apr. 1838), at Hannover (31 May 1838), at Munich (18 Aug. and 6 Sept. 1839), in England (18 June, 5 July, and 12 July 1838), and in Paris (13 Aug. 1838). Gauss Papers, Göttingen UB, Ms. Dept.

13. Weber reported to Gauss on experimental work in Leipzig on 16 Mar. 1838 and on 28 Jan. 1842, Gauss Papers, Göttingen UB, Ms. Dept. Poggendorff referred to Weber's cooperation in his work in "Ueber die Wirklichkeit des Uebergangswiderstands bei hydroelektrischen Ketten," *Ann.* 52 (1841): 497–547. Weber published twenty-four papers in the years 1838–42.

14. Gauss to Weber, 21 May 1843, Gauss Papers, Göttingen UB, Ms. Dept.

15. Gauss's vote in the report by the Göttingen U. Senate of 21 Jan. 1838, Göttingen UA, CDLX VI C460 (1) 1838. Also Heinrich Weber, *Weber*, 53–54.

16. Gauss to Weber, 12 Mar., 8 June, and 10 July 1838; Weber to Gauss, 18 June 1838; Gauss Papers, Göttingen UB, Ms. Dept. Göttingen U. Curator Hoppenstedt to Gauss, 14 Apr. 1838 (draft); Gauss to Hoppenstedt, 1 May 1838; G. W. Müller to Hoppenstedt, 17 May 1838; Listing Personalakte, Göttingen UA, 4/V b/108. Heinrich Weber, *Weber*, 43–73, gives a detailed discussion. Wiederkehr, *Weber*, 79–80, bases a brief discussion of Gauss's efforts on his letters cited above.

arguments, they also had a new understanding of their own, which they had derived from Weber and Gauss's work and which they now used as the main argument for keeping Weber; namely, that the physical cabinet was no longer a "mere collection" of instruments but a delicate tool, a "quite different category." The Göttingen physics institute, now set up "entirely for the present state of mathematical and scientific physics," had lately acquired such highly perfected instruments and apparatus that only an experienced physicist could keep it from being damaged. The faculty subtly reminded the ministry of the state's investment: many of the instruments had been constructed in the course of scientific research, and a person without Weber's understanding of the research could not properly understand the nature of the instruments and might destroy them. This was especially true of the "physico-mathematical apparatus," the prorector wrote, for it was subject to much greater changes than any other apparatus and therefore required far subtler handling. The physical cabinet, which now no longer served merely for the experimental lectures, had to be preserved for the experiments and measurements that advanced science.[17]

Getting a successor for Weber was no easy matter. The government of Hannover, whose action against the "Göttingen Seven," as the seven dismissed professors were called, was received with criticism and dismay in many parts of Germany, had to stand by its action so as not to lose face with the other German governments or make them uneasy. That meant it had to find successors for the Göttingen Seven who were as distinguished in their fields as the men who had been fired (who included such renowned scholars as the Germanists Jacob and Wilhelm Grimm).[18] With respect to the physics professorship, the Hannover government had the special problem of having to appease Gauss, of even holding him in Göttingen.[19] Having deprived him of Weber, they felt that they should allow him to select another physicist for Weber's chair with whom he could work. In fact, Gauss *must* select him; only Gauss could get them a worthy successor to Weber, since the strong disapproval of Hannover in university circles made it a point of honor for German physicists not to seek Weber's job. (The few physicists who either applied for the position or who were recommended for it by others were later automatically excluded from consideration by Gauss and therefore also by the government.[20])

When Gauss finally agreed to advise the government on the physics appoint-

17. Vote by Göttingen U. Senate, 21 Jan. 1838; Göttingen U. Prorector and Senate to Curator, 30 Jan. 1838; Göttingen UA, CDLX VI C460 (1) 1838. The latter is also in file 4/V h/18. The arguments were repeated in the report by Prorector and Senate to Curator, 9 May 1838, Göttingen UA, 4/V h/18.

18. Weber to Gauss, 18 June 1838; Draft of a letter by Curator Hoppenstedt, 3 Sept. 1838; Schele, a government official in Hannover, to Stralenheim, 8 Nov. 1838; Stralenheim to Hannover government, 13 Nov. 1838; and report to the government by Stralenheim and Hoppenstedt, 18 Feb. 1839; Listing Personalakte, Göttingen UA, 4/V b/108.

19. Hoppenstedt to Gauss, 14 Apr. 1838; G. W. Müller to Hoppenstedt, 17 May 1838; Hoppenstedt to an official, 12 Nov. 1838; Listing Personalakte, Göttingen UA, 4/V b/108. Heinrich Weber, *Weber*, 53–54, quotes Gauss's remark to Humboldt that his age and the danger of losing time for his work would make it difficult for him to leave Göttingen; but others expected him to leave. The despondent tone of Gauss's letters to Hannover and of his statements to the Göttingen faculty justified such expectations but may in part have been designed to pressure the Hannover government into bringing Weber back.

20. Gauss to "Cabinetsrath," 31 July 1838, Listing Personalakte, Göttingen UA, 4/V b/108.

ment—letting them know that he was doing it only because Weber wanted him to[21]—he demanded a successful researcher for the same reason as he had given at the time of Weber's appointment: the new professor of physics would have to belong to the Göttingen Society of Sciences. But Gauss's expectations of the candidates were higher now. If an "unworthy" person, by which he meant any "mediocre" physicist, were to be brought to Göttingen and admitted to the mathematical class of the society, Gauss would leave the society. "Compendium wisdom" and "collector's diligence" had their place, he wrote, but not in the mathematical class of the society. Gauss could accept only a physicist "who can preserve and increase Göttingen's fame through works that claim to be of lasting value in the annals of science."[22]

Gauss's three candidates for Weber's position were, however, once again chosen with his specific needs in mind rather than in accordance with the criteria he stated. In order, they were: Carl August Steinheil, Gerling once again, and Listing. Steinheil, a Munich physicist who was then curator of the Bavarian state physics collection and a professor at Munich University, was known to Gauss for his work on electromagnetic telegraphy. Gerling was still not considered the equal of Weber or Steinheil in "productive genius" by Gauss, but as before Gauss credited him with experience, and he was Gauss's friend, which he did not omit to mention. In his recommendation of Listing, Gauss stated that Listing had published nothing but his dissertation so far and that his teaching experience was limited to one year at a trade school. Nevertheless, Gauss thought that Listing was a "young man of very exceptional talent," with "thorough understanding of natural science and thorough mathematical education, who only lacks a suitable position to do excellent work in the future."[23] What brought Listing that recommendation was no doubt his recent cooperation with Weber in bringing his institute at the Hannover trade school into the Magnetic Union.[24]

Steinheil was so well situated in Munich that, as the Hannover government realized at once, there was no hope of getting him for Göttingen with the means they had to offer.[25] Gerling was not a particularly satisfactory second choice for Hannover because of his political past—he was suspected of being "an adherent of the new-fangled constitutional system"—but the government had to call him to avoid the embarrassment of appointing a totally inexperienced and unknown young man to a Göttingen chair.[26] Gerling was inclined to exchange his professorship at Marburg for that at Göttingen as long as he was given the same advantages that he enjoyed at Marburg, above all a new physics institute with a fixed annual budget and a salary guaranteed for life. In addition, he wanted to be sure that he was *not*

21. Gauss to Hoppenstedt, 1 May 1838.
22. Gauss to "Cabinetsrath," 31 July 1838.
23. Gauss to "Cabinetsrath," 31 July 1838.
24. Weber to Gauss, 31 May 1838.
25. Stralenheim's report to the Hannover government, 13 Nov. 1838.
26. Stralenheim to "colleague," 21 (or 20) Sept. 1838, Listing Personalakte, Göttingen UA, 4/V b/108. Also Stralenheim's report, 13 Nov. 1838.

being called to Weber's chair.[27] Gerling's demands infuriated the Hannover officials, who immediately broke off negotiations.[28] Now they had to appoint Listing to satisfy Gauss, but to spare themselves at least some embarrassment they left Weber's professorship vacant and appointed Listing extraordinary professor with the assignment of teaching the experimental physics lectures and supervising the physical cabinet.[29]

Listing's appointment prepared the way for the dual representation of physics at Göttingen that Weber had envisioned. Listing, who might have been promoted to Weber's chair had he proved to be another young Weber, soon incurred the government's displeasure because he attracted so few students—Weber later thought that that was not entirely Listing's fault, since there were not many students in any case—and because he did not produce "important literary works."[30] The task of running the institute, of gradually enlarging it, and of equipping the new laboratory facilities, together with his teaching, absorbed most of Listing's energy, even exceeding it at times.[31] In his research he did not profit as Weber had from the link between the astronomical observatory and the physical cabinet, because his interests lay outside the areas of physics that Gauss and Weber had cultivated. As a consequence, Listing remained an extraordinary professor throughout the decade of Weber's absence from Göttingen University; Listing's was to become a permanent second physics position beside the then vacant ordinary professorship.

The earliest cases of two ordinary professorships of physics at a German university usually had one thing in common: a particularly desirable physicist was available at a critical moment. When Göttingen University acquired two professorships of physics in 1849, it was, as we will see, because Weber was known to want to return to his former position. In the early 1840s, again because of Weber's availability, Leipzig University very nearly brought about the creation of two professorships of physics.

27. Gerling was interested in a mathematical professorship at Göttingen, which had become vacant through the death of its occupant. As professor of mathematics as well as of physics at Marburg, Gerling could expect to be called to a mathematical professorship, and he asked for assurance that the chair he was being offered was that of mathematics. Gerling to "Cabinets-Rath" (probably Hoppenstedt), 31 Dec. 1838. The official communication of the Göttigen U. Curator with Gerling on 22 Nov. 1838 refrained from naming the chair he was being offered, which was unusual practice. Internal official communications—from Stralenheim to the Hannover government, 13 Nov. 1838, and from Schele to Stralenheim, 17 Nov. 1838 and 17 Jan. 1839—identify the professorship in question as being Weber's; it is clear that the Hannover officials were well aware of the physicists' views with regard to Weber's professorship. All documents here referred to are in Listing Personalakte, Göttingen UA, 4/V b/108.

28. Stralenheim to Schele, 9 Jan. 1839; Schele to Stralenheim, 17 Jan. 1839; Stralenheim to Gerling, 29 Jan. 1839; Listing Personalakte, Göttingen UA, 4/V b/108.

29. Listing's appointment, 14 Mar. 1839; Göttingen U. Curator to Listing, 18 Mar. 1839; Listing Personalakte, Göttingen UA, 4/V b/108.

30. Draft of a letter by Hoppenstedt to Listing, which was not sent because it was too critical of Listing and might have upset Gauss; correspondence between Hoppenstedt and Stralenheim about the draft; and the letter that was actually sent to Listing, dated 22 Nov. 1842; Listing Personalakte, Göttingen UA, 4/V b/108.

31. Listing to Curator, 3 Mar. 1846, Göttingen UA, 4/V h/8. Listing to the Hannover government, 21 Jan. 1848, Göttingen UA, 4/V h/10. Listing to Curator, 2 Jan. 1853, Listing Personalakte, Göttingen UA, 4/V b/108. These are a few of the more important reports.

Soon after Fechner fell ill in 1840, Weber received the first indirect inquiry from the Saxon minister of education as to whether he would be willing to take either a temporary professorship at Leipzig, substituting for Fechner (whose public lectures had been taken over by K. W. H. Brandes, a local gymnasium teacher), or the directorship of the polytechnic in Dresden.[32] E. H. Weber, to whom the inquiry had been addressed, answered for his brother that a temporary position would be unacceptable and that Weber would consider a position outside a university only if it guaranteed him the freedom to continue his scientific research.[33] This reply brought a formal, direct inquiry to Wilhelm Weber suggesting the position in Dresden in 1841. On the understanding that he "could not give up" scientific work, Weber went to Dresden to see if the Saxon offer suited his ideas about the kind of activity he wanted for himself. He learned that his ideas were still "too new" to be realizable.[34]

The Saxon government renewed its efforts to hire Weber when it found that Fechner was still too ill to return to his duties in the academic year of 1841–42. Although Brandes was now Privatdocent, the ministry pressed the faculty to agree to a more experienced teacher of physics at the university. Specifically, they wanted to bring in Weber. Some members of the faculty put loyalty to Fechner before scientific considerations, and they asked for another period of grace, "at least until Easter 42." Meanwhile the ministry was to ensure that Weber would not be lost to them if Fechner's condition turned out to be hopeless.[35] The Leipzig mathematician Moritz Wilhelm Drobisch judged the matter from a scientific rather than a collegial point of view. He argued that even if Fechner were to resume lecturing in 1842, the physical apparatus would still remain unused for scientific investigations for a long time, because Fechner would not be able to subject his eyes (which were seriously affected by his illness) to the strain of experimenting except in lectures. Drobisch saw "a certain moral obligation toward the sciences . . . not to leave unused for years a valuable, sufficiently funded apparatus." "The present state of the sciences and the demands on the universities" recommended Weber's appointment and his use of the apparatus, "particularly for scientific investigations." If Weber wanted, he might also take over the lectures, but Drobisch could also conceive (as his words imply) of having Weber at the university in a pure research position.[36] His colleagues of the philosophical faculty as a body could not agree to such a position: an appointment of Weber, under conditions that protected Fechner's interests, should be "not only to use our precious physical apparatus" but also to carry the "obligation to give physics lectures."[37]

32. "Universitätsnachrichten. Leipzig," in *Leipziger Repertorium* 1 (1843): 223–24, on 224. Heinrich Weber, *Weber*, 74.

33. Weber to Gauss, 3 Feb. 1841, Gauss Papers, Göttingen UB, Ms. Dept.

34. Weber to Karl von Richthofen, 9 Apr. 1841, Göttingen UB, Ms. Dept., Phil. 182.

35. Dean A. Westermann to Rector and Philosophical Faculty of Leipzig University, 29 July 1841, Fechner Personalakte, Leipzig UA, PA 451.

36. Drobisch's vote in the faculty in response to Westermann's request for opinions above, n.d., attached to Westermann's letter.

37. Leipzig Philosophical Faculty to Saxon Ministry of Culture and Public Education, 5 Oct. 1841, Fechner Personalakte, Leipzig UA, PA 451.

The Saxon government reopened negotiations with Weber, and this time they succeeded. In April 1842 Weber agreed to the appointment to the Leipzig chair of physics, but he was given leave to remain in Göttingen until the spring of 1843.[38] With respect to Fechner, he and the ministry made an agreement that Weber would return to him the directorship of the physics institute and his place in the philosophical faculty together with the income associated with it if and when Fechner could return to work. In that case, Weber would get the directorship of a new laboratory then to be established alongside the directorship of the magnetic observatory to be built for him immediately.[39]

A few months after Weber's arrival in Leipzig, Fechner's illness suddenly took a dramatic turn for the better.[40] Fechner did not return to teaching right away, but he did return to physics to publish one last paper in it. He never claimed the physics professorship again—his scholarly interests had turned elsewhere, toward philosophy, aesthetics, and psychology—and it was for that reason that two professorships for physics at Leipzig, an arrangement for which Weber had laid the groundwork, did not come into effect then but was postponed for nearly a half century.

In his last paper on physics, published in the *Annalen der Physik* in 1845, Fechner took up the problem of connecting the laws of electric induction with those of electrodynamics.[41] His starting point was a law, enunciated by Lenz in 1834, relating Ampère's electrodynamic motion of conductors to Faraday's electromagnetically induced currents.[42] To explain the origins of Lenz's law, which was regarded as only an empirical rule, Fechner proposed a physical connection between Ampère's and Faraday's phenomena. From two "fundamental laws" that referred the interaction of current elements to the combined action of positive and negative "particles of electricity" simultaneously moving in wires in opposite directions, Fechner analyzed the simpler cases of interaction between wires.[43] He assumed that electrical particles of the same sign attract one another when they move in the same direction and that electrical particles of the opposite sign attract one another when they move in opposite directions and, further, that the attraction is along the line connecting the particles. He then showed that if a neutral wire is moved toward a parallel wire carrying a current, a current is induced in the former wire and, as a result, a pon-

38. Weber to Gauss, 24 Apr. 1842, Gauss Papers, Göttingen UB, Ms. Dept.
39. Saxon Ministry of Culture and Education to Leipzig Philosophical Faculty, 7 May 1842, Fechner Personalakte, Leipzig UA, PA 451.
40. Weber to Gauss, 25 Oct. 1843, Gauss Papers, Göttingen UB, Ms. Dept.
41. G. T. Fechner, "Ueber die Verknüpfung der Faraday'schen Inductions-Erscheinungen mit den Ampèreschen elektro-dynamischen Erscheinungen," *Ann.* 64 (1845): 337–45.
42. The law reads: If a wire moves in the neighborhood of a galvanic current or a magnet, a galvanic current is induced in it, the direction of which is such that it would have caused a motion in the wire that would have been exactly the opposite of the one given it, provided it was movable only along the line of the motion. E. Lenz, "Ueber die Bestimmung der Richtung der durch elektrodynamische Vertheilung erregten galvanischen Ströme," *Ann.* 31 (1834): 483–94, on 485.
43. Fechner regarded currents as charges in motion, and he related the forces on current elements to forces on these charges. He resolved the forces into components parallel and perpendicular to the wires; the parallel component is the induced electromotive force causing currents to arise, and the perpendicular component is the ponderomotive force driving the wires together or apart.

deromotive force arises between the two wires. Fechner predicted that a charged rod turning on its axis would behave like a magnet and that, conversely, an approaching magnet would cause a charged rod to turn, but he knew that these and similar consequences would be hard to test, since Gauss and Weber had shown that enormous velocities of electrical machines and powerful electrifications are required to produce measurable induced currents. In any event, Fechner did not have the necessary apparatus to test the theory himself.

Neither did Fechner have the necessary mathematical skill to develop the theory. In his analysis of the motions of electricity in wires, he could only give the direction of the forces causing them, not their strength. His accomplishment fell short of what he and most of his colleagues understood by an adequate physical theory; in the 1840s, it was widely regarded as a severe limitation for a theory to be confined to qualitative statements.

Fechner was not able to deduce Ampère's and Faraday's phenomena from the laws of the electric force as Poisson would have done.[44] But that did not really matter to him now, for he knew that Weber had derived the fundamental law of electrical action, from which all that Fechner had found and much else could be deduced. Fechner offered his theory merely as a forerunner of Weber's. When Weber's theory came out the following year, Weber acknowledged Fechner as the first to have "really succeeded" in revealing the "inner connection" between Faraday's, Ampère's, and Lenz's laws. He approved of Fechner's "somewhat generalized Ampère's law"; his own law was only more general yet.[45]

Shortly before Weber was deprived of his institute at Göttingen, he had explained to a minister in Hannover his ambition in science: he strove "to do science thoroughly and to use every means that serves the search for truth," "to advance equally on the road of observation as well as that of experiment, of measurement, and of calculation, and to reach a common goal on them all." This was the "only" way to obtain "a higher success and true gain."[46] The appointment to the Leipzig chair of physics not only gave him the means to continue his research in an institute of his own, but—as Poggendorff and other friends of Weber in Berlin would have argued—it allowed him to work independently and along *all* the "roads" of physical research. Poggendorff had long thought that Weber's "servant's" role in his collaboration with Gauss instead of that of the independent researcher had hindered

44. For Fechner, the authoritative theoretical approach to electrical phenomena was Poisson's; namely, the reduction of all phenomena to laws of attraction and repulsion of electricity. But he allowed that the difficulties in applying Poisson's investigations to actual cases encountered in the laboratory still forced physicists to seek information about the phenomena from experiments rather than to seek from the experiments merely confirmations of Poisson's investigations. In considering Faraday's alternative to Poisson's approach, Fechner did not think that a quantitative expression of Faraday's curved lines of force was possible. The "composition and resolution of the actions of infinitely many points," as Faraday's approach required, was "too difficult for the calculus." G. T. Fechner, "Ueber Elektricität durch Vertheilung," *Ann.* 51 (1840): 321–50, on 341–43.

45. It includes induction due to changing intensity of current as well as Fechner's induction due to the motion of steady currents. Weber, "Elektrodynamische Maassbestimmungen" (1846), 178–79.

46. Weber to "Cabinets-Minister," 8 Feb. 1837, Göttingen UA, 4/V h/15.

him; Gauss received recognition for their joint work while Weber was nearly ignored. Soon after Weber had lost his job in Göttingen, Poggendorff expressed his
hope to him that "in science, too, you may belong to yourself alone again."[47] In the
new position at Leipzig, Weber found the subject he was to make his own, electrodynamics.

Weber had a better financial basis for his work at Leipzig than at Göttingen. He
received so much more in salary—nearly twice what he got at Göttingen—that he
voluntarily contributed 200 thaler of it to the annual budget of the physics institute.
The institute budget proper (500 thaler) was also nearly twice that of Göttingen's
institute, and in addition Weber was given a small salary (200 thaler) for an assistant.[48] He was granted a new magnetic observatory, and until that was completed
he could use the "beautiful subterranean vaults of our university building" to set up
the magnetic apparatus. For the researches on galvanism that occupied him in 1843
and 1844, he found in the instrument collection at the university "several very
sensitive electrometers [made] according to Bohnenberger's direction," which he
used to perform "Volta's fundamental experiment" in various ways "with definite
success." Fechner had used the electrometers for the same purpose, Weber noted.
Soon Weber added to the collection some instruments of his own design, which
were more suitable for "quantitative determinations."[49]

With measuring instruments Weber studied the action of a charged sphere on a
sphere whose halves were made of different metals. He took observations of the
resulting motion with a telescope, believing they would be of interest in connection
with certain theoretical questions.[50] Gauss at long distance encouraged him to extend his observations and suggested changes in the experimental arrangement. He
also suggested that Poisson's fundamental equations for the distribution of electricity
on an electrically homogeneous conductor might be incomplete: more might be involved than the inverse-square action of the electrical elements on one another,
Gauss thought, and he wondered if there was not also "a kind of molecular action"
that acts much more strongly. Given the inverse-square force alone, Gauss told
Weber, "I cannot formulate any idea of the cause of Volta's fundamental theorem;
in the event of the participation of molecular forces, one might be able to think of
something that is accessible to calculation." But these were still immature thoughts
that could only ripen or be disproved through the addition of "*experience*," he explained.[51] Weber lost interest in his two-metal sphere when he found fault with his
earlier results, and he returned to his electrodynamometers. The first perfected one,

47. Poggendorff to Weber, 6 Apr. 1839, in Heinrich Weber, Weber, 60–61.
48. Weber to a Hannover government official, 28 (or 23) Apr. 1848, Weber Personalakte, Göttingen UA, 4/V b/95a.
49. Weber to Gauss, 9 Apr., 5 Aug., and 24 Dec. 1843, Gauss Papers, Göttingen UB, Ms. Dept.
50. Weber to Gauss, 24 Dec. 1843. The theoretical problem was to establish the distribution of
electricity on the two-metal sphere and the dependence of that distribution on the distance from the
second sphere; it was to be done in such a way that the electrical difference at the border between the
two metals could be calculated from the measurable moment of rotation.
51. Gauss to Weber, 27 Jan. 1844, Gauss Papers, Göttingen UB, Ms. Dept.

which the Göttingen mechanic Meyerstein had built for him in 1841, Weber now could at last set up for use in the Leipzig physics institute.[52] Weber was ready to question the foundations of electrodynamics and to subject them to experimental and mathematical investigations.

In 1845 Weber sent Gauss a manuscript on electrodynamics containing an equation for the interaction of two current elements that was to be an improvement over Ampère's. Gauss's response, delayed by two months, was critical of Weber's equation; Gauss added that he had worked on a similar theory ten years before. Weber half apologized for entering Gauss's domain: his interest in electrodynamics, in which Fechner and Möbius encouraged him, had led him to work on a subject that, as he realized from the beginning, was "above his head."[53] But he persisted, and the paper that resulted became the first of his eight major publications between 1846 and 1878 under the series title "The Determination of Electrodynamic Measures."

Weber's paper in 1846 was a masterwork of theoretical and measuring physics, and it together with the sequel publications reconstructed the physics of electricity in much the same way that Gauss's work had reconstructed the physics of magnetism. For the rest of his career, Weber worked on problems related to this paper, and it and Neumann's theory of induction set the problems and direction for much of German research in electrodynamics for the next thirty to forty years.[54]

As its title reveals, Weber's paper was built upon his understanding of the inseparability of mathematical physics from the physics of exact measurement. His main theoretical achievement in the paper was to derive a single fundamental law for all of electrical physics, uniting the theories of electrostatics, electrodynamics, and Voltaic induction; to him this achievement was inseparable from his work on electrodynamic measures.

In the preamble to the paper, Weber discussed the state of electrodynamics, which meant that he discussed mainly Ampère's work, since other physicists had added almost nothing to it. Ampère, Weber said, had devoted only a part of his work to the phenomena and laws of the interaction of conductors, and Ampère himself had said that the work was incomplete and had repeatedly pointed out what remained to be done, both theoretically and experimentally. Ampère had found the task of experimentally deriving a quantitative electrodynamic law impossible because he lacked suitable, precise measuring instruments. The experiments Ampère did do Weber did not find to be a satisfactory proof of his electrodynamic law. Moreover, Ampere had lacked the time to continue his theoretical investigations, and others had not followed up his discussion of the theoretical possibility of a more fundamental law of interaction between pairs of electric particles. After Ampère, the interaction of conductors was repeatedly shown to be an experimental fact but under circumstances that allowed no quantitative determinations. Physicists had not taken

52. Weber to Gauss, 25 Apr. 1844, Gauss Papers, Göttingen UB, Ms. Dept. Weber, "Elektrodynamische Maassbestimmungen" (1846), 36.

53. Weber to Gauss, 18 Jan., 1 Feb., and 31 Mar. 1845; Gauss to Weber, 19 Mar. 1845; Gauss Papers, Göttingen UB, Ms. Dept.

54. Wiederkehr, Weber, 101.

up such determinations because they shied away from the "great difficulties" in-volved. What instrumental means had been available up to then for electrodynamic experiments were not only very difficult to use but also did not allow as many differ-ent and precise observations as they did in electromagnetic experiments, which physicists tended to prefer for that reason.[55]

That physicists were convinced of the accuracy of Ampère's law without direct proof did not, to Weber's mind, remove the need for such a proof. He was surprised that with the "general striving to determine all natural phenomena by number and measure and thus to obtain a foundation for theory that is independent of sense perception or mere guessing," no one had yet attempted to make precise measure-ments in electrodynamics. Weber made the first attempt at such measurements not only to prove the fundamental laws of electrodynamics but also to offer them as a "source for completely new investigations."[56]

In the first part of the paper, Weber reported on his experiments to confirm the source and distance dependencies of Ampère's law. Ampère had discussed his exper-iments and their significance for his theory and had carefully described his instru-ments, but he had neglected to give the details: he said nothing about how often he repeated the experiments, how he varied them, or what data he obtained from them. Weber doubted that Ampère's experimental means could support his claim that his law was "derived only from experience." The main difficulty was that Ampère con-nected the movable conductor to the battery in such a way that the friction canceled out all or most of the electrodynamic force that was to be observed. To prove am-père's law experimentally, Weber had to develop an instrument in which friction was an "unnoticeable fraction" in comparison with the electrodynamic force.[57]

To exclude friction and make "real measurements" had long been a concern of Weber's. In his 1846 paper he described an instrument he had constructed twelve years before that enabled him to eliminate the friction that had vitiated Ampère's experiments. Weber's apparatus consisted of a wire coiled around a thin wooden frame, which was suspended by two fine metal wires that also conducted current through the coil; the coil, or "bifilar roll," was set in motion by a second coil of wire, or multiplicator. It was the use of the suspension of the bifilar roll as the connection to the battery that eliminated the friction. Gauss's earlier bifilar magne-tometer had taught Weber the "whole significance" of the instrument for measure-ments. Following Gauss, Weber let the rotational moment of the bifilarly suspended apparatus serve as a measure of *any* rotational moment given to the bifilar roll, here the rotational moment due to electrodynamic force. To read the instrument accu-rately, he adopted the mirror attached to the bifilar roll, the telescope, and the scale that Gauss had used in his magnetometer.[58]

The elaborate instruments Weber used for most of his investigations in 1846 followed the original bifilar idea, though he made some modifications. Weber's com-

55. Weber, "Elektrodynamische Maassbestimmungen" (1846), 29–30.
56. Weber, "Elektrodynamische Maassbestimmungen" (1846), 34–35.
57. Weber, "Elektrodynamische Maassbestimmungen" (1846), 31–35, quotations on 31, 35.
58. Weber, "Elektrodynamische Maassbestimmungen" (1846), 35.

plete apparatus included a separate galvanometer consisting of a magnetometer and a multiplicator, since it was necessary to have an independent means of measuring the intensity of the current, and a commutator, a battery, and two telescopes with which he made observations of the dynamometer and the magnetometer.[59] With this apparatus, Weber made a series of measurements of the angular displacement of the oscillating bifilar roll. The tangents of the angles of displacement gave him the measure of the displacing force, and he found "complete agreement" between his measured values and those he calculated from Ampère's law. To Weber's satisfaction, his measurements had provided at last a "complete proof of Ampère's fundamental law."[60] Weber next showed that with his electrodynamometer he could measure Faraday's "Volta-induction," which involved the motion of electricity in wires. This part of electrical science was not contained in Ampère's law explicitly, but it was implicitly, as Weber went on to argue.[61]

Weber's theoretical intention with regard to Faraday's induction was to generalize Ampère's law so that it extended to induction phenomena (and indeed to *all* electric phenomena). Voltaic induction still lacked a quantitative theory, and Weber wanted to develop one in conjunction with the development of measures for induction: "When one . . . occupies oneself with the connection between *electrostatic* and *electrodynamic* phenomena, one need not be guided only by the more general scientific interest of penetrating the existing relations between the different parts of physics, but one may also envision a more specific purpose that concerns *measure determinations of Voltaic induction from a more general fundamental law of the pure theory of electricity*. These measure determinations of Voltaic induction now belong to the *electrodynamic measure determinations* that are the main object of this treatise." Weber thought it was "self-evident" that the "establishment of such measure determinations is most intimately linked with the establishment of the *laws* that govern the phenomena in question, so that the one cannot be separated from the other."[62] He confirmed this through his work on the theory of induction.

Having determined in the experimental first part of the paper the correctness of Ampère's law for the phenomena Ampère considered, Weber directed the second part of the paper to the theoretical construction and application of a more general law than Ampère's. Unlike Ampère's law, which concerns the action of currents in

59. Both wire coils were placed so that the diameter of the cylinders about which the wire was wound was vertical. The arrangement of the coils with respect to one another was such that the axis of the cylinder of one was at right angles to that of the other, and that one of the two coils was inside the other. Either the outer or the inner coil could be the bifilar roll with bifilar suspension; whichever arrangement, it had to allow enough room for the suspended coil to rotate freely in a horizontal plane about its vertical central diameter. Since some experiments required that the stationary coil, the multiplicator, could also be placed at various distances from and at different locations about the moveable bifilar roll, Weber came to prefer the multiplicator to be placed inside the bifilar roll rather than the other way around; it could then be relocated without disturbing the suspension of the bifilar roll. This was the main modification of the instrument. Weber, "Elektrodynamische Maassbestimmungen" (1846), 36–40, 54–58.
60. Weber, "Elektrodynamische Maassbestimmungen" (1846), 69–80, quotation on 79.
61. Weber, "Elektrodynamische Maassbestimmungen" (1846), 92–107.
62. Weber, "Elektrodynamische Maassbestimmungen" (1846), 132–34, on 134.

ponderable wires,[63] Weber's law concerns the action of the imponderable electric masses within the wires. Weber, like Fechner, assumed that currents are electric masses in motion; according to this assumption, any element of current contains an equal number of positive and negative electric masses moving with the same speed but in opposite directions in the wire, and the measure of the current is the number of electric masses passing through a cross section of the wire in unit time.

The quantitative statement of Weber's assumption is that the current i equals aeu, where a is a constant, e is the mass of positive electricity per unit length of conductor, and u is its velocity along the conductor. With the substitution of this definition of current, applied to each of the two kinds of electricity separately, into Ampère's law, and after many solid pages of manipulations of formulas, Weber derived the mutual force between a pair of electric masses in relative motion. (To connect this force with Ampère's force, which is responsible for moving ponderable wires, Weber assumed that the electric force is transferred to the wires through their resistance to the motion of the electric masses within them.) Weber combined the new force with Coulomb's "fundamental principle" of electrostatics to arrive at the "general fundamental principle *for the whole theory of electricity*":[64]

$$\frac{ee'}{r^2}\left[1 - \frac{1}{c^2}\left(\frac{dr}{dt}\right)^2 + \frac{2r}{c^2}\frac{d^2r}{dt^2}\right],$$

where to simplify the equation the constant c replaces the constant a. By this formula for the mutual action of two electric masses, e and e', separated a distance r, electrodynamics and electrostatics are no longer separate branches of electricity, as they are, for example, in Ampère's scheme of the division of the sciences. Rather, electrostatic action, represented by the first term in the bracket, is the limiting case of electrodynamic action when the relative velocity dr/dt and the relative acceleration d^2r/dt^2 of the electric masses vanish.

The action expressed by Weber's law is instantaneous and directed along the line connecting the electric masses, in agreement with the long-standing example of the gravitational force. But in its dependency not only on the separation of the pair of electric masses but also on their relative motion, it differs from the gravitational

---

63. Ampère's "fundamental principle" of electrodynamics is

$$\frac{-ii'}{r^2}\left(\cos\epsilon - \frac{3}{2}\cos\theta\cos\theta'\right)ds\,ds',$$

which expresses the ponderomotive force between current elements. In this formula ds and ds' are the elementary lengths of the two currents i and i', and ϵ, θ, and θ' refer to the angles that the positive currents in the two elements make with one another and with the connecting line r between them. Weber, "Elektrodynamische Maassbestimmungen" (1846), 69–70.

64. The two constants are proportional: $a = 4/c$. The symbol e is the electric mass as measured in electrostatics, and so it is simply proportional to the e, the electric mass per unit length, in Weber's definition of current. This derivation of the new law from Ampère's law is on 151–57 of the 1846 paper; Weber's direct derivation of the law from "experience," based partly on observation and partly on Ampère's law, is on 134–48. Wilhelm Weber, "Elektrodynamische Maassbestimmungen" (Excerpt), *Ann.* 73 (1848): 193–240, reprinted in *Werke* 3:215–54, on 244.

force. All physicists who discussed Weber's law remarked on this feature, so that to the German historian of physics Ferdinand Rosenberger, writing in the 1880s, Weber's law appeared as a "revolutionary achievement of the first order."[65] Weber, of course, was aware of the departure of his law from the expected form, and from the start he sought to forestall objections to it on this account. He wrote: "The laws giving the dependence of forces on given physical relations are called *physical fundamental laws,* and according to the purpose of physics, they are not meant to give an *explanation* of the forces by their true causes, but only a clearly presented and useful general method for the *quantitative* determination of the forces by means of the fundamental measures established in physics for space and time." For that reason one cannot object, "from a physical point of view," if a force is represented by a function of time as well as of distance. Both time and space are measurable quantities and, by their nature, suited for exact quantitative determination. Weber observed that his law, with its dependence on time, was unlike Newton's gravitational law, but this was no objection to it, since any analogy used in the formulation of new laws was to be followed only so long as it led to correct results. Once it ceased to do so, it was to be abandoned for new approaches, such as the one Weber's fundamental law represented. Weber thought that physicists might "well expect" other forces to show a similar dependency on motion as his force, which introduced an "entirely new element" into the concept of force.[66]

In the shortened version of the 1846 paper that Weber published in the *Annalen der Physik* in 1848, he followed up the derivation of his fundamental law by giving an expression for its potential, in keeping with the example provided by Gauss's work on magnetism.[67] (Weber did not actually use the potential in these early papers, however.)

The constant c was of great importance to Weber's work in electrodynamics. From the way it enters the fundamental law, c is seen to be the limiting velocity with which two electric masses must move relative to one another for them to exert no mutual force.[68] That was its physical meaning for Weber. The practical importance of c arose from its place in Weber's development of a system of absolute measures for electrodynamics.

The fruitfulness of the use of absolute measures in magnetism made the establishment of absolute measures in electrodynamics an unquestioned goal. In fact, the first "fundamental measures" that Weber established for current intensity, electromotive force, and resistance[69] made use of the absolute measures of magnetism, that is, of the measure of the action of a current by the motion of a magnet.[70] Weber

65. Rosenberger, *Geschichte der Physik,* 507.

66. Weber, "Elektrodynamische Maassbestimmungen" (1846), 149–50.

67. Weber, "Elektrodynamische Maassbestimmungen" (Excerpt) (1848), 245.

68. Wilhelm Weber, "Elektrodynamische Maassbestimmungen insbesondere Widerstandsmessungen," *Abh. sächs. Ges. Wiss.* 1 (1852): 199–381, reprinted in *Werke* 3:301–471, on 368.

69. Weber had no independent measure for resistance in 1846 but derived one from the measures of electromotive force and current intensity.

70. Weber, "Elektrodynamische Maassbestimmungen" (1852), 320–21, 358. Also Riecke, "Weber," 20.

recognized, however, that electrodynamic measures need not depend on magnetic measures but can be established on the basis of Ampère's fundamental law of electrodynamics and the law of Voltaic induction; in other words, an electric current can be measured by another current. Weber developed fundamental measures for current intensity, electromotive force, and resistance on this electrodynamic basis.[71] Finally, he developed a third system of electrodynamic measures by adopting the measures established in electrostatics; any electromotive force, for example, can be expressed in terms of the measure established for electric force in electrostatics. This measure is not a measure peculiar to electrostatics, however, but is the same as the measure of force in mechanics; Weber wanted to derive a measure of current intensity, and hence a measure for resistance, from measures used in mechanics.[72]

To use the measures of mechanics in electrodynamics, Weber had to find a rule by which all the measurements that he had made using the other two measuring systems could be converted. He recognized that this rule could be derived only from his fundamental law, not from any other law (such as Ampère's) that had preceded it. The conversion of the measures involved the ubiquitous constant c: for example, to convert his measurements of current intensity from electrodynamic measures to mechanical ones, Weber had to multiply the measurements by $c/4$. It was obvious to Weber that as long as c was not actually measured, the "special" systems—the electromagnetic and the electrodynamic measures—would continue to be indispensable for "practical uses in electrodynamics."[73] Without the determination of c, moreover, Weber's fundamental law was incomplete, capable of predicting quantitites only in ratios in which c cancels out. With his friend the Marburg physicist Rudolph Kohlrausch, Weber measured the constant and published its value in 1855.[74] This work, which brought the absolute system of measures in electrical physics to an inner conclusion, Weber delayed as long as he did because of the difficulty in carrying out the measurement, especially the part connected with static electricity, for which Kohlrausch's expert assistance was invaluable.[75]

Weber remarked on the closeness of the measured value of c to the velocity of light, noting mainly the physical dissimilarity of their origins. For him, the constant c was a "real" velocity of electric masses, whereas the velocity of light was not the

71. Weber, "Elektrodynamische Maassbestimmungen" (1852), 358–65. The "electromagnetic" fundamental measures are not identical with the "electrodynamic" ones. The measure of current intensity in the former system is related to that in the latter system as $\sqrt{2}$ to 1; the fundamental measure of electromotive force in the former system is related to that in the latter system as 1 to $\sqrt{2}$.

72. Weber, "Elektrodynamische Maassbestimmungen" (1852), 365–68.

73. Weber, "Elektrodynamische Maassbestimmungen" (1852), 366–68.

74. Wilhelm Weber and Rudolph Kohlrausch, "Ueber die Elektricitätsmenge, welche bei galvanischen Strömen durch den Querschnitt der Kette fliesst," Ann. 99 (1856): 10–25, reprinted in Weber, Werke 3:597–608. Weber had already announced the value of c in remarks to the Saxon Society in 1855 when he submitted his and Kohlrausch's paper "Elektrodynamische Maassbestimmungen insbesondere Zurückführung der Stromintensitäts-Messungen auf mechanisches Maass." Wilhelm Weber, "Vorwort," Verh. sächs. Ges. Wiss. 17 (1855): 55–61, reprinted in Werke 3:591–96, on 594. In their paper in the Annalen in 1856, Weber and Kohlrausch gave $c = 439{,}450 \times 10^6$ millimeters per second.

75. Riecke, "Weber," 20–21; Leon Rosenfeld, "The Velocity of Light and the Evolution of Electrodynamics," Nuovo Cimento, supplement to vol. 4 (1957): 1630–69, on 1633. Weber, "Vorwort" (1855), 592.

velocity of any body but of a wave motion.[76] When in 1864 Weber deduced, as Kirchhoff had also deduced, that current oscillations in a perfectly conducting circuit travel with a velocity $c/\sqrt{2}$, a value even closer to the velocity of light, he remarked that one should not hold "great expectations" for establishing an "inner connection" between optics and electricity through this numerical coincidence.[77]

In the 1840s Weber was prominent among a number of physicists in Germany who succeeded in connecting the laws belonging to previousy separated groups of facts. But he did not, nor did any of his colleagues then, succeed in establishing the fundamental connection between the laws of electricity and those of light. That achievement was to come later in the century and, in its theoretical formulation, it was to come to Germany from abroad.

Weber's researches, which dealt at the time with resistance measurements, were interrupted again in 1849. In the spring of 1848, the political situation in Hannover had already changed enough to allow preparations for Weber's return to Göttingen. Weber had "great interest" in returning, for he wanted to help reestablish there the "lively scientific sphere of activity" of which he had been a part and which he had left with great reluctance. The "magical attraction" of Göttingen for Weber was the promise of renewed scientific collaboration with Gauss.[78]

Assuming that Göttingen University needed physics lectures that would attract students, Weber thought that the Hannover government would consider "inadmissible" an appointment that did not include the obligation to lecture as its main purpose. That was acceptable to Weber: "My purely scientific work is too insignificant for me to want to base demands on it, or to be able to do so." Weber, who apparently knew of the official dissatisfaction with Listing, only feared that in his own case, as in Listing's, the ministry might hold unrealistic expectations for his teaching.[79]

The circumstances of Weber's dismissal in 1837 made a new appointment at Göttingen a sensitive matter. Weber wanted to be certain that the appointment to his former chair would be made only because it was in the interest of physics at Göttingen. He also wanted to be certain that both he and Listing were needed, so that he would not be encroaching on Listing's position. The immediate official letter to Weber offered him an ordinary professorship "especially for the subject of physics." It added that university teachers once again considered Göttingen a "place of residence as pleasant as it is suitable for scientific life."[80]

76. Weber, "Vorwort" (1855), 595. Wilhelm Weber and Rudolph Kohlrausch, "Elektrodynamische Maassbestimmungen insbesondere Zurückführung der Stromintensitäts-Messungen auf mechanisches Maass," Abh. sächs. Ges. Wiss. 3 (1857): 221–90, reprinted in Weber, Werke 3:609–76, on 652.

77. Here Weber wrote the measured value for $c/\sqrt{2}$ as $310{,}740 \times 10^6$ mm/sec. Wilhelm Weber, "Elektrodynamische Maassbestimmungen insbesondere über elektrische Schwingungen," Abh. sächs. Ges. Wiss. 6 (1864): 571–716, reprinted in Werke, vol. 4, Galvanismus und Elektrodynamik, zweiter Theil, ed. Heinrich Weber (Berlin, 1894), 105–241, on 157.

78. Weber to a Hannover government official, 28 (or 23) Apr. 1848.

79. Weber to unknown (probably Sartorius von Waltershausen), 14 Apr. 1848, Weber Personalakte, Göttingen UA, 4/V b/95a.

80. Weber to unknown, 14 Apr. 1848; Weber to "Regierungsrath," 22 May 1848; Göttingen U. Curator to Weber, 15 Apr. 1848; Weber Personalakte, Göttingen UA, 4/V b/95a.

Weber visited Göttingen in May to see for himself. Staunchly, if implicitly, in support of Listing, Weber reported to the government that he found the same lack of interest in physics among the students, particularly the medical students, that he had earlier in 1837. The fault lay with a general disregard for physics, which appeared, on the one hand, in the inadequate preparation of the students for studying physics and, on the other, in the absence of adequate physics requirements in examinations given by the medical faculty. Two physics professors working together on the problem might make a difference, and in general Weber thought it was time to give the physical sciences "double representation" at Göttingen. It had already happened at "many other universities," since physics had grown to such an extent that nobody was capable anymore of equally encompassing all of its branches.[81]

The arrangement for the "double representation" of physics at Göttingen that Weber suggested was based on research interests. Weber proposed that he be appointed professor of experimental physics because he had broad experience in experimental physics; by contrast, he had only limited experience in a few areas of mathematical physics, which he had acquired through his researches. He proposed that Listing, in light of his mathematical background, be appointed professor of mathematical physics. Weber insisted that in any case Listing, as the current representative of experimental physics, had the right to choose the position he wanted. If Listing should choose experimental physics, Weber was prepared to take on mathematical physics. Weber made only two conditions for his return: one, that Listing be promoted to ordinary professor so that he would be of equal rank with Weber; and two, that each of them be given an independent and sufficient budget for his work.[82] Weber's suggestion was precisely what the ministry wanted. Listing was *told* of the change, not given a choice.[83] Having been informed that he would be professor of experimental physics, Weber asked for an immediate extraordinary grant for the physical cabinet so that he would not lose too much time in moving his research from Leipzig to Göttingen. He wanted a large amount (which he eventually fixed at 3000 thaler) later for "renewal" of the physical cabinet, which was "urgently" needed "every 25 or 50 years" if an institute was to meet the "demands of the times." Weber's financial requests were approved, and he officially accepted the Göttingen position in October 1848. He moved back to Göttingen the following spring.[84]

The creation of two ordinary professorships for physics at Göttingen University

81. Weber to "Regierungsrath," 22 May 1848.

82. Weber to "Regierungsrath," 22 May 1848.

83. Göttingen U. Curator to Listing, 31 July 1848; Listing's answer, 8 Aug. 1848; Listing Personalakte, Göttingen UA, 4/V b/108. The Göttingen curator had already made up his mind that Listing should not continue as professor of experimental physics. To gain the desired decision from the government, he misrepresented Weber's answer above: he wrote that Weber would come "if he were given the direction of the physical cabinet to the extent that it is necessary for his subject, *experimental* physics, and if the present extraordinary professor of physics Listing were appointed ordinary professor of *mathematical* physics." Report by Göttingen U. Curator to King of Hannover, 16 June 1848, Weber Personalakte, Göttingen UA, 4/V b/95a. When Weber learned that Listing had not been asked, he asked Gauss to obtain Listing's agreement to the arrangements directly before he accepted the offer from Hannover. Weber to Gauss, 21 June 1848; Gauss to Weber, 26 June 1848; Gauss Papers, Göttingen UB, Ms. Dept.

84. Weber to the Göttingen U. Curator, 8 July and 5 Oct. 1848; Curator to Weber, 28 Aug. 1848; Weber Personalakte, Göttingen UA, 4/V b/95a.

was followed by the creation of two physics institutes. As Weber had been given to understand during the negotiations over his appointment, he was to get the existing physical cabinet, except for instruments that he did not need and found more suitable for mathematical physics, and he was to get the rooms of the existing physical cabinet. Listing, on the other hand, had been left with the impression that both the apparatus and the rooms would be divided between him and Weber.[85] Both had understood the ministry correctly: it intended Weber to have the physical cabinet by and large as it was, and it also intended Listing to get part of it, but a very small part. The separation of instruments and rooms was carried out, although because of the two physicists' desire to accommodate one another and because of Weber's momentary position of strength, Listing received a larger share than was officially intended, which gave him some means for experimental research.[86]

The two physics institutes did not satisfy the needs of their directors. Nearly two decades later, Weber was still waiting for over half of the money he had requested for the improvement of his instrument collection. (Listing fared so badly that he went into personal debt as a result of buying instruments.) To advance his research, Weber resorted to his old ingenuity at devising apparatus with what means he had; he now also claimed for his research a part of the annual institute budget and space in the institute.[87] As he reported to the curator in 1851: "At least the private practical work of the professor of physics was provided for."[88] Aside from Gauss, only Weber among German university physicists could then make such a claim for his "private" research. He had gained the right because by representing physics research in every context for the last twenty years, he had contributed to implanting his view of the university physicist in the official mind.

Electrical Researchers at Königsberg and Berlin

In the mid-1840s the Prussian Academy of Sciences brought out two extensive papers on electric induction by Neumann. Their purpose was not to present the capabilities of a new instrument in testing a law, as Weber's had been in part. They were strictly mathematical: by mathematical manipulation, Neumann proceeded from a set of established electrical laws to new laws governing the phenomena of induction.

Earlier Neumann had done research on problems from various parts of physics, especially as they connected with crystals. His first published researches in the 1820s treated mainly the geometrical properties of crystals, but from the early 1830s they

---

85. Weber to Göttingen U. Prorector, 3 Apr. 1849, Göttingen UA, CDLX VI C 460 (1).

86. Göttingen U. Prorector Fuchs to Curator, 5 Apr. 1849, Göttingen UA, 4/V h/19.

87. Listing to Göttingen U. Curator, 2 Jan. 1853, Listing Personalakte, Göttingen UA, 4/V b/108; Listing's inventory of his mathematical-physical institute as of 1849 in Listing to Göttingen U. Curator, 3 Sept. 1855, Göttingen UA, 4/V h/8. "Bericht des Professors Wilhelm Weber, die Instrumenten-Sammlung des physikalischen Instituts betreffend" to Göttingen U. Curator, 13 Aug. 1849; Curator to Weber, 22 Aug. 1849; Göttingen UA, 4/V h/19. Weber to Curator, 4 Apr. 1851, Göttingen UA, 4/V h/10.

88. Weber to Göttingen U. Curator, 10 May 1851, Göttingen UA, 4/V h/21.

treated their thermal, elastic, and optical properties as well. Drawn to optical researches particularly by Fresnel's recent wave theory of light, Neumann questioned Fresnel's application of the theory to the problem of double refraction in crystals. In his first work in optics, Neumann set out to supply a proper theory for this phenomenon by deriving optical laws from the equations of mechanics, extending C. L. M. H. Navier's laws of elastic oscillations for noncrystalline bodies to crystalline ones.[89]

In general, in his early optical work, Neumann followed the French authors Navier, Poisson, and Cauchy in approaching the subject from a molecular standpoint. Later, however, he came to treat the smallest parts of bodies as similar to the bodies themselves, endowed with similar properties: he studied the optical properties of deformed bodies by treating a deformed body as a collection of homogeneous, infinitesimal deformed volume elements. Using the same approach, he studied total reflection, reflection and refraction at crystal interfaces, elastic properties of crystals, and other phenomena inside and outside optics. In all of this, Neumann's procedure was "deductive"; for him the physical theory always came first, and after that he made observations in the form of exact measurements.[90]

The culmination of Neumann's researches in physics came in the 1840s. At that time, he brought to completion the optical researches that had occupied him for ten years, and he made a profound study of a new subject, electrical induction. Like Gauss, Fechner, and Weber, he addressed the principal theoretical problem of bringing Faraday's induced currents into relationship with known physical laws. His approach differed from theirs in that he did not make hypotheses about the nature of electric currents (though he spoke of the motion of the "fluid"), nor did he make hypotheses about the nature of the ultimate forces of attraction and repulsion between electrical quantities. He did not need physical hypotheses like these to establish the mathematical laws of induced currents, which was his only concern.[91]

Neumann's first paper on electrodynamics in 1845[92] was not an easy work for his contemporaries. They found its German highly convoluted and its mathematical notation idiosyncratic. Jacobi, who did the proofreading of Neumann's paper in Berlin, wrote to Neumann about the problems he had with it, the "most dreadful" being Neumann's peculiar way of writing certain differentials.[93] He asked Poggendorff, who of all the Berlin physicists seemed to know Ampère's work most thoroughly, to report on Neumann's paper to the Prussian Academy. But Poggendorff, preparing

89. Franz Neumann, "Theorie der doppelten Strahlenbrechung, abgeleitet aus den Gleichungen der Mechanik," Ann. 25 (1832): 418–54.

90. Voigt, "Neumann," 259–60, 257. Wangerin, Neumann, 96–97, 102. Volkmann, "Franz Neumann als Experimentator," 932; Neumann, 14.

91. Volkmann, Neumann, 18. Wangerin, Neumann, 107.

92. Franz Neumann, "Die mathematischen Gesetze der inducirten elektrischen Ströme," Abh. preuss. Akad., 1845, 1–87, read 27 Oct. 1845, reprinted as vol. 10 of Ostwald's Klassiker der exakten Wissenschaften, ed. Carl Neumann (Leipzig, 1889). An excerpt appeared as "Allgemeine Gesetze der inducirten elektrischen Ströme," Ann. 67 (1846): 31–44.

93. Jacobi observed that Neumann's use of capital "D" instead of the usual lowercase "d" made the expression "DsE" look "quite like a product of three factors." Jacobi to Neumann, 6 Jan. 1846, quoted in Koenigsberger, Jacobi, 359. The abbreviated version of this paper appearing in the Annalen used the lowercase "d."

the report only from excerpts of Neumann's results and from some formulas furnished
by Jacobi, produced such a clumsy account, Jacobi thought, that none of the physicists at the meeting could have gotten a clear idea of Neumann's work. The paper
might as well have been written in Chinese, Jacobi wrote to Neumann, since Poggendorff could not have understood the first line of it. Given the novelty of Neumann's "technical expressions," however, Neumann was not without blame in the
debacle either, Jacobi suggested; with a few long explanations he could have made
his work easier for other physicists to understand.[94]

For all its difficulty, Neumann's first paper on electrodynamics proved influential
both for its content and as an example of mathematical physics. In abstract mathematical language, with little physical explanation, Neumann set out nearly all that
was quantitatively known about induction. He stated Lenz's law, which asserts that
the direction of an induced current is such as to oppose the motion of the conductor
causing the induction, and he stated the law of proportionality between the induced
current and the speed with which the conductor is moved. To enable him to combine the first two, he stated several more laws: the proportionality of the induced
current and the action of the inducing current; the independence of the induced
electromotive force from the material of the conductor; and the proportionality of
the induced current and the induced electromotive force, or Ohm's law. From these
simple, quantitative laws, in a few steps Neumann derived the "general law of linear
induction," the fundamental equation of his theory. It is itself a simple law, written,
as Ampère's law is, for a differential element of wire: $E \cdot Ds = -\epsilon v C \cdot Ds$. In
words, it says that the induced electromotive force in an element of wire is proportional to the total inducing action on it.[95]

Upon this foundation, Neumann built an elaborate mathematical structure. By
integrating the differential law around a closed circuit and over a finite time, he
obtained the "integral current," or "finite action of the current," which is the quantity that is usually measured. Of special significance for the subsequent development
of electrodynamics was Neumann's proof that the electrodynamic action of two
closed currents on one another has a "potential":[96]

$$V = \frac{1}{2}jj' \int \int \frac{\cos(Ds, D\sigma)}{r} Ds D\sigma,$$

where j and j' are the intensities of the two currents s and σ. The change in the
potential measures the mechanical work done by the electrodynamic force. With the

94. Jacobi to Neumann, 5 Dec. 1845, in Koenigsberger, Jacobi, 355.
95. The differential element of wire is Ds, the induced electromotive force in it $E \cdot Ds$, and the
inducing action on it $-\epsilon v C \cdot Ds$, where v is the velocity of the element of wire, C the component of
the inducing action on the element in the direction of its motion, as determined from Ampère's law, and
ϵ a constant. Neumann, Die mathematischen Gesetze, 17.
96. Neumann, "Allgemeine Gesetze," 39; Die mathematischen Gesetze, 69. This potential law is
discussed in Wangerin, Neumann, 123; Rosenberger, Geschichte der Physik, 510–12; Edmund Hoppe, Geschichte der Elektrizität (Leipzig, 1884), 438–48; Arnold Sommerfeld and R. Reiff, "Standpunkt der Fernwirkung. Die Elementargesetze," Encyklopädie der mathematischen Wissenschaften mit Einschluss ihrer Anwendungen, vol. 5, Physik, ed. Arnold Sommerfeld, pt. 2 (Leipzig: B. G. Teubner, 1904–22): 3–62, on
27–34.

aid of the potential Neumann rewrote the "integral current," and in general the potential allowed him to express in an especially simple way the various possibilities of induced currents.

Neumann claimed for his first publication in electrodynamics the derivation of a "unique law of induction," with which he treated the simpler cases of induction in linear conductors. He did not get around to publishing an intended extension of the theory to more general conductors, but in a final paper on electrodynamics in 1847, he generalized the analysis to wire circuits of variable dimensions.[97]

At the beginning of 1846 Jacobi wrote to Neumann from Berlin that he was "at once" going to send a reprint of Neumann's paper on electrodynamics to Weber, "who was here recently and was very interested in the work."[98] Since Weber published his electrodynamic theory after he had received the version of Neumann's paper prepared for the *Annalen der Physik*, he was able to discuss Neumann's theory together with his own. Neumann's mathematical results "can hardly be doubted," Weber wrote, either with respect to their inner connection or with respect to their connection to the empirical rules. Since Neumann had derived them in a completely different way than he had his, Weber thought it would be "interesting" to compare the two.[99] Weber showed that Neumann's law agrees with his for all cases in which induction is due to magnets or closed currents, but that it does not apply when open currents are involved.[100]

Neumann, too, in his second publication on electrodynamics, compared the two theories. He developed a general expression for induction from Weber's law and showed that only in the case in which the inducing circuit consists of a moving and fixed part does Weber's law differ from his own; here the two laws attributed opposite directions to the induced electromotive force.[101]

Neumann's and Weber's reconciliations of this discrepancy illuminate their approaches to physics. Responding to Weber's mode of presenting his work (one assumes), Neumann took what was for him an unusual step; he included in his paper a schematic account of the experimental arrangement with which he had established his equation for the electromotive force in the case in question. Neumann also subjected the derivation of this equation from Weber's law to a careful examination and concluded that the derivation was incomplete. With the necessary adjustments, he established a complete agreement between the two theories.[102]

Weber, too, wanted agreement, but he was not satisfied with the way Neumann

97. Franz Neumann, "Ueber ein allgemeines Princip der mathematischen Theorie inducirter elektrischer Ströme," *Abh. Preuss. Akad.*, 1848, 1–71; read 9 Aug. 1847.

98. Jacobi to Neumann, 6 Jan. 1846, quoted in Koenigsberger, *Jacobi*, 359.

99. Weber argued that Neumann's law does not apply to open currents since it is based on Lenz's law, which applies only to closed currents. Weber, "Elektrodynamische Maassbestimmungen" (1846), 180, 182.

100. Wilhelm Weber, "Bemerkungen zu Neumann's Theorie inducirter Ströme," *Verh. sächs. Ges. Wiss.*, 1849, 1–8, reprinted in *Werke* 3:269–75; "Elektrodynamische Maassbestimmungen" (1852), 405–27.

101. Neumann's discussion here from "Ueber ein allgemeines Princip" is quoted in Weber, "Bemerkungen zu Neumann's Theorie," 270–71.

102. Weber reprinted Neumann's description of his apparatus alongside that of the apparatus he used to check Neumann's results. Weber, "Elektrodynamische Maassbestimmungen" (1852), 409–17.

had reached it. He repeated Neumann's experiment, first in a version of his own and then more or less as Neumann had described it, finding that it bore out Neumann's theory exactly. He next examined Neumann's derivation of the induction law from his own fundamental law to see if Neumann had taken into account all "given relative motions of electric fluids" and their changes. Weber convinced himself that his and Neumann's laws were only different ways of reaching the same result. Neumann's general principle, he said, refers to currents and conductors as a whole; that is, only to their intensity and position at the beginning and end of an induction. It immediately yields the sum of the electromotive forces, but it says nothing about the intervening details. The obvious advantage of a simple and general law like Neumann's is its ease of application. What Weber's law gives is a "rule" for indirectly obtaining the electromotive forces by summing over all "elementary actions," so that if one wants the induction law for a certain case one must take account of all elementary actions. Weber found that Neumann in his effort at reconciling their theories had overlooked a particular elementary action, a change in the motion of the electrical particles occurring in the experiment. Carrying through a physical analysis and then a theoretical development, Weber came to the satisfactory result that his and Neumann's theories are indeed in agreement.[103] Neumann thought that the resolution of their differences was a "very brilliant success." After this, Weber's law acquired wide authority in Germany for some time and entered the textbooks as the preferred mathematical theory of electric induction.[104]

Mathematical laws in physics generally contain constants, the measurement of which belonged to the daily work of the mathematical physicist in the 1840s. The numerical value and physical meaning of constants could arouse intense interest among physicists. Lacking a technical name for the new constant ϵ relating electromotive and electrodynamic forces in his theory, Neumann referred to it in one place as a "current" and in another place as a "concept" of a magnitude; related to the "mysterious connection" between all bodies, still concealed in "deep mysteries," this constant, he said, was the "true physical problem of all induction phenomena."[105] Neumann posed the measurement of this constant as a prize problem in 1846 at Königsberg.[106]

The problem was solved by a member of Neumann's seminar, Gustav Kirchhoff. Reporting on this work in the *Annalen der Physik*, Kirchhoff remarked: "The mathematical laws of induced electric currents have been set out by Neumann and Weber; in the expression, which both have found for the intensity of an induced current, . . . a constant occurs, which must be determined by experiments once and for all and which Neumann designates by ϵ. This I have undertaken to determine." The natural way to do it, Kirchhoff decided, was to give to the two closed conductors containing the inducing and the induced currents a shape for which he

103. Weber, "Elektrodynamische Maassbestimmungen" (1852), 405–27; quotation on 418.
104. Rosenberger, *Geschichte der Physik*, 513.
105. Neumann to Jacobi, 5 Feb. 1846, in Koenigsberger, *Jacobi*, 361–62. Neumann, *Die mathematischen Gesetze*, 21.
106. Wangerin, *Neumann*, 177.

could readily calculate the potential. Then with a magnetic needle he measured the intensity of the two currents and computed the numerical value of ϵ.[107] Kirchhoff's measurement of ϵ "deserves to be set alongside the works of Gauss and Weber," Bunsen said in recommending Kirchhoff a few years later for his first chair of physics.[108] It was the highest form of praise for a young mathematical physicist in the middle of the nineteenth century.

Kirchhoff, the son of a Königsberg lawyer, entered the local university originally to study mathematics. But he vacillated, as he was drawn to chemistry for a time and then to physics, which he finally decided for, even at the risk of subjecting himself to "boring observations and even more boring calculations." The boredom he spoke of referred to earth-magnetic measurements, by now a common means of introducing students to observations. He described his experience with them to his brother: "Of the first [boring observations] I have recently had a small sample; there I sat from 10 o'clock in the evening to 2 o'clock in the Albertinum behind a telescope and, in a temperature of only 1°, observed a magnet every 15 seconds, the position of which I had to write down. Still with a cigar and some small sand cakes, which our concerned mother had filled my pockets with, the 4 hours passed as quickly as an arrow, sooner than I had thought."[109]

Kirchhoff was won over to physics largely because of Neumann, who became his main teacher. A member of Neumann's seminar from 1843, Kirchhoff soon revealed a "talent" for physics.[110] In 1845, while still a member of the seminar, Kirchhoff published in the *Annalen der Physik* a mathematical solution to a problem of the distribution of electricity and its experimental proof.[111] "I thank you very much for the treatise," Poggendorff wrote to Neumann about Kirchhoff's paper: "It is very interesting in its own right, and especially as the first in a new field."[112] In this paper, Kirchhoff accepted without question Ohm's law for currents in conducting solids. To extend its application, he needed to introduce no physical hypotheses about the nature of electricity and electric forces; he needed only Ohm's law to determine completely the distribution of electricity in an infinitely thin, unbounded plane with any number of entry and exit points for current and, within experimental accuracy, in a real circular metal plate of finite thickness with one entry and one exit wire. To adapt Ohm's law for his problem, he wrote it in terms of a function he called the electric "tension," which determines the flow of current. The tension satisfies Laplace's equation for two dimensions, and for a circular plate the mathematical methods of potential theory predict circles of constant tension. Kirchhoff verified the circles by touching the plate with a pair of wires connected through a

107. Gustav Kirchhoff, "Bestimmung der Constanten, von welcher die Intensität inducirter elektrischer Ströme abhängt," *Ann.* 76 (1849): 412–26, reprinted in Gustav Kirchhoff, *Gesammelte Abhandlungen* (Leipzig, 1882), 118–31, quotation on 118 (hereafter cited as *Ges. Abh.*).

108. Bunsen to Baden Ministry of the Interior, 26 July 1854, Bad. GLA, 235/3135.

109. Kirchhoff to his brother Otto, n.d., quoted in Warburg, "Kirchhoff," 205.

110. Wangerin, *Neumann*, 177. Luise Neumann, *Neumann*, 368.

111. Gustav Kirchhoff, "Ueber den Durchgang eines elektrischen Stromes durch eine Ebene, insbesondere durch eine kreisförmige," *Ann.* 64 (1845): 497–514, reprinted in *Ges. Abh.*, 1–17.

112. Poggendorff to Neumann, 20 June 1845, Neumann Papers, Göttingen UB, Ms. Dept.

galvanometer. At the close of the paper, he developed useful laws for the distribution of current in complicated wiring circuits. These results especially interested Poggendorff, as they were close to his and Weber's work.

Kirchhoff's first paper attracted the attention of scientists in Berlin. Weber, when he visited Berlin, read Kirchhoff's paper and made such a "fuss" over it that Poggendorff became enthusiastic and gave a lecture on the last part of it. Jacobi hoped Kirchhoff would come to Berlin, where he could serve, Jacobi told Neumann, as interpreter of Neumann's difficult writings. For Kirchhoff to come, it meant that money had to be found for him, which was no simple matter. Jacobi urged Neumann to forego his customary passivity and for once "force" himself to make the effort; to do something for Kirchhoff, Neumann needed to write to the government and perhaps also to Humboldt. "As far as you yourself are concerned," Jacobi explained to Neumann, "you must not think that anything personal *against* you is involved, but there just isn't the necessary enthusiasm for the subject to do away with financial hindrances." In the spring of 1846, Neumann could write to Jacobi that Kirchhoff had received a travel grant and that his sponsors were going to ask the minister to add some extra money.[113]

Although Jacobi wanted Kirchhoff in Berlin for personal reasons, he thought that Kirchhoff would profit more by going to Paris. But, as he reported to Neumann, the Berlin physicists Magnus and Poggendorff doubted, on the basis of their experience, that Kirchhoff would be able to work in Paris. It would be better for him, they believed, to come to Berlin to perfect his chemistry, working with Magnus and Rose. He should bring some experimental work of his own, and once he was there they would help him get the apparatus he needed.[114] When Kirchhoff arrived in Berlin with his stipend, he took the Berlin physicists' advice and gave up his plan of going to Paris; he stayed on in Berlin and habilitated there. He continued to work on the laws of conductors, but mainly he did research in a new field, elasticity. On Jacobi's advice, he sent a note on his new research to the Paris Academy of Sciences, helped "with his French" by Emil du Bois-Reymond. He was befriended in Berlin not only by Jacobi and du Bois-Reymond, but also by Poggendorff, Magnus, Dirichlet, Gustav Karsten, and Knoblauch.[115] In general, Kirchhoff was introduced to an extended scientific society of experienced researchers who appreciated his original talent and advised him on how best to cultivate it.

In a series of publications in the *Annalen*, Kirchhoff developed more applications of Ohm's law, generalizing his own laws of current distribution to any number of wires and connections, and generalizing his laws for wires to laws for connected three-dimensional conductors.[116] In August 1848 he visited Weber in Leipzig, re-

113. Jacobi to Neumann, 5 Dec. 1845, and 6 Jan. and 2 Apr. 1846; Neumann to Jacobi, 20 Mar. 1846; quoted in Koenigsberger, *Jacobi*, 355–66.

114. Jacobi to Neumann, 2 Apr. 1846 (p. 366).

115. Kirchhoff to Neumann, 29 Feb. and 13 Oct. 1848, Neumann Papers, Göttingen UB, Ms. Dept. Kirchhoff to his brother Otto, 20 Sept. 1848, quoted in Warburg, "Kirchhoff," 207.

116. Gustav Kirchhoff, "Ueber die Auflösung der Gleichungen, auf welche man bei der Untersuchung der linearen Vertheilung galvanischer Ströme geführt wird," *Ann.* 72 (1847): 497–508; "Ueber die Anwendbarkeit der Formeln für die Intensitäten der galvanischen Ströme in einem Systeme linearer Leiter auf Systeme, die zum Theil aus nicht linearen Leitern bestehen," *Ann.* 75 (1848): 189–205; reprinted in *Ges. Abh.*, 22–33 and 33–49, respectively.

turning to Berlin with yet another project: "In our conversation, Professor Weber and I also brought up how desirable it would be to replace the considerations by which Ohm arrives at his equations with others that link up more closely to the rest of the theory of electricity. Later I thought of a way of deriving these equations which seems to me to be preferable to Ohm's."[117] Ohm's derivation was unsatisfactory because of its conflict with electrostatic principles.[118] It is always "desirable," Kirchhoff wrote, to derive the laws of currents from those of electrostatics, here Ohm's law from Coulomb's; Kirchhoff accomplished this by identifying the potential of the electrostatic force with the tension or "electroscopic force" of Ohm's theory. For the assumptions of electrostatics to apply to currents, Kirchhoff imagined that each particle of electricity, positive or negative, is at rest on a material molecule before the electrostatic force drives it to the next. This conception of current was Weber's, with whose theory of electricity Kirchhoff expected to reconcile his own ideas "in a natural way."[119] But he found it a "difficult" problem to derive the general laws of closed currents from Weber's fundamental law of electric action (which he succeeded in doing only in 1857); it was nonetheless a necessary step toward subsuming all parts of electrical theory "under one point of view," which was the promise of Weber's theory.[120]

Kirchhoff's work in electricity in the 1840s reflected the new directions in teaching and research in physics in Germany. As a member of the mathematical-physical seminar in Königsberg, Kirchhoff had been instructed in mathematical and measuring methods; following that, as a participant in the Berlin colloquium and physical society, he had joined the company of other researchers. From the time he entered physics, he had been able to draw on major German contributions to electrical theory: he worked with Ohm's galvanic law, with Neumann's law of electrical induction, and with Weber's fundamental law of electric action. Like Weber, Kirchhoff did not get to Paris after graduation as he had hoped, but that was not so important any longer.

From early on, Kirchhoff had a preferred direction within physical research. When his Königsberg mathematics teacher Friedrich Julius Richelot told him that he was in line for a call to Breslau University as extraordinary professor for experimental physics, he knew that he could not turn down the offer. But he did not really want it: what would be fitting and welcome, he told his parents at the time, was a "call for mathematical physics"; he knew of no positions for that subject, and so he moved to Breslau in 1850 with the thought that it might be good for him to try experimental physics and to tear himself away from his usual range of ideas.[121]

117. Kirchhoff to Neumann, 13 Oct. 1848.

118. Ohm assumed the electricity in a conductor is at rest if it is spread with uniform density throughout the volume of the conductor, whereas according to electrostatics free electricity can exist in equilibrium only on the surface of the conductor. Gustav Kirchhoff, "Ueber eine Ableitung der Ohm'schen Gesetze, welche sich an die Theorie der Elektrostatik anschliesst," *Ann.* 78 (1849): 506–13, reprinted in *Ges. Abh.,* 49–55.

119. Kirchhoff to Neumann, 13 Oct. 1848.

120. Kirchhoff, "Ableitung der Ohm'schen Gesetze," 54–55.

121. Kirchhoff to his parents, n.d., quoted in Warburg, "Kirchhoff," 207.

Researches on Theories of Forces and of Heat at Berlin

The knowledge of several scientific subjects—mathematics, physics, and physiology—bore especially important results in Hermann Helmholtz's research, as he himself explained: "possessing some geometrical ability, and equipped with a knowledge of physics, I had, by good fortune, been thrown among medical men, where I found in physiology a virgin soil of great fertility; while, on the other hand, I was led by the consideration of the vital processes to questions and points of view which are usually foreign to pure mathematicians and physicists."[122] In particular, Helmholtz believed that his good fortune could be seen in his first work on physics, which Magnus described as a "rare example of versatile knowledge."[123] In this work, he introduced the principle of the conservation of force, which he came to through his concern with the convertibility of forces within his ongoing work on physiological heat and muscular metabolism.

Helmholtz worked out the principle of the conservation of force soon after completing his education in Berlin. While a student at the gymnasium in nearby Potsdam where his father taught classical languages, he had decided that he wanted to study physics. Since his father could afford this plan only if he studied physics within a medical education, in 1838 he entered the Friedrich-Wilhelms-Institut in Berlin. This state medical-surgical institution trained army physicians by providing them with a free medical education at Berlin University. Helmholtz wrote his dissertation at the university on the physiology of nerves under Johannes Müller and received his M.D. in 1842. In 1843 he published his first independent investigation in Müller's *Archiv* and that year took up his duties as army surgeon at Potsdam. There at the army post, he set up a small physical-physiological laboratory.[124] He also kept up the scientific associations he had formed at Berlin University.

In Berlin, Helmholtz was drawn into the circle of Müller's students, befriending especially du Bois-Reymond and Brücke, who were united in their desire to eliminate from physiology the concept of life force, in their eyes an unscientific concept left over from nature philosophy. They wanted to see how far physics and chemistry could go in explaining life processes, which brought them into contact with physicists in Berlin, above all with Magnus.[125] Because a state examination for physicians required Helmholtz to spend a half year in Berlin, in the winter of 1845–46 he worked regularly in Magnus's private laboratory. Du Bois-Reymond, who had participated in Magnus's physical colloquium, introduced Helmholtz to the newly formed Berlin Physical Society, which was soon to provide the first audience for his work on the conservation of force. He regularly attended the meetings of the society, and for the first volume, as for later volumes, of the *Fortschritte der Physik*, he reported on researches in physiological heat.[126]

122. Helmholtz, "Autobiographical Sketch," 280.
123. Magnus to du Bois-Reymond, 2 Aug. 1847, quoted in Koenigsberger, *Helmholtz* 1:71.
124. Koenigsberger, *Helmholtz* 1:55.
125. Koenigsberger, *Helmholtz* 1:44, 50.
126. Koenigsberger, *Helmholtz* 1:58, 62, 64.

Helmholtz's work on the conservation of force required a sound knowledge of mathematical physics, which he had acquired in his early years in Berlin. He had read extensively in the literature; in 1841, for example, after his first medical examinations were over, he was left with some free time, which he devoted to the study of mathematics and the advanced parts of mechanics. On his own, or with a friend, he studied the writings of Laplace, Biot, Poisson, Jacobi, and others. He attended no lectures in mathematical physics or in mathematics at Berlin; in these subjects he was largely self-taught.[127]

By 1847, the year of his publication on the conservation of force, Helmholtz had already been "convinced for years," according to his friend and biographer Leo Koenigsberger, of the validity of a principle of this sort. He recognized that the question of whether living beings are to be understood by the action of a life force or by the action of the same forces that occur in lifeless nature is closely connected with a conservation principle for forces. He also recognized that to establish to the satisfaction of the scientific world a mathematically formulated conservation principle would require a series of investigations in various parts of physiology and physics. In 1845, for example, he published a paper in which he tested his physical understanding of a difficult physiological problem, namely, the chemical changes occurring in muscles owing to their mechanical action. Studying frogs with the help of a self-constructed electrical machine and a Leyden jar, he succeeded in demonstrating these changes and even obtained quantitative results. For even more exact results, he had to determine the relations between the action of muscles and the heat developed, which required new investigations. In the *Fortschritte der Physik* for 1845, which appeared in 1847, Helmholtz published a report on theories of physiological heat which he later acknowledged as belonging to his work on the conservation of force.[128]

In February 1847, while still an army surgeon at Potsdam, Helmholtz wrote to du Bois-Reymond that in his latest reworking of an essay on the conservation of force, he had "thrown overboard everything that smells of philosophy," and he was anxious for du Bois-Reymond's opinion of how it would go down with the physicists. That summer, Helmholtz read the completed work to the Berlin Physical Society, where it aroused enthusiasm, at least among some members. Helmholtz immediately sent it to Magnus asking him to forward it to Poggendorff for publication in the *Annalen der Physik*. Poggendorff appreciated the importance of the problem Helmholtz addressed and his handling of it, but he rejected the paper. It was too long to be fitted into the *Annalen* that year, Poggendorff said; but his main reason for rejecting it had to do with its nature: "The *Annalen* is necessarily dependent above all on experimental investigations," and Poggendorff would have to sacrifice some of these if he wished to "open the door to theoretical" investigations like Helmholtz's.

127. Koenigsberger, *Helmholtz* 1:42, 45, 51, 56.

128. Hermann Helmholtz, "Ueber den Stoffverbrauch bei der Muskelaktion," *Archiv für Anatomie, Physiologie und wissenschaftliche Medicin*, 1845, 72–83. In his *Wissenschaftliche Abhandlungen*, 3 vols. (Leipzig, 1882–95), 1:3–11 (hereafter cited as *Wiss. Abh.*), Helmholtz included as the first paper under "The Theory of Energy" his report, "Bericht über die Theorie der physiologischen Wärmeerscheinungen für 1845," *Fortschritte . . . 1845* 1 (1847): 346–55.

Through Magnus, Poggendorff recommended that Helmholtz have the work published privately. Helmholtz accordingly approached the Berlin publisher G. A. Reimer, to whom he explained that the work would not be expensive to produce: it was not long, required no copper plates, and had "relatively little mathematical type." The subject of the work was the generalization of a "fundamental law of mechanics," he explained further; he had reached his result by "extensive and exact" work on "all branches of physics." Privately, he had learned of considerable interest in this work; he submitted to Reimer letters about it from Magnus, du Bois-Reymond, and Brücke, and he added that Müller could testify to his scientific ability. He realized that he could expect no money from its publication and only wanted fifteen free reprints. Reimer agreed to publish it and, to Helmholtz's surprise, paid him an honorarium.[129]

From his study of the older mechanical treatises, Helmholtz learned the strong proof of the impossibility of perpetual motion. In his physiological studies, he questioned the possibility of perpetual motion outside mechanics, in heat, electricity, magnetism, light, and chemistry. His solution to the problem of determining precisely which relations must obtain between natural forces so that perpetual motion is impossible in general was the principle of the conservation of force.[130]

Helmholtz based the principle on either of two maxims, which he proved equivalent. One is that from any combination of bodies, it is impossible continuously to produce moving force from nothing. The other is that all actions can be reduced to attractive and repulsive forces that depend solely on the distance between material points. The problem of science is, he said, to reduce all phenomena to unchanging causes, which are the unchanging forces between material points. As the "solvability of this problem is also the condition of the complete comprehensibility of nature," the problem of "theoretical natural science" will be solved once this "reduction of natural phenomena to simple forces is completed and at the same time is proven to be the only possible reduction the phenomena allow."[131]

The impossibility of unlimited moving force had been adopted as a maxim by Carnot and Clapeyron in their theoretical studies of heat, and Helmholtz made it his "purpose" to extend it throughout "all branches of physics." The maxim is equivalent in mechanics to the principle of the conservation of "living force" (or "vis viva" or "kinetic energy"). Helmholtz proved that this principle requires that the forces be "central," that is, that they depend on the distance between material points and act along their joining line. He showed that the increase in the living force of a material point due to the action of a central force equals the sum of the "tension forces" due to the change in the position of the point. Mathematically, Helmholtz's statement reads:

129. Helmholtz to du Bois-Reymond, Feb. 1847; Poggendorff to Magnus, 1 Aug. 1847; Magnus to du Bois-Reymond, 2 Aug. 1847; Helmholtz to G. A. Reimer, 14 Aug. 1847; quoted in Koenigsberger, *Helmholtz* 1:68–72, 78–79.
130. Koenigsberger, *Helmholtz* 1:80–82.
131. Hermann Helmholtz, *Ueber die Erhaltung der Kraft, eine physikalische Abhandlung* (Berlin, 1847); reprinted in *Wiss. Abh.* 1:12–68, on 16–17.

$$\frac{1}{2} mQ^2 - \frac{1}{2} mq^2 = -\int_r^R \varphi \, dr,$$

where m is the mass of the point, q and Q are the velocities of the point at the initial and final positions r and R, and φ is the intensity of the central force. Generalizing the statement to apply to any number of interacting points, Helmholtz concluded that the sum of the living forces and the tension forces is constant. This he called the "principle of the conservation of force."[132]

Helmholtz applied this conservation principle to some mechanical theorems and then to the other parts of physics, which provided the truly interesting cases and the testing ground. A supporter of the mechanical theory of heat, he accounted for the apparent loss of living force of two bodies after undergoing an inelastic collision by the conversion of their living force into tension forces and heat. He was especially interested in applying the conservation principle to electricity, magnetism, and electrodynamics, subjects which offered manifold instances of force conversions. For example, he deduced the electromotive force of two metals in a cell by equating through the conservation principle the heat developed chemically in the cell to that developed electrically in the wire. In this example, in which heat serves as a measure of the forces, he brought together nearly all of the known quantitative laws of electric current: Ohm's law, Lenz's law for the heat developed in a length of wire, James Prescott Joule's more general law for the heat developed in any circuit, the laws of complex circuits that Kirchhoff was then working out, and Faraday's law of electrolysis.[133] In another example, Helmholtz applied the conservation principle to connect the chemical, thermal, and mechanical processes entering the electrodynamic interaction of a fixed, closed current produced by a cell and a nearby magnet free to move in space. Here he made use of Neumann's potential for a closed current; with it and by simple mathematical steps, he derived a number of Neumann's cases of induced currents. In addition to recovering these known results, he derived a new result, showing the power of the conservation principle to link the parts of physics; by equating his and Neumann's formulas for the current in the wire, he showed that Neumann's empirical, undetermined constant from electrical theory ϵ is the reciprocal of the mechanical equivalent of heat.[134] In these examples, to apply the con-

132. Helmholtz, "Erhaltung der Kraft," 17–25.

133. Helmholtz, "Erhaltung der Kraft," 35, 49–57. We wish to acknowledge discussions with Stephen M. Winters, who is at work on a deep and comprehensive study of Helmholtz's researches in physics, beginning with Helmholtz's principle of conservation of force.

134. Helmholtz wrote the law of conservation of force for a closed current that moves a magnet as $aA Jdt = aJ^2 Wdt + J \, dV/dt \, dt$ (where a is the mechanical equivalent of a unit of heat, A the electromotive force, J the current, W the resistance, and V the potential), which states, in mechanical units, that the electrochemical action on the left, which produces the current, is spent in part in heating the wire and in part in increasing the living force of the magnet. Solving the equation, Helmholtz obtained

$$J = \frac{A - \dfrac{1}{a} \dfrac{dV}{dt}}{W},$$

servation principle, Helmholtz did not need a detailed knowledge of the mathematical form of the acting central forces, the existence of which the principle presumably guaranteed. The forces were often still unknown or problematic; for example, with regard to Weber's fundamental law of electric action, which relates the force between electric masses to their relative motion, Helmholtz observed that no hypothesis had yet been established that could reduce inductive phenomena to "constant central forces."[135]

Throughout his paper on the conservation of force, Helmholtz referred not only to theoretically founded laws but also to a good deal of experimental work on the establishment of laws by Riess, Poggendorff, Weber, and others. He pointed to his predictions as waiting to be tested. His purpose was not just theoretical; it was also to show the experimental significance of the new results he obtained by joining established laws by means of the conservation principle. He concluded his study with the observation that the "complete confirmation" of the conservation principle was a main task of physics in the immediate future.[136]

But as Poggendorff noted when he rejected it, Helmholtz's paper did not report original experiments. For that reason it could seem overly speculative to experimental physicists, who were not at first persuaded of the conservation principle.[137] When physicists did admit it into their literature, they did so with caution. "I have received the first part of the physics annual report," Helmholtz wrote to du Bois-Reymond about the *Fortschritte der Physik* for 1847, "and was not a little surprised to see my *Erhaltung der Kraft* placed by Karsten with physiological heat phenomena, although I had submitted it written up separately." Later Helmholtz reported for the *Fortschritte* on related papers by Robert Mayer and others, and he took the occasion to place his own paper in the physical context he had originally intended for it.[138]

The task of persuading physicists of the conservation principle was not entirely Helmholtz's in any case. With marked differences of approach and purpose, Mayer and several other natural scientists in the 1840s worked on problems arising from a widely shared belief in the unity of nature and the indestructibility and transformability of forces.[139] As one of several statements of the measure of the relations be-

---

which differs from Ohm's law by the appearance of $(1/a)(dV/dt)$, a new electromotive force arising from the change in separation of the current and magnet; this electromotive force causes a change in J, which is the "induced" current. Helmholtz, "Erhaltung der Kraft," 61–63. Later Helmholtz returned to, and improved, his derivation of the interaction of a closed current and a magnet by including the effects of self-induction.

135. Helmholtz, "Erhaltung der Kraft," 61–65.
136. Helmholtz, "Erhaltung der Kraft," 68.
137. Koenigsberger, *Helmholtz* 1:79–80.
138. Helmholtz to du Bois-Reymond, 15 Jan. 1850, quoted in P. M. Heimann, "Helmholtz and Kant: The Metaphysical Foundations of *Über die Erhaltung der Kraft*," *Stud. Hist. Phil. Sci.* 5 (1974): 205–38, on 232–33, especially n. 104 on 233.
139. On the scientific, technical, and philosophical issues to which scientists contributing to the establishment of the conservation law responded, individually and collectively, there has been some recent discussion. It includes Heimann, "Helmholtz," "Mayer's Concept of 'Force': The 'Axis' of a New Science of Physics," *Historical Studies in the Physical Sciences* 7 (1976): 277–96 (hereafter cited as *HSPS*), and *Metaphysics and Natural Philosophy: The Problem of Substance in Classical Physics* (Brighton: Harvester

tween the forces of nature, Helmholtz's came to be regarded as the mathematical foundation for the principle of the conservation of "energy." Within a few years, Helmholtz acknowledged that his terms "living force" and "tension force" were synonymous with W. J. M. Rankine's "actual [kinetic] energy" and "potential energy" and that Rankine's term "conservation of energy" was preferable to his own "conservation of force."[140]

With Helmholtz's principle, the several, often qualitative, assertions of the conservation and convertibility of forces received precise expression. The many newly discovered relations between the forces of nature did not require any major change in the understanding of these forces, which derived from the example of Newton's gravitational force; this was one of the more remarkable implications of Helmholtz's paper. Physicists who accepted Helmholtz's reasoning were concerned, on the most fundamental level, with just those things mechanics was concerned with: material points, constant central forces, relative positions and motions, the laws of motion and associated principles such as the principle of virtual velocities, and the principle of the conservation of force, or energy, which Helmholtz saw as an extension of the principle of the conservation of living force in mechanics. Helmholtz claimed that his paper of 1847 was independent of metaphysical considerations; later, in 1881, when he included it in his collected papers, he acknowledged that he had been indebted to Kant's philosophy in his view that the law of causality was essential for understanding nature and that central forces were ultimate causes. He derived his conservation principle within a certain picture of the physical world, one governed by mechanical concepts and laws. It was one of the great conceptions of nature underlying much nineteenth-century physical research, and in Germany Helmholtz gave it a complete definition; over the course of his long career, he developed its implications throughout physics.[141]

Intended expressly for "physicists," Helmholtz's 1847 paper must be counted as one of the most impressive first publications in the history of physics. Helmholtz had the highest regard for the principle he developed there, speaking of it fifteen years later, for example, as the most important scientific advance of the century because it encompassed all laws of physics and chemistry.[142] On the occasion of Helmholtz's hundredth birthday, in 1921, his former student Wilhelm Wien could write that the significance of the principle was still growing.[143] But in 1847 Helmholtz was not a physicist, and after delivering the paper he returned to his physiological researches,

Press, 1982), 105–26; Thomas S. Kuhn, "Energy Conservation as an Example of Simultaneous Discovery," in Critical Problems in the History of Science, ed. M. Clagett (Madison: University of Wisconsin Press, 1959), 321–56; Yehuda Elkana, "Helmholtz' 'Kraft': An Illustration of Concepts in Flux," HSPS 2 (1970): 263–98.

140. Heimann, "Helmholtz," 206.

141. Heimann, "Helmholtz," 208–9, 234–38. Helmholtz, "Zusätze (1881)," in Wiss. Abh. 1:68–75, on 68.

142. Helmholtz's talk, "On the Application of the Law of the Conservation of Force to Organic Nature," on 12 Apr. 1861, discussed in Koenigsberger, Helmholtz 1: 373.

143. Wilhelm Wien, "Helmholtz als Physiker," Naturwiss. 9 (1921): 694–99, on 694.

which, like his physical researches, provided a field for applying and testing the conservation principle.

In 1848, the year after publishing his paper on the conservation principle, Helmholtz left the military service to begin teaching, first as a teacher of anatomy at the Berlin Academy of Arts and then a year later as extraordinary professor for physiology at Königsberg University. At Königsberg, he came into association with Neumann, whom he found "somewhat difficult to approach," "hypochondriacal, shy, but a thinker of the first rank."[144] Neumann was soon to be of help to Helmholtz in his researches on the rate of propagation along nerves. Helmholtz engaged him in his efforts to determine the duration of electric currents induced by sudden current fluctuations, which were a means for irritating animal parts in his studies of nerves. By theoretical insight, Helmholtz was led to a new mathematical principle governing the phenomenon, and with its aid Neumann did integrations and set out theorems that enabled Helmholtz to test the principle experimentally.[145]

Helmholtz published the theoretical and experimental researches on this problem as a pure physics paper in the *Annalen der Physik* in 1851.[146] The "theoretical discussion" he based on the laws of complicated circuits that Kirchhoff had derived from Ohm's law in 1847 and on Neumann's law of the potential of two currents. Ohm's law, which until then had been applied only to nearly constant currents, Helmholtz applied to the currents he was studying, and with its help he derived the mathematical principle governing the course of the induced currents in question.[147] From his measurements and calculations, he concluded that within 1/10,000th of a second after a current in a spiral is interrupted, all inducing action in it stops. This result showed him that the time intervals belonging to electric currents are of a different order of smallness than those of nerve actions, which enabled him once again to return to his main subject, physiology, specifically nerve physiology.[148]

Although at this time Helmholtz did principally physiological research, he took an interest in and had contact with Neumann, Kirchhoff, Weber, and other mathematical physicists, whose work frequently bore directly on his own. For example, in the same year, 1851, that Neumann helped him with his research in Königsberg, Helmholtz wrote to the physiologist Carl Ludwig in connection with a professorship of physics in Zurich that Kirchhoff was suited for the job because of his "most admi-

144. Helmholtz to du Bois-Reymond, 15 Jan. 1850, quoted in Koenigsberger, *Helmholtz* 1:117.
145. Koenigsberger, *Helmholtz* 1: 145.
146. Hermann Helmholtz, "Ueber die Dauer und den Verlauf der durch Stromesschwankungen inducirten elektrischen Ströme," *Ann.* 83 (1851): 505–40. Helmholtz entered this paper in *Wiss. Abh.* (1: 429–62) as his first paper on "electrodynamics."
147. Helmholtz's mathematical law for the current intensity J is

$$J = \frac{A}{W}\left(1 - e^{-\frac{W}{P}t}\right),$$

where A is the electromotive force, W resistance, P potential, and t time. The law asymptotically approaches Ohm's law without induction. Helmholtz, "Ueber die Dauer," 429–38, on 434.
148. Koenigsberger, *Helmholtz* 1:147.

rable acuteness and clarity in the most complicated relationships." Again in the fall
of that year, during a tour of physiological laboratories, Helmholtz looked up Weber,
who showed him "much interesting physical apparatus" in the Göttingen physics
institute; in a letter to his wife after this meeting, Helmholtz wrote that the "physicist Weber, after Neumann, is no doubt the first mathematical physicist in Germany."[149]

The first critical examination of Helmholtz's reasoning behind the principle of
the conservation of force came from Rudolph Clausius in 1853. The truth of the
principle, Clausius argued, does not depend on central forces, not at least mathematically. Helmholtz replied that he was speaking from a physical, not a mathematical, standpoint and went on to reaffirm the starting point of his original work.
Clausius raised a number of other objections, mainly having to do with definitions
of concepts, but his main response to Helmholtz's work of 1847 was admiration:
despite its inexactness here and there, it had, "in my view, through the many beautiful ideas it contains, great scientific value."[150] For several years, Clausius in his
own work had made important use of one of the main supports of Helmholtz's principle, the convertibility of work and heat together with its precise measure. He had,
that is, begun to develop the mechanical theory of heat, which was to remain his
central interest and the subject of his lasting accomplishments.

Of all the physicists we discuss in this study, Clausius is the first of whom we
can say that "all of his accomplishments lay in the area of theoretical physics."[151]
He never made experimental physics the subject of his researches, although he held
positions that required him to lecture on experimental physics and to direct experimental institutes. He was a physicist who connected his theoretical studies with
experiments done by others.

The son of a school official who was also a clergyman, Clausius studied at the
gymnasium in Stettin in Prussia. From there he entered Berlin University in 1840,
where he was strongly drawn to Leopold von Ranke's lectures and even considered
making history his field. He heard lectures, too, by Magnus, Dirichlet, and other
physicists and mathematicians, in all spending three and a half years studying mathematics and the natural sciences. He concluded his studies with the examination
qualifying him to teach at Prussian gymnasiums. For the next six years he taught at
one of the Berlin gymnasiums and at the same time pursued his scientific interests
through his connection with the university physicists; a participant in Magnus's colloquium from its beginning, he remained close to Magnus. He also pursued his scientific interest through an institution open to him because of his job: in 1846 he

149. Letters from Helmholtz to Carl Ludwig and to Helmholtz's wife in 1851, quoted in Koenigsberger, *Helmholtz* 1:148, 155.
150. Rudolph Clausius, "Ueber einige Stellen der Schrift von Helmholtz 'Über die Erhaltung der
Kraft,' " *Ann.* 89 (1853): 568–79, on 578–79. Clausius and Helmholtz's exchange, which extended into
the following year, is discussed in Heimann, "Helmholtz," 234–35.
151. Walther Nernst, "Rudolf Clausius 1822–1888," in *150 Jahre Rheinische Friedrich-Wilhelms-Universität zu Bonn 1818–1968. Bonner Gelehrte. Beiträge zur Geschichte der Wissenschaften in Bonn. Mathematik
und Naturwissenschaften* (Bonn: H. Bouvier, Ludwig Röhrscheid, 1970), 101–9, on 101.

became a member of the "Seminar für gelehrte Schulen," a seminar at Berlin University which, as he described it, had the purpose of giving younger secondary school teachers an opportunity to continue their scientific education through independent scientific work. Clausius received his doctorate after he had been a member of this seminar for two years, and he continued in it until 1850, when he was appointed teacher of physics at the Berlin Artillery and Engineering School (Vereinigte Artillerie- und Ingenieurs-Schule), where he was charged with all physics instruction, including experimental physics. That same year he also became Privatdocent at Berlin University, where he taught physics from a mathematical-physical standpoint. Both positions together took up twelve hours a week and paid him a small salary of 550 thaler, allowing him time to prepare a series of impressive publications.[152]

Clausius revealed his theoretical bent in the opening remarks of his first publication in 1847. He pointed out that too little was known about daylight, his subject, because the methods of measuring the intensity of light were incomplete; the resulting lack of reliable measurements had led to a lessened interest in theoretical investigations, which was unfortunate. For by making hypotheses to bridge gaps in our knowledge, Clausius explained, we can construct general formulas, and by comparing their consequences with "reality," we can confirm or disprove the hypotheses. He described his first publication as an "attempt to determine more precisely the light-dispersing and luminous effects of the atmosphere through theoretical considerations."[153]

Clausius's dissertation dealt with the same subject. By a highly mathematical analysis, he arrived at conclusions about the cause of the reflection of sunlight in the atmosphere, proving that reflecting masses in the atmosphere—either the atmosphere itself or foreign masses floating in it—must be tiny vapor bubbles in the shape of thin plates with parallel surfaces. He showed that if the masses had any other shape, we would, for example, see a fixed star as an object larger than the sun.[154] The year following his dissertation he published a study of the equations of motion of an elastic body, which he introduced by referring to a recent experimental publication by Regnault on the compression of liquids and to the "very solid mathematical investigations" by the great French authors "Navier, Poisson, Cauchy, Lamé, and Clapeyron." Their theories essentially agreed with one another, and yet their results disagreed with certain facts. To discover the reason for the disagreement between theory and reality, Clausius examined several of their starting assumptions concerning the nature of molecular actions. The facts showed that elasticity theory was not a "closed" subject, and Clausius concluded his critical study by urging phys-

152. Clausius's vita submitted to President of the Swiss Education Council on 17 June 1855; Georg Sidler to President, 31 Mar. 1855, A Schweiz. Sch., Zurich. Helmholtz, "Clausius," 1–2.

153. Rudolph Clausius, "Ueber die Lichtzerstreuung in der Atmosphäre und über die Intensität des durch die Atmosphäre reflectirten Sonnenlichtes," Ann. 72 (1847): 294–314, on 294–95. This paper is an abstract of two papers appearing in the Journ. f. d. reine u. angewandte Math. 34 (1847): 122–47 and 36 (1848): 185–215.

154. Clausius's dissertation in 1848 was published: "Ueber die Natur derjenigen Bestandtheile der Erdatmosphäre, durch welche die Lichtreflexion in derselben bewirkt wird," Ann. 76 (1849): 161–88.

icists to multiply their experimental efforts to create "secure foundations for an extended theory."[155]

In the *Annalen der Physik* in 1850, Clausius published a paper on the "moving force of heat,"[156] which belongs to the group of theoretical researches affirming connections between the parts of physics, here heat and mechanics. To build upon this connection, Clausius had to resolve an apparent conflict arising from two stages in the development of heat theory. In the first stage, heat was held to be a fluid substance, or caloric, which was the viewpoint Carnot applied in 1824 in his work on the motive power of heat. In explaining the work done by a steam engine by the transfer of a certain quantity of caloric from a hot to a cold body, Carnot assumed that the quantity of caloric is conserved in the process: the caloric moves from the hot to the cold body in analogy with the fall of water from a high to a low elevation in the operation of a waterwheel, and if the engine is run in reverse, the same work transfers the caloric from the cold to the hot body, completing a full cycle. Carnot derived a theorem that states that the efficiency of an engine, the maximum work that a quantity of heat can produce, depends only on the two temperatures between which it operates and not on the nature of the working substance, steam or whatever. Taking up the theory ten years later, Clapeyron developed, as Carnot had not, the mathematics of heat theory, including a graphical representation of the Carnot cycle. In 1850 Clausius worked directly with Clapeyron's results.

In the second, more recent stage in the development of the theory, heat in bodies was held to be a kind of motion rather than a conserved caloric fluid. In 1849 William Thomson called attention to an apparent conflict between Carnot's principle and Joule's recent experimental findings on the generation of heat by currents and fluid friction. These findings suggested that heat is not conserved in the production or consumption of work, bringing into question Carnot's assumption of caloric and supporting Joule's view that heat is the mechanical vibration of the particles of bodies. Other facts, however, suggested that Carnot's principle is correct. As a way out of this impasse, Thomson looked to new experiments either to confirm Carnot's principle or to lay the foundation for a new theory of heat. Clausius's response was to say that what was needed was not new experiments but a new theoretical analysis.[157]

In Part I of the 1850 paper, Clausius introduced the first principle of the theory of heat, that of the equivalence of heat and work: whenever heat produces work, the principle says, a proportional quantity of heat is consumed, and conversely. To make intelligible this equivalence, Clausius had only to assume that heat is the measure of the "living force" of the moving particles of bodies; he did not need to assume any particular form for the motion. By combining this first principle with the

---

155. Rudolph Clausius, "Ueber die Veränderungen, welche in den bisher gebräuchlichen Formeln für das Gleichgewicht und die Bewegung elastischer fester Körper durch neuere Beobachtungen notwendig geworden sind," *Ann.* 76 (1849): 46–67, on 46, 51, and 66.

156. Rudolph Clausius, "Ueber die bewegende Kraft der Wärme und die Gesetze, welche sich daraus für die Wärmelehre selbst ableiten lassen," *Ann.* 79 (1850): 368–97, 500–524.

157. Martin J. Klein, "Gibbs on Clausius," *HSPS* 1 (1969): 127–49, on 130–31.

known gas laws, Clausius analyzed the relations between heat and work in the expansion and compression of a gas in a reversible engine. From this analysis, he arrived at certain consequences, such as the constant difference between the specific heat of a gas at constant pressure and the specific heat at constant volume.

To obtain further consequences, in Part II of the paper Clausius enlarged the foundations of the theory of heat to include Carnot's principle alongside the first principle. He retained the part of Carnot's principle that says that a transfer of heat occurs when work is done, only modifying the principle to allow some of the heat to be consumed during the transfer. His proof of the principle was a variation on Carnot's own reductio ad absurdum: he showed that Carnot's conclusion about the maximum work that a heat engine can produce remains valid by showing that its denial implies the transfer of heat from a cold to a hot body without a net expenditure of work; this result contradicts our universal experience of the unassisted passage of heat from hot to cold bodies. It seems, Clausius concluded, "*theoretically justified*" to accept the essential part of Carnot's theorem, which is that the maximum work depends only on the quantity of heat transferred and on the two temperatures.[158]

By combining the consequences of the first principle with those of the second, Clausius determined that for gases "Carnot's function"—an important function of temperature introduced by Clapeyron in his infinitesimal analysis of the Carnot cycle—is proportional to the absolute temperature, in agreement with Clapeyron and with recent measurements: $A(a + t)$, where t is the temperature and a and A are constants. The value of the constant a, "ideally" the same for all gases, or of its inverse $1/a$, had been experimentally determined for air by Regnault and by Clausius's teacher Magnus, The other constant A, or its inverse $1/A$, is the work equivalent of heat, which Clausius calculated from data on air and water vapor; the agreement of his value with the values that Joule had obtained in other ways confirmed for him the "correctness of Carnot's fundamental principle in the form it has assumed through the connection with the first fundamental principle."[159]

Clausius understood in 1850 that the resolution of the outstanding problem of the theory of heat was not to pick the correct fundamental law, Carnot's or otherwise, but to recognize that there are two laws, independent of one another and equally fundamental.[160] When in 1876 Helmholtz together with Kirchhoff and Werner von Siemens proposed Clausius as a corresponding member of the Prussian Academy of Sciences, they singled out his paper of 1850: "Over twenty-five years ago, he [Clausius] made a discovery of the greatest importance in theoretical physics, in that he found the law that has received the name of the second fundamental law of the mechanical theory of heat."[161] Upon Clausius's death twelve years later, Helmholtz told the Berlin Physical Society that in its "high significance, general validity, and

158. Clausius, "Ueber die bewegende Kraft," 503.
159. Clausius, "Ueber die bewegende Kraft," 378, 524.
160. Klein, "Gibbs on Clausius," 131.
161. Letter by Helmholtz, Werner von Siemens, and Kirchhoff, 14 Feb. 1876, proposing Clausius as corresponding member of the Prussian Academy of Sciences, Document 9, in Christa Kirsten and Hans-Günther Körber, eds., *Physiker über Physiker* (Berlin: Akademie-Verlag, 1975), 87.

fruitfulness," the second law was given its first rigorous formulation and development by Clausius. This law, Helmholtz continued, "is not only one of the most important but also one of the most surprising and original accomplishments of the old and the new physics: important because, so far as we now know, this law is one of the few [laws] that can claim an absolute general validity independent of all the diversity of natural bodies and because it reveals the most surprising connections between the most distant branches of physics."[162]

Following his original paper on the mechanical theory of heat, Clausius paid close attention to announcements of new experiments bearing on it. Later in 1850, for example, he responded to a paper in which William Thomson reported an experimental confirmation of the lowering of the freezing point of water by an increase of external pressure; Clausius wanted to show that this result agreed with his own theory. In 1851, he again responded to Thomson, this time to argue that Thomson was wrong to think that his theory could not explain why steam from the safety valve of a high-pressure boiler is not scalding.[163] In these and other papers, Clausius cited results by a good many experimenters, and he suggested further experiments, for example, those that might determine the relationship between the latent heats of various vapors and their tensions;[164] but he did no experiments himself, limiting his publications to critical discussion and theory.

Soon Clausius applied his heat laws to electrical discharge and thermoelectricity, theoretically joining those two prolific transforming powers of nature, heat and electricity. "It is known that in a manner similar to the production of mechanical work through the application of heat, electric currents also can be used to give rise in part to various mechanical actions, in part to heat," Clausius observed in a paper in 1852. These phenomena, which were especially interesting because of their "practical applications," could be given a "rigorous mathematical treatment" to expose their "inner connectedness."[165] Clausius imposed on the phenomenon of electric discharge a definite measure through the "fundamental laws of mechanics," adding to them, as equals, his own laws on heat. Most of the cases of electric discharge that he discussed were "too complicated" to allow a "very rigorous" comparison between theory and experiment. But where the comparison was possible, he found a reasonable agreement, which encouraged him to view his results as a new confirmation of the mechanical theory of heat. (He used published data by the Berlin physicists Dove and Riess, and since he was in direct contact with Riess, he asked him to make additional measurements expressly for his paper.)[166] In this paper and

162. Helmholtz, "Clausius," 3.

163. Rudolph Clausius, "Notiz über den Einfluss des Drucks auf das Gefrieren der Flüssigkeiten," Ann. 81 (1850): 168–72; "Ueber das Verhalten des Dampfes bei der Ausdehnung unter verschiedenen Umständen," Ann. 82 (1851): 263–73.

164. Rudolph Clausius, "Ueber den theoretischen Zusammenhang zweier empirisch aufgestellter Gesetze über die Spannung und die latente Wärme verschiedener Dämpfe," Ann. 82 (1851): 274–79.

165. Rudolph Clausius, "Ueber das mechanische Aequivalent einer elektrischen Entladung und die dabei stattfindende Erwärmung des Leitungsdrahtes," Ann. 86 (1852): 337–75, on 337.

166. Clausius, "Ueber das mechanische Aequivalent," 338, 375.

in others, such as a related paper that year on Leyden jars, the "main instrument for machine electricity," Clausius had to make simplifying mathematical assumptions; but in the discussion, he always returned to the actual, more complex apparatus required to make the measurements.[167]

In 1854, in a sequel to his 1850 paper, Clausius reformulated his modified version of Carnot's principle, illustrating the task of mathematical physics of finding clearer and more useful forms for a new law. Again placing the second law of the mechanical theory of heat alongside the first as an equally fundamental law of experience, this time he stated it in words as: heat cannot pass from a colder to a warmer body without some related change occurring at the same time. With the help of this principle, he derived a theorem concerning what he called the "equivalence value" of a transformation between heat and work. In a reversible cycle, there are two kinds of transformations: the production of work by a transfer of heat from a hot to a cold body, and the expenditure of work in the transfer of heat from a cold to a hot body. The "equivalence value" of these two transformations is a quantity that is conserved in a reversible cycle and that, in this sense, replaces heat, which is no longer conserved. The equivalence value, Clausius determined, takes the form of the ratio of heat Q to absolute temperature T: Clausius showed that the quantity dQ/T is a complete differential as dQ is not, so that for a reversible cycle the "analytical expression of the second fundamental principle of the mechanical theory of heat" is:

$$\int dQ/T = 0.$$

By speaking of the second law of the theory as the law of equivalence of transformations, Clausius made formal its analogy with the first law, that of the equivalence of heat and work.[168]

Independently of Clausius, Thomson also introduced a second fundamental law of the mechanical theory of heat, and other researchers such as K. H. A. Holtzmann at the technical school in Stuttgart seemed to be groping toward one. Thomson's law came in 1851, the year after Clausius's, and he acknowledged Clausius's priority. So it was Clausius who, with his paper of 1850, created a distinct science of the mechanical theory of heat or, as it came to be called, thermodynamics; that anyway was the considered judgment of one of the foremost experts in the subject, Josiah Willard Gibbs, a champion of Clausius's direction in it. Gibbs elaborated: "If we say, in the words used by Maxwell some years ago, that thermodynamics is 'a science with secure foundations, clear definitions, and distinct boundaries,' and ask when those foundations were laid, those definitions fixed, and those boundaries traced,

167. Rudolph Clausius, "Ueber die Anordnung der Elektricität auf einer einzelnen sehr dünnen Platte und auf den beiden Belegungen einer Franklin'schen Tafel," *Ann.* 86 (1852): 161–205, on, for example, 173, 198. Quotation on 161.

168. Rudolph Clausius, "Ueber eine veränderte Form des zweiten Hauptsatzes der mechanischen Wärmetheorie," *Ann.* 93 (1854): 481–506. Eduard Riecke, "Rudolf Clausius," *Abh. Ges. Wiss. Göttingen* 35 (1888): appendix, 1–39.

there can be but one answer. Certainly not before the publication of that memoir."[169]

Like Weber in electricity, Clausius in the mechanical theory of heat strove to lay foundations for an entire branch of physics. Clausius and Weber together with Neumann, Kirchhoff, and Helmholtz, other authors of encompassing theoretical studies we have discussed here, accounted for much of the German contribution in 1845–50 to the establishment of the great classical theories of physics of the nineteenth century.

169. Josiah Willard Gibbs, "Rudolf Julius Emanuel Clausius," *Proc. Am. Acad.* 16 (1889): 458–65; quoted in Klein, "Gibbs on Clausius," 129–30, where Clausius's work is discussed in light of Gibbs's observation.

7

Contributions of Mathematicians to Physics: Dirichlet, Riemann, and Carl Neumann

The advances of physical theories in the first half of the nineteenth century demonstrated to German physicists the importance of powerful mathematical techniques for their subject. Some of the techniques they owed to the German mathematician Gauss, who not only developed them but also applied them to physical problems. During Gauss's later years and after his death, other German mathematicians developed mathematical techniques useful in physics and, as Gauss did, applied them. In this chapter we discuss two of the more important of these mathematicians from the middle years of the century, Dirichlet and Bernhard Riemann, both of whom ended their careers in Gauss's chair at Göttingen. It was fitting, for in that position they continued their predecessor's work on the connections of mathematics and physics. We also discuss the Leipzig mathematician Carl Neumann, who saw his work on physical problems as a continuation into the late nineteenth century and beyond of the tradition of Gauss, Dirichlet, and Riemann.

Gauss's Importance for Physics

The discussion about a replacement for Gauss at Göttingen University in 1855 brought out the importance of mathematics for the physical sciences. At the time of his death, Gauss was professor both of higher mathematics and of astronomy, so the question arose of whether he should be succeeded by an astronomer or by a mathematician. Since specialization was a necessary and accepted fact of scientific life by then, nobody expected to find another person qualified in both fields, and it was certainly necessary to appoint an astronomer since the astronomical observatory could not to be left unused. But it was an open question whether they should look for an astronomer eminent enough to command Gauss's large salary or for an eminent mathematician instead. The question was put to Weber, to whom the answer

170

was clear; in giving it he expanded on the value of higher mathematics for the physical sciences, the appreciation of which he had acquired over his nearly thirty years of close association with the finest German mathematicians.

Higher mathematics was needed more than astonomy for university instruction, Weber argued; it was "of the greatest importance and indispensable not only for the education of actual mathematicians but also for the education of astonomers and physicists, as indeed in higher education in all exact sciences and their applications." He further argued that an appointment in higher mathematics would enhance the Göttingen Society of Sciences: a good mathematician would guarantee its "brilliant" position in the scientific world, which a good astronomer could not do, even if it would be a pleasure to have one in the society. Weber explained that in the class of the society concerned with higher mathematics and the "theoretical" natural sciences, natural phenomena are presented in their "causal connections, linked together by mathematical laws": these "sciences are dominated by higher mathematics, which is the queen of the sciences, as Gauss called it, because in its abstract foundation and rigorous philosophical deduction it is completely independent, and because the ends of the threads running through all researches in the other sciences come together in it." Higher mathematics was more important than astronomy for furthering related subjects: for one science to be important to another, the close relationship of the two was not decisive in itself; they must also differ in a way that allowed them to complement one another. So by this argument, if a physicist and an astronomer were to undertake joint research, neither would bring anything new to the work of the other. "The mathematician, on the other hand, can display all the riches of his science and the results of his own researches in a suitably chosen astronomical or physical investigation that he undertakes with an astronomer or with a physicist, and through it he in turn gains incentive and stimulation to explore new areas of mathematical problems." Weber's final argument for the need for an appointment in higher mathematics had to do with the reputation of Göttingen University. Gauss—whose only equals were Archimedes and Newton, in Weber's view—had given Göttingen the "dominating position in the world," and to maintain that position it was necessary that Gauss's chair go to a "creative genius of higher mathematics."[1]

Dirichlet as Gauss's Successor

The generation of mathematicians following Gauss's inherited not only his more than formidable mathematical legacy. "The immense colossus that has been called into being by the works of an Euler, Lagrange, Laplace demands the most enormous strength and exertions in thinking if one wants to penetrate its inner nature and not merely fiddle around at the surface. To become its master, so that one does not have to be afraid every second of being crushed by it, one is driven by an impulse that

    1. Weber to Warnstedt, 5 Apr. 1855, Dirichlet Personalakte, Göttingen UA, 4/V b/134.

does not allow one to stop and rest until one stands above it and can survey the whole work."[2] This assessment of contemporary mathematics is from a letter in 1823 by the nineteen-year-old C. G. J. Jacobi, who was going to devote himself to mathematics.

The year before, Jacobi's future close friend Dirichlet, then a seventeen-year-old student, left Germany for Paris, where for five years he worked on mastering the "immense colossus," in Jacobi's words. There he was befriended by Fourier, who awakened his interest in mathematical physics, a field which he was to pursue with great success.[3]

Upon his return to Germany on Humboldt's advice, Dirichlet took a degree at Bonn University, taught briefly at Breslau University, and then taught for many years at Berlin University and also at a Berlin military school, the Allgemeine Kriegsschule. He came into personal contact with German mathematicians, including Gauss (with whom he had already been in touch in connection with his earliest mathematical work, which had originated in Gauss's *Disquisitiones Arithmeticae*). Early on, he became friends with Weber, who spent several months in the winter of 1828 in Berlin to further his studies, much of the time in the company of Dirichlet and the mathematician Jacob Steiner. Dirichlet had Weber among his auditors at his lecture on Fourier's heat theory, and later, particularly after Weber was no longer working with Gauss, it was Dirichlet who helped Weber with mathematical problems of his electrical theory. (Weber's visits with Poggendorff in Berlin were always also visits with Dirichlet and with the family of Dirichlet's wife, the Mendelssohns, the "most distinguished meeting point of art and science in Berlin.")[4]

When Gauss's professorship at Göttingen fell vacant at his death in 1855, in Weber's judgment Dirichlet was the only candidate for it. At the highest level of mathematical research, Germany had long had only one man, Gauss, Weber argued: Gauss's greatness could be recognized only by foreign, mainly French, mathematicians such as Lagrange and Laplace, until the late 1820s when mathematics in Germany was suddenly enriched by the nearly simultaneous appearance of Dirichlet, Jacobi, Gotthold Eisenstein, and Niels Henrik Abel. Of these four, only Dirichlet was still alive, and he was the only mathematician worthy to succeed Gauss. Reflecting Weber's view, the official call went to Dirichlet, who was told that Göttingen "urgently" needed an outstanding mathematician for the continued advancement of higher mathematics and of the "natural sciences that are based on mathematical laws." Dirichlet accepted. Contributing to his decision to leave Berlin for Göttingen was the prospect of a scientific collaboration with Weber such as Gauss had enjoyed. Dirichlet also saw the move as a chance to gain more time for his researches, since

2. Jacobi to his uncle Lehmann, quoted in Koenigsberger, *Jacobi*, 8.

3. Koenigsberger, *Jacobi*, 9; Hermann Minkowski, "Peter Gustav Lejeune Dirichlet und seine Bedeutung für die heutige Mathematik," in Minkowski, *Gesammelte Abhandlungen*, ed. David Hilbert, 2 vols. (Leipzig and Berlin: B. G. Teubner, 1911), 2:447–61, on 449. E. E. Kummer, "Gedächtnissrede auf Gustav Peter Lejeune Dirichlet," in G. *Lejeune Dirichlet's Werke*, ed. L. Kronecker and L. Fuchs, 2 vols. (Berlin, 1889–97), 2:311–44, on 319.

4. Minkowski, "Dirichlet," 449–50. Heinrich Weber, *Weber*, 11–15, 96–97. Koenigsberger, *Jacobi*, 34, 57, 100. Quotation from Weber to Warnstedt, 5 Apr. 1855.

he would now be freed from the extra teaching at the Berlin military school. Above all, Dirichlet could not refuse the "greatest glory" of becoming Gauss's successor.[5]

By this time, Dirichlet had long been one of the cultivators of mathematical physics in Germany. Fourier's heat theory had inspired his work in that field as it had inspired his mathematical work on infinite series and definite integrals. Dirichlet wrote the entry on recent "mathematical physics" for Dove and Moser's *Repertorium der Physik* in 1837, in which Dirichlet presented, among other topics, the representation of arbitrary functions by Fourier's sine and cosine series. Dove remarked that this representation had recently found so many applications in the analytical treatment of physical problems that it was necessary to give a systematic account of the mathematical considerations on which the series are based.[6]

Dirichlet was also inspired by Gauss's studies on the potential, a subject that shortly came to be viewed as a developing discipline within mathematics.[7] He developed it further, and he was one of the first to give special lectures on it, a practice which all German universities subsequently followed. The lectures on the potential that Dirichlet gave at Göttingen in the winter of 1856–57 were transcribed and published as a complete textbook on the mathematical treatment of "forces that act according to the inverse square of the distance."[8] From an analysis of the action of any number of point-masses on another point-mass, Dirichlet drew two conclusions on which his general theory of the potential rests. First, each component of force on a point-mass M owing to the action of other point-masses m is the partial derivative of a single function, the "potential" v. The x-component of the force is written as:

$$X = kM\frac{d}{dx}\sum\frac{m}{r}, \text{ or simply, } X = M\frac{d}{dx}v,$$

where k is a constant and r is the distance of masses m from M. Second, the potential satisfies Laplace's equation: $d^2v/dx^2 + d^2v/dy^2 + d^2v/dz^2 = 0$. To generalize the equations for the potential of point-masses to that of finite bodies, Dirichlet replaced the finite sum by an integral: $v = \int k/r \, dT$, where k is the density of matter and dT is the volume element. For mathematical physics as a whole, the significance of these equations is that they apply not only to Newton's gravitational force but also to the electric and magnetic forces. The form of the mathematical expression for all

5. Weber to Warnstedt, 5 Apr. 1855; Warnstedt to Hannover Ministry, 21 Apr. 1855; Göttingen U. Curator to Dirichlet, 23 Apr. 1855; Dirichlet Personalakte, Göttingen UA, 4/V b/134.

6. Kummer, "Dirichlet," 325, 333; Heinrich Wilhelm Dove, "Vorwort," and Dirichlet, "Ueber die Darstellung ganz willkührlicher Funktionen durch Sinus- und Cosinusreihen," in Heinrich Wilhelm Dove and Ludwig Moser, eds., *Repertorium der Physik*, vol. 1 (Berlin, 1837), iii–vi, on iv, and 152–74, respectively.

7. Hans Salié, "Carl Neumann," in *Bedeutende Gelehrte in Leipzig*, ed. G. Harig, vol. 2 (Leipzig: Karl-Marx-Universität, 1965), 13–23, on 21.

8. Gustav Lejeune Dirichlet, *Vorlesungen über die im umgekehrten Verhältniss des Quadrats der Entfernung wirkenden Kräfte*, ed. F. Grube (Leipzig, 1876).

three forces is $Mm\,f(r)$; for electricity and magnetism the force is negative, for gravitation it is positive.

Dirichlet's three active years at Göttingen were "especially filled" with thoughts about physical questions, according to a biographer. He had found a rigorous proof for the stability of our planetary system and a new general method for treating and solving the differential equations of mechanics. But Dirichlet was now, as he had always been, reluctant to begin writing down his results, and no more than a few hints became known of his work, which was brought to an end by his death in 1859. His contribution to mathematical physics during these last years was through his lectures, in which he treated certain mathematical problems that were of great importance for electricity. Dirichlet's lectures were continued by Riemann, who succeeded him at Göttingen.[9]

Riemann's Lectures and Researches

Bernhard Riemann was nearly twenty years younger than Dirichlet, so that by the time he entered Göttingen University in 1846, it was possible to get a first-rate education in higher mathematics in Germany. Riemann immediately took two of Stern's courses and in his second semester Gauss's lectures on the method of least squares. But despite Gauss's presence, Göttingen was not then the best university in Germany for an aspiring mathematician, since Gauss taught only a limited range of subjects and his mathematical colleagues did not measure up to the best who were to be found elsewhere, principally in Berlin. So during the next two years, from 1847 to 1849, Riemann acquired the larger part of his mathematical education in Berlin from Dirichlet, Jacobi, and Eisenstein. He then returned to Göttingen to round out his education with lectures on the natural sciences and philosophy. Of the former, Weber's lectures on experimental physics were of "greatest interest" to him; in the latter, he concentrated on the philosophy of Johann Friedrich Herbart. After completing the lecture courses, he became a member of both the pedagogical seminar and the mathematical-physical seminar, where he remained until his graduation in 1851, apparently intending to earn a living soon as a secondary school teacher.[10] In the mathematical-physical seminar he distinguished himself immediately, especially in his work on optical problems in Listing's part of the seminar, and he was awarded one of the student stipends in his first year. In the second year Weber put him in charge of preparing the new members of his part of the seminar for laboratory exercises, a task for which Riemann received a small salary.[11] As a

9. Minkowski, "Dirichlet," 459. Felix Klein, *Vorlesungen über die Entwicklung der Mathematik im 19. Jahrhundert*, pt. 1, ed. R. Courant and O. Neugebauer (New York: Chelsea, 1967), 99.

10. Richard Dedekind, "Bernhard Riemann's Lebenslauf," in *Bernhard Riemann's gesammelte mathematische Werke und wissenschaftlicher Nachlass*, ed. H. Weber (Leipzig, 1876), 507–26. This biography and Riemann's Personalakte in the Göttingen UA, 4/V b/137, are our main sources for details about his career.

11. "Jahresbericht 1850/51"; Ulrich to Göttingen U. Curator, 2 Aug. 1851; Göttingen UA, 4/V h/20.

member of the seminar and as an assistant, he was praised for his "excellent" researches and lectures.[12]

The seminar stipend and assistant's salary were intended more to give Riemann financial help, which he badly needed, than to encourage and reward his work. As Weber remarked later, by this time Riemann had long ceased to be a student and was already a "true professional scholar." Gauss thought so highly of Riemann's researches that he refused to draw him away from his "higher calling," as he might have when Riemann expressed mild interest in the—as Gauss termed it, "mechanical"—work of observer at the astronomical observatory in 1851. Gauss "counted Riemann among the few who are talented primarily for higher mathematical researches and of whom one must make higher demands because they carry within them the strength to meet them." He especially valued Riemann's "creative talent for finding new questions and points of view for mathematical research in the field of higher mathematical physics and for being able to build on them."[13]

The research that brought high praise to Riemann in the four years before he became Privatdocent at Göttingen dealt with several different parts of mathematics and physics: the introduction of complex variables into the theory of functions, trigonometric series, the foundations of geometry, the search for a connection between the fundamental laws of the parts of physics, and Weber and Kohlrausch's measurement of Weber's constant c. To Riemann, these disparate mathematical and physical areas of research evidently seemed ultimately related. That likelihood was first suggested by a paper he prepared for the pedagogical seminar in 1850 "on the extent, arrangement, and method of instruction in the natural sciences in gymnasiums," in which he expressed his understanding of mathematics as the means of uniting all parts of physics: "One can set up a completely self-contained mathematical theory, which proceeds from the elementary laws that are valid for individual points to processes in the actually given continuously filled space, without distinguishing whether it is gravity, electricity, magnetism, or the equilibrium of heat that is being treated."[14]

Riemann's mathematical researches in these years were intended to earn him academic credentials. He wrote his dissertation on the "foundations for a general theory of functions of a variable complex quantity," a subject he had debated with Eisenstein in Berlin, when he held that a partial differential equation is the essential definition of a function of a complex variable. His next mathematical research was meant as qualification for his habilitation in the winter of 1853–54; in it he treated the possibility of representing functions by trigonometric series, a part of mathematics "so important for physics." Habilitation required yet another piece of work from him, a sample lecture, which he gave "on the hypotheses that are the foundation of geometry." Gauss had chosen this topic from the three submitted by Riemann because he wanted to find out what such a young man had to say on such a difficult

12. "Jahresbericht 1851/52," Göttingen UA, 4/V h/20.
13. Weber to Göttingen U. Curator, 10 Mar. 1855, Riemann Personalakte, Göttingen UA, 4/V b/137.
14. Dedekind, "Riemann's Lebenslauf," 513.

subject. Gauss came away from the lecture "speaking with unusual excitement about the depth of Riemann's ideas."[15]

Simultaneously with these mathematical studies, Riemann developed, as Weber described it, "a larger piece of work by which he intends to establish an inner connection mainly between optics and electrical theory in a way that no one else has thought of before." Weber expected Riemann's discovery of such a connection and its realization to be "of very great importance and truly epoch-making."[16] Riemann described his work as having an even more ambitious scope: an "investigation of the connection between electricity, galvanism, light, and gravity."[17]

With the posthumous publication of Riemann's collected works, including manuscripts—Riemann died in 1866, at age forty, before he could finish his physical theory—his goals were more fully revealed. In writings dating from the early 1850s, he said that his main task was to develop a new conception of the known laws of nature, which would make possible the use of experimental data on the interactions between heat, light, magnetism, and electricity in the investigation of the connection of the laws. He was led to this understanding by Newton's and Euler's works on the one hand and by Herbart's psychology on the other.[18] His new conception required a world-space continuously filled with material.[19] He thought of this material as an incompressible, homogeneous fluid without inertia, which flows into ponderable atoms, there disappearing from the phenomenal world and entering the mental world. Oscillations, which we perceive as light and heat, are propagated through the material, and its pressure on ponderable matter produces the phenomena of gravitation. He placed at the head of his theory a mathematical law with two parts; one part describes gravitation and electrostatic attraction and repulsion, and the other part describes the propagation of light and heat and also electrodynamic and magnetic attraction and repulsion.[20] Riemann's goal was a total theory of physics based on a single encompassing mathematical law.

In the spring of 1854, Rudolph Kohlrausch came to Göttingen for two weeks to work with Weber on the determination of the constant c in Weber's law, and they invited Riemann to participate in their experiments. Riemann took the occasion to

15. Bernhard Riemann, "Grundlagen für eine allgemeine Theorie der Functionen einer veränderlichen complexen Grösse" (1851); "Ueber die Darstellbarkeit einer Function durch eine trigonometrische Reihe" (1854); "Ueber die Hypothesen, welche der Geometrie zu Grunde liegen" (1854); in Werke . . . Nachlass, 3–47, 213–53, on 214, and 254–69. Dedekind, "Riemann's Lebenslauf," 517.

16. Weber to Göttingen U. Curator, 10 Mar. 1855.

17. Riemann to his brother Wilhelm, 28 Dec. 1853 and 26 June 1854, cited in Dedekind, "Riemann's Lebenslauf," 515.

18. Bernhard Riemann, "Fragmente philosophischen Inhalts," in Werke . . . Nachlass, 475–506, on 475.

19. Dedekind recalled a conversation in which Riemann spoke with admiration of Newton's third letter to Bentley in which Newton referred to direct action at a distance as an "absurdity." Dedekind, "Riemann's Lebenslauf," 521. Riemann quoted that passage from Newton's letter in his posthumously published writings on gravitation and light. Riemann, "Fragmente," 498.

20. Riemann developed these ideas in a fragment entitled "Neue mathematische Principien der Naturphilosophie," to which he added the note "found on 1 March 1853," suggesting that he thought these principles were important. (He made it clear immediately that by "Naturphilosophie" he meant natural philosophy.) In his Werke . . . Nachlass, 502–6.

discuss with Kohlrausch his explanation—drawn from his work on the connection between electricity, light, and magnetism—of Kohlrausch's measurements of the electrical residue in a Leyden jar. Kohlrausch encouraged Riemann to work out the theory for this phenomenon. This was an important opportunity for Riemann, as he explained to his brother, "because it is the first time that I could apply my work to a previously unknown phenomenon, and I hope that the publication of this work will help to give my larger work a favorable reception."[21] It was Kohlrausch's precise measurements of the phenomenon that made it such a desirable test for Riemann's law for the motion of electricity.[22] Riemann submitted a paper on it to the *Annalen der Physik* only to withdraw it because of a suggested change that he did not want to make. In its place he published a paper on the theory of Nobili color rings,[23] an "important" subject that also allowed for "very precise measurements"; the "laws according to which electricity moves can be very precisely tested on it."[24]

The winter of 1854–55 was Riemann's first semester as Privatdocent. At the time a Göttingen colleague recommended him for a position at the new Zurich Polytechnic as a "pioneering genius" in research, though an inexperienced teacher.[25] But the Göttingen mathematicians and physicists did not want to lose him; they knew that Gauss was dying, and they saw Riemann as "indispensable" for the "school" of advanced mathematics that Gauss had established at Göttingen, which "must under no circumstances be allowed to collapse."[26] For his first lectures on the theory of partial differential equations with applications to physical problems, Riemann got a "very numerous" audience (for such a subject) of seven students.[27] To ensure that he would stay at Göttingen, he was given a small salary, and in 1857 at Weber's request a promotion to extraordinary professor. Both as Privatdocent and then as extraordinary professor, Riemann taught "pure and applied mathematics";[28] in addition to purely mathematical subjects, he lectured on higher mechanics and on the mathematical theories of gravitation, elasticity, and electricity and magnetism, and on selected physical problems.[29] In the summer of 1859 Riemann succeeded Dirichlet in Gauss's chair.[30]

21. Riemann to his brother Wilhelm, 26 June 1854, in Dedekind, "Riemann's Lebenslauf," 516–17.

22. Bernhard Riemann, "Neue Theorie des Rückstandes in electrischen Bindungsapparaten" (1854), in *Werke . . . Nachlass*, 345–56, on 345.

23. Bernhard Riemann, "Zur Theorie der Nobili'schen Farbenringe," *Ann.* 95 (1855): 130–39, reprinted in *Werke . . . Nachlass*, 54–61.

24. Riemann to one of his sisters, 9 Oct. 1854, quoted in Dedekind, "Riemann's Lebenslauf," 518.

25. W. Sartorius von Waltershausen to [Studer?], 22 Dec. 1854, A Schweiz. Sch., Zurich, document number 31 in file dated 1855.

26. Sartorius von Waltershausen to Göttingen U. Curator, 11 Feb. 1855, Riemann Personalakte, Göttingen UA, 4/V b/137.

27. Weber to Göttingen U. Curator, 10 Mar. 1855.

28. Göttingen U. Philosophical Faculty to Curator, 11 June 1854; Göttingen U. Curator to Riemann, 9 Nov. 1857; Riemann Personalakte, Göttingen UA, 4/V b/137.

29. "Verzeichnis der von Riemann angekündigten Vorlesungen," in *Bernhard Riemann's gesammelte mathematische Werke. Nachträge*, ed. M. Noether and W. Wirtinger (Leipzig: B. G. Teubner, 1902), 114–15. Also marginal note on Riemann's lectures, in a draft of the letter of his appointment to ordinary professor, 30 July 1859, Riemann Personalakte, Göttingen UA, 4/V b/137.

30. Riemann's letter of appointment, 30 July 1859. Dedekind, "Riemann's Lebenslauf," 522.

Riemann modeled his lectures on the partial differential equations of physics after those he had heard Dirichlet give in Berlin. He introduced these lectures with the observation that "a scientific physics" existed only since the discovery of the differential calculus.[31] Although the basic concepts of physics such as acceleration and center of attraction had not changed since Galileo and Newton, the mathematical methods of physics had changed. Riemann had in mind especially the method of proceeding from fundamental laws of physics relating to spatial and temporal points to laws relating to the extended bodies and time intervals that we perceive. This method demands partial differential equations. Reviewing the subject historically, Riemann observed that it was not until sixty years after Newton's *Principia* that d'Alembert solved the first physical problem that led to a partial differential equation. It was another sixty years after that before Fourier, in his theory of the conduction of heat, developed general methods for solving physical problems that led to partial differential equations. Since then, the basic laws of physics that could be tested by experiment had all been formulated as partial differential equations.

Riemann devoted the first half of his lectures to purely mathematical subjects: definite integrals, infinite Fourier series, ordinary differential equations, and, most important, partial differential equations. "With the physical phenomena we want to observe," Riemann explained, "more [than one] independent variable quantities enter: time and the three spatial coordinates" and with them, "therefore, partial differential equations." Of these, "linear partial differential equations of the second order are of the greatest interest because most physical questions lead to such equations." The general form of the most important partial differential equation in physics is, for the x-component,

$$l \frac{\partial^2 u}{\partial x^2} + m \frac{\partial^2 u}{\partial x \partial t} + n \frac{\partial^2 u}{\partial t^2} + p \frac{\partial u}{\partial x} + q \frac{\partial u}{\partial t} + ru = s,$$

with corresponding equations for the y- and z-components.[32] Riemann devoted much of the second half of his lectures to studying special cases of this general equation in several parts of physics; specifically, in the theories of the motion of heat, oscillations of elastic bodies, the motion of fluids, electricity, magnetism, and gravitation.[33]

Riemann's published lectures in their original form—and in later expanded versions brought out by others[34]—provided physicists with a compendium of mathe-

31. Dedekind, "Riemann's Lebenslauf," 518. Bernhard Riemann, *Partielle Differentialgleichungen und deren Anwendung auf physikalische Fragen*, ed. Karl Hattendorff (Braunschweig, 1869). Quotation from the second edition (1876), p. 1.

32. Riemann, *Partielle Differentialgleichungen*, 107–8.

33. Karl Hattendorff brought out Riemann's lectures in two volumes in 1876; the second volume, which continued Riemann's applications of partial differential equations to additional branches of physics, he entitled *Schwere, Elektricität und Magnetismus, nach den Vorlesungen von Bernhard Riemann* (Hannover, 1876).

34. Riemann's lectures became one of the classic German texts, kept up to date, passing from editor to editor, while retaining the original author's name and benefiting from his renown. What Hattendorff

matical methods useful for solving physical problems. They did more than that: they exhibited the generalizing and unifying power of the methods in the various parts of physics. In principle, to calculate most of the phenomena of the physical world, the physicists had only to solve one of the special cases of a general partial differential equation under the appropriate initial and boundary conditions.

Riemann told his auditors and readers that mathematics had played the leading role in the recent historical development of physical theory. Physicists who learned from him recognized that, at the very least, they needed advanced mathematical training, especially in techniques for handling partial differential equations. Riemann's lectures, it is worth noting here, were published in 1869, just as theoretical physics was beginning to be regularly represented in German universities and before published lectures by physicists on theoretical physics had begun to appear. They served as an early, important textbook as well as a mathematical aid in theoretical research.

In addition to working on the general foundations of a theory uniting all parts of physics, Riemann worked on specific problems in several branches of mathematical physics, in electricity, optics, and acoustics. Even then, his intention in some of this work was, as we have seen, to test his general theory. In other instances, he meant the particular physical case to serve mathematics (which would ultimately serve physics again): "This investigation does not claim to furnish experimental research with useful results," he wrote in an announcement of a paper on the propagation of planar air waves of finite wave length; "the author wishes it to be considered only as a contribution to the theory of nonlinear partial differential equations."[35] His approach followed precedent: for the integration of linear partial differential equations the most fruitful methods were not found by developing the general concept of the problem but by treating special physical problems, and the new methods Riemann arrived at in this way he expected to benefit the study of more general problems.

Riemann's work on electrodynamics was that which most directly related to his objective of a total theory of physics. In a paper entitled "Contribution to Electrodynamics," which he presented to the Göttingen Society in 1858, he revealed his high expectations: this work, he announced with his opening words, "brings into close connection the theory of electricity and magnetism with that of light and of radiant heat."[36] In a letter at the time he claimed the "discovery of the connection between electricity and light," and although he had been told that Gauss had already discovered a connection, he thought that his was different and correct.[37] In

brought out as two separate volumes, based on lectures Riemann gave in separate semesters, Heinrich Weber later brought out as one work in two volumes: *Die partiellen Differential-Gleichungen der mathematischen Physik. Nach Riemann's Vorlesungen*, 4th rev. ed., 2 vols. (Braunschweig: F. Vieweg, 1900–1901).

35. Bernhard Riemann, "Selbstanzeige der vorstehenden Abhandlung" (1859), in *Werke . . . Nachlass*, 165–67, on 165.

36. Bernhard Riemann, "Ein Beitrag zur Elektrodynamik" (1858), posthumously published in *Ann.* 131 (1867): 237–43, reprinted in *Werke . . . Nachlass*, 270–75, on 270.

37. Dedekind, "Riemann's Lebenslauf," 521. The letter, for which Dedekind does not give a date, is to Riemann's sister Ida.

this paper, Riemann generalized Poisson's equation for the electrostatic potential by adding to it a second-order time derivative of the potential to arrive at an equation of propagation, a wave equation with a source term. Riemann solved the equation using a so-called retarded potential, which he showed leads to experimentally confirmed results.[38] Riemann did not publish the paper, and when it appeared posthumously it was immediately criticized by Clausius, who pointed out a mathematical error in it and suggested that Riemann had withdrawn the paper because of it.[39] But the theory was widely noticed, and, as we will see, Carl Neumann, for one, found it a stimulus to develop his own electrodynamic theory.

To introduce his electrodynamic theory, Riemann stated the "experimental law" of the potential between two conductors carrying currents, which he reformulated by invoking Weber's assumption about the nature of currents. He then showed that the same potential results from his own "new theory," the fundamental equation of which is the following partial differential equation for the potential function U:

$$\frac{\partial^2 U}{\partial t^2} - \alpha^2 \left(\frac{\partial^2 U}{\partial x^2} + \frac{\partial^2 U}{\partial y^2} + \frac{\partial^2 U}{\partial z^2} \right) + \alpha^2 4\pi\rho = 0,$$

where ρ is the density of electric masses, and α is a constant with units of velocity. To identify the two expressions for the potential, the experimentally confirmed and his own, he only had to equate α with $c/\sqrt{2}$, where c is Weber's constant. From the closeness of Weber and Kohlrausch's values of $c/\sqrt{2}$ with the velocity of light, Riemann concluded that the actions of electric masses on one another are, within experimental accuracy, propagated with the velocity of light.[40]

In his lectures at Göttingen in 1861, which were published in 1876, Riemann proposed a new "fundamental law" of electrodynamics.[41] This law was another variant of Weber's, differing from Weber's in that the total relative velocity of a pair of electric masses enters in place of the relative velocity only along the line between the masses. This time Riemann did not derive the electrodynamic action from a finite propagation of the potential function but from Lagrange's law, which he constructed from the kinetic energy T of the electrical system, an electrostatic part S of the potential depending only on position, and an electrodynamic part D of the potential depending on both position and velocity. The latter part, since it depends on both position and velocity, might be considered as belonging either to the kinetic energy or to the potential energy in the Lagrangian function. Since that function for gravitation-type forces—the kinetic minus the potential energy—was no guide in deciding on the sign of a velocity-dependent potential, Riemann decided the question by appealing to the principle of the conservation of energy. If electrical

38. Riemann was apparently the first to use a retarded potential, but because of the delay in the publication of the work, the first published use of it was by Ludwig Lorenz in 1861. Rosenfeld, "The Velocity of Light," 1635.

39. Rudolph Clausius, "Ueber die von Gauss angeregte neue Auffassung der elektrodynamischen Erscheinungen," *Ann.* 135 (1868): 606–21, on 613–18.

40. Riemann, "Ein Beitrag zur Elektrodynamik," 272, 275.

41. Riemann, *Schwere, Elektricität und Magnetismus*, 313–37.

motions are such that energy is conserved, then the potential D, or the negative value of it, the potential energy, must be grouped with T in the Lagrangian function; to be precise, a necessary and sufficient condition for the conservation of energy is:

$$\delta \int_0^t (T - D + S)dt = 0,$$

which is what Riemann called the "extended law of Langrange."[42] By giving D one form, he showed that Lagrange's law yields Weber's fundamental law of electric action; by giving it another form, he showed that it yields his own fundamental law. In demonstrating the applicability of an extended Lagrangian formalism to electrodynamics and in this way developing electrodynamics from the same first principles as mechanics, Riemann showed that the electrodynamic force can be treated like familiar forces that do not have velocity-dependent potentials. In general, in his work on electrodynamics, Riemann showed that this rapidly developing subject offered a challenging field to mathematicians interested in physical questions.

Carl Neumann's Lectures and Researches

Riemann's work on electrodynamics stimulated another mathematician—the last of our examples of mathematicians who contributed to physics—Carl Neumann. Like Riemann, Neumann developed a theory founded on the finite propagation of electrodynamic actions, and like Riemann's, his theory was taken seriously by physicists; at least two of them, Weber and Clausius, corresponded with him about it.

Throughout his long career, Carl Neumann worked as a mathematician, not as a physicist. But as a student at Königsberg University, he had studied physics with his father, Franz Neumann, along with mathematics, and later as a working mathematician he dealt almost exclusively with mathematical problems arising from physics. For forty-three years, beginning in 1868, he held one of Leipzig's two mathematical professorships. It was Möbius's old position, which Weber described as a professorship for "higher mechanics, which essentially encompasses mathematical physics."[43] Although Neumann's physical interests did not enter the deliberations at the time of his hiring,[44] his lectures at Leipzig covered potential theory, mechanics, and all parts of mathematical physics. His researches were equally wide ranging in subject, though in approach they were always mathematical; he sometimes compared the consequences of his mathematical hypotheses with experimental results, but he did no experiments himself, leaving them to the physicists.[45] Because of the empha-

42. Riemann, *Schwere, Elektricität und Magnetismus*, 316–18.

43. Weber to Göttingen U. Curator, 22 May 1848, Weber Personalakte, Göttingen UA, 4/V b/ 95a.

44. Neumann was hired as a mathematician who could teach "higher" mathematics, not as a mathematical physicist. Neumann Personalakte, Leipzig UA, Nr. 774 and other documents.

45. O. Hölder, "Carl Neumann," *Verh. sächs. Akad. Wiss.* 77 (1925): 154–80, on 167.

sis of his teaching, he counted a number of physicists among his students at Leipzig.[46]

Before moving to Leipzig, Neumann taught mathematics at Tübingen University. For his inaugural lecture there in 1865, he chose the subject of the "present standpoint of mathematical physics." He had no quarrel, he said, with the widespread claim that natural science was rapidly advancing, but he did have one with the claim that the advance applied to theory as well as to the number of discoveries. In certain parts of physics, theories seemed fairly well established. In certain other parts, however, such as electricity and magnetism, the existing theories were not likely to endure for long. Even though Weber's law of electric force, for example, accounted with full exactness for the observed phenomena, the very principles in this area of physics were still in question. The rotating elementary electric systems that Weber invoked to explain permanent magnetism seemed to Neumann to be overly complicated, a sign that new physical ideas might be needed and, as well, new mathematical ideas, especially ideas on "space and time."[47]

In his research and in his teaching Neumann related the theoretical needs of electricity and magnetism to potential theory, the part of mathematics in which he did his most important work.[48] In 1868, he presented a new and complete electrodynamic theory making full use of the potential.[49] He introduced the theory with the observation that the parts of physics fall into two classes corresponding to the basic forces used to explain their phenomena: those parts of physics whose forces are determined by the relative positions of particles, which include the gravitational, elastic, and capillary forces, and those parts whose forces depend on conditions such as velocity and acceleration in addition to relative positions. Unlike the forces of the first class, those of the second class, which include frictional, magnetic, perhaps optical, and above all electrodynamic forces, do not necessarily obey the law of the conservation of "living force." Since the law relates kinetic and potential energy, and since for the second class of forces the potential energy is unknown, the problem of electrodynamic theory, Neumann concluded, is to determine the potential energy.

Neumann came to his new "principles" of electrodynamics after studying Weber's law of electric action and finding a potential for it, which he regarded as more fundamental than the force itself. (He was unaware that Weber had found a potential for his law in 1848.) Riemann's electrodynamic theory, published in 1867, showed Neumann how the electrodynamic force, a force of the second class, could be derived from the potential of the electrostatic force, a force of the first class, by assuming that the potential is propagated with finite velocity. To his surprise, he found that the usual electrostatic, or Newtonian, potential together with Riemann's progressive propagation leads to the expression for the potential he had already discovered for Weber's law. Neumann regarded as the major innovation of his theory,

46. Salié, "Carl Neumann," 15.
47. Carl Neumann, *Der gegenwärtige Standpunct der mathematischen Physik* (Tübingen, 1865), 4–5, 18–19, 29–32.
48. Hölder, "Carl Neumann," 156, 168.
49. Carl Neumann, "Die Principien der Elektrodynamik" (1868), *Math. Ann.* 17 (1880): 400–434.

as it was of Riemann's, the progressive nature of the moving electrical impulse, as determined by the potential.[50]

Neumann put these several ideas together: by assuming that the potential between a pair of electrical points in relative motion propagates with the constant velocity c and that the emitted potential has the Newtonian form mm_1/r, he derived as the "effective" received potential the potential for Weber's law:

$$\frac{mm_1}{r}\left[1 + \frac{1}{cc}\left(\frac{dr}{dt}\right)^2 \right].$$

Declaring that Hamilton's variation principle is "unconditionally valid," and extending its application from dynamics to electrodynamics and from potentials of forces of the first class to potentials of forces of the second, Neumann derived from the variation of the action integral the known laws of electric attraction and induction and, at the same time, a form of the principle of the conservation of living force that embraces electrodynamics.[51]

Responses to Neumann's theory dealt, predictably, with his unorthodox use of dynamical principles and his propagated potential. The author of a report on electrical theories for the British Association was puzzled by Neumann's concept of energy, which was of a kind "quite different from any that we have experience of," being neither potential nor kinetic.[52] With regard to the finite propagation of the potential, Weber wrote to Neumann that it "may be spoken of only under the assumption of a *higher mechanics* (as, e.g., of the propagation of waves in air only on the grounds of the mechanics of air)." Weber had in mind a possible physical propagation through a medium. In reply, Neumann said that he preferred to view temporally separated actions as "primary (not further explicable)" rather than as "secondary (referred back to simpler processes)."[53] This was in keeping with Neumann's understanding of physical explanation: to "explain" is to reduce phenomena to the "fewest possible fundamental ideas," which are themselves inexplicable, or "incomprehensible."[54]

Clausius wrote to Neumann that he agreed that "a definitive unification of the electrodynamic and electrostatic laws would belong to the greatest advances that have been made in physics in a long time."[55] But the way Neumann tried to realize this objective did not satisfy Clausius, who regarded the theory as mathematically

50. Neumann, "Die Principien der Elektrodynamik," 402.

51. Neumann, "Die Principien der Elektrodynamik," 405, 420. At the time, Neumann was unaware of Riemann's earlier but still unpublished derivation in his Göttingen lectures of the electric force from an electrodynamic potential through the variation principle. Neumann's note added in 1880 at the end of the 1868 paper, p. 434.

52. J. J. Thomson, "Report on Electrical Theories," *Report of the Fifty-Fifth Meeting of the British Association for the Advancement of Science* (London, 1886), 97–155, on 122–23.

53. Carl Neumann quoted Weber's letter to him in the postscript to his 1868 paper, "Die Principien der Elektrodynamik," 433–34

54. Carl Neumann, *Der gegenwärtige Standpunct*, 17.

55. Clausius to Carl Neumann, 1 Nov. 1869, Gustav Wiedemann Personalakte, Leipzig UA, Nr. 1061.

faulty. In defense of it, Neumann took pains to clear up Clausius's misunderstanding of the nature of the propagation. Neumann supposed that because of his historical reference to Riemann's theory, Clausius thought he had in mind a propagation similar to that of light.[56] He realized now that he had expressed himself too pictorially; he was not thinking so much of a "propagation" of something as of a "transmission" of a "command" between electrical bodies requiring time. To clarify his meaning, Neumann spelled out the differences between light and the electrical potential of his theory: light is independent of the emitting body, whereas the potential depends on the relative positions of emitting and receiving bodies; light intensity falls off with distance, whereas the potential is unchanged; light is only partially absorbed when it falls on a body, whereas the potential is completely absorbed. Light and Neumann's potential have only one similarity: both are characterized by a great, constant velocity, but even this similarity is not exact, since the two velocities are not identical. In all of this, Neumann stressed the superficiality of the analogy between electrodynamics and optics.[57] The concepts and principles of his electrodynamics were not close enough to those of optics to suggest to Neumann a connection between these two parts of physics.[58]

Neumann was not interested in the physical properties of a medium that might explain the finite velocity of electric actions; rather he was interested in, for example, the parallel ways that space and time enter the mathematical formulation of the potential. This abstract work on electrodynamic theory resembled certain mathematical work in mechanics concerned with deciding the principles underlying the established laws. The resemblance extended to the substance of the theory as well: so close, in fact, were the concepts of Neumann's dynamics of electrical points to those of the dynamics of material points that he neglected to distinguish between electrical and ponderable masses, a slip he corrected in his next publication.[59] Neumann showed that like mechanical theory, electrodynamic theory could be developed from Hamilton's variation principle.[60] At the same time he found—as Weber, Riemann, Clausius, and other authors of contending theories found—that the concepts and principles of mechanics had to be given extended meanings in electrodynamics. In electrodynamics in the second half of the nineteenth century, as in mechanics earlier, the development of mathematical methods of physics went hand in hand with the analysis of the physical foundations of the subject.

Neumann believed in a harmony between the intellect and the external world, which made mathematics, astronomy, physics, mineralogy, and chemistry appear to him as parts of a "single great whole." To his regret these sciences had increasingly

56. Carl Neumann, "Notizen zu einer kürzlich erschienenen Schrift über die Principien der Elektrodynamik," Math. Ann. 1 (1869): 317–24, on 324.

57. Sommerfeld and Reiff, "Standpunkt der Fernwirkung. Elementargesetze," 51–52.

58. Neumann was to hold reservations about Maxwell's theory, which joined optics to electrodynamics. At best he saw Maxwell's equations as a "provisional foundation (an intermediate step)." Letter to Arnold Sommerfeld, 30 May 1903, Sommerfeld Papers, Ms. Coll., DM.

59. Neumann, "Notizen," 318.

60. Neumann said that he was directed to the variation method of his electrodynamic theory by his earlier work on the mechanical theory of elasticity. Neumann to Sommerfeld, 30 May 1903.

grown apart in the course of the nineteenth century;[61] Jacobi, Dirichlet, and Riemann had worked equally in mathematics and physics, but after them, Neumann believed, one came to expect mathematics only from mathematicians and physics only from physicists.[62] The result was the impoverishment of both. He regarded mathematics as a subject in need of constant nourishment from mechanics and the natural sciences. To doubt this, he thought, would be presumptuous and harmful to further progress all around.[63]

The grounds for Neumann's regret over advancing specialization in mathematics and physics were to remain. There would be other mathematicians of Neumann's outlook, but never very many. Hermann Minkowski, Marcel Grossmann, and David Hilbert were among the later mathematicians, whom we will meet, who provided mathematical methods for physics and who worked with them on physical questions. Mathematicians continued to be of help to physicists as the needs of physical theory came to include bodies of mathematical knowledge not contained in Riemann's original manual on the partial differential equations of physics. But the position of intermediary between mathematics and physics, as Riemann was seen to hold, was increasingly taken over by a new kind of specialist, the theoretical physicist. The theoretical physicist might consult or even collaborate with a mathematician, but he always worked as a physicist rather than as a mathematician. As a physicist, he was knowledgeable in mathematics, and although he did not do original research in mathematics, he was capable of adapting new mathematics to physical uses and, in the process, of offering mathematicians new mathematical opportunities.

In this chapter we have discussed the work by mathematicians on potential theory or, as it was sometimes called, the "theory of attraction," and on the partial differential equations of physics. Both became frequent subjects of special lecture courses at German universities, taught occasionally by physicists but usually by mathematicians. The number of special courses does not adequately represent the amount of instruction offered in these two subjects, since they were incorporated into lectures on all parts of theoretical physics.[64]

61. Carl Neumann, "Worte zum Gedächtniss an Wilhelm Hankel," Verh. sächs. Ges. Wiss. 51 (1899): lxii–lxvi, on lxiv.

62. Salié, "Carl Neumann," 18.

63. Heinrich Liebmann, "Zur Erinnerung an Carl Neumann," Jahresber. d. Deutsch. Math.-Vereinigung 36 (1927): 174–78, on 175.

64. During the academic year 1886–87, for example, potential theory was announced as the subject of special courses at ten German universities and partial differential equations of physics at six of them. The number of special courses gradually fell off; for example, eight special courses in potential theory were announced in 1900–1901, two in 1913–14. Deutscher Universitäts-Kalender.

8

Developments in Switzerland and Austria Bearing on German Physics

Switzerland enters our study of the development of physics in Germany during this period through the establishment of a new physics position. The position, a professorship for mathematical physics at the new Zurich Polytechnic, was first filled by Germany's outstanding young theoretical physicist, Clausius. At Zurich, Clausius taught mathematical physics together with technical physics for many years, while at the same time he did much of his most important research in theoretical physics. After Clausius, the position continued to be held by outstanding theoretical physicists from Germany.

Austria enters our study here for a different reason: its universities produced a theoretical physicist for Germany, Ludwig Boltzmann. Before the end of the century, Boltzmann would be called to three of the most important ordinary professorships for theoretical physics at German universities, and he would, in fact, occupy two of them.

Physics for a New Polytechnic in Switzerland

In 1854 the community of German scientists was stirred by the news that the Swiss federal government was establishing a technical school in Zurich. The new school advertised over 40 positions in European daily papers, and it received 189 applications within three months, over half of them from Germany.[1] Two of the positions were intended for physics, one for "general" physics and one for technical physics. The school did not pin itself down to a position for "mathematical physics," though in its description of the positions it included the subject among the "mathematical-

1. Gottfried Guggenbühl, "Geschichte der Eidgenössischen Technischen Hochschule in Zürich," in *Eidgenössische Technische Hochschule 1855–1955* (Zurich: Buchverlag der Neuen Zürcher Zeitung, 1955), 3–260, on 68. *100 Jahre Eidgenössische Technische Hochschule. Sonderheft der Schweizerischen Hochschulzeitung* 28 (1955): 46.

physical" subjects ranging from "pure mathematics" to "higher engineering,"[2]

The planners of the new school, influenced especially by J. W. von Deschwanden, the rector of the Zurich industrial school who would become the first director of the Zurich Polytechnic, took as their model not the French technical schools but the German, particularly the polytechnics at Karlsruhe and Stuttgart, which Deschwanden knew well. The main effect on the Zurich Polytechnic of the planners' preference for the German model was that it became a collection of *Fachabtheilungen*, or specialized departments, devoted to professional education for the different branches of engineering, for architecture, and for secondary education in science and mathematics. The engineering and architecture departments of the polytechnic developed programs that consisted largely of required courses, which took up thirty to forty hours of the student's time each week.[3] One of the required courses was technical physics, initially planned for the first year. The course in general physics was left to the education department, which at first had no specific requirements.[4]

Since the physicists of the polytechnic were to share the collection of instruments and the rooms of the physics professor at the Zurich Kantonsschule, a secondary school, until the polytechnic had acquired or erected its institutes, the Swiss education council wisely appointed the current physics professor at the Kantonsschule, Albrecht Mousson, as the first professor for general or experimental physics at the polytechnic.[5] For the professorship of technical physics, they first wanted Rudolph Kohlrausch, who had taught at a technical school in Kassel before becoming extraordinary professor of physics at Marburg University. In early 1855, when Kohlrausch was offered the Zurich job, he had just completed a joint investigation with Weber; with Kohlrausch, Weber wrote in support of his candidacy, the polytechnic would acquire "an important scientific talent in the full development of his powers," guaranteeing the school "a higher scientific importance right from the beginning." Weber added that it would be difficult to find a person better suited for the position. The planners of the polytechnic, to their disappointment, soon discovered that Weber was right: for when Kohlrausch turned them down out of love for "physics without purpose," they were forced, for lack of another candidate like Kohlrausch, to change their plans.[6]

In his refusal to President Kern of the Swiss education council, Kohlrausch criticized the planned physics curriculum for engineering students. He pointed out

2. Heinrich Buff to an unnamed Swiss colleague, 26 Oct. 1854; B. Studer to President of the Swiss Education Council Kern, 10 Dec. 1854; W. Sartorius von Waltershausen to an unnamed Swiss colleague, 22 Dec. 1854; Rudolph Kohlrausch to Kern, 23 Jan. 1855; A Schweiz. Sch., Zurich.

3. Guggenbühl, "Zürich," 19, 35. Studer to Kern, 12 June 1855, A Schweiz. Sch., Zurich.

4. Kohlrausch to Kern, 12 Feb. 1855, A Schweiz. Sch., Zurich. A. Frey-Wyssling and Elsi Häusermann, *Geschichte der Abteilung für Naturwissenschaften an der Eidgenössischen Technischen Hochschule in Zürich 1855–1955* ([Zurich], 1958), 8.

5. Albrecht Mousson to (presumably) Kern, 30 Aug. 1855; Kohlrausch to Kern, 23 Jan. 1855; "Auszug aus dem Protokoll der 112. Sizung des schweizerischen Bundesrathes" to "Schulrath der polytechnischen Schule, in Zürich," 24 Aug. 1855; A Schweiz. Sch., Zurich.

6. Kohlrausch to Kern, 23 Jan. and 12 Feb. 1855; Wilhelm Weber to Kern, 1 Jan. 1855; Studer to Kern, 30 May 1855; A Schweiz. Sch., Zurich.

that if the school intended to teach technical physics in the five technical departments in the first year of the program, students would not have a chance to take an elementary course in experimental physics first. The task of providing them with the "knowledge of the laws of nature" that technical physics presupposes would then naturally fall to the professor of technical physics, who would have to begin his course with basic physics. As a consequence, he would not have time to take up the "wave theory and with it a large part of optics" and, in general, any "deeper theoretical" subjects. If, on the other hand, the school intended to give students first an experimental physics course and only after that a technical physics course, Kohlrausch advised President Kern, it should not look for a pure physicist like himself but for someone who was at the same time a "theoretically thoroughly trained physicist," who would be a match for his knowledgeable students and a physicist with an inner drive toward the application of physics. The polytechnic did not want a "physicist whose thoughts prefer to rummage in hypotheses," since "some purely theoretical work, begun on the side," might well "occupy his mind so much that his office becomes a burden to him." To assure the interests of technical physics, they should hire a scientifically trained specialist in it.[7]

Kohlrausch's friend Weber, who was less inclined to insist on a strict correspondence between teaching and research, only required a proper theoretical basis for a physicist's work in physics: "Physics forms a bond and a point of unification for mathematical and exact experimental research, the two main levers of the polytechnic sciences, to which it thus gives a center," and "in this connection the treatment of physics from the point of view of *mathematical physics and higher mechanics* is of special importance for the higher scientific position of a polytechnic school."[8] Weber believed that while Kohlrausch would do fine in technical physics, the practical direction of the polytechnic would not keep him from the "pursuit of new investigations in which the theoretical interest dominates."[9] That technical physics might suffer under these circumstances did not occur to Weber. ("Theoretical," as used by Kohlrausch and Weber in this discussion, was opposed to "technical," or "applied." The experimental research that Kohlrausch did was to establish basic physical theories, and in this sense the closely associated experimental and theoretical research was, in their view and terminology, all "theoretical.")

The Zurich planners now decided to substitute mathematical physics for technical physics as the subject of the second physics professorship, influenced perhaps by Weber and, no doubt, by the physics curriculum at the Karlsruhe Polytechnic, their model. Only two years before, in 1853, the professor of physics at Karlsruhe, Wilhelm Eisenlohr, had introduced mathematical physics there. He supplemented the regular four-hour lecture course on experimental physics with two new related courses: a three-hour course on the mathematical treatment of physics problems for advanced students (taught in the winter), and a three- to four-hour course of exercises in physics (taught in the summer), which he regarded as essential for a full

7. Kohlrausch to Kern, 12 Feb. 1855.
8. Weber to Kern, 1 Jan. 1855.
9. Weber to Kern, 9 May 1855, A Schweiz. Sch., Zurich.

understanding of the first course. In the exercises, students were taught to measure length, time, weight, and quantities from all parts of physics such as wavelengths, heat conductivities, coefficients of expansion, and magnetic forces according to absolute measures; they were also taught to calibrate instruments, to use telescopes, microscopes, and most other standard optical instruments, and to make thermometers and artificial magnets. They were, in short, taught measuring physics, which was part of the responsibility of a teacher of mathematical physics.[10]

There was another, perhaps decisive, inducement for the Zurich Polytechnic to consider a mathematical rather than a technical physicist: as it happened, an outstanding mathematical physicist, Clausius, was willing to take the job. When Weber pointed out that the mathematical physics would be important for the scientific standing of the polytechnic, he implied that it should be represented by a separate physics professorship, for he added Clausius to the planners' list of candidates. Weber said of Clausius that "next to Neumann in Königsberg and Kirchhoff in Heidelberg," he had "excelled in this direction [mathematical physics], especially with his papers on heat theory." Poggendorff thought Clausius the "most suitable" for them, too, "since you are looking for a candidate especially for mathematical physics," and Clausius had "turned toward the mathematical direction." He added that "if by technical physics you mean machine theory and such, I believe that you can very well assign it to Clausius." Most important for the Zurich planners, Clausius had already indicated to Poggendorff his willingness to go to Zurich under the right conditions.[11]

After the planners of the polytechnic had settled on Clausius as the second physics professor, Mousson negotiated with him on the division of their teaching duties. Mousson proposed to teach technical physics in the five technical departments and experimental physics in the department of education and to supervise the physical apparatus; he suggested that Clausius teach mathematical physics and physical geography and direct the physical seminar. Clausius agreed, unaware that it left him with nothing to teach. Mathematical physics was not a requirement for any of the departments, and with the demands that the required subjects made on the technical students, it was unlikely that many would have time for an extra course. It was the same for physical geography, which Deschwanden had not found time for in the schedule of courses. And the physical seminar had not yet been decided on. One of the planners noted that Clausius's agreement had perhaps been more "theoretical" than "practical." "Swiss honesty" required that Clausius be told that Mousson would be getting the lion's share of student fees and that Clausius would be like an "extraordinary [professor] lecturing to empty benches beside the main professor." Dissatisfied, Clausius would leave Zurich again, the planner warned, and indeed if the subject were to be divided as Mousson proposed, the polytechnic could do without the second physics professorship altogether.[12]

10. Lehmann, "Karlsruhe," 245–46.
11. Weber to Kern, 1 Jan. 1855; Poggendorff to Brunner, 18 May 1855; A Schweiz. Sch., Zurich.
12. Studer to Kern, 12 June 1855. Mousson's motives were honorable; he always said that he was taking over technical physics only as a favor to the Swiss Education Council.

To give Clausius something to do and to ensure his equality with Mousson and prevent conflict between them, Clausius was appointed "professor of physics . . . preferably for mathematical and technical physics and director of the physical exercises."[13] In spite of the wording of the appointment, the planners considered technical physics to be Clausius's main subject and mathematical physics a subsidiary one. His technical students were now expected to be prepared for "a physics with technical applications" (rather than "specialized technology"), since they were expected to have had a general physics course before entering the polytechnic. In Clausius's course on technical physics, the planners thought, he could "stimulate the young people to enter more especially into individual parts of physics, that is, to take courses on mathematical physics and physical work."[14] Clausius's appointment also included the provision that he might have to teach experimental physics alternately with technical physics. What German physicists such as Weber and Poggendorff or the Göttingen scientist W. Sartorius von Waltershausen had seen as a chance for their best mathematical physicists (Waltershausen had proposed Riemann, Richard Dedekind, and Ernst Schering for mathematical physics as well as mathematics[15]) turned out to be only an afterthought; the physics appointments were traditional. Berlin tried to hold Clausius by offering him a tenured position much like the untenured one at Zurich, a professorship at the Berlin trade school, but it was too late. Clausius had already accepted in Zurich.[16]

In March 1857 Clausius was also appointed ordinary professor in the philosophical faculty of Zurich University. He acquired with this position no new duties and no additional income, for the university students attended his lectures at the polytechnic.[17]

In the first years after the opening of the polytechnic in the fall of 1855, physics instruction took the following form: Mousson and Clausius both gave a main one-year course, Mousson the basic one on experimental physics to be taken in the students' first year (but not required of all), Clausius the course on technical physics required of the technical students and to be taken in their second year after suitable preparation. In addition, Clausius offered specialized lecture courses on mathematical physics.

Mousson's lectures took up six hours per week; in addition, the regular students and some of the "large number" of auditors attended a *Repetitorium*, or review session. Mousson divided up his subject so that he treated "mechanical physics," acoustics, and heat theory in the winter semester and the theories of light and of magnetism and electricity in the summer, "everything on an experimental basis, but not without the use of elementary mathematics."[18]

13. "Auszug aus dem Protokoll," 24 Aug. 1855.
14. Studer to Kern, 12 June 1855.
15. Sartorius von Waltershausen to an unnamed Swiss colleague, 22 Dec. 1854.
16. Clausius to Swiss Education Council, 27 Nov. 1857, A Schweiz. Sch., Zurich.
17. Letter of appointment by the Directors of Education of the Canton of Zurich, 2 Mar. 1857, Clausius file, STA K Zurich, U. 110b. 1, Nr. 14.
18. Mousson, "Bericht über das Fach der Experimental-Physik 1856–57," dated 27 Nov. 1857 (the date on the document reads 27 Nov. 1854, which can only be an error), A Schweiz. Sch., Zurich.

Clausius taught technical physics in four-hour courses. His students at first were the second-year students of the five technical departments—the school of architecture, the engineering school, the mechanical-technical school, the chemical-technical school, and the school of forestry—plus some candidates for secondary school teaching and a few medical students from the university, who came as auditors. He gave lectures "combined with the necessary experiments," during which he did not ask the students any questions. He also spent some of his time going over the material with his students: at first he asked them, one or a few each time, to give a summary of the previous lecture at the beginning of each class; later he set aside a whole hour for going over the material again after completing a section of his subject. He took up those parts of physics most completely that found application in practice, and he left out parts that were unimportant for applications. He left out, for example, all of acoustics and parts of optics such as polarization in crystals and diffraction, but he treated the parts of optics needed to understand optical instruments. Stressing especially the theory of steam, he covered the theory of heat "in all its extensions" because of "its many applications." (His student Carl Linde, later one of the first to make important applications of the second law of heat theory, remembered Clausius as devoting more time to heat theory than to any other part of physics.) He also covered all parts of electricity and magnetism—machine electricity, galvanic electricity, magnetism, and electromagnetism—(though not in as much detail as heat) because if he had treated only parts of it, students could not have understood it. He said he spent extra time on the application of these subjects, especially on "galvanoplastics" and electric telegraphy.[19]

As at a university, at the polytechnic Clausius was free to devote his courses on mathematical physics to whatever special subjects he chose; he chose to emphasize the methods of mathematical physics. In 1856–57, for example, he offered "Introduction to Mathematical Physics and Theory of Elasticity" in the winter semester and "Magnetism and Electricity Treated Mathematically" the following summer. Most of the first course, he reported, consisted of a connected treatment of the parts of analytical mechanics used in mathematical physics, concluding with the theoretical derivation of the laws of elasticity and of the most important phenomena based on those laws, "mainly according to Cauchy's and Poisson's manner of treating them." In the second course, he treated the theory of the potential function, "which is extensively used in magnetism and electricity," according to Laplace, Green, and Gauss. He followed that with a discussion of machine electricity, galvanic currents, and, as far as time permitted, electrodynamics.[20] In the following year, Clausius devoted the first semester to acoustics and optics, "in which the different phenomena of sound and light such as reflection, refraction, interference, polarization, and double refraction are derived from the fundamental principles of the wave theory." In the summer semester, he started all over again, this time combining analytical

19. Clausius, "Bericht über den Unterricht in der technischen Physik, . . . während des Schuljahres 1855/56," 6 Nov. 1856, A Schweiz. Sch., Zurich. Grete Ronge, "Die Züricher Jahre des Physikers Rudolf Clausius," Gesnerus 12 (1955): 73–108, on 82.
20. Clausius, "Beitrag zum Jahresberichte der 6ten Abtheilung über das Schuljahr 1856/7, in Bezug auf die mathematische Physik," 18 Nov. 1857, A Schweiz. Sch., Zurich.

mechanics with potential theory in one course, "Introduction to Mathematical Physics and Potential Theory," which he intended as preparation for his lectures on electrodynamics and magnetism.[21] Each time, he reported, he had enthusiastic students, though not many, "as is in the nature of the case."[22] His most industrious students were from the education department, but he also drew a few as auditors from Zurich University.

Whether he discussed technical or theoretical physics, lecture material or research, Clausius's orientation was thoroughly scientific. Already in his early years in Berlin, as Helmholtz later reported, Clausius impressed him and others in their circle "with the acuteness of his mathematical thinking and with his knowledge" (although "locked" into his "own world of thoughts," he was not particularly communicative). One of his students in technical physics at the Zurich Polytechnic echoed Helmholtz: he remembered Clausius as deep and also as quiet and rather dry.[23]

At the Zurich Polytechnic it soon developed that a scientific emphasis was not wanted. Mousson's experimental physics course was demoted to preparatory status; "limited to the simplest physical laws and avoiding everything that has scientific significance, [it] would be about on the level of a good gymnasium or better industrial school [course]." Delicate experiments would be impossible, for as Mousson sarcastically explained, "if they are not to be merely games, [they] demand at once entry into theory, which one wants to prevent from penetrating our technical schools." He cautioned the faculty that unless they firmly "entered the lists" for the scientific side of their institution, it would be able to meet neither the "growing demands of modern technology nor the standpoint of other institutions of equal rank."[24]

21. Clausius, "Beitrag zum Jahresberichte der VIten Abtheilung über das Schuljahr 1857/58 in Bezug auf die mathematische Physik," 8 Dec. 1858, A Schweiz. Sch., Zurich.

22. Clausius, "Beitrag," 18 Nov. 1857. The proposed physical seminar apparently could not be realized with the space and means available to Clausius during the early years. He and Mousson complained repeatedly that they lacked space for student exercises.

In 1857 the Swiss physicist Heinrich Wild, one of Franz Neumann's students, proposed to the Swiss education authorities to meet what he evidently saw as an unrecognized need in physics instruction at the Zurich Polytechnic. He asked to be allowed to become lecturer of physics there to teach "selected chapters of mathematical physics," to give lectures on physical chemistry, and to set up "physical exercises with accompanying measuring observations after the model of Neumann's and Kirchhoff's seminars." Wild to President Kappeler, 1 Dec. 1857; Wild's vita, 1 Dec. 1857.

Asked to evaluate Wild's publications, Clausius described Wild's photometer and polarimeter as a valuable invention. Clausius also praised the "rigorous mathematical treatment and the execution of some difficult calculations" in Wild's other work, though it "did not bring any essentially new results." Clausius found Wild "completely qualified" to become Privatdocent, but he did not comment on Wild's proposed courses, which must have struck him as presumptuous and revealing of Wild's ignorance of the difficult circumstances at the polytechnic. Clausius to Kappeler, 20 Dec. 1857. Wild left after three semesters, and the next Privatdocent of physics was not admitted until after the new institute was completed.

Mousson's proposals for physics in 1867 again include his and Clausius's intentions of having a seminar: he included for the third year of the program of the sixth department "above all: physical exercises or physical seminar." It was to be one of the main responsibilities of the second, "higher," physics professor, that is, of Clausius's successor. Mousson to President of the Swiss Education Council, 14 Sept. 1867. All documents in A Schweiz. Sch., Zurich.

23. Helmholtz, "Clausius," 2. Ronge, "Clausius," 82.

24. Mousson to Director of the Polytechnic, 28 June 1860, A Schweiz. Sch., Zurich.

The problem with the technical physics course that Kohlrausch had predicted arose even earlier. The course was designed to provide the polytechnic students with a scientific foundation for their technical professions, and Clausius expected them to enter the course with a knowledge of the "main theories of elementary physics, which are taught in the first course in general experimental physics"; he also expected them to be "familiar with mathematics to the extent that they can follow the calculations, which cannot always be carried out without the use of the differential and integral calculus."[25] He found that the chemistry students in particular were not ready for his course. In 1857, he suggested changes in the requirements, and on the basis of them it was proposed that chemistry and forestry students be required from then on to take Mousson's experimental physics course instead of technical physics.[26] In 1860, students in the mechanical-technical section asked to be excused from technical physics (and from Dedekind's course on the calculus) and to be allowed to substitute a practical course such as road and waterway construction.[27] Such requests repeatedly led the faculty and school administration—who had little understanding of what the physicists were aiming at—to seek a more "useful" program for physics. When Clausius left the Zurich Polytechnic in 1867, Mousson proposed a revision of the physics program to the Swiss education council; based on Mousson's "long years of experience," the program included technical physics as a two-hour course "only required for a very few."[28]

Clausius as Theoretical Physicist at Zurich

Technical physics and theoretical physics came together in Clausius's work not only in his teaching but also in his research. He often called attention to the applications of the parts of physics he was working on theoretically; for example, in a research paper in 1852 he wrote with regard to the mechanical equivalent of an electric discharge: "All of these phenomena in themselves are already of great interest, which is still greatly increased by the practical applications that one has made of them or possibly can make; but in addition these very effects are capable of a rigorously mathematicaly treatment and thus seem especially suited for an investigation of their inner connection among themselves and with the acting cause."[29] The subjects that Clausius found most important for practical applications, which he accordingly emphasized in his course on technical physics, are the subjects he treated in his research: machine electricity (by which he meant electricity producing mechanical action), electrolysis, and, above all, heat theory.

Soon after moving to Zurich, Clausius gave an academic address on the nature

25. Clausius to Swiss Education Council, 10 June 1857, A Schweiz. Sch., Zurich.

26. "Auszug aus dem Protokoll der Special-Conferenz der Abtheilung IV des schweizerischen Polytechnikums. X. Sitzung 24 Juni 1857," 26 June 1857; "Bemerkungen zum Programm 1857/58," addressed to the President of the Swiss Education Council, no author or date given; A Schweiz. Sch., Zurich.

27. Gustav Zeuner to Director of the Polytechnic, 18 Apr. 1860, A Schweiz. Sch., Zurich.

28. Director Bolley to President of the Swiss Education Council, 17 June [?] 1860, A Schweiz. Sch., Zurich. Mousson to President of the Swiss Education Council, 14 Sept. 1867, A Schweiz. Sch., Zurich.

29. Rudolph Clausius, "Ueber das mechanische Aequivalent einer elektrischen Entladung und die dabei stattfindende Erwärmung des Leitungsdrahtes," Ann. 86 (1852): 337–75, on 337.

of heat, in which he expressed his understanding of the great conception of nature to which he had dedicated himself and of which he had become a principal developer. Heat—both radiant heat and heat in bodies—is a form of the motion of particles, Clausius explained. When the ponderable molecules of a body vibrate, they set up progressive waves in the finely particulate ether, and when these waves strike another body, they in turn set up vibrations in its ponderable molecules; the moving molecules, which all bodies are constituted of, fill the universe with ethereal vibrations proceeding in all directions. The unity of the phenomena of nature extends even further: waves in heat radiation are essentially the same as light waves, the only difference being that the eye can perceive the latter but not the former. Heat, moreover, is the "true moving principle," Clausius explained, without which all bodies would be brought to an equilibrium state by mutual forces, and the earth would become dead and unchangeable. Wherever there is motion or life, there is heat; heat drives steam engines, causes the weather, and in general runs the "great machine of nature."[30] That is the great and universal meaning of heat, of compelling interest to both the physicist who determines its laws and the engineer who applies them.

At Zurich, Clausius turned to an aspect of the theory of heat that he had not dealt with in his earlier researches, though he had long thought about it: the molecular motions constituting heat. In his 1850 paper laying the foundations for the mechanical theory of heat, Clausius had not discussed molecular motions because he wanted to keep the results that depend on general principles separate from those that depend on molecular assumptions. In 1857, however, he took up the subject in print, prompted by a paper published the year before by August Krönig, which advanced molecular ideas similar to, if somewhat simpler than, his own.[31]

Clausius shared Krönig's view that gas molecules do not vibrate about equilibrium positions but move uniformly in straight lines until they collide with other molecules or with the walls of their container. Clausius introduced three assumptions about molecules and their forces and motions, which together define an ideal gas: molecules are so small that the volume they occupy can be ignored; the duration of a collision is small compared with the time between collisions; and the attractive forces between molecules are negligible. To develop the mathematical theory in accordance with these assumptions, Clausius ascribed a single, mean velocity u to all of the molecules of a contained gas, although he recognized that different molecules probably have different velocities. By molecular-mechanical reasoning, he derived the basic equation of the theory, the ideal gas law:

30. Rudolph Clausius, *Uber das Wesen der Wärme, verglichen mit Licht und Schall* (Zurich, 1857). Quotations on 29, 31.

31. Rudolph Clausius, "Ueber die Art der Bewegung, welche wir Wärme nennen," *Ann.* 100 (1857): 353–80. This and later writings by Clausius on the kinetic theory are discussed in Stephen G. Brush, *The Kind of Motion We Call Heat: A History of the Kinetic Theory of Gases in the 19th Century*, vol. 1, *Physics and the Atomists* (Amsterdam and New York: North-Holland, 1976), 168–82; Edward E. Daub, "Rudolf Clausius and the Nineteenth Century Theory of Heat" (Ph. D. diss., University of Wisconsin-Madison, 1966), and "Atomism and Thermodynamics," *Isis* 58 (1967): 293–303; Elizabeth Wolfe Garber, "Maxwell, Clausius and Gibbs: Aspects of the Development of Kinetic Theory and Thermodynamics" (Ph.D. diss., Case Institute of Technology, 1966), and "Clausius and Maxwell's Kinetic Theory of Gases," *HSPS* 2 (1970): 299–319; and Klein, "Gibbs on Clausius."

$$p = \frac{nmu^2}{3v},$$

where p is the pressure of the gas, v is the volume, n is the total number of molecules, and m is the mass of an individual molecule. Clausius did not know either of the key molecular quantities, n and m, but he knew their product, the total mass of the gas, which enabled him to calculate the mean velocities of different gases at normal atmospheric conditions.

By this theory, Clausius strengthened the mechanical connectedness of the parts of physics: he derived the ideal gas law along with other results by analyzing the collisions of a large number of molecules according to the laws of mechanics (at the same time, by speaking of mean values, circumventing the impossible task of analyzing the motion of each molecule individually). Clausius argued that his molecular-mechanical reasoning could even yield some limited knowledge of the invisible molecular world itself; for example, knowledge of the need to regard molecules as complex bodies and not as point-masses or simple elastic spheres. Although in his mathematical theory Clausius used only the translational motion of molecules, he recognized other modes of motion, and he closed the paper by showing that translational living force does not account for all of the heat in a gas. The proportion of translational living force to total living force is a function of the specific heats of the gas at constant volume and pressure, and specific heat values show, Clausius argued, that in the more complex gases, more of the total living force must be accounted for by internal molecular rotations and vibrations. For Clausius, molecules are real physical bodies, and his study of them in 1857 contributed to what would become a distinct branch of physics, the kinetic theory of gases.

In the following year, in a sequel publication, Clausius introduced his most original contribution to the molecular theory of gases: the concept of "mean free path," which, Maxwell said, opened up a "new field of mathematical physics."[32] Clausius published it in response to recent criticisms of molecular theories, of his own theory as well as of Joule's and Krönig's. In particular, Clausius took seriously the question C. H. D. Buys-Ballot posed: if molecules move in straight lines at great velocities, as Clausius had concluded, then different gases in contact with one another ought to mix quickly; for example, why does tobacco smoke hang in layers, and why does it take minutes to detect the odor of chlorine when it is released across the room? In his answer, Clausius argued on probabilistic grounds that the path a molecule traverses between collisions is short compared with the dimensions of a room. To begin with, he asked what the probability is that a molecule will move a distance x through a gas, say, the air in a room, without entering the sphere of action of another molecule. By assuming the molecules of the gas to be at rest and to be distributed with uniform density, he showed that the probability is $e^{-\alpha x}$, where α is a constant to be determined. If a number of free molecules are projected at the gas, a certain fraction will collide with the first layer of fixed molecules, another fraction with the second layer, and so on. If each of these fractions is mul-

32. Quoted in Daub, "Rudolf Clausius," 127.

tiplied by the corresponding path length and if the sum of their products is divided by the total number of free molecules, the result is the "mean free path" between collisions; Clausius showed this to be $l' = 1/\alpha = \lambda^3/\pi\rho^2$, where λ is the mean separation between neighboring molecules, and ρ is the radius of the sphere of repulsive action of molecules. (If the fixed molecules in this example are allowed to move with a common velocity, the path, denoted by l, is reduced by a factor of $3/4$.) Since neither λ nor ρ was known, Clausius supposed as a best guess that the volume of the gas is a thousand times greater than the volume of all of the spheres of action, in which case, $l = 61\lambda$. All physical and chemical evidence pointed to an extremely small value for α, so that the mean free paths of molecules must be small, too, and the probability that a molecule will travel far beyond its mean free path is small. This result shows why, Clausius concluded, a cloud of smoke in a room retains its shape for a long time and why the molecular theory of gases is credible.[33]

The suggestion of a statistical method in Clausius's analysis of molecular collisions was taken up by Maxwell, and the two entered into a critical exchange, in the course of which Clausius used the mean free path to give an early rigorous treatment of the conduction of heat in gases.[34] Maxwell's derivation of his famous law that statistically distributes velocities of all values among the molecules of a gas drew objections from Clausius. Only once, in 1874, did Clausius use Maxwell's distribution law, and he seems to have rejected it in the end. Clausius accepted the idea of the disorder of molecular motions, and he recognized the error in likening molecular motions to ordered motions, such as those resulting from central collisions in a line of elastic spheres. But unlike Maxwell (and Boltzmann), he never fully valued the statistical approach, and he relied on analytical mechanics together with molecular assumptions in his continuing work on the mechanical theory of heat. He preferred to study order, not disorder. From 1862 on, he worked toward a molecular-mechanical interpretation of "entropy," the term he introduced in 1865 for the quantity entering the second law, and the related, if now forgotten, concept of "disgregation."[35]

In 1864 Clausius republished a collection of his papers on the mechanical theory of heat, entitled *Abhandlungen über die mechanische Wäremetheorie*. He had been urged to do this because interest in the theory had spread beyond the readers of the physics journals, specifically of the *Annalen*, where almost all of his papers had appeared. Because, as he said, his papers on the theory had "contributed essentially to its foundation and development," the collection served as an early, thorough intro-

33. Rudolph Clausius, "Ueber die mittlere Länge der Wege, welche bei der Molecularbewegung gasförmiger Körper von den einzelnen Molecülen zurückgelegt werden; nebst einigen anderen Bemerkungen über die mechanische Wärmetheorie," *Ann.* 105 (1858): 239–58.

34. In general, the mean free path proved valuable for investigating, at least in first approximation, a variety of phenomena in gases, such as diffusion and viscosity. Daub, "Rudolf Clausius," 134–43. Garber, "Clausius and Maxwell's Kinetic Theory," 304–6. Stephen G. Brush, *Kinetic Theory*, vol. 1, *The Nature of Gases and of Heat* (Oxford and New York: Pergamon, 1965), 23–25.

35. Klein, "Gibbs on Clausius," 148. Daub, "Rudolf Clausius," 142–43. Garber, "Clausius and Maxwell's Kinetic Theory," 307–9, 317. Brush, *Motion We Call Heat* 1:181–82.

duction to it. He did not republish all of his papers on the subject but only those in which the basic theory was developed from "simple fundamental laws." He withheld other papers that made use of hypotheses about molecular motions or that dealt with electricity, reserving them for future volumes of an intended, connected, comprehensive treatise. Twelve years later he brought out a second edition, which was called for, he explained, because the mechanical theory of heat was now an "extensive and independent branch of science" that could not easily be learned from a collection of original papers. This time he completely reworked it to form a "connected whole," so that it was now a proper "textbook" for the subject.[36]

The mechanical theory of heat had "introduced new ideas into science" and with them "specific mathematical considerations." Clausius's work on the theory had been criticized, misunderstood as he believed, and in his book on the subject he elucidated unfamiliar mathematical points and notations that had given rise to "misunderstandings" of the concepts occurring.[37] He knew that to establish the mechanical theory of heat or any other theory of physics, it was essential to reach clarity on the methods of mathematical physics.

"A contribution to mathematical physics" was the subtitle Clausius gave to his book *Die Potentialfunction und das Potential*, which he published in 1859. The potential theory was then a principal subject of his lectures on mathematical physics. His book was intended to clarify useful distinctions such as that between the "potential function" and the "potential" and, in general, to make the potential theory more accessible to physicists. The theory had acquired great importance in physics, Clausius said, through the explanation of phenomena by the actions of elementary forces and the reduction of them to "simple mechanical principles." It had become an indispensable tool of mathematical physics; Clausius along with Neumann, Kirchhoff, Helmholtz, and others who worked theoretically made constant use of the potential throughout physics. In 1870 Clausius brought out a second edition of this book, which corrected certain features that gave it the appearance of a mathematical

36. Rudolph Clausius, *Abhandlungen über die mechanische Wärmetheorie. Erste Abtheilung* (Braunschweig, 1864). Quotations from "Vorrede," v–x. The second revised edition is entitled *Die mechanische Wärmetheorie*, vol. 1, *Entwickelung der Theorie, soweit sie sich aus den beiden Hauptsätzen ableiten lässt, nebst Anwendungen* (Braunschweig, 1876). Quotations from the preface to the English translation of the second edition by W. R. Browne, *The Mechanical Theory of Heat* (London, 1879), vii–viii.

37. In general, together with the extensive mathematical development of theories of electricity and heat in the middle of the century, a variety of mathematical notations appeared side by side in the literature. Clausius called attention to this in his book on heat theory: to distinguish between the left-hand term and the first term on the right in the equation $dz/dx = dz/dx + dz/dy \, dy/dx$, Clausius said, various authors had suggested $1/dx \cdot dz$ or $d(z)/dx$ or dz/dx. Clausius, *Abhandlungen*, 4. We note that a variety of notations were used in electrical theory too: Weber used dd for the second derivative instead of the more concise and later standard d^2; Franz Neumann used in addition to the then standard derivative and integrals signs, d and $\int$, the unfamiliar signs D and S; Kirchhoff used ∂ for a partial derivative, which came to be the standard notation, while there were others then who still wrote d. Wilhelm Weber, "Elektrodynamische Maassbestimmungen," *Ann.* 73 (1848): 193–240, for example, on 229. Franz Neumann, "Inducirte elektrische Ströme" (1845), for example, p. 10 in the reprint. Gustav Kirchhoff, "Ueber die Anwendbarkeit der Formeln für die Intensitäten der galvanischen Ströme in einem Systeme linearer Leiter auf Systeme, die zum Theil aus nicht linearen Leitern bestehen," *Ann.* 75 (1848): 189–205, for example, on 191.

memoir; it was now clearly a textbook for physicists, as he intended it to be.[38]

Misunderstandings inevitably arose in the course of research, as physicists groped for a correct understanding of the phenomena. Eventually physicists had to reach agreement on a range of matters such as terminology, definitions, units, standards, notations, and concepts, and as their research advanced, this follow-up work had to be done over and over again. The rapid developments in theoretical physics in the middle years of the nineteenth century invited Clausius's kind of reworking of them. The result was the systematic, useful, and up-to-date textbook.

Clausius as Practical Physicist at Zurich

Clausius's position at Zurich included a responsibility that was rarely the lot of mathematical physics teachers then: he was co-director with Mousson of the physics collection and, in effect, co-creator of the new physics institute at the polytechnic. He differed from other teachers of the subject in another respect; whereas they usually wanted access to instruments and a laboratory to further their research, he did his research without using the experimental means that were available to him.

From the beginning of his career in Berlin, Clausius's work had earned him the reputation of being a pure theorist. "All of his papers are of a purely mathematical-physical nature, based on the existing observations of others," Bunsen wrote of him in 1854; "there are no experimental papers by him, and it is unknown to the faculty [of Heidelberg University, which was then considering Clausius for a professorship] if he is even familiar with experimental physics from practical experience."[39] Soon after, Weber remarked in his recommendation of Clausius for the Zurich job that he did not know if Clausius "had made experimental physics the special object of his work."[40] Clausius had not.

But Clausius did have practical experience, for in Berlin he was then teaching experimental physics and, according to a Berlin colleague, he was even earning praise as a skillful experimenter.[41] He was also closely associated with experimentalists in Berlin, with his teacher Magnus, with Dove, and, through his work, with Riess.[42] His appointment to the Zurich Polytechnic acknowledged his experience as a teacher of experimental physics.

Clausius had to put his practical knowledge of physics to immediate use: "Since I came to a newly established institution, the Federal Polytechnic, when I was called to Zurich," he explained, "I, together with my special colleague, Professor Mousson, had to take on the task of equipping a new physical cabinet, for which purpose we received a one-time credit of 40,000 francs and an annual credit of first 2,000 francs and later 2,400 francs. Naturally, under these circumstances we were forced to oc-

---

38. Rudolph Clausius, *Die Potentialfunction und das Potential. Ein Beitrag zur mathematischen Physik* (Leipzig, 1859) and 2d ed. (Leipzig, 1870). Quotations from iii–vi, 1st ed.
39. Bunsen to Baden Ministry of the Interior, 26 July 1854, Bad. GLA, 235/3135.
40. Weber to Kern, 9 May 1855.
41. Georg Sidler to Kern, 31 Mar. 1855, A Schweiz. Sch., Zurich.
42. Clausius, "Ueber das mechanische Aequivalent," 365, 371.

cupy ourselves a great deal with the question of which objects are necessary for a well-equipped physical cabinet and from whom they can best be obtained."[43] As Clausius and Mousson expected to have a new institute within about two years, they immediately began to plan a complete institute in which they would not only lecture but also conduct laboratory exercises for students, particularly exercises in measuring methods, which was then a regular feature of instruction in mathematical physics. Part of their plan was that they and some of their students would also do some research. Among the first instruments they ordered were expensive measuring apparatus that would serve both experimental work and laboratory exercises for students: for example, Weber's "electrodynamic measuring apparatus" of 1846; the induction apparatus H. D. Ruhmkorff had begun making in 1850; a rheostat for measuring galvanic resistance, which Wheatstone had introduced in 1843; Melloni's apparatus to study heat radiation; and scales, the most expensive item on the list.[44] As it turned out, they had to wait nine years for their institute. Their efforts to offer students exercises in laboratory techniques, not to mention opportunities to do research, were frustrated by lack of space, as they kept on preparing for a working institute. In the early 1860s, when their hope of soon moving to a new institute was revived, they added to their basic measuring equipment more weights, a telescope (they had asked for two more), a galvanometer, and Regnault's apparatus for determining specific heat.[45]

When Clausius and Mousson finally did move, they explained that now the most "important direction" was "exact measuring work."[46] "Although some beautiful, in part very beautiful, measuring instruments are already on hand," they reported, "we are far from having the means to be able to undertake exact investigations in the different areas of physics. We even lack the most elementary basis, namely, fully exact measures." They regarded the completion of their collection as all the more urgent since they had begun the practical exercises for older students the previous fall, which Mousson described as instruction in "exact investigation." These exercises could "hardly be carried through satisfactorily without a certain selection and number of reliable measuring apparatus."[47] Clausius and Mousson added the latest refined thermometers "for very exact measurements of temperature," accurate to 1/100th of a degree; a "rheostat for galvanic resistance measurements according to more recent construction, which is supposed to give greater exactness than those in use so far";[48] a "simple and ingenious spherometer . . . for determin-

43. Clausius to Würzburg University Senate, 18 May 1867, Clausius Acte, Würzburg UA, Nr. 404.

44. Mousson and Clausius, "Jahresbericht über die physicalische Sammlung der polytechnischen Schule für 1856," 12 Jan. 1857, A Schweiz. Sch., Zurich. Descriptions of many of the instruments that were acquired for the Zurich Polytechnic can be found in Rosenberger, Geschichte der Physik, here, for example, on 513 and 522.

45. For our account of the polytechnic's physical collection, we consulted Mousson and Clausius's annual reports for the years 1856–66, all in the A Schweiz. Sch., Zurich.

46. Mousson, writing also for Clausius, "Jahresbericht über die physicalische Sammlung der polytechnischen Schule für das Jahr 1864," 4 Jan. 1865.

47. Mousson to Swiss Education Council, 5 Apr. 1867, A Schweiz. Sch., Zurich. Mousson, "Jahresbericht," 4 Jan. 1865.

48. Mousson and Clausius, "Jahresbericht über die physicalische Sammlung des schweizerischen Polytechnikums für das Jahr 1865," Dec. 1865.

ing the thickness of thin wires, metal sheets, plates, etc.," capable of measuring widths as small as 0.001 millimeter.[49] The basic equipment they acquired also included large magnets (the large electromagnet they bought in 1862 took up a third of their annual budget for a down payment only) and induction apparatus, particularly Ruhmkorff's, of "such strength [as] could be constructed only in recent years," giving sparks twenty-four to twenty-seven centimeters in length (as compared with their first induction apparatus, which gave sparks of only three to four centimeters).[50]

That Clausius and Mousson were planning a laboratory that could be used for research was evident not only from their acquisitions of measuring instruments but also from their attention to up-to-date equipment. Few of the items they acquired dated from before 1830, and those that did were usually meant for lecture demonstrations. Several times Clausius and Mousson ordered instruments right after their introduction into physics; they attended the international exhibitions in Paris and London to see and buy the latest equipment on the spot. In 1861, for instance, they acquired a Becquerel phosphoroscope and a series of phosphorescent tubes, a description of which had appeared in the Annales de chimie et physique only in 1859.[51]

They kept the collection up to date also in the sense that they acquired the apparatus used in the most important current researches in physics. This meant that the part of physics that made the most demands on their budget for instruments was "electricity and galvanism."[52] Of the part of physics in which they did their own chief research at this time they could report in 1862 that the recent "acquisitions for mechanical and molecular physics as well as for heat are insignificant, [since] the most important [instruments] are pretty well on hand."[53] A related part of physics, heat radiation, made larger demands as it took on increasing importance in the early 1860s. Melloni's apparatus, which was among their first orders and which they received in 1859, was used to investigate the heat spectrum of the sun and the permeability of various substances for heat radiation;[54] in 1861 they acquired an "improved" spectroscope; in 1865 they acquired from Ruhmkorff a "thermoelectric pile of linear construction"—the "only" instrument with which they could investigate the thermal properties, particularly the heat distribution, of the spectrum of the sun—and a large, exact spectroscope with several prisms for "more advanced and measuring analysis."[55]

As Mousson's co-director, Clausius gained experience also in assembling a collection of instruments for lecture demonstrations in the general course on experi-

49. Clausius and Mousson, "Jahresbericht über die physicalische Sammlung des schweizerischen Polytechnicums für das Jahr 1866," 31 Dec. 1866.

50. Mousson and Clausius, "Jahresbericht über die physicalische Sammlung des schweizerischen Polytechnikums für 1863," 4 Jan. 1864.

51. Clausius and Mousson, "Bericht über die physicalische Sammlung des schweizerischen Polytechnikums 1861," 6 Jan. 1862. Rosenberger, Geschichte der Physik, 473.

52. For example, in Clausius and Mousson, "Bericht über die physicalische Sammlung der polytechnischen Schule für das Jahr 1858," 11 Jan. 1859.

53. Clausius and Mousson, "Bericht," 6 Jan. 1862.

54. Rosenberger, Geschichte der Physik, 230.

55. Clausius and Mousson, "Bericht," 6 Jan. 1862; "Jahresbericht," Dec. 1865.

mental physics (although he did not have to teach it again until after he left Zurich). Their purchases included Ampère's apparatus for showing the effects of galvanic currents on one another; Faraday's rotational apparatus demonstrating the action of electricity in creating mechanical work; a model of a Watt steam engine; a Fessel wave machine for illustrating wave motion; large models of the eye, ear, and throat; and a much talked about apparatus by Edouard Carré for making ice by evaporating ammonia, which amply explained the principle involved, Clausius and Mousson reported, as it produced a pound or more of ice during the course of a lecture. Many of the items he and Mousson bought for the Zurich lectures appeared on his list of needed equipment for the physics institute at Würzburg,[56] which he directed as the ordinary professor of physics from 1867.

Clausius and Mousson needed not only instruments but space for working with them. Their "over-full" cabinet[57] in the Kantonsschule (to which they added over four hundred new pieces before they could move to new quarters), their "much used" auditorium, and the unfurnished and unheated small chamber that was their only place for research left them with hardly room to turn around. When, two years after the polytechnic opened, a student asked them to be allowed to specialize in physics and to do independent work, they had no place where he could work during the winter.[58] They themselves planned experimental research (to be carried out by Mousson, we presume): in 1859 they reported the purchase of two instruments that they had made "less with regard to instruction than for the purpose of special scientific investigations." Their justification was that "at institutions where experimental sciences are taught, the teachers are generally granted the right to use, in a modest way, the means of the collection that they are in charge of to the advantage of their own investigations."[59] They believed that they could claim this right. But their circumstances clearly worked against them, and their most important acquisitions were, after all, the apparatus used in teaching. As they explained in 1860 when asked about the addition of an earth-magnetic observatory at the polytechnic, the technical curriculum demanded so much of the students' time that not many students would be available to make earth-magnetic measurements.[60] In this case, as in assembling their institute, Clausius and Mousson did not refuse any means that might stimulate higher scientific activity in their field, but they did not hold high expectations for it to develop at the polytechnic. As a practical physicist there, Clausius served primarily as an expert on instruments and on institute organization and not as a director of experimental research.

Nevertheless, Clausius profited from his work with Mousson. Although he did theoretical research, he—unlike most mathematical physicists then—could claim long experience in running a complete institute, which was important in gaining

56. Clausius to Würzburg U. Senate, 18 May 1867.
57. Mousson, also writing for Clausius, to the President of the Swiss Education Council, 16 Nov. 1857, A Schweiz. Sch., Zurich.
58. Mousson to President of the Swiss Education Council, 16 Nov. 1857; Clausius and Mousson, "Bericht über die physicalische Sammlung der polytechnischen Schule 1857," 20 Jan. 1858.
59. Clausius and Mousson, "Bericht," 11 Jan. 1859.
60. Mousson, Clausius, and Wolf to President Kappeler, 26 June 1860, A Schweiz. Sch., Zurich.

him his first university chair at Würzburg. No physicist hoping for a successful career in physics could then get around the need for such experience; for success meant a university chair and an institute directorship, positions which always entailed the responsibility of teaching experimental physics. (As it happened, the completely neglected physical cabinet at Würzburg required Clausius to do all over again what he had just done with Mousson at Zurich.)

Mousson, too, was satisfied with their cooperation: on Clausius's departure from Zurich, he worked out a program for physics at the polytechnic stipulating that in the future the second physicist should continue to be his equal with regard to the physics collection.[61] Eight years later, after Clausius's position had been filled by quickly rising young physicists such as August Kundt and Friedrich Kohlrausch, it went to H. F. Weber in whose laboratory the student Albert Einstein was to work.

Training "Scientific" Physicists in Austria

In Austria, "scientific" physics training was established about fifteen years before Ludwig Boltzmann turned up to take advantage of it.[62] In 1844, the professor of physics Andreas von Ettingshausen obtained permission to give lectures on "higher physics" and on the "latest advances in this science";[63] this was the beginning of instruction in mathematical physics at Vienna University.

Ettingshausen belonged to the philosophical faculty, which at Austrian universities was still a two-year preparatory school corresponding to the last two years of the German gynmasium; strictly prescribed, the curriculum of the philosophical faculty included eight hours per week of physics in the second year. The chairholder for physics was, in effect, a gymnasium teacher, and only Ettingshausen's extra physics lectures, which were "free" (that is, not required), were at the university level. His innovation was well received, and three years later he was given an *extraordinary* professorship for higher physics in place of the regular physics chair (though he soon resigned in favor of a position in technical education).

In the course of general university reforms in Austria in 1849–50, a "physics institute" was created at Vienna University which had the purposes of a seminar and a laboratory course. It was an institution separate from the physics chair, now occupied by August Kunzek, who under the new arrangement was responsible for physics lectures for a general audience of teaching candidates, pharmacy students, and, later, medical students. The physics institute was to give a small number of "ordinary" students (twelve to begin with) who intended to teach physics, chemistry, or physiology an opportunity to acquire a knowledge of physics sufficient for "successful

61. Mousson to President of the Swiss Education Council, 14 Sept. 1867.
62. "Vortrag des Staats-Ministers Richard Graf v. Belcredi" addressed to the Emperor of Austria, 20 Sept. 1866, Stefan file, Öster. STA, 4 Phil, credits Ettingshausen with being among the first to start the scientific treatment of physics in Austria.
63. "Vortrag . . . Belcredi," 20 Sept. 1866. Also *Geschichte der Wiener Universität von 1848 bis 1898*, ed. Akademischer Senat der Wiener Universität (Vienna, 1898), 262–366, where physics and mathematics at Vienna are discussed for the fifty years the book covers, along with the philosophical faculty in general.

teaching" and to acquire "mechanical skill in physical experimenting"; at the same time, it was to give them the "necessary directions for independent researches in the field of physics."[64] To help the program succeed, the government took pains to provide the first director of the institute, Christian Doppler, with the necessary financial and material means.

While Doppler was director, the course at the institute consisted of three semesters of "demonstrative experimental physics with exercises in the laboratory" for ten hours each week.[65] Kunzek, who had lost most of his physical apparatus to the new institute, offered theoretical physics "with a mathematical basis"; his main courses on mathematical physics were substantial, usually taking up five hours a week. Besides Doppler and Kunzek, Joseph Petzval, the ordinary professor of mathematics, taught mathematical subjects related to physics such as analytical mechanics, elasticity, wave theory, and dioptrics.

In 1852 Doppler left the directorship of the physics institute because of failing health. His replacement Ettingshausen—who here returns to our story—divided the three-semester program of the institute into two semesters of basic training and one semester of research. The first semester was devoted to instruction in experimental techniques in physics, the second to the acquisition of the technical skills physicists then needed to maintain and construct physical apparatus and to prepare experiments, and the third to further training "through practical physical studies and independent work." The activities of the first two semesters occupied ten hours per week; during the third semester there were no more regular classes, and students spent the whole day working in the institute.

To the practical program of the institute Ettingshausen added lecture courses in mathematical physics and also what appears to have been a colloquium on current physics. The physicist Josef Stefan wrote about the small circle of older students interested in "mathematical studies" that Ettingshausen repeatedly gathered around him to discuss the "most difficult areas of mathematical physics with [his] usual clarity."[66] The lecture catalogs list courses on the latest advances in physics in which the students were expected to give presentations. These courses Ettingshausen soon devolved onto young physicists he had trained.

When Ettingshausen assumed the directorship of the physics institute, he brought with him a student, Josef Grailich, who specialized in mathematical physics and in crystal physics. In 1855 Grailich became Privatdocent for crystallography, crystal physics, and general physics, and two years later he was appointed extraordinary professor of higher (or mathematical) physics at the university.[67] Grailich

---

64. *Geschichte der Wiener Universität*, 286–87, 289.

65. "Öffentliche Vorlesungen an der K. K. Universität zu Wien," Vienna University Archive. We have used the volumes covering the semesters beginning with the summer semester 1849 through the winter semester 1867–68 (except summer semester 1851 for which the volume is missing).

66. Josef Stefan, obituary of Ettingshausen, in *Almanach Wiener Akad.* 28 (1878): 154–59, on 155.

67. "Grailich, Josef," *Österreichisches Biographisches Lexikon 1815–1950* 2 (Graz and Cologne: H. Böhlaus, 1959): 46–47. The entry in the *Lexikon* gives 1855 as the date of Grailich's appointment to extraordinary professor. Internal evidence supports 1857, the date given by *Geschichte der Wiener Universität*.

offered his lectures on mathematical physics within the institute, while mathematical physics also continued to be taught outside it by the professors of physics and
mathematics. Grailich also took an active part in the practical work of the institute,
directing student research, involving students in his own research,[68] and conducting
the colloquium. There is good reason to think that he was being groomed by Ettingshausen to succeed him as director one day. Then in 1859, at age thirty, this gifted
physicist died.

The physics institute in the mid-1850s had three students who soon commanded
attention as physicists in their own right: Stefan, who came in 1853, and Victor
von Lang and Ernst Mach, both of whom came in 1855.[69] All three began doing
research soon after they entered the physics institute. Stefan, who also became a
highly skilled experimentalist, displayed his preference for theoretical physics—he
was "above all a theoretical physicist," his student Boltzmann was to write later—
from the beginning. Taking up one of Ettingshausen's research areas, he wrote his
first paper on the "general equations for wave motion," publishing it in the *Annalen
der Physik* in 1857. Also in 1857 he presented a paper on the "absorption of gases"
to the Vienna Academy of Sciences, which won him a second patron, the physiologist Carl Ludwig, with whom he collaborated on his next research.[70] He took his
doctorate in 1858, becoming Privatdocent for mathematical physics at Vienna University that same year.[71] Lang began publishing research in 1856; he worked closely
with Grailich on crystal physics, but he also published on mathematical physics, in
particular, on the "newer theory of light."[72] After he had received his doctorate,
Lang went to Heidelberg to study with Kirchhoff and then to Paris to work with
Regnault. (In going to Kirchhoff, Lang followed the example of Ettingshausen, who
a few years earlier had expressed his admiration for Kirchhoff by making a trip to
Breslau especially to meet him.[73] Boltzmann, in his turn, would go to Kirchhoff
too.[74]) In 1859 Lang became Privatdocent at Vienna University. Mach also did
research with Ettingshausen's support. While a student in the Vienna physics insti-

68. See, for example, Josef Grailich, *Krystallographisch-optische Untersuchungen* (Vienna and Olmüz,
1858), viii; Josef Grailich and Edmund Weiss, "Über das Singen der Flammen," *Sitzungsber. Wiener Akad.*
29 (1858); or Alois Handl and Adolf Weiss (like Edmund Weiss, students at the physics institute),
"Untersuchungen über den Zusammenhang in den Änderungen der Dichten und Brechungsexponenten
in Gemengen von Flüssigkeiten und Verbindungen von Gasen," *Sitzungsber. Wiener Akad.* 30 (1858):
389–441, a paper starting from Grailich's work and carried out with his help and encouragement.

69. Eduard Süss, obituary of Stefan, in *Almanach Wiener Akad.* 43 (1893): 252–57. "Commissions-
bericht über den in der Sitzung vom 17. Juni l. J. gestellten-Antrag, die Errichtung einer ausserordent-
lichen Lehrkanzel der mathematischen Physik betreffend," 2 July 1863 (contains vitae for Lang, Mach,
and Edmund Reitlinger), Öster. STA, 5 Graz Phil, Physik. Also John T. Blackmore, *Ernst Mach. His
Work, Life, and Influence* (Berkeley, Los Angeles, and London: University of California Press, 1972), 13.

70. Boltzmann, "Josef Stefan," 94, 97, 99. Süss's obituary of Stefan, 253. Walter Böhm, "Stefan,
Josef," *DSB* 13: 10–11, on 10.

71. Stefan's career is described in the "Vortrag" of Minister of Culture and Education Carl von
Stremayr to the Emperor, 27 Oct. 1878, Stefan file, Öster. STA, 4 Phil.

72. "Commissionsbericht," 2 July 1863.

73. Ettingshausen to Bunsen (we think), 14 Mar. 1854, Bad. GLA, 235/3135.

74. Engelbert Broda, *Ludwig Boltzmann. Mensch, Physiker, Philosoph* (Vienna: Franz Deuticke, 1955),
4; Ludwig Boltzmann, *Gustav Robert Kirchhoff* (Leipzig, 1888), reprinted in *Populäre Schriften*, 51–75, on
52.

tute, he tried to settle experimentally the controversy over the Doppler effect in sound.[75] In 1860 he received his doctorate, and in 1861, like Stefan and Lang shortly before him, he became Privatdocent at Vienna University.

Ettingshausen's program at the institute was productive: by 1861 he could point to nearly fifty research papers by his students appearing in the periodicals of the Vienna Academy of Sciences, and he could point to several students who had embarked successfully on academic careers, the Privatdocenten Stefan, Lang, and Mach, along with assistants at various scientific institutes and workers in sciences other than physics.[76]

In this liberal promotion of the young physicists in his institute Ettingshausen had for years circumvented a rule that students who had received their doctorate could no longer work in the physics institute. In Austria before 1872, the doctorate of philosophy was an easily acquired degree, requiring no more than a final examination.[77] Since the three semesters at the institute tended to come at the end of a physics student's three years at the university, the rule meant that Ettingshausen's students were officially excluded from his laboratory facilities after a brief time, regularly only a semester, of independent research; that is, the rule excluded them before they had a chance to do the kind of substantial investigations that earned physicists a doctorate at the German universities. In 1861 Ettingshausen tried to get approval of graduate research at his institute by proposing that it be open to so-called members. Membership would be available to Austrian physicists who had completed the three-year course at the university or a complete technical course, who had already worked at the physics institute as regular students, and who had produced at least one paper accepted for publication by the academy. Members would be entitled to free use of the institute's instruments and premises for their research as long as they did not interfere with its regular purposes. Ettingshausen even had in mind the first members, naming Lang and Mach along with five others,[78] but his plans apparently remained unrealized when a serious illness the next year forced changes in the administration of the institute. The lack of advanced students was to dog Viennese physicists for years to come and had much to do with Boltzmann's deciding twice to leave Austria for Germany.

By the early 1860s at Vienna University, Stefan, Mach, and Edmund Reitlinger, an Austrian who had studied with Weber in Göttingen but who was now also at the Vienna physics institute, were the principal teachers of "higher" physics at Vienna University. Ettingshausen taught when his health allowed it.

Ettingshausen had supported Grailich, a mathematical physicist like himself, and when Grailich died the man who replaced him in Ettingshausen's planning was

75. Ernst Mach, "Ueber die Aenderung des Tones und der Farbe durch Bewegung," *Ann.* 112 (1861): 58–76, on 65, 76. See Erwin N. Hiebert, "The Genesis of Mach's Early Views on Atomism," in *Ernst Mach. Physicist and Philosopher*, vol. 6 of Boston Studies in the Philosophy of Science, ed. R. S. Cohen and R. J. Seeger (Dordrecht-Holland: D. Reidel, 1970), 79–106, on 80.
76. Ettingshausen to Austrian Ministry of State, 21 Oct. 1861, Öster. STA, 4 Phil, Physik.
77. *Geschichte der Wiener Universität*, 268.
78. Ettingshausen to Austrian Ministry of State, 21 Oct. 1861.

Stefan. To begin with, Stefan took over Grailich's courses on mathematical physics at the institute; his first lectures treated the "physics of molecular forces," and in the following years, while he was still Privatdocent, they treated the "theory of heat conduction according to Fourier," the "theory of light," the "theory of heat," and the "theory of elasticity." When in 1862 Ettingshausen, because of illness, was forced to ask for an assistant's position, he recommended Stefan for it. Expecting the assistant to succeed him some day, Ettingshausen wanted someone who could be appointed "ordinary university professor of physics with the right to give lectures on the theoretical part of this science and on the branches of mathematics that are its basis"; Stefan was qualified by his published research as well as by his five years of teaching. The ministry also favored Stefan because he was considered an excellent mathematician who might be able to fill what they considered a gap in the curriculum "consisting in this, that the theoretical part of physics is not represented at all and the related science of higher mathematics insufficiently."[79] (The ministry meant that it was not represented by a professorship, since Grailich's extraordinary professorship had not been filled again.) In January 1863 Stefan was made co-director of the physics institute and ordinary professor of "higher mathematics and physics."[80] Three years later Ettingshausen retired so that the ministry could offer his position to Stefan as an inducement for him to remain at Vienna University rather than accept an offer from the Vienna Polytechnic; Stefan now became sole director of the physics institute.[81]

During this time at Vienna, Mach lectured on such methodological or historical subjects as "methods of physical research" and the "principles of mechanics and mechanical physics in its historical development"; in the winter of 1863, he added lectures on psychophysics and the theory of sensation and perception. He also gave lectures on physics prepared especially for medical students, which, in addition to satisfying his own interest,[82] served a practical purpose. In the reforms at the Austrian universities in the late 1840s, the natural science courses that had been taught in the medical faculty were moved to the philosophical faculty,[83] and in the 1850s courses on physics for medical students and for students of pharmacy appeared in the Vienna lecture catalog. Mach, needing an income, took on the responsibility for an already established—and no doubt reasonably profitable—part of the physics curriculum.

Simultaneously with Stefan, Reitlinger was Privatdocent for mathematical physics at Vienna University from 1859 and also assistant at the physics institute, at times substituting for Ettingshausen as Stefan was to do. In his lectures, he specialized in electrotechnology and the recent developments in electricity, interests relat-

79. "Vortrag" of Minister of State Anton Ritter von Schmerling, 20 Dec. 1862, Stefan file, Öster. STA, 4 Phil. The minister's presentation includes Ettingshausen's request and recommendation of Stefan.
80. Appointment by the Ministry of State, 26 Jan. 1863, Stefan file, Öster. STA, 4 Phil.
81. Vienna U. Philosophical Faculty to Minister of State, 18 July 1866; "Akte," Ministry of State, 1 Oct. 1866, containing Stefan's appointment; "Vortrag . . . Belcredi," 20 Sept. 1866; Stefan file, Öster. STA, 4 Phil.
82. Blackmore, Mach, 14–15.
83. Geschichte der Wiener Universität, 268.

ing to his training at Göttingen. In time, he extended his courses to the history of
physics in general and to "inductive logic as the foundation of physical research,"
and after Mach left, he took over Mach's physics lectures for medical students and
also his lectures on topics such as the "physics of sense perceptions" and the "relationship of physics to psychology and logic."

Mach's and Reitlinger's branching out to subjects uniting physics with physiology and philosophy began something of a tradition at Vienna, which later Mach
and, after him, Boltzmann consolidated. In part, it was encouraged by the accidents
of the institutional arrangements we have described. In the absence of regulations
permitting graduate research at the physics institute without an official affiliation,
Ettingshausen and the philosophical faculty allowed an unusually large number of
Privatdocenten. Having located the main teaching of theoretical physics within his
institute, however, Ettingshausen had unintentionally robbed the remaining Privatdocenten of the specialized courses that were usually their domain at the German
universities.

In 1863, the year Stefan became co-director of the Vienna physics institute,
Graz University requested a new extraordinary chair for mathematical physics.[84] The
position was more important than the title indicates, since it was created for the
sole reason that the professor of physics at Graz was held to be no longer competent
to teach physics adequately, and the new extraordinary professor would in fact be
the main physicist there.[85] The candidates for the position were Stefan's fellow Privatdocenten at Vienna: Lang, Reitlinger, and Mach.[86] Lang, who had fifteen published research papers in both mathematical and experimental physics to his credit,
got the job. A year later, Mach was appointed professor of mathematics at Graz
University, so that when Lang returned to Vienna University in 1865 as Kunzek's
successor to the ordinary chair of physics, Mach was in a position to recommend
Reitlinger as Lang's replacement at Graz.[87] Instead, Mach himself was appointed
ordinary professor of mathematical physics at Graz in 1866,[88] and Reitlinger became
ordinary professor of physics at the Vienna Polytechnic that same year.[89] With all
of this shuffling, 1866 proved a remarkable year for Ettingshausen. Of his students
of ten years before, four now occupied important Austrian chairs of physics, and the
Prague chair of physics would soon be added to the list.[90] Moreover, that year the
finest product of Ettingshausen's institute appeared before the world of physics: Boltz-

84. The documents relating to the establishment of the extraordinary chair for mathematical physics
at Graz University are contained in two files for 1863 in Öster. STA, 5 Graz Phil. Physik. See also Hans
Schobesberger, "Die Geschichte des Physikalischen Institutes der Universität Graz in den Jahren von
1850–1890" (manuscript), Graz UA.

85. Report by the Ministry of State and the Ministry of Finance, 10 July 1863, Öster. STA, 5 Graz
Phil. Physik, a. o. Lehrkanzel.

86. Graz Philosophical Faculty to Ministry of State, July 1863, Öster. STA, 5 Graz Phil. Physik.
Also "Commissionsbericht," 2 July 1863.

87. Mach to the Graz Philosophical Faculty, 10 Oct. 1865, Graz UA, N. 20 Phil. Dec. 1866.

88. "Vortrag" of the Minister of State Richard von Belcredi, 9 Apr. 1866; Mach's appointment, 19
Apr. 1866; Öster. STA, 5 Graz Phil. Physik.

89. *Geschichte der Wiener Universität*, 291.

90. Mach moved to Prague in 1867.

mann, still a student, made an auspicious debut with his paper "On the Mechanical Significance of the Second Law of Mechanical Heat Theory."

Boltzmann as Theoretical Physicist at Vienna

Boltzmann came to Vienna University in 1863 and studied with Kunzek and Ettings-hausen, as well as with Lang and Stefan.[91] In 1865 he entered the physics institute where Stefan, who now became his principal teacher, continued the practice estab-lished by Ettingshausen of devoting the means of the institute to research. The work of Stefan's students was noticed as far away as England, where Maxwell commented on their "excellent papers" and on the desirability of good experimental training such as that offered in Vienna. Boltzmann was mainly a theorist, but like Stefan he was also a good experimentalist. He later wrote that Stefan's institute became for him for the rest of his life the "symbol of serious experimental work pervaded by intellectuality," the spirit of which he strove to recreate in his own institutes with-out, he felt, ever quite succeeding.[92]

When Boltzmann entered the Vienna physics institute as student in 1865, he also entered a scientific program that had guided the research of teachers and stu-dents there for more than a decade. Ettingshausen sought to advance physics by reducing problematic phenomena to motions of molecules—"molecules" of matter and "molecules" of ether—and applying to them the laws of mechanics. In his text-book in 1839, for example, he had written that further develoments in the wave theory of light depended not on new discoveries but on "advances of theoretical mechanics" such as Cauchy's.[93] Dividing inanimate nature between them, Ettings-hausen's students worked out his program.

Grailich, one of the first students, devoted himself to the study of the physical properties of crystals from the molecular point of view. His paper on crystallographic optical investigations, which won the prize of the Vienna Academy of Sciences in 1857, bore the motto: "Only the general investigation of crystals can create the foundations of future molecular theory."[94] He believed that it was time to learn what happens at the molecular level in physical processes, and his work engaged several of the other students at the institute; he developed the mathematical theory and then collaborated with them or set them to work independently on series of mea-surements in support of the theory. After Grailich's death, Lang carried on his pro-gram.

Mach was one of the students in the institute who studied fluids from the mo-

91. Report by the Ministry of Culture and Education, 28 June 1869, Öster. STA, 5 Graz Phil. Physik. It contains Boltzmann's vita.

92. Boltzmann, "Josef Stefan," 100.

93. See, for example, Andreas von Ettingshausen, "Über die neueren Formeln für das an einfach brechenden Medien reflectirte und gebrochene Licht," *Sitzungsber. Wiener Akad.* 18 (1855): 369–91. Quotation from Baumgartner and Ettingshausen, *Naturlehre*, 410.

94. Grailich, *Krystallographisch-optische Untersuchungen*, v.

lecular point of view. Like Grailich, he approached the subject with a sense of embarking on a comprehensive and important task. He wrote in 1862: "The present note is to be regarded as the beginning of a long series of investigations concerning the molecular action of fluids—which investigations may be at least as important as the study of gases and crystals."[95] Much as he might have hoped that his subject would equal in importance the subjects of the institute's two outstanding senior students, Grailich's crystals and Stefan's gases, he did not carry out his project because (it has been suggested) his areas of investigation were not essential to the support of atomic theory.[96] Ettingshausen's illness in 1862 brought to an end his efforts to arrange formal access to the institute for Mach; this was sufficient cause for Mach to stop the experiments, for he had no means of his own.[97] Mach's teaching also led him away from this research, although for the time being he was busy writing a textbook on physics from the point of view of molecular mechanics for the medical students he was teaching. He wrote the book in Ettingshausen's spirit and dedicated it to him.[98]

Stefan also followed the general program of the institute, working in several parts of it. His earliest topic, the "general equations for wave motion," was related to Ettingshausen's researches on optics and his conception of the light ether as a system of oscillating material points.[99] Stefan's second paper dealt with gas absorption,[100] and he continued to work on gas theory, eventually developing the experimental means of confirming it. In particular, he solved the difficult experimental problem of measuring the heat conductivity of the different gases, which had been calculated from the theory on the assumption that as heat spreads through a gas, motion is gradually propagated from molecule to molecule. A third early interest of Stefan's was Maxwell's electromagnetic theory (Boltzmann recalled that Stefan gave him Maxwell's papers to read while he was still a student, around 1865). Stefan showed that Maxwell's views could be reconciled with the older theory: electricity as a state of motion in the ether was compatible with Ettingshausen's approach. This could also be seen from Boltzmann's translation of Maxwell's terminology to fit the molecular terminology: "The mechanical heat theory teaches [us] that the ponderable molecules of bodies are continuously in motion; this view we can transfer also to ether molecules."[101] (Another of Ettingshausen's early students, Simon Subič, published a treatise, "Characteristics of a Molecular Physics and a Mechanical Theory of Electricity and Magnetism," in 1862, but because he showed himself an incom-

95. In Ernst Mach, "Ueber die Molekularwirkung der Flüssigkeiten," *Sitzungsber. Wiener Akad.* 46 (1863): 125–34. Quoted by Hiebert, "The Genesis of Mach's Early Views on Atomism," 82.

96. Hiebert, "Genesis," 95.

97. Blackmore, *Mach*, 14, passim.

98. Hiebert, "Genesis," 86. For a different view than ours of Mach's position vis-à-vis that of the physicists who were at the Vienna physics institute with him, see Blackmore, *Mach*, 24.

99. Josef Stefan, "Allgemeine Gleichungen für oscillatorische Bewegungen," *Ann.* 102 (1857): 365–87.

100. Josef Stefan, "Bemerkungen über die Absorption der Gase," *Sitzungsber. Wiener Akad.* 27 (1857): 375–430.

101. Boltzmann, "Josef Stefan," 96–98; "Über Maxwells Elektrizitätstheorie" (1873), in *Populäre Schriften*, 11–24, quotation on 20.

petent physicist he earned only Stefan's ridicule with it, and on the basis of Stefan's criticism he lost the physics position at Graz University for which Stefan was evaluating him.[102])

The problem in the mechanical theory of heat that Boltzmann began to work on soon after entering the Vienna physics institute was well suited to Ettingshausen's approach to physics. In the mechanical theory, heat is defined as a kind of motion and so is subject to the laws of mechanics, but at the time Boltzmann took up the subject, the law of increase of entropy, the second fundamental law of the theory, had not yet been derived from purely mechanical principles. In 1866 Boltzmann provided a derivation.[103]

The first of the two fundamental laws of the mechanical theory of heat, which asserts the quantitative equivalence of heat and mechanical energy, could be given a mechanical interpretation by interpreting heat as a form of mechanical energy.[104] The parallel problem of mechanically interpreting the second law was more complex; to solve it, Boltzmann gave the concept of temperature a mechanical definition, which was the crux of his proof of the law.

Guided by the condition that "no heat, hence no living force of the motions of the atoms," is communicated when two bodies of the same temperature come in contact, Boltzmann derived the condition that on the average an atom of one body does not receive any living force from an atom of the other body. From this condition of equilibrium and from other considerations, he defined the temperature of an atom as its average-over-time, or "mean," living force:

$$T = \frac{\int_{t_1}^{t_2} \frac{mc^2}{2} \, dt}{t_2 - t_1}.$$

To arrive at the entropy, he also needed to express the heat, Q, the other quantity that enters into its definition in terms of the motion of an atom. For this purpose he analyzed in detail the effect of adding an infinitely small heat, or living force, δQ to an atom moving in a closed path; as in the least action principle, he analyzed the effect by taking the variation of the integral of the living force of the atom. By showing that $1/T$ is an integrating factor of δQ and by considering both reversible and irreversible processes, he derived the second law in the general form that Clausius had given to it: $\int dQ/T \leq 0$. This was the first reasonable mechanical interpre-

102. "Commissions-Bericht" by Graz U. Philosophical Faculty, 15 Jan. 1869; Stefan to Ministry of Culture and Education, 8 Apr. 1869; Öster. STA, 5 Graz Phil. Physik.

103. Ludwig Boltzmann, "Über die mechanische Bedeutung des zweiten Hauptsatzes der Wärmetheorie," Sitzungsber. Wiener Akad. 53 (1866): 195–220; reprinted in Wissenschaftliche Abhandlungen, ed. Fritz Hasenöhrl, 3 vols. (New York: Chelsea, 1968), 1:9–33 (hereafter cited as Wiss. Abh.). This paper is discussed in detail in René Dugas, La théorie physique au sens de Boltzmann et ses prolongements modernes (Neuchâtel-Suisse: Griffon, 1959), 153–57.

104. For then, in the mathematical statement of the first law, $dQ = dE + dW$, the heat Q is an energy term like the other two quantities, E internal energy and W external work.

tation of the second law.[105] Boltzmann did not regard his proof as depending on the theory of heat but on the general mechanical principle of least action, to which he gave a "more general form."[106]

Clausius, too, was determined to secure a mechanical proof of the second law; ignorant of Boltzmann's, he arrived at a similar proof several years later.[107] Clausius discussed the least action principle in connection with the proofs, claiming that he had discovered a new principle of mechanics similar to, but more general than, Hamilton's; his and Boltzmann's proofs alike endowed a variational principle with a significance in the mechanical theory of heat parallel to that of the energy principle. (Not one to repress a joke even when it was aimed at otherwise esteemed colleagues, or at himself, Boltzmann wrote in 1870 from Heidelberg, where he was visiting Kirchhoff, that he had used Hamilton's principle in his latest paper "because this is now in fashion, and after all, I must show that I've learned a little bit about the latest fashion abroad. I would no more determine forces without Hamilton's principle that I would go out without a walking stick."[108]) Boltzmann called Clausius's attention to his earlier proof, which resulted in an inconclusive priority discussion in which Boltzmann stressed what their proofs had in common and Clausius what they did not.[109]

Boltzmann came to realize that he had claimed too much for his first proof. To express the second law in mechanical terms, he had restricted the motion of atoms to periodic paths, which was unrealistic in light of the probable complex motions of gas particles. In the meantime, from Maxwell's papers on the theory of gases he had learned that gases have to be described statistically. In 1868 he supplied a new derivation of Maxwell's law of the distribution of velocities among molecules, and with it he generalized Maxwell's theory of gases.[110] He soon applied his newly acquired statistical understanding to the old problem of the second law, publishing in 1871 a second, "analytic" proof of it. This time he treated the problem of nonperiodic motion by introducing the probability of a molecule in a given state. Now the second law became a theorem in a "new and as yet unnamed discipline—statistical mechanics," in which the laws of probability enter alongside those of mechanics.[111]

105. Boltzmann, "Über die mechanische Bedeutung." Dugas, La théorie physique, 157.

106. Boltzmann's principle allows variations in the limits of integration as well as in the living force supplied to the body.

107. Rudolph Clausius, "Ueber einen auf die Wärme anwendbaren mechanischen Satz," Ann. 141 (1870): 124–30.

108. Boltzmann to Director (Stefan?), 26 June 1870, STPK, Darmst. Coll. 30.7.

109. Ludwig Boltzmann, "Zur Priorität der Auffindung der Beziehung zwischen dem zweiten Hauptsatze der mechanischen Wärmetheorie und dem Prinzip der kleinsten Wirkung," Ann. 143 (1871): 211–30, in Wiss. Abh. 1: 228–36; Rudolph Clausius, "Bemerkungen zu der Prioritätsreclamation des Hrn. Boltzmann," Ann. 144 (1871): 265–74.

110. Ludwig Boltzmann, "Studien über das Gleichgewicht der lebendigen Kraft zwischen bewegten materiellen Punkten," Sitzungsber. Wiener Akad. 58 (1868): 517–60, reprinted in Wiss. Abh. 1: 49–96.

111. Ludwig Boltzmann, "Analytischer Beweis des zweiten Hauptsatzes der mechanischen Wärmetheorie aus den Sätzen über das Gleichgewicht der lebendigen Kraft," Sitzungsber. Wiener Akad. 63 (1871): 712–32, reprinted in Wiss. Abh. 1: 288–308. Martin J. Klein, "Mechanical Explanation at the End of the Nineteenth Century," Centaurus 17 (1972): 58–82, on 61–62; Paul Ehrenfest, vol. 1, The Making of a Theoretical Physicist (Amsterdam and London: North-Holland, 1970), 97–100.

Boltzmann's new understanding was to prove more fruitful for the further development of heat theory than Clausius's and his own earlier understanding.[112]

Upon earning his doctorate in 1866, Boltzmann became assistant at the Vienna physics institute. In 1868 he qualified as Privatdocent for mathematical physics;[113] as Austrian Privatdocenten apparently had to seek approval from the ministry for their intended lectures when they asked to be allowed to habilitate, Boltzmann submitted to them a full program. He told the ministry that in his first lecture course, the "fundamental principles of mechanical heat theory," he was going to show why the mechanical heat theory is preferable to the caloric theory, derive the first and second fundamental laws, and in light of these laws discuss the nature and properties of solid bodies, fluids, vapors, and gases. In following semesters he planned to teach "theoretical optics," taking up theories of the motion of the ether, Huygens's principle, and the equation of a wave surface; he planned in addition to teach the "theory of electricity," taking up in it the potential theory and Ampère's and Weber's formula for the interaction of currents and its relation to Faraday's view of these interactions.[114] From Boltzmann's list of topics it is clear that from the outset of his career, his interest was directed toward the fundamental questions of physical theory in his teaching as well as in his research.

In 1869, at the age of twenty-nine, Boltzmann was promoted to ordinary professor for mathematical physics at Graz University;[115] from there he moved to Vienna University in 1873 as ordinary professor of mathematics. These earliest professorships did not represent the full range of Boltzmann's interests nor did they give him adequate opportunity to develop them. He was too much the product of the Vienna physics institute, of Stefan's view that the "true physicist" is both experimenter and theorist, not to work experimentally as well as mathematically. During his first years at Graz he visited Heidelberg and Berlin, where he did experimental work. In Helmholtz's laboratory in Berlin, he investigated "with Thomson's electrometer the change in capacity of condensers by means of insulating intermediate layers, a rather lengthy and time-consuming investigation, which I took on more to come into as close contact with Helmholtz as possible and to disprove as well as I might the view that a calculating physicist can never do experiments than because I was particularly interested in the subject itself"; but he was fascinated by the precision of the instruments he was using.[116] After returning to Graz, he wrote to Helmholtz that he was continuing the experimental investigation he had begun in Berlin, remarking that he could work on it only when the Graz physics institute was not needed for lectures, since there was

112. Daub, "Rudolf Clausius," 180–81.
113. The documents on Boltzmann's habilitation at Vienna University are in Boltzmann file, Öster. STA, 4 Phil.
114. Dean of Vienna U. Philosophical Faculty to Ministry of Culture and Education, 9 Mar. 1868; Boltzmann, "Plan der Vorlesungen, welche der Gefertigte an der Universität zu Wien zu halten beabsichtigt," Mar. 1868; Boltzmann file, Öster. STA, 4 Phil.
115. Documents on Boltzmann's appointment at Graz University, Öster. STA, Graz Phil. Physik.
116. Boltzmann to Director (Stefan?), 2 Feb. 1872, STPK, Darmst. Coll. 30.7.

not enough space for both teaching and research. Shortly after taking up his new job at Vienna, Boltzmann wrote again to Helmholtz that the move had interrupted him in the middle of his investigation of the dielectricity of gases and crystallized bodies. Boltzmann was now mathematical professor and as such he was responsible for a subject that, he said, was "always further from me than physics"; he was disappointed in his "wish to get a position where a physical cabinet would be at my disposal for my work," which he thought would be "much more suitable" for him.[117] Even in Vienna in his unsuited job, Boltzmann continued to do experimental work, which could not have been too difficult given his good relations with Stefan. Eventually, in 1876, his wish for a physical cabinet was granted through his appointment to the chair of "experimental physics" at Graz University.

117. Gisela Buchheim, "Zur Geschichte der Elektrodynamik: Briefe Ludwig Boltzmanns an Hermann von Helmholtz," NTM 5 (1968): 125–31, on 126, 128, 129.

9

Physics at German Universities from 1840 to 1870

Owing in large part to the organization work of the physicists we have discussed so far, the German pattern of physics education and research at the universities was more or less established by 1870. The initiative, drive, and inventiveness of a Weber or a Magnus were uncommon; the extent to which other physicists were able to achieve comparable arrangements depended mainly on the finances and interests of their respective states. What Robert von Mohl said of the state of Baden and its universities was generally the case: scientists rarely could command state finances for their scientific needs.[1] By this time, a scientist who had a reputation for excellent research was placed ahead of colleagues who did not, but his reputation was no guarantee that once he was appointed he would be furnished with adequate means to continue his work. Nor was excellent research enough, except in rare instances, for a scientist to receive an appointment that was not dictated by local and curriculum needs: the German states could not afford to compete with one another only for the glory of having the best scientists, much as university faculties might urge them in that direction.[2] Neither could they afford to promote young scientists for no other reason than to reward research, as the unhappy consequences of Prussia's promotions of this kind showed.

To a large degree, the fate of physics at a particular university depended on the importance of the university to the state; that is, on whether it was the only university in that state, a provincial university in a state that had several, or the university in the capital of a state with several universities. The nineteen German universities in this period fell into these categories: Berlin and Munich Universities

---

1. Robert von Mohl, *Lebens-Erinnerungen* (Stuttgart and Leipzig: Deutsche Verlags-Anstalt, 1902), 1: 221.

2. To give an example: after Dirichlet's death, some members of the Göttingen faculty hoped to use his salary to bring another great scientist, not necessarily a mathematician, to their university. The medical faculty in particular wanted Helmholtz, then still a physiologist; but it lost out to the argument that Göttingen already had a satisfactory physiologist in Rudolph Wagner, that a mathematician should be hired instead, and that Riemann, who was already at Göttingen, should be advanced. Warnstedt, "Vortrag betr. die Ausfüllung der durch das Ableben des Professors Lejeune-Dirichlet entstandenen Lücke auf der Universität Göttingen" (1859), Riemann Personalakte, Göttingen UA, 4/V b/137. Also Warnstedt to Rudolph Wagner, 18 May 1859, R. Wagner Correspondence, Göttingen UB, Ms. Dept.

belong to the capitals of Prussia and Bavaria; Heidelberg University was not in the capital of Baden, but it served as the main university during this period, Freiburg serving as the second university; Erlangen and Würzburg were the provincial universities of Bavaria; Greifswald, Halle, Breslau, Bonn, and Königsberg were the Prussian provincial universities before 1866; and Marburg, Giessen, Tübingen, Jena, Kiel, Rostock, Göttingen, and Leipzig were the only universities in their respective states. The universities that were the only ones had the advantage that they alone educated and certified the professionals and bureaucrats of their states; by that undivided responsibility, they acquired a certain claim to their governments' attention and support. The universities in states with more than one university had the same responsibilities, but none had a monopoly on them.

Physics at "Only" Universities

Physics at an "only" university had a better chance of getting adequate support than elsewhere because it was one of the basic sciences for medical education. As a professional field, medicine drew students in much larger numbers than the natural sciences; for this reason, physicists had long relied in large part on medical students for the audience for their main lectures on experimental physics. To enhance the physics curriculum according to the new views of physics education, physicists wanted to ensure that medical students took their physics studies seriously; if medical students were required to submit to their examinations, they could be brought into the laboratory practice courses as well as to the lectures. Throughout this period, physicists had to struggle to get the support of the medical faculties of their universities; for not all of these faculties saw the "urgent necessity" of so much physics, nor were they easily persuaded to require physics examinations by the physics professors rather than by their own, since that meant relinquishing a part of their control over the training of medical students to outsiders.[3]

Leipzig University was one of the earliest to require its medical students to pass an examination on all "theoretical" basic knowledge, "especially on physics," before they were allowed to take medical courses.[4] The Leipzig physicists accordingly had no shortage of students. Hankel, who succeeded Weber there in 1849, started with fifty-five students in his lectures and during the next thirty years watched their number climb to over four hundred; in addition, he had a substantial number of students in his laboratory practice courses, the enrollment reaching forty-two by 1862.[5] (By contrast, physicists attracted only small numbers to their classes at the Prussian provincial university of nearby Halle, whose medical students generally had taken their physics lectures at other universities.[6])

3. See n. 102, chap. 4. Also Wilhelm Weber to "Cabinets-Minister," 8 Feb. 1837, Göttingen UA, 4/V h/15.

4. Weber to "Cabinets-Minister," 8 Feb. 1837; Dean of the Leipzig U. Medical Faculty Karl August Kuhl to E. H. Weber, 11 May 1837; Göttingen UA, 4/V h/15.

5. *Festschrift zur Feier des 500jährigen Bestehens der Universität Leipzig* (Leipzig: S. Hirzel, 1909), vol. 4, pt. 2, p. 58.

6. Blume to "Geheim-Cabinetsrath," 17 Mar. 1831, Weber Personalakte, Göttingen UA, 4/V b/95a.

At Tübingen as at Leipzig, physics enjoyed the support of the medical faculty. When J. G. C. Nörrenberg, professor of astronomy, mathematics, and physics there, retired in 1851, the Württemberg government had already set aside the funds for two ordinary professorships to replace his. One of these professorships was for physics alone. The government arrived at its decision from the increasing "*practical* importance" of physics "for those professions that are based on the natural sciences," especially medicine, in which "the methods of investigation that are peculiar to physics" now exert great influence. They chose a physicist of "practical" background, the Württemberger Eduard Reusch, who until then had been teaching at Württemberg's polytechnic school in Stuttgart. Reusch was to convey the methods of physics to medical students as he had conveyed them to technical students, namely, by being a stimulating lecturer who could be clear on his subject even to students who knew no higher mathematics.[7] Reusch knew, as physicists then did, that general lectures were not enough, that physics had to be an examination requirement before most students would do serious work in it;[8] so the initial gain for physics at Tübingen consisted only in getting a separate professorship, not in raising the level of instruction. Between 1859 and 1863, physics at Tübingen received further support from the side of medicine. At the instigation of the medical faculty, the natural sciences formed a separate faculty to which all medical students were assigned at the beginning of their studies; from there they could graduate to the medical faculty only by passing examinations in the natural sciences, which included physics.[9] Through these changes, Tübingen physics was brought considerably closer to the standards of the best university physics instruction: it now had an ordinary professorship for physics, and from 1865 on, Reusch offered regular "practical physical exercises."[10] Since at Tübingen physics depended so largely on medicine for its students, however, Reusch did not succeed in equally advancing its mathematical side.[11] Tübingen, he sadly admitted after losing Carl Neumann in 1868, was still no place for a good mathematician.[12] The mathematical-physical seminar was established the next year, which was to help.[13]

7. Report of the Ministry of Church and School Affairs to the King, 25 Oct. 1851, HSTA, Stuttgart, E14 Bü 1471.

8. Reusch to Tübingen U. Philosophical Faculty, 16 June 1859, in *Quellen zur Gründungsgeschichte der Naturwissenschaftlichen Fakultät in Tübingen 1859–1863*, ed. Wolf von Engelhardt and Hansmartin Decker-Hauff (Tübingen: J. C. B. Mohr [Paul Siebeck], 1963), 55–57.

9. Klüpfel, *Tübingen*, 161.

10. *Festgabe*, 1.

11. The knowledge of physics was "rare and inadequate" among physicians, Reusch wrote in 1859 (*Quellen*, 57). Around that time, medical students anywhere in Germany could still have so imperfect an understanding of physics that they might expect to learn its most important lessons without knowing any mathematics. An author of a reference book on physics intended for medical students described the mathematical formulas in other physics books as decorations. Foreword to Rudolf Wagner, *Taschenbuch der Physik* (Leipzig, 1851).

Through private study, the medical student Helmholtz acquired a comprehensive knowledge of mathematics in the early 1840s because he intended to use physics in his physiological researches. His fellow students Brücke and du Bois-Reymond, although they were equally committed to such a program, did not acquire that knowledge, which, as they later acknowledged, gave Helmholtz a considerable headstart. Koenigsberger, *Helmholtz* 1: 44.

12. Reusch to Franz Neumann, 3 Oct. 1868, Neumann Papers, Göttingen UB, Ms. Dept.

13. Tübingen, *Festgabe*, 14.

Teaching was the other profession beside medicine for which students could be required to study physics, and, as we have seen, physicists made use of their connection with teacher training to advance their field in general. Aside from medicine and teaching, no other profession then offered a particularly strong argument for physics at the universities. Appeals for government support rarely mentioned that students preparing to become bureaucrats, for example, needed to know physics.[14] The use of physics in technical professions—which were then, like medicine, education, and law, to a large extent in the service of the state—was acknowledged, but that did little to help physics at the universities, since students preparing for technical professions as a rule got their education elsewhere. While most universities offered courses in "technology," usually as part of a major in "economics," it was rarely an important subject there. The capital of most states had a technical school, which had grown out of the former military academy at the court. So Leipzig University was supplemented by the Dresden Polytechnic, Göttingen by a polytechnic school in Hannover, Tübingen by one at Stuttgart, Marburg by one at Kassel; and of the three states with more than one university, Baden, Bavaria, and Prussia, the latter two also had more than one polytechnic school. Only Giessen, Kiel, Rostock, and Jena were not supplemented by polytechnic schools in their states in this period; as a consequence, these four universities became involved in one way or another with technical training, which influenced, for better or worse, their physics teaching.

The involvement with technical training had a negative influence on physics at Rostock and Kiel and a beneficial one at Giessen. (Jena's involvement came only after this period.) Rostock and Kiel, as port cities, had naval schools, which shared faculty members with the local university and which consumed much of the time of the university's natural sciences teachers. Rostock University was so small and poor that it was the one remaining German university that still did not have a professor of physics at all. Physics was taught there in part by the professor of mathematics Hermann Karsten and in part by the professor of chemistry Franz Schulze, who were both also kept busy by duties related to naval instruction. Hermann Karsten taught navigation at the university, directed the school of navigation, and also edited an "astronomical almanac for sailors." The absence of instruction beyond the general physics lectures—Rostock had neither a physics laboratory course nor a seminar—suggests that there were few if any students with a scientific interest in physics and that Karsten and Schulze saw no need, or lacked the inclination, to promote a more thorough study of physics. At the turn of the century, Rostock's physics lecture hall still accommodated only forty-eight students.[15]

14. Gerling at Marburg complained of the lack of student interest in mathematics and the natural sciences because state officials were not expected to have a knowledge of these subjects; he looked hopefully to a new law then being discussed that would establish general examinations and introduce a certification of future officials from the institute of political economy that would reflect a knowledge of mathematics and physics. Gerling to the Hessen government, 15 Aug. 1831, STA, Marburg, Bestand 307d, Nr. 21.

15. Gerhard Becherer, "Die Geschichte der Entwicklung des Physikalischen Instituts der Universität Rostock," *Wiss. Zs. d. U. Rostock, Math.-Naturwiss.* 16 (1967): 825–30, on 826, 829.

At Kiel, Gustav Karsten, the professor of physics and mineralogy from 1851, put most of his resources for physics at the service of a scientific meteorology and other undertakings of practical value; he, too, taught at the local naval school at the same time that he taught at the university. Karsten had come to Kiel from Berlin, where he had been a member of the small, exclusive circle of young scientists that included Helmholtz and Clausius, and he had been co-founder of the Berlin Physical Society. At Kiel, he taught the expected courses on experimental physics and even mathematical physics occasionally, he conducted practical exercises, and he directed researches in physics by a few students. But physics did not flourish there—even for the big experimental lecture course he had only ten to fifteen students—and the local means were essentially lost to physics during most of Karsten's long tenure there, which extended to 1894.[16] Karsten had found an arena for his organizational talents in areas other than physics, which, given Kiel's geographical location and maritime function, were more important there and therefore more profitable.

Giessen University, which was the one university at which physics profited from the connection with technical training, between 1837 and 1875 served as both the university and the polytechnic for its state. It not only offered courses on technical subjects as the other universities did, but it also allowed students to earn doctorates of philosophy by majoring in engineering or technology. It was then the only institution of higher education in Germany to do so, a practice which stopped with the founding of the polytechnic school in Darmstadt in 1877.[17] As early as 1838 Giessen acquired an ordinary professorship exclusively for physics, to which Heinrich Buff was appointed. In Buff, the university acquired a physicist with excellent scientific connections through his experimental training with Gay-Lussac and Liebig; it acquired as well a physicist with experience in technical education, since Buff had taught at the polytechnic school in Kassel. Most important for physics at Giessen, Buff brought with him the inclination and conviction of a "scientific" experimental physicist, who from the beginning firmly believed in the importance of mathematics for the natural sciences. Because of the double function of Giessen as a university and a technical school, Buff could hope for an audience in addition to the expected medical students for his comprehensive lectures in physics.[18] He could also expect to attract some of the many chemistry students attracted to Giessen by Liebig. This

16. Charlotte Schmidt-Schönbeck, *300 Jahre Physik und Astronomie an der Kieler Universität* (Kiel: F. Hirt, 1965), 65–73; B. Schwalbe, "Nachruf auf G. Karsten," *Verh. phys. Ges.* 2 (1900): 147–59 (inaccurate in a number of pertinent details); Leonhard Weber, "Gustav Karsten," *Schriften d. Naturwiss. Vereins f. Schleswig-Holstein* 12 (1901): 63–68; W. Wolkenhauer, "Karsten, Gustav," *Biographisches Jahrbuch und Deutscher Nekrolog* 5 (1900): 76–78. The details of the financial support for physics at Kiel are given in a report by the Göttingen U. Curator to Minister v. Gossler, 16 Oct. 1883, Göttingen UA, XVI. IV. C. v, and in a letter by Curator Warnstedt, formerly an official in Copenhagen, to Rudolph Wagner [1854?], Rudolph Wagner Correspondence, Göttingen UB, Ms. Dept.

17. M. Biermer, "Die Grossherzoglich Hessische Ludwigs-Universität zu Giessen," in Wilhelm Lexis, ed., *Das Unterrichtswesen im Deutschen Reich*, vol. 1, *Die Universitäten im Deutschen Reich* (Berlin: A. Asher, 1904), 562–74, on 564.

18. Lorey, "Physik . . . Giessen," 87–96. Buff's views on physics instruction may be gathered from his reports on the establishment of a mathematical-physical seminar at Giessen in 1861, Giessen UA, Phil H Nr. 36.

was another connection of physics with technical training, since Liebig trained his students for technical jobs in chemistry. Buff, originally a chemist himself, taught physics with the needs of chemistry and pharmacy in mind.[19] In 1846 a newspaper noted that whereas attendance at most German universities had been declining for the last several years, at Giessen University it had constantly increased. In part, the newspaper went on, this had to be ascribed to the many means that had been brought together at Giessen "for the thorough study of the natural sciences"; if the university could add to its faculty an excellent botanist and zoologist, there would be few other universities in Germany "where physicians, manufacturers, men with technical professions, pharmacists, and farmers could prepare themselves more thoroughly for their speciality than here."[20]

If a university physicist was assured students because of favorable circumstances for teaching, such as those at Tübingen and Giessen, he could expect state support. As so many of the German physicists of that period did, Reusch at Tübingen in 1851 started with almost nothing. His predecessors had enjoyed the adequate quarters of the Tübingen observatory, because they had also been the local astronomers,[21] but as a professor of physics only, Reusch had to make do with an inadequate auditorium and two rooms for the physical cabinet. He managed some modest improvements. First, he adapted the auditorium for experimental lectures by installing elevated seats.[22] This change from low seats, which were literally at the feet of the lecturer on his raised podium (the place where admiring students of great teachers gathered, according to academic legend), to stepwise elevated seats with a good view *down* on the lecturer and his experimental table was introduced to science lecture halls in the nineteenth century.[23] Elevated seating, as the first permanently installed and specialized feature of science lecture halls, contributed to the change from all-purpose university auditoriums, which had often been used for science lectures in the past, to separate physics lecture halls. It also shifted the expense of furnishing physics lecture halls from the physics professors, whose responsibility it had been at many universities, to the states. Second, Reusch accumulated many valuable instruments, the most important of which were the precision instruments for electricity and magnetism that had become almost prescribed tools for physicists after Gauss and Weber.[24] The acquisition of such instruments tended to be the first step toward acquiring a modern physics institute; their value and complexity, their need of careful maintenance and permanent placement where they would be used, and their use

---

19. Borscheid, *Naturwissenschaft*, 39, suggests that physics at Giessen profited from Liebig's presence there but makes the common mistake of considering Liebig's views on laboratory instruction as out of keeping with contemporary views, even an "offense against the spirit of the times."

20. Borscheid, *Naturwissenschaft*, 39 n. 84.

21. Gerling described the favorable conditions Tübingen offered him twenty years earlier; letter to the government in Kassel, 15 Aug. 1831, STA, Marburg, Bestand 307d, Nr. 21. Also *Festgabe*, 9–10.

22. *Festgabe*, 1. Klüpfel, *Tübingen*, 122.

23. Eduard Schmitt, "Hochschulen im allgemeinen," 4–53, on 9, and Hermann Eggert, "Universitäten," 54–111, on 81; both in *Handbuch der Architektur*, pt. 4, sec. 6, no. 2aI.

24. Klüpfel, *Tübingen*, 122.

in instruction as well as in research all sooner or later demanded an appropriate location. They demanded it, moreover, of the state whose property the instruments now were. The specialized lecture halls and laboratories and the delicate, yet large instrumental arrangements inevitably suggested that they be given a special building. At Tübingen, a building for a physics institute was considered as early as 1863;[25] the plans that Reusch was asked to draw up came to nothing, but such false starts were fairly typical. The slow acquisition of the material means for physics consumed the entire careers of many German physicists in this period.

Buff took the initiative early in acquiring a physics institute at Giessen, where Liebig's example held the promise of success. In 1838, Buff created an institute in a wing of his own house, but he had it acknowledged as the official Giessen physics institute from the beginning. He received reimbursement for the furnishings of the auditorium and laboratory in his house, into which he moved the instrument collection used by his predecessor, and from 1844 he even received rent from the state for these rooms that he provided for the institute. His institute had space for faculty and students to do research and space for laboratory exercises, which from 1862 were conducted in the physical seminar. In addition, Buff's work was supplemented by that of junior colleagues, who also received not only a salary but money and facilities for instruments, an unusual arrangement then.[26]

Physics at Provincial Universities

The provincial universities of Baden, Bavaria, and Prussia were, as a rule, at a disadvantage with respect to the other German universities. Redistributions of territory following the wars at the beginning of the century had brought new universities to all three states; for example, Greifswald University to Prussia, Erlangen University to Bavaria, and Freiburg University to Baden. Many other universities had been closed, uncomfortable reminders to Erlangen and Freiburg of their own possible fate. A newly acquired small university such as Erlangen might be unwelcome to its new state because it had lost its properties or other sources of income and was now financially dependent on the state.[27] If it retained its properties and could still largely support itself, it might be unwelcome all the same because of religious differences, as Freiburg was;[28] or, as Greifswald, it might not fit the ministry's plans for educational reform.[29] In any case, the uncertainty about their future affected the expectations and material demands of these universities just as it affected how much their states were willing to give.

25. *Festgabe*, 1.
26. See details below, pp. 242–43.
27. Theodor Kolde, *Die Universität Erlangen unter dem Hause Wittelsbach, 1810–1910* (Erlangen and Leipzig: A. Deichert, 1910), especially 96–164. Robert von Mohl's (cited in Württemberg, Statistisches Landesamt, *Statistik . . . Tübingen*, 23) and Riese's (*Hochschule*, 65) descriptions of the nineteenth-century German universities as state institutions for education no longer possessing any "private property to speak of" applies to most of them.
28. Borscheid, *Naturwissenschaft*, 70–71, 75. Riese, *Hochschule*, 74.
29. Lenz, *Berlin*, vol. 2, pt. 1, p. 11.

Yet another threat to their future was the loss of students. Freiburg came close to extinction several times during our period for this reason as well as for the reason of religious differences. It first lost its Swiss students—Freiburg attracted them earlier because of its convenient location—when Switzerland founded universities at Bern and Zurich. Then in 1836 it lost many of the students in the philosophical faculty, when the task of preparing entering students for the professional faculties was assigned to the gymnasiums.[30] This second loss was so great that by the winter semester of 1841–42, the enrollment in the philosophical faculty was down to two. The professor of physics, G. F. Wucherer, who used to have approximately fifty students, now combined his lectures on experimental and theoretical physics into one course to which he added popular lectures on practical subjects or on great discoveries in physics to attract what students he could.[31] Any attempt at raising the level of physics instruction to a scientific one, as might have been possible after the elementary studies were taken over by the gymnasiums, was precluded by the lack of students.[32] Even a vigorous physicist such as Johann Müller, a man of thirty-five when he succeeded Wucherer in 1844 and a former student of scientists of the caliber of Plücker, Buff, and Liebig, could not make a difference.[33] Soon after he came to Freiburg, in 1846, he started a seminar for mathematics and the natural sciences together with the professor of mathematics Ludwig Öttinger and other science professors, but in 1853 the seminar was canceled because it attracted no students.[34] Müller was asked in 1850 to give the lecture course on experimental physics throughout the academic year instead of in the summer only, which was the measure of his modest success.[35] Until 1869 he did not lecture on theoretical physics, which was partly covered by Öttinger's lectures on mechanics, and he did not offer student laboratory practice. The physics seminar was not revived until after 1870.

The material means for physics at Müller's disposal corresponded to the condition of the university as a whole. Müller's collection of instruments, which had been acquired from a monastery that had been secularized, had been set up in several rooms in a wing of the university building long before his arrival. Within these rooms, some space was converted into a lecture hall for mathematics and physics

30. Fritz Baumgarten, *Freiburg im Breisgau* (Berlin: Wedekind, 1907), 118–19. Gericke, *Mathematik . . . Freiburg*, 54–59.

31. *Aus der Geschichte . . . Freiburg*, 16.

32. *Aus der Geschichte . . . Freiburg*, 17, claims that when Wucherer retired in 1842, his position was left vacant for lack of students. Wucherer died in April 1843 of a paralyzing disease; his end was perhaps anticipated, for only two months later Dove received the first inquiries about his interest in the Freiburg chair of physics. In January 1844, he was offered the job. He declined, recommending instead Moser, who was offered it in April 1844. Moser was willing to go to Freiburg if he could have a physical cabinet with an annual fund to supplement it as well as a salary in excess of the 1000 thaler he was getting at Königsberg. Apparently Freiburg could not offer him these conditions. The negotiations for a successor to Wucherer had begun promptly, but they dragged on for over a year, which caused a break in physics instruction. Dove to "Regierungs-Director," 31 Jan. 1844; Moser to "Professor," 26 Apr. 1844; both in Bad. GLA, 235/7525.

33. Von L., "Müller: Johann Heinrich Jakob," *ADB* 22 (1970): 633–34.

34. Freiburg U. Senate to Baden Ministry of the Interior, 7 Sept. 1846, Bad. GLA, 235/7766. Gericke, *Mathematik . . . Freiburg*, 62.

35. Müller to Freiburg U. Senate, 25 Sept. 1850, Bad. GLA, 235/7767.

and, presumably, other sciences; botany was still taught in it in the 1870s, impeding the preparations for the experimental physics lectures. Other rooms remained completely unchanged and still lacked gas and water pipes in the 1870s, which made them useless for physics. And yet this location served as the Freiburg physics institute until the end of the century. The regular institute budget from 1832 to 1858 of 300 gulden (approximately 170 thaler), which included the salary for a servant, by the end of this period was less that half of what physics institutes at most other universities received; it was not enough even for the needs of instruction and the maintenance of the instruments. It was raised to 400 gulden in 1860, after Müller had required small extraordinary grants for several years; occasionally he received larger amounts for "unavoidably necessary new apparatus of some importance." These modest means did not allow Müller to acquire the precision instruments necessary for research and for student exercises, but over the years he managed to equip the institute for the many demonstration experiments he liked to include in his lectures.[36]

That Müller's plight reflected the conditions of Freiburg University and not his own failings as a physicist is confirmed by a request for a Ruhmkorff electric induction apparatus, which he together with three other science professors at Freiburg made in 1861. They explained that they hoped to use it both for instruction and for research and that it could be used not only for physics and chemistry but also for physiological and even mineralogical investigations. They pointed out that Heidelberg University and Karlsruhe Polytechnic, their sister institutions in Baden, already had their Ruhmkorffs, and Robert Bunsen and Kirchhoff had used theirs in their brilliant discoveries.[37] Between them, the four professors did not have the thousand francs that the apparatus cost in Paris, since the budgets for their institutes were so small that they were completely consumed by day-to-day expenses.

Although Müller lacked all means for systematic research, he participated in physics as best he could, as did his neighbor Reusch who was almost equally hampered in research. No other institute directors published more frequently in the *Annalen* around 1870 than they did. They appeared in nearly every volume; the frequency of their communications was matched only by their brevity, Müller's of three pages and Reusch's of five pages. The differences between their publications, as far as their value to physics was concerned, were small despite the somewhat better state of the Tübingen institute. Müller did not pretend to do research; a prolific textbook writer, he reported measurements with a "vibration chronoscope," which he said he would describe in the coming seventh edition of his *Lehrbuch der Physik*.[38]

36. *Aus der Geschichte . . . Freiburg*, 14–18. Emil Warburg, "Das physikalische Institut," in *Die Universität Freiburg*, 91–96, on 93–94. Freiburg U. Senate to Baden Ministry of the Interior, 8 May 1860, Bad. GLA, 235/7767. According to the latter source, Freiburg physics got occasional small extraordinary grants in the years immediately before 1860. Borscheid, *Naturwissenschaft*, 75, is not entirely correct in claiming that it got nothing at all.

37. Müller and other faculty members to Baden Ministry of the Interior, 10 Feb. 1861, Bad. GLA, 235/7767.

38. Johann Müller, "Ein Vibrations-Chronoskop und Versuche mit demselben," *Ann.* 136 (1869): 151–54.

Reusch's series of brief crystallographic studies of mica show that he intended to do at least a minimum of research, but they also reveal the limitations he worked under, both of his material means and of his mathematical ability. He used the mica of the Tübingen physical cabinet, the origins and chemical composition of which he did not know and which was in bad condition and insufficient for him to draw firm conclusions. After his first publication on the subject, colleagues in Berlin and Vienna sent him good mica, which allowed him to continue and modify his findings. By stacking lamina of mica to imitate different crystals, evidently expecting to learn something about molecular structure, he saw the possibility of a mathematical treatment of the optical effects and invited a "calculator" to work it out, conscious of his own "very elementary mathematical knowledge."[39]

The Bavarian provincial university of Würzburg fared similarly to Freiburg: physics had almost no existence there, not even an ordinary professorship to itself. From 1828 until 1866, it was taught by a "professor of physics and general chemistry," a position held by G. W. Osann. In the 1860s, Osann gave a regular five-hour lecture course on physics "in connection with . . . general chemistry," classes for reviewing physics exercises, a one-hour free lecture course on wave theory in its application to acoustics and optics, and a practical introduction to physical and chemical experiments, which, given Osann's equipment, must have been a demonstration course rather than one in which students participated.[40] That is, Osann gave Würzburg medical students a general idea of physics and chemistry and did not carry the physics curriculum beyond that. As his successor Clausius was to find, Würzburg had no students with the mathematical preparation for advanced physics in any case.[41] Osann's instrumental equipment consisted of thirty-three pieces—some scales and some apparatus for lecture demonstrations—of which only three were in good condition in 1867. His double appointment at such a late date and the condition of the Würzburg physical cabinet—about which Clausius said that "far from corresponding to the present state of the science, it even lacked very many of the most necessary apparatus without which, in my view, one cannot even give a lecture on experimental physics that is worthy of a university"—were holdovers from a time when the cost of science instruction at a provincial university could almost be held to the price of half a professor's salary.[42]

The state of physics at Erlangen University also seems to have been determined by how cheaply Bavaria could get its physicists. After the long career of C. W. G.

39. Eduard Reusch, "Ueber die Körnerprobe am zwei-axigen Glimmer," Ann. 136 (1869): 130–35; "Untersuchung über Glimmercombinationen," Ann. 138 (1869): 628–37, on 632–34. Reusch to Franz Neumann, 24 Aug. 1879, Neumann Papers, Göttingen UB, Ms. Dept.

40. Osann's Personalakte, Würzburg UA, Nr. 690. Reindl, Würzburg, 38, 101. Verzeichniss der Vorlesungen welche an der Königlich-Bayerischen Julius-Maximilians-Universität zu Würzburg . . . gehalten werden (Würzburg, [annual]).

41. Würzburg U. Senate to Bavarian Ministry of the Interior (draft), 13 Jan. 1869, Clausius Personalakte, Würzburg UA, Nr. 404. In his mathematical lectures on electrical theory, Clausius had about fourteen auditors, but among them only three capable of "complete understanding and honest participation." The three were not students but two ordinary professors of medicine and an assistant, according to this file.

42. Clausius to Würzburg U. Senate, 18 May 1867, Clausius Personalakte, Würzburg UA, Nr. 404.

Kastner came to an end in 1857, and after his successor, the energetic and highly recommended experimentalist Rudolph Kohlrausch, died within his first year there, Erlangen had to make do with beginners, first with Wilhelm Beetz and after him with Eugen Lommel.[43] Both physicists came from teaching jobs below the university level and both had sought employment outside of Germany, in Switzerland. They had, as a result, two advantages over other physicists: they would come for a smaller salary than an experienced physicist, and they did not dare to make great demands for instruments and facilities. Erlangen University offered Beetz and Lommel next to nothing in facilities: the lecture hall was poor, and the rooms of the institute could barely hold the beginnings of a collection.[44] Nevertheless, Beetz managed to do experimental research there, and Lommel, who was more of a mathematical physicist in his research, made it possible for his students to do experimental investigations.[45] Both Beetz and Lommel made their tenure at Erlangen into a stepping stone to prestigious positions in Munich.

Beginning in the 1860s, there were signs of a more competitive attitude in some of the provincial universities, which had an effect on physics. A good example is the negotiation over Osann's successor at Würzburg. By 1866 Osann's health had deteriorated to a point where the Bavarian ministry began thinking about replacing him. They wanted both a physicist and a chemist this time, since they intended to separate Osann's two fields at last. The ministry had not yet decided whether a new ordinary professorship could be created for physics or whether they should make do with an extraordinary professorship for the time being. They put the question before the philosophical faculty, directing it to submit it to the medical faculty as well, since the medical faculty, "because of its great number of students, must take a very great interest in the quality of the physicist." The medical faculty wanted as good a physicist as possible and right away, which decided the matter, since its wishes could only be met by a new ordinary, not extraordinary, professorship. The philosophical faculty had no equally clear idea of what it wanted or even of the need for good physics at Würzburg.[46]

43. Kolde, *Erlangen*, 424–25.
44. Kolde, *Erlangen*, 469–70.
45. Friedrich Kohlrausch, "Wilhelm v. Beetz. Nekrolog," in *Gesammelte Abhandlungen*, ed. Wilhelm Hallwachs, Adolf Heydweiller, Karl Strecker, and Otto Wiener, 2 vols. (Leipzig, J. A. Barth, 1910–11), 2:1048–61 (hereafter cited as *Ges. Abh.*). C. Voit, "Wilhelm von Beetz," *Sitzungsber. bay. Akad.* 16 (1886): 10–31. Ludwig Boltzmann, "Eugen von Lommel," *Jahresber. d. Deutsch. Math.-Vereinigung* 8 (1900): 47–53. C. Voit, "Eugen v. Lommel," *Sitzungsber. bay. Akad.* 30 (1900): 324–39. Clausius recommended Lommel as a mathematical physicist to the Zurich Polytechnic when Lommel became Privatdocent there in 1866; in 1869 the polytechnic offered Lommel a professorship, which he declined. Clausius to President of the Swiss Education Council, 27 Feb. 1866, A Schweiz. Sch., Zurich.
46. Recklinghausen to Franz Neumann, 5 Mar. 1866, Neumann Papers, Göttingen UB, Ms. Dept. Recklinghausen wanted Neumann's recommendation of a very good physicist. It appears from a letter by another Würzburg professor to Neumann later, on 29 Dec. 1866, in the same collection, that Neumann responded by recommending his own students, Georg Quincke and Heinrich Wild. They did not meet the criterion of the Würzburg faculty members, who wanted the best and got Clausius.
The separation of physics from chemistry was formally announced to the Würzburg University Senate by the Bavarian Ministry of the Interior on 14 Mar. 1867, Clausius Personalakte, Würzburg UA, Nr. 404.

The next question to be settled was whom to appoint to the new chair. The Würzburg faculty was divided on the criteria to be used in choosing candidates. Some members held that Bavarian professorships should be filled with Bavarians if at all possible, and they presented an all-Bavarian list of candidates. Other members were guided by the view, which was supported by much past experience, that provincial universities could only hope for second-rate professors because the state would not pay for better. Their list of candidates was headed by a gymnasium teacher—who in over ten years of teaching had published a physics text, a book of geography, and two papers—an extraordinary professor, and a Privatdocent, all of whom had the advantage of being not too expensive.[47]

Both of these factions of the faculty were swept aside by a third, who saw Würzburg University in competition with all universities in western and southern Germany, especially with the best universities among them, Göttingen, Heidelberg, and Bonn. This third faction pointed out that the best universities had recently made the "greatest efforts to bring their teaching staff and their means of instruction to ever greater levels of perfection." Not to be left behind, Würzburg should go after the best possible physicist who had an established reputation as an outstanding teacher and a researcher into the "highest problems of science." It did not matter if the new physicist was "a Bavarian or a Prussian, a Swiss or an Austrian," as long as he was honorable and the best. This faction wanted Clausius, to be precise, and the government agreed, even though it knew that Clausius's appointment would involve considerable expense for the improvement of the Würzburg physics institute. (The three other candidates whom the Würzburg academic senate proposed in case Clausius did not come were Beetz, Wild, and Quincke: Beetz and Wild were ordinary professors, and Quincke was an extraordinary professor whose desirability was enhanced by his owning an excellent private collection of instruments.) The case for Clausius was based primarily on his creativity as a physics researcher and his standing as one of the "greatest" of contemporary physicists.[48] Not too many years earlier, the faculty of a provincial university such as Würzburg might have mentioned someone like Clausius as the most desirable candidate and then settled for three local or inexpensive candidates who qualified mainly by their teaching.

Following upon its success in acquiring Clausius, when Clausius later moved to Bonn, Würzburg wanted to hire Kirchhoff away from Heidelberg to replace him.[49] The Bavarian ministry opposed their plan then because of Kirchhoff's poor health.[50] But when Würzburg's physics chair became vacant again two years later, in 1872, Kirchhoff was offered the job this time, and he turned it down.[51] In asking Kirch-

47. Report of the Würzburg U. Senate to Bavarian Ministry of the Interior, 13 Jan. 1867, Osann Personalakte, Würzburg UA, Nr. 690. Unidentified Würzburg professor [name illegible] to Franz Neumann, 29 Dec. 1866, Neumann Papers, Göttingen UB, Ms. Dept.

48. Würzburg U. Senate report, 13 Jan. 1867. Clausius had received the finest recommendation from Kirchhoff. For the Bavarian ministry's approval of Clausius for Würzburg: Ministry of the Interior to Würzburg U. Senate, 14 Mar. 1867, Clausius Personalakte, Würzburg UA, Nr. 404.

49. Rudolf Wagner to Göttingen U. Curator, 5 Mar. 1869, Friedrich Kohlrausch Personalakte, Göttingen UA, 4/V b/156.

50. Reindl, Würzburg, 39.

51. Baden Ministry of the Interior, 12 Feb. 1872, Kirchhoff Personalakte, Bad. GLA, 76/9961.

hoff, Würzburg had tried to win out not only over Heidelberg but also over Berlin, which shortly before had offered Kirchhoff its physics chair and had been turned down.[52] Würzburg had acted on the conviction that provincial universities had the same right to scientific and scholarly excellence as universities in the capitals.

Although Würzburg could hold Clausius for only two years, physics there profited from the initiative of the faculty members who had wanted the best. Beginning at Würzburg in the fall of 1867, Clausius taught experimental physics as a five-hour lecture course extending over two semesters, which drew more students than the lecture hall could hold. He also introduced mathematical-theoretical courses.[53] His importance as a physicist made it possible for him to secure the money to bring Würzburg's physical cabinet up to date. He was granted the approximately 10,000 gulden he needed—Bavarian universities could, with the government's permission, take on large loans for such purposes—and he left behind an institute consisting of a lecture hall, a workroom for the director, and a number of rooms containing the instrument collection, which would meet "all demands of modern times." In this institute, his successor, August Kundt, set up the laboratory and acquired W.C. Röntgen as the first assistant.[54]

But Clausius could not provide students with sufficient mathematical preparation to take his advanced theoretical courses. He left Würzburg in 1869 in part because he hoped to find them at Bonn.[55]

At the Prussian provincial universities, financial support for physics would seem ample when compared to that at the southern provincial universities. With the exception of Greifswald, the physics institutes at the Prussian provincial universities were supported as well as the most productive physics institutes at German universities outside Prussia, such as those at Göttingen, Heidelberg, and Leipzig. At Bonn University, physics received 400 thaler annually until 1865, when its budget was doubled; at Königsberg, physics received 508 thaler annually during this period; at Breslau, it received 428 thaler in the 1840s; at Halle, physics and chemistry, which were combined, received 520 thaler.[56] In addition, Bonn and Halle had money for natural sciences seminars, which included physics, and each of the Prussian universities had at least two physicists' salaries. For comparison with non-Prussian universities: at Göttingen, physics received 300 thaler until 1849 and after that 500; at Heidelberg, it received between 500 and 600 thaler at its peak in the 1860s during

52. Kirchhoff to du Bois-Reymond, 9 June 1870, STPK, Darmst. Coll. 1924.55. Baden Ministry of the Interior, 10 June 1870, Kirchhoff Personalakte, Bad. GLA, 76/9961.

53. *Verzeichniss der Vorlesungen . . . Würzburg*. Würzburg U. Senate to Bavarian Ministry of the Interior (draft), 13 Jan. 1869, Clausius Personalakte, Würzburg UA, Nr. 404. Clausius's first two-hour theoretical lecture courses were on "electricity in mathematical treatment" and on "mechanical heat theory"; later he gave a three-hour lecture course each semester on "optics [or electricity] in special treatment with experiments," the "special treatment" referring to mathematics.

54. Bavarian Ministry of the Interior to Würzburg U. Senate, 14 Mar. and 23 Mar. 1867; Clausius to Würzburg U. Senate, 18 May 1867; "Senatsbericht zum vorgesetzten Staatsministerium," 4 June 1867; Ministry's approval of the request for the money, 11 June 1867; Würzburg U. Senate to the Bavarian Ministry of the Interior, 5 Oct. 1868; Würzburg U. Senate to Bavarian Ministry of the Interior (draft), 13 Jan. 1869; Clausius Personalakte, Würzburg UA, Nr. 404.

55. Würzburg U. Senate to Bavarian Ministry of the Interior (draft), 13 Jan. 1869.

56. These amounts show only that Prussian physics received as much money as physics anywhere, not that physics got its fair share. See n. 36 in chap. 1. Rönne, *Unterrichts-Wesen* 2:433–62.

Kirchhoff's tenure; and at Leipzig, it received 500 thaler while Weber was there in the 1840s, which included the 200 thaler he donated from his salary to the institute budget.[57]

Like budgets, facilities for physics at provincial Prussian and non-Prussian universities were more or less comparable. The instrument collections and institute rooms were uniformly unremarkable at all of the provincial universities at the beginning of our period. Only Kirchhoff at Heidelberg received a new institute, consisting of half of a building; elsewhere improvements were left up to the physicists working with their regular budgets.

But to a greater degree than physicists at Göttingen, Heidelberg, and Leipzig, physicists at Prussian provincial universities were hindered in their attempts to build up physics. The difficulties they experienced in this period, which were similar to Neumann's at Königsberg, stemmed largely from the appointment and promotion policies of the ministry of culture. As the histories of Prussian physics institutes show, the Prussian ministry all too frequently disregarded—and made it a policy to disregard—the customary arrangement of having one ordinary professor administer a university physics institute. What money and facilities there were for physics at a university were rendered useless, or at least difficult to use effectively, because the ministry appointed second ordinary professors of physics or extraordinary professors of physics with whom the chairholder was then expected to share his institute and equipment, if indeed he did not have to cede them to the new man.[58] It also promoted talented young physicists regardless of the availability of established university chairs and without giving them adequate means for their work. In this, it was following the old Humboldtian notion of advancing scholarship through uninhibited competition among scholars, pitting the young against the established. But the competition was not backed up with the financial means necessary for it to work. The result was hardship for all young scholars,[59] and among physicists and other natural scientists it achieved nothing but loss of time and opportunity; for aside from lacking a salary, young physicists also found themselves condemned to scientific inactivity for lack of materials for their work. Many of the best physicists left Prussia.

The small Prussian—formerly Swedish—university of Greifswald was the least dependent on state support of all the Prussian universities, as most of its income still came from real property. Nevertheless, Altenstein, the Prussian minister of culture, beginning with one of his earliest ministerial evaluations in 1818, judged Greifswald University to be "completely unnecessary." Agreements with Sweden prevented him from closing it, but he planned to "influence" the provincial goverment to use the university's money for other things.[60] This plan was apparently realized: in the late

57. Our figures here are taken from the sources we cite where we discuss in detail physics at these individual universities. On Prussia, our figures agree with Rönne.

58. The problem originated with the ministry, not with the faculties. During Altenstein's ministry, the faculties had practically no say in matters of appointments or promotions, not even their traditional one of proposing three candidates for an opening on the faculty. The conflict over this issue and the resulting difficulties are described in Lenz, Berlin, vol. 2, pt. 1, pp. 404–15.

59. Lenz, Berlin, vol. 2, pt. 1, pp. 418–25.

60. Lenz, Berlin, vol. 2, pt. 1, p. 11.

1830s, physics got only sixty thaler annually and other fields got equally small amounts, but every year the government administrator of the university put aside several thousand thaler for "unexpected expenses" and other such categories that are not found in any other Prussian university budget.[61]

Conditions for physics in the 1840s at Greifswald were much what they had been since the beginning of the century: the now elderly professor of physics G. S. Tillberg taught his subject along with mathematics and astronomy, while the professor of mathematics and astronomy also taught physics and had permission to use the collection of old instruments and models, which constituted the physical cabinet.[62] Into this setting, in 1848, the Prussian ministry introduced the promising young physicist Ottokar von Feilitzsch, who had been trained by Plücker at Bonn and by Magnus at Berlin.[63] Tillberg, who guessed that the new extraordinary professor had been sent there to replace him, refused him access to the physical cabinet and all cooperation. Feilitzsch had no choice but to provide his own lecture hall and equipment. The ministry did nothing to help him, and it may even have worsened the situation when it promoted him to ordinary professor in 1853, over Tillberg's resistance, without improving his working conditions.

We can see the influence of the Greifswald arrangements on Feilitzsch's career by looking at his work. He published five papers in his first years at Greifswald, among them two long experimental series of investigations of diamagnetism. In these, for the most part, he used very modest means which he built himself; the larger items he used were limited to a telescope, a battery, magnets, and the like. He did not make measurements, even though he was testing some of Weber's results. Rather, he was "speaking of an *approximate* measure," he wrote in one case, "for I am far from attributing *more* than the characteristic of an observation to these investigations, which are carried out with the crudest means." Only once could he credit the Greifswald physical cabinet with contributing a piece of equipment, a good French prism. As he concluded the last of the series of researches in 1853, he said that he would continue them, but he did not.[64] He published next five years later—and then only a very brief paper—in 1858, a year after his and Tillberg's collections had been ordered to be combined and given to him.[65] By that time, Feilitzsch had spent nearly a decade of his most productive years without adequate means for research. Now, thinking that conditions might improve for him at last, he wrote to Neumann to learn about conditions at Königsberg; his questions show that he hoped for an up-to-date institute.[66] What Feilitzsch actually received at

61. Rönne, Unterrichts-Wesen, 447–50.

62. Festschrift zur 500-Jahrfeier der Universität Greifswald (Greifswald: Universität, 1956), 2:457–59.

63. Poggendorff noted that Feilitzsch was a member of Magnus's first colloquium. Feilitzsch spoke of Plücker as his "revered teacher" in his paper "Eine Theorie des Diamagnetismus. Magnetismus des Wismuth. Erweiterung der Ampère'schen Theorie," Ann. 82 (1851): 90–110.

64. Ottokar von Feilitzsch, "Erklärung der diamagnetischen Wirkungsweise durch die Ampère'sche Theorie," Ann. 87 (1852): 206–26, 427–54; 92 (1854): 366–402, 536–77. Quotation on 390.

65. Festschrift . . . Greifswald, 458. The paper is "Magnetische Rotationen unter Einfluss eines Stromleiters von unveränderlicher Gestalt," Ann. 105 (1858): 535–43.

66. Feilitzsch to Franz Neumann, 1 June 1857, Neumann Papers, Göttingen UB, Ms. Dept. Feilitzsch asked Neumann about the amount of the budget, the income of the physics institute in general,

Greifswald was so little that it could not help his career much either as a teacher or as a researcher: three rooms, a small budget, and a mechanic. These conditions, remaining unchanged for decades, even after the ministry had agreed to a new institute in 1867, allowed for no research to speak of—he published almost nothing more—and also forced him to limit the number of his students, preventing him from offering courses in laboratory practice, not to mention student research.[67] Feilitzsch's years of enforced inactivity in physics no doubt impeded the development of physics at Greifswald; for careers were built on research by then, and university physics institutes grew with their directors' reputations as reflected in offers from other universities.[68]

At another of Prussia's provincial universities, Breslau, the physicists came into conflict over the use of instruments, provoked in part by malice and in part by the practice of forcing physicists into coexistence at the same university under inadequate working conditions. The new Breslau University of 1811 had been created by uniting two older universities, and as a consequence it began with two ordinary professors of physics, who also taught other subjects. In 1832 one of the ordinary professorships of physics was held by Georg Friedrich Pohl, a Hegelian, a friend of like-minded ministry officials, and Ohm's nemesis; the other one was transformed that year into a salaried extraordinary professorship and given to the then unsalaried extraordinary professor Moritz Frankenheim.[69] Because of the separate origins of the two positions, which entailed a separate administration of their means, the arrangement worked satisfactorily for a time. Pohl had charge of the main physics collection, though he never used it either for research or for student laboratory practice.[70] Frankenheim, independently, had a small instrument collection and a small budget to maintain it, which furnished the means for his physics lectures; he, like his successors in the extraordinary professorship, was expected to teach experimental physics. He also had "just barely" enough means for scientific investigations.[71] When Pohl died in 1849, Frankenheim became his successor, at the faculty's request. But the ministry refused to appoint him director of the main physics collection; for although Pohl had never watched Frankenheim at work—Frankenheim impressed the

---

and how many teachers had to share the institute. He wanted to know if there were extra amounts for salaries for an assistant, a servant, and a mechanic; what the conditions of the rooms of the institute were and if the rooms were connected with the official living quarters of the director; if regular meteorological or magnetic observations were being made in the physics institute; and if the rooms and the budget sufficed to allow individual students to do "experimental exercises or small independent, perhaps physical-physiological investigations."

67. *Festschrift . . . Greifswald,* 458–59.

68. Feilitzsch was mentioned as a candidate for the Marburg chair of physics in 1864 (Hessen Ministry of the Interior to Marburg U. Senate, 10 Mar. 1864), but the philosophical faculty rejected his candidacy because he did not have adequate scientific achievements (Marburg U. Philosophical Faculty to Marburg U. Senate, 17 Mar. and 3 June 1864). In their view, he had already been outdistanced by Melde, who had become Privatdocent only four years earlier and Gerling's assistant in 1857. All documents in STA, Marburg, Bestand 305a.

69. Lummer, "Physik," 440–48. (Not an entirely reliable source.)

70. Moritz Frankenheim to Franz Neumann, 15 Nov. 1849, Neumann Papers, Göttingen UB, Ms. Dept.

71. E. E. Kummer to Franz Neumann, 22 June 1849, Neumann Papers, Göttingen UB, Ms. Dept.

critical physicist O. E. Meyer with his "very great aptitude for experimental methods"—Pohl had judged him as lacking a "higher scientific sense and the art of experimenting." The ministry believed Pohl. For access to instruments, it threatened Frankenheim with a complete dependence on the new extraordinary professor, who instead of inheriting the independent collection that came with his position became the custodian of the main collection.[72]

In the end, the ministry made Frankenheim co-director with the new man, Kirchhoff. Frankenheim, who had twenty-two years of experience as an experimental physicist and who was charged with the main experimental physics lectures, was made the equal of a man at the beginning of his career who, by his own account, "lacked all practice" in experimental physics.[73] Frankenheim foresaw with anguish—and correctly—that the shared administration of the collection would paralyze his teaching and research and would create bitterness and animosity between him and Kirchhoff, in spite of his good opinion of Kirchhoff as a physicist.[74] For Kirchhoff the situation was difficult, too, particularly since the ministry had not defined in detail their respective rights and duties. Kirchhoff did make some experimental investigations while he was at Breslau, but older colleagues such as Bunsen, Neumann, and Weber saw that the situation was a hindrance to his work and after four years helped to move him to an ordinary professorship at Heidelberg.[75] Hermann Marbach, Kirchhoff's successor, was too preoccupied with his duties as a secondary school teacher to play much of a role at the university.[76] As a result, Frankenheim had all of the institute funds at his disposal, and although he was not very productive as a researcher, he used his skill as an experimentalist to improve the Breslau collection of physics apparatus; by the end of his tenure, in the 1860s, Frankenheim could report that "few similar institutes" surpassed Breslau's in the number and value of its

72. Frankenheim to Neumann, 15 Nov. 1849. O. E. Meyer to Franz Neumann, 6 Feb. 1861, Neumann Papers, Göttingen UB, Ms. Dept. In Kummer to Neumann, 22 June 1849, Kummer asked Neumann to recommend a successor to Frankenheim in the extraordinary professorship, explaining that the "main thing for the faculty as for me is that we get a young man who is quite capable in his science as well as as a teacher." Kummer was then thinking of Knoblauch in Berlin, the only suitable young physicist he knew of. There is nothing in Kummer's letter to indicate that the faculty envisioned as irregular a role for the new extraordinary professor, who turned out to be Kirchhoff, as the ministry was to give him.

73. Warburg, "Kirchhoff," 207.

74. Frankenheim to Neumann, 15 Nov. 1849.

75. Warburg, "Kirchhoff," 208, shows that Robert Bunsen initiated the move. At Bunsen's request, which Kirchhoff transmitted, Weber, Ettingshausen, and Franz Neumann all sent him their recommendations of Kirchhoff: Weber to Bunsen, 12 Mar. 1854; Ettingshausen to Bunsen, 14 Mar. 1854; Neumann to Bunsen, 20 Mar. 1854; Bad. GLA, 235/3135.

76. Hermann Marbach was described by the Breslau crystallographer F. F. Runge as a "quite capable man for the optical relations of crystals," who differed from those contemporary crystallographers who were satisfied with knowing mathematics and physics only superficially (Runge to Franz Neumann, 28 Aug. 1867). Marbach had studied Neumann's researches and, with Kirchhoff's encouragement, had done "exceptionally good work" in the early 1850s (Marbach to Neumann, 9 Oct. 1856; Meyer to Neumann, 30 Mar. 1867). He was the Prorector of the Breslau Realschule from 1850 and also Privatdocent at the university from 1855, taking over from Kirchhoff. Despite Meyer's condemnation of Marbach in 1867 as a "quite useless unscientific man" (Meyer to Neumann, 30 Mar. 1867), the main obstacle to Marbach's work at the university was his secondary school teaching, as Meyer conceded after Marbach's death. Meyer wrote then that Marbach was "by nature a very talented man and could have achieved important [work] if the [secondary] school had not absorbed all of his energy" (Meyer to Neumann, 10 May 1873). All letters in Neumann Papers, Göttingen UB, Ms. Dept.

instruments; Frankenheim's successor, O. E. Meyer, remarked on the "excellent measuring apparatus." In 1866 the collection had been moved into "splendid observation halls," which were supplemented by a large lecture hall and quarters for an extraordinary professor of physics, so that Breslau could enter the next period much better prepared, thanks to Frankenheim, than Königsberg or Greifswald.[77]

The physicists at Halle found that even with the best will, their coexistence in one institute could not be productive for everyone. Perhaps because Schweigger was professor of both physics and chemistry, the ministry of culture kept promoting Schweigger's outstanding students to supplement physics instruction. In the late 1820s, for example, Halle had two extraordinary professors, Wilhelm Weber and L. F. Kämtz, in addition to Schweigger. The physicists were to share the Halle institute, and Schweigger cooperated, but since the institute building was also his home and he their senior, the implementation of the ministry's order became a delicate matter. Weber and later Wilhelm Hankel, another of Schweigger's students, did not stay long after their promotions but left Prussian service. Kämtz, on the other hand, stayed for over ten years before he, too, left in 1842;[78] he had been promised an annual sum for the purchase of apparatus, but instead, like Feilitzsch, he got a promotion to ordinary professor, making him in 1834 "an ordinary professor of physics without apparatus," as he described himself with bitterness a few years later. He depended on Schweigger for every instrument he needed, even for his lectures, which were on both experimental and mathematical physics; never having all the instruments to make his lectures what he knew they should be "deeply depressed" him. Experimental research was "completely impossible."[79]

After Kämtz had left Halle, Schweigger gave up chemistry and devoted himself only to physics. He had a junior colleague in the Privatdocent C. S. Cornelius, but since Cornelius was not much of a physicist, and perhaps because Schweigger now no longer carried the double burden, they were left undisturbed by further promotions for the time being. With Schweigger's advancing age, however, Halle in 1853 again acquired a second ordinary professor of physics, the prolific Knoblauch, by then doing experimental physics at Marburg, and again the arrangement worked against the younger physicist. In his first four years at Halle, the years before Schweigger's death, Knoblauch did not produce a single research paper. Only after he had inherited Schweigger's chair and institute in 1857 did he return to his former work and publishing habits.

In addition to its ignorance of, or indifference to, the material needs of physicists,[80] the Prussian ministry of culture often seemed not to care whether a candidate

77. Lummer, "Physik," 444. Meyer to Neumann, 30 Mar. 1867.

78. Willy Gebhardt, "Die Geschichte der Physikalischen Institute der Universität Halle," *Wiss. Zs. d. Martin-Luther U. Halle-Wittenberg, Math.-Naturwiss.* 10 (1961): 851–59, especially on 855–58. *Bibliographie der Universitätsschriften von Halle-Wittenberg 1817–1885*, ed. W. Suchier (Berlin: Deutscher Verlag der Wissenschaften, 1953), 340, 350, 634, 635. Wilhelm Schrader, *Geschichte der Friedrichs-Universität zu Halle*, 2 vols. (Berlin, 1894), 2: 80–81, 286.

79. Kämtz to "Geheimrath," 31 Dec. 1837, Listing Personalakte, Göttingen UA, 4/V b/108. Also, in the same file, Gruber to Mühlenbruch, 2 Feb. 1838.

80. Jacobi to Franz Neumann, "ca. 20 Jan. 1845," Neumann Papers, Göttingen UB, Ms. Dept. The ministers who were favorably disposed toward the sciences rarely had access to the king, according

fit a particular position or not. That arbitrariness affected physics at Breslau and Bonn: at the former university negatively, at the latter, quite by chance, positively.

At Breslau, physics was affected by the combination of students who were too poorly prepared in mathematics and of mathematics professors who were too good. During Pohl's and Frankenheim's tenures, the physics lectures attracted an average of thirty to forty students, a good attendance for a provincial university;[81] that number of students might have been sufficient to bring physics to a scientific level if the students had been better prepared in mathematics, but the Breslau professors of mathematics either could not or would not begin their instruction at a low enough level. The mathematics professor Ferdinand Joachimsthal, for example, looked for a Privatdocent to teach mechanics, trigonometry, and introductory analysis; and H. E. Schröter could not make himself understood even when he might have taught elementary subjects during his years as Privatdocent and extraordinary professor.[82] To keep his students, Frankenheim was therefore forced to make his physics courses largely practical and even technical. He hoped to establish a mathematical-physical seminar after he had obtained the ordinary professorship of physics in 1850, but he could not realize his plan for more than a decade, not until 1863.[83] While Kirchhoff was in Breslau, he taught mathematical physics, but as was to be expected, he did not succeed in arousing much interest in the subject; his students included colleagues such as Bunsen, which suggests that the level of the course was beyond most students' preparation.[84] In 1861 Frankenheim tried to persuade O. E. Meyer, a recent Königsberg graduate who was looking for a university at which to habilitate, to become Privatdocent at Breslau to teach "theoretical" physics. With a realistic view of the circumstances there, Frankenheim proposed that he give lectures on practical uses of mathematics in physics. "All the mathematics that is to be applied comes down to a few interpolation formulas," Meyer reported scornfully on the proposal; he rejected so modest a beginning to his career, as he had rejected teaching mechanics, trigonometry, and introductory analysis. An official at the Prussian ministry agreed with Meyer that he was too good for Breslau. The Breslau faculty saw the matter differently: to them, Meyer was an impractical physicist for whom they had no need; they would have preferred a physicist of "Jolly's direction," the experimental physicist at Munich.[85]

In 1864 Meyer came to Breslau after all, but as successor to the mathematician Lipschitz, in an extraordinary professorship used for mathematics, rather than as a physicist.[86] Meyer was expected to give mathematics lectures, but he concluded from

to Jacobi; of the cabinet ministers who did have access, "the one is hostile to the sciences, the other is indifferent to them," and they "ruin the best intentions."

81. Lummer, "Physik," 447.

82. Meyer to Franz Neumann, 6 Feb. 1861, Neumann Papers, Göttingen UB, Ms. Dept.

83. Frankenheim to Neumann, 15 Nov. 1849. Festschrift . . . Breslau, 440.

84. Warburg, "Kirchhoff," 207; Meyer to Neuman, 6 Feb. 1861.

85. Meyer to Neumann, 6 Feb. 1861.

86. Both Lummer and Olesko have said that Meyer came to Breslau as "extraordinary professor for mathematical physics" (Lummer, "Physik," 443), and that in 1865 he was promoted to ordinary professor for mathematical physics and remained in that position for the rest of his career (Olesko, "Emergence," 515, passim). They are contradicted by Meyer (letter to Franz Neumann, 16 July 1864, Neumann Papers,

the negotiations with the Prussian ministry of culture that "I may at the same time consider myself Kirchhoff's successor, that is, I may assume that I am being employed not only for mathematics but also for physics." As with Kirchhoff, with Meyer the ministry followed its practice of leaving matters undetermined. "All this does not rest on official arrangements but merely on a private agreement between Schröter and Olshausen [a ministry official]. Both are acting on the view that Kirchhoff's position has not yet been filled again, even though Marbach was promoted to extraordinary professor of physics. Both . . . are wishing that mathematical physics . . . would again be taught at Breslau." Officially Meyer was not told what to lecture on or even assigned a special subject. He intended to exploit the vagueness of his appointment "to win back for mathematical physics in Breslau the ground that it has lost since Kirchhoff's departure," using even his mathematical lectures toward that end.[87] In his enthusiasm, Meyer forgot his own conclusion that not much ground had ever been gained there for mathematical physics.[88] Nor, as it turned out, did he have much time to devote exclusively to improving the conditions for mathematical physics. The ministry, with its usual disregard for proper qualifications, made Meyer the main representative of experimental physics only three years later, when Frankenheim retired from the directorship of the physics institute.[89] Meyer's new duties deflected most of his energies from mathematical physics: he did not remain "faithful" to his original plan of devoting his life to mathematical physics, as he said much later.[90] As Breslau lost the full-time mathematical physicist Meyer wanted to be, it hardly gained an adequate experimentalist. Others elsewhere judged him to be unsuitable for chairs of experimental physics, and he himself described his teaching of experimental physics as "popular" physics.[91] He did succeed in maintaining mathematical physics at Breslau as a regular feature of the curriculum, but the ministry's appointment policy had once again deprived experimental physics of the most effective use of its resources.

At Bonn, experimental physics was handed over to mathematicians entirely, while the chair of physics was officially vacant for thirty-five of the first forty years

Göttingen UB, Ms. Dept.) and by Rudolf Sturm, "Mathematik," in *Festschrift . . . Breslau* 2:434–40, on 438, who states that Meyer was appointed ordinary professor of mathematics in 1865 and that he was succeeded by an extraordinary professor of mathematics, Paul Bachmann, when Meyer switched to physics in 1867. Since Meyer's promotion in 1865 was to a personal ordinary professorship, given to him to prevent him from accepting an offer from the Braunschweig Polytechnic, and not to a chair, the reversal of his position to its original form of an extraordinary professorship would have been a matter of common practice. The extraordinary professorship for mathematics was apparently reserved for teaching the parts of mathematics that bore on physics, given the selection of the two Dirichlet students, Lipschitz and Bachmann, as well as of Meyer.

87. Marbach was promoted in 1861. Meyer to Neumann, 16 July 1864.

88. Meyer, too, found that the Breslau students' "preparation and their scientific interest lag very far behind the conditions in Göttingen," where Meyer had come from. Meyer to Franz Neumann, 23 Mar. 1865, Neumann Papers, Göttingen UB, Ms. Dept.

89. Meyer to Neumann, 30 Mar. 1867.

90. Meyer to Franz Neumann, 10 Dec. 1893, Neumann Papers, Göttingen UB, Ms. Dept.

91. Meyer to Neumann, 10 Dec. 1893. Meyer was rejected by the Bonn faculty in 1868 because he was "no experimenter." Lipschitz to Franz Neumann, 14 June 1868, Neumann Papers, Göttingen UB, Ms. Dept.

of its existence. Bonn was fortunate enough, however, to acquire a mathematician, Plücker, who turned out to be an excellent experimental physicist when the job was thrust upon him; by chance, physics flourished at Bonn.

Division of Labor

Given adequate financial support, the key to a well-functioning physics institute was a division of labor that did not divide the means. How that was achieved did not matter too much; only it appears to have been important that the main professor of physics have a free hand in coordinating the local physicists' work.

What could be expected of a well-functioning physics institute by this time was, first, a comprehensive physics program and, second, some research, although expectations for the latter were still rather modest. When asking for money for research facilities, physicists sometimes still had to remind their governments that research ought to be expected: Jolly wrote to his ministry in 1846 that the state was justified to expect the university teacher to give public evidence of his studies from time to time, and Reusch similarly wrote in 1848 that he ought to be expected to contribute to the developments of the field instead of merely following them.[92]

Our examples of physics at Bonn and Marburg give an idea of the variety of ways in which these expectations could be met effectively. At the same time they show that toward the end of our period, individual solutions to the problem of managing physics were giving way to a growing standardization of institute organization, made necessary by increasing numbers of students, a corresponding expansion of instruction and teaching facilities, and develoments in research.

The first Bonn professor of physics, C. W. G. Kastner, left in 1821 after only three years. His lectures were taken over by the professor of astronomy and mathematics, K. D. von Münchow, who taught mechanics and experimental physics, and by the second professor of mathematics, W. A. Diesterweg, who taught "mathematical physics" or "applied mathematics" in addition to pure mathematics.[93]

One of their earliest students was Julius Plücker, who, after rounding out his studies in Berlin and in Paris, came to Bonn as Privatdocent for mathematics and physics in 1825.[94] At his request, in 1828 he was promoted to extraordinary professor over the faculty's objection that Bonn had all the mathematics instructors it needed.[95] Plücker taught the mathematical treatment of physics problems; some-

92. Jolly to Baden Ministry of the Interior, 12 June 1846, Bad. GLA, 235/3135. Reusch to "Studienrath," 19 Jan. 1848, STA, Ludwigsburg, E 202/883.

93. Barbara Jaeckel and Wolfgang Paul, "Die Entwicklung der Physik in Bonn 1818–1968," in *150 Jahre . . . Bonn*, 91–100, on 91. Heinrich Konen, "Das physikalische Institut," in *Geschichte der Rheinischen Friedrich-Wilhelm-Universität zu Bonn am Rhein*, vol. 2, *Institute und Seminare, 1818–1933*, ed. A. Dyroff (Bonn: F. Cohen, 1933), 345–55, on 346. *Vorlesungen . . . Bonn*. Friedrich von Bezold, *Geschichte der Rheinischen Friedrich-Wilhelms-Universität von der Gründung bis zum Jahr 1870* (Bonn: A. Marcus and E. Weber, 1920), 223.

94. Plücker, "Curriculum Vitae"; Heinrichs to Bonn U. Philosophical Faculty, 18 Aug. 1824; and letter dated 28 Apr. 1825; Plücker Personalakte, Bonn UA.

95. Bonn U. Philosophical Faculty, remarks on Plücker's request for promotion, 16 Oct. 1827; Bonn U. Philosophical Faculty to Rehhaus, 16 Oct. 1827; Plücker Personalakte, Bonn UA.

times he devoted a whole course to some important work by one physicist, for example, to mechanics according to Poisson or to Laplace's theory of capillary action. His courses attracted students even though his subjects were difficult and even though his courses competed with those of the two ordinary professors.[96]

Plücker left Bonn in the early 1830s, but he was brought back almost immediately to succeed Diesterweg, who died in 1835, as the ordinary professor of mathematics. In that capacity, he taught pure mathematics and mechanics. When Münchow died in 1836, Plücker was also appointed temporary director of the physical cabinet and given permission to offer physics lectures. Since the arrangement was to last only until the appointment of a new professor of physics, Plücker continued to devote himself primarily to mathematics for a few more years.[97] But the ministry's negotiations for a new physicist, for example, with Dove,[98] were unsuccessful, and the longer the provisional arrangement lasted, the more involved Plücker became with physics. In the summer of 1842, following the government's request that physics be taught the year round, he went beyond the general experimental physics lectures and offered for the first time "a full course for the sake of practical exercise in experimenting and for discussion of the phenomena and apparatus." This course the faculty expected to be "especially fruitful and stimulating."[99]

The vacancy of the Bonn chair of physics until 1856 attracted a stream of hopeful Privatdocenten, some of whom Plücker no doubt needed, given his double burden of mathematics and physics. One of these was the Berlin physicist Gustav Radicke, who, working on his own, had made himself a specialist in "theoretical optics" and had published a handbook of optics as well as some research on the subject. His papers were strictly mathematical, taking their observational data from other physicists, which is the direction his teaching took. Despite his inappropriate background, his lack of success as a teacher at Bonn, and his discontinuation of almost all research, the Prussian ministry of culture settled on him to become the Bonn representative of experimental physics. It promoted him to extraordinary professor in 1847 as an attempt to restrict Plücker to mathematics again. But it was too late: Radicke could not fill the part the ministry had intended for him because of ill health, and Plücker was just then coming into his own as an experimental physicist.[100]

Like physicists at other Prussian universities, Plücker had only very limited space for his teaching and research—the physical institute, which dated from 1819, con-

96. The nature of Plücker's lectures can be seen in *Vorlesungen . . . Bonn.* K. D. von Münchow testified to Plücker's success as a teacher, given his subjects, thinking it a "good sign" that he attracted students at all. In Bonn U. Philosophical Faculty remarks, 16 Oct. 1827.

97. Alfred Clebsch, "Zum Gedächtniss an Julius Plücker," in *Julius Plückers Gesammelte Mathematische Abhandlungen,* ed. A. Schoenflies (Leipzig, 1895), 1: ix–xxxv. Notice of Plücker's temporary appointment as a substitute for Münchow as of 27 July 1836 to the Bonn U. Philosophical Faculty, 10 Aug. 1836, Plücker Personalakte, Bonn UA.

98. Dove to "Regierungs-Director," 31 Jan. 1844.

99. Bonn U. Philosophical Faculty, remarks on Plücker's plan, 2–8 Dec. 1841, Plücker Personalakte, Bonn UA.

100. Bezold, *Bonn,* 401. For the nature of Gustav Radicke's early articles, see his "Berechnung und Interpolation der Brechungsverhältnisse nach Cauchy's Dispersionstheorie und deren Anwendung auf doppeltbrechende Krystalle," *Ann.* 45 (1838): 246–62, 540–57.

sisted of an auditorium and two rooms—but he made good use of what he had and·
his budget of 400 thaler. He acquired apparatus mainly for the areas of his own
research, which were magnetism, spectroscopy, and discharges in gases; there he
could choose knowledgeably, and he bought excellent equipment, much of it from
France. He hoped to start systematic instruction in physics laboratory practice from
the mid-1850s on, but lacking a student laboratory, he could do no more for the
time being than to make his own laboratory available to selected students for research.[101] One of these students, Wilhelm Hittorf, became his research collaborator
and teaching assistant before becoming, after a brief period as Privatdocent at Bonn,
professor of physics at the nearby Münster Academy.[102] Student laboratory practice
became available to Bonn students after the experimental physicist Adolph Wüllner
had become Privatdocent at Bonn in 1865; he was at the same time teacher of
physics at the agricultural academy at nearby Poppelsdorf, where he had a physics
laboratory to which he admitted Bonn students.[103]

From the late 1840s on, physics and mathematics at Bonn were organized
around Plücker's activities. Although he continued to teach both subjects, his research for more than a decade centered on experimental physics. Accordingly his
junior colleagues in these fields came to be people who supplemented his work in
mathematics and mathematical physics. In 1844 two more Privatdocenten, Eduard
Heine, Dirichlet's student, and Feilitzsch followed Radicke from Berlin to Bonn.
Both were trained in mathematics and mathematical physics. Like Feilitzsch, Heine
taught mathematical physics at first, but after he was promoted to extraordinary
professor in 1848, he supplemented Plücker in mathematics, the area of his research,
rather than in physics.[104] In 1850 Plücker acquired in August Beer the junior colleague who for many years was to complete the physics program at Bonn. Beer was
Plücker's student and was skilled in experimental work, but he was primarily a mathematical physicist specializing in optics.[105] Soon after becoming Privatdocent in
1850, he published his most important early work, Einleitung in die höhere Optik. It
was praised as the first German textbook that contained mathematical physics; it
contained original research, too, such as the connections Beer established between
Cauchy's difficult theoretical investigations and experimental optics.[106] As Privat-

101. Konen, "Das physikalische Institut," 347. Jaeckel and Paul, "Physik in Bonn," 91–92.
102. Adolf Heydweiller, "Johann Wilhelm Hittorf," Phys. Zs. 16 (1915): 161–79, on 162. Also
Gerhard C. Schmidt, "Wilhelm Hittorf," Phys. Bl. 4 (1948): 64–68, on 64.
103. Report by the Bonn U. natural science section to the Philosophical Faculty (in two drafts),
undated [July 1868], Plücker Personalakte, Bonn UA. The report stressed that after a year and a half,
some of Wüllner's Bonn students had already produced "several very good papers"; from an appendix to
an undated draft by Lipschitz that year, it appears that four of these experimental papers had already been
published in the Annalen. The Bonn curator described Wüllner's facilities at Poppelsdorf as a "rather
nice" cabinet and laboratory. His letter to Clausius, 11 Mar. 1869, Clausius Personalakte, Bonn UA.
104. Hans Freudenthal, "Eduard Heine," DSB 6:230; Vorlesungen . . . Bonn.
105. August Beer to Bonn U. Philosophical Faculty, 24 July 1850; report on Beer's habilitation by
Noeggerath, 5 Aug. 1850; Beer Personalakte, Bonn UA.
106. August Beer, Einleitung in die höhere Optik (Braunschweig, 1853). Plücker characterized the
book in the Bonn U. Philosophical Faculty's remarks on Beer's request to forward his book to the Prussian
Ministry of Culture, 28 Feb. 1853, Beer Personalakte, Bonn UA. Of theoretical and mathematical textbooks on physics in Germany, Merz called Beer's the "first important work of this kind." John Theodore
Merz, A History of European Thought in the Nineteenth Century, 4 vols. (1904–12; reprint, New York:
Dover, 1965), 1: 44n.

docent, Beer set out to teach "physics and the parts of mathematics that are close to it."[107] Within a few years, his teaching and research had "turned primarily to mathematical physics, on which so few are as yet working."[108] In 1854, for example, Beer was considered alongside one of those few who were working on mathematical physics, Kirchhoff, for the Heidelberg chair of physics.[109] He was a successful teacher, leaving few students for the Privatdocent for mathematics Lipschitz, who from 1857 to 1862 offered lectures on subjects similar to Beer's, such as the theory of Newtonian forces, potential theory, and partial differential equations used to solve physical problems.[110] In 1855 Beer was promoted to extraordinary professor, and a year later, at the same time that Plücker was at last permanently assigned the Bonn chair of physics, he became ordinary professor of mathematics.[111]

What Bonn physics still lacked in the 1860s was a seminar for mathematics and mathematical physics, subjects that were not covered in the Bonn seminar for the natural sciences. Plücker planned such a seminar but had to put it off because Beer by then was not well enough to participate, and Plücker could not take on the additional work by himself.[112] When Beer died in 1863, at age thirty-eight, he was succeeded by Lipschitz, against Plücker's wishes; when in 1866 the seminar was established with Lipschitz as one of its directors, Plücker almost had to be ordered to participate.[113]

Lipschitz did not inherit the lectures on mathematical physics along with Beer's chair of mathematics; they were taken over instead by the physicists Wüllner and Eduard Ketteler, who came to Bonn as Privatdocenten in 1865.[114] Wüllner was

107. Beer to Bonn U. Philosophical Faculty, 24 July 1850.

108. F. Argelander's remark to Bonn U. Philosophical Faculty, June 1854, Beer Personalakte, Bonn UA.

109. Bunsen to Baden Ministry of the Interior, 26 July 1854, Bad. GLA, 235/3135. The Heidelberg faculty considered Beer's book on optics to be original research.

110. Konen, "Das physikalische Institut," 348. Lipschitz to Franz Neumann, 12 Aug. 1858, Neumann Papers, Göttingen UB, Ms. Dept.

111. Beer was first recommended for promotion to extraordinary professor by the Bonn U. Philosophical Faculty in 1854 (evaluations by Plücker, Argelander, and others in his Personalakte). Prussian Ministry of Culture to the Bonn Philosophical Faculty, 11 Aug. 1856, Beer Personalakte, Bonn UA.

112. Plücker to Bonn U. Curator Beseler, undated, received 13 Sept. 1864; also Curator Beseler to Minister of Culture Mühler, 14 Sept. 1864; N.-W. HSTA, NW5 Nr. 558.

113. Curator Beseler to Bonn U. Philosophical Faculty, 6 Oct. 1866, Plücker Personalakte, Bonn UA. In his report to the minister on 14 Sept. 1864, Beseler described the bad relations between Plücker and Lipschitz; he referred to them again on 11 Sept. 1866 in a request that the ministry decide on the statutes of the Bonn mathematical seminar because Plücker and Lipschitz refused to work together on them. N.-W. HSTA, NW5 Nr. 558. After Plücker's death, Lipschitz said that he was only then introducing an "absolutely rigorous" method into Bonn mathematics, an apparent slight on Plücker and Beer. Lipschitz, "Separatvotum, eingeliefert in der Sitzung der philosophischen Facultät vom 17ten Juli 1868," Plücker Personalakte, Bonn UA.

114. Obituary of Eduard Ketteler in Leopoldina 37 (1901): 35–36. "Vita" in Ketteler's dissertation, "De refractoribus interferentialibus," Ketteler Personalakte, Bonn UA. Documents relating to Ketteler's habilitation: Bonn U. Curator Beseler to Ketteler, 30 Mar. 1865; Ketteler to Bonn U. Philosophical Faculty, 31 Mar. 1865; remarks by the Faculty on Ketteler's request to habilitate, 5 Apr.–12 May 1865; report by the Philosophical Faculty on his habilitation colloquium, 19 May 1865; report by the Philosophical Faculty to Bonn U. Curator, 9 June 1865; Ketteler to Dean of the Philosophical Faculty Kampshulte, 4 Nov. 1865; Ketteler Personalakte, Bonn UA.

Aachener Bezirksverein deutscher Ingenieure, "Adolf Wüllner," Zs. d. Vereins deutsch. Ingenieure 52 (1908): 1741–42. Wüllner described his early career in his application to the Zurich Polytechnic for the position Clausius had held, 6 June 1867, A Schweiz. Sch., Zurich.

promoted to extraordinary professor in 1867 because of offers from abroad, and in 1870 he left Bonn for the technical school at Aachen. Ketteler eventually became the first professor of theoretical physics at Bonn. The researches of his early years, which fall into our present period, exemplified that balance of experiment and theory characteristic of the work of physicists who were trained by the best physicists of the period, such as Plücker, Magnus, and Kirchhoff.

Ketteler had begun his university studies in Bonn, spending two years there before moving to Berlin, where he studied three more years, earning a doctorate under Magnus in 1860. After completing his dissertation, he continued to do research at Berlin and then at Heidelberg. For the problem of the dispersion of light in gases, he developed a method that had only recently become practical because of Bunsen and Kirchhoff's discoveries in spectroscopy; in Heidelberg, Kirchhoff allowed him to use the laboratory and the apparatus of the physics institute for his work. In 1864 Magnus presented Ketteler's work to the Prussian Academy of Sciences for publication,[115] on the strength of which Ketteler became Privatdocent for physics at Bonn in 1865.

In the next two years, while teaching related subjects such as the "connections between, and the methods of determining, the most important optical constants" and the "theory of interference phenomena," Ketteler made preparations for a "larger and comprehensive experimental investigation" of the optical relations of gases and vapors. He set himself the task of experimentally investigating the dispersion of light in all of its relations and to examine the different attempts at a theoretical explanation of it. He believed that "rigorous experiments" were needed to obtain the "extremely delicate" measurements for completing the data and bringing order to the field. He was able to carry out this work because the Prussian Academy gave him substantial financial support and because Plücker, who had returned to mathematical research, let him use the rooms at the Bonn physics institute.[116]

The practice at the Bonn institute during Plücker's last years—he died in 1868—of making research space available to the extraordinary professor was followed at Marburg through most of our period. Like Plücker, the ordinary professor of physics at Marburg, Gerling, had a multiple appointment, representing mathematics and astronomy in addition to physics. He provided well for his fields; to carry out his many duties, he requested and received an older building that could accommodate all of them. For physics he had a lecture hall for about fifty students, five rooms containing instruments, which were set up in such a way that they could be used at their permanent location, a room for students participating in magnetic observations, an office for himself, family living quarters, and an annual budget of 400 thaler to maintain it all. Most important, he wanted all of the facilities to be used. Because he inclined to mathematics and astronomy in his researches more than to physics, he asked as early as 1831 for a salaried Privatdocent or extraordinary profes-

115. Ketteler to Bonn U. Philosophical Faculty, 31 Mar. 1865.
116. Ketteler to Dean of the Bonn U. Philosophical Faculty H. von Sybel, 27 June 1870; Clausius's evaluation of Ketteler's work included in the Philosophical Faculty's report, 29 June 1870, Ketteler Personalakte, Bonn UA. Quotations from the letter to Sybel.

sor for physics to take over part of the teaching. It took some years before he got what he wanted, but from the mid-1840s the institute had at least one physicist in a junior position working in it most of the time. The institute was also used by students for laboratory exercises and for some research.[117]

Few German universities in this period could claim junior physicists who were as productive as Marburg's. They included Knoblauch, Marburg's first extraordinary professor of physics from 1849 to 1852 (from 1852 to 1853 he was ordinary professor, Marburg for a moment having two ordinary professors of physics); Rudolph Kohlrausch, extraordinary professor from 1852 to 1857; Wüllner, Privatdocent from 1858 to 1862; and Franz Melde, Gerling's assistant at the institute from 1857, Privatdocent from 1860 to 1864, and extraordinary professor from 1864 to 1866. They all did research in experimental physics. Using a spacious and well-equipped private "cabinet," Knoblauch earned a good reputation as an experimentalist in the subject of radiant heat, publishing six papers on it.[118] Kohlrausch apparently had much of the Marburg physics institute at his disposal, as he listed among the advantages he enjoyed at Marburg the annual budget of the physics institute. To his major collaboration with Weber on electrical experiments, Kohlrausch brought the apparatus he was using at Marburg and the results of his experimental research.[119] Wüllner published eight experimental papers in his first two years at Marburg and four pamphlets and books on experimental subjects in the next two years, which included the first volume of his famous textbook on experimental physics.[120] Melde was promoted at Marburg for his "many" experimental researches in optics and acoustics, which were praised by Weber, Kirchhoff, Jolly, Knoblauch, and Müller.[121] All four of these

117. Gerling first described what he needed in a letter to the Hessen government on 15 Aug. 1831, STA, Marburg, Bestand 307d, Nr. 21. He described the completed institute in his *Nachricht* in 1848. The purpose of Gerling's report on the institute was to point out the need for a scientifically trained assistant. Progress reports on the institute by Gerling to Gauss are found in letters of 8 Aug. and Dec. 1833 and 17 Oct. 1841, in *Christian Ludwig Gerling an Carl Friedrich Gauss. Sechzig bisher unveröffentlichte Briefe*, ed. T. Gerardy (Göttingen: Vandenhoeck und Ruprecht, 1964), 63, 68, and 81. See also O. F. A. Schulze, "Zur Geschichte des Physikalischen Instituts," in *Die Philipps-Universität zu Marburg 1527–1927*, ed. H. Hermelink and S. A. Kaehler (Marburg: Elwert, 1927), 756–63, on 757–59.

118. Karl Schmidt, "Carl Hermann Knoblauch," *Leopoldina* 31 (1895): 116–22. Knoblauch was well off, and by private means he could augment whatever he found at Marburg for his research. Tyndall reported in his paper "Ueber die Gesetze des Magnetismus," *Ann.* 83 (1851): 1–37, that Knoblauch put at his disposal "excellent apparatus and three of his rooms" (p. 37). Knoblauch's experiments were based on the analogy between heat and light; by a careful description of the properties of heat radiation, he wanted to establish the "optical" behavior of heat (Rosenberger, *Geschichte der Physik*, 386–94). In 1854 Bunsen wrote that Knoblauch had proven himself to be a skilled experimenter with his experimental series on radiant heat. Bunsen to Baden Ministry of the Interior, 26 July 1854.

119. Rudolph Kohlrausch to President Kern of the Swiss Education Council, 23 Jan. 1855, A Schweiz. Sch., Zurich. Kohlrausch said here that he also had a salary of 700 thaler, which was fairly large for an extraordinary professor, and he commanded "several hundred thaler annually" from the local scientific society and through his collaboration with Weber. As a "surrogate" for all these privileges, he had to ask "at least" for the directorship of an institute elsewhere. See also *Catalogus professorum academiae Marburgensis; die akademischen Lehrer der Philipps-Universität in Marburg von 1527 bis 1910*, ed. F. Gundlach (Marburg: Elwert, 1927), 394–95. Bunsen wrote about Kohlrausch in 1854: "Among the younger physicists, Professor Kohlrausch in Marburg has quickly made a good name for himself through his investigations on tension electricity." Bunsen to Baden Ministry of the Interior, 26 July 1854.

120. Wüllner listed his publications in his application to the Zurich Polytechnic, 6 June 1867.

121. P. Losch, "Melde, Franz Emil," *Biographisches Jahrbuch und Deutscher Nekrolog* 6 (1901): 338–40; obituary of Franz Melde, *Leopoldina* 37 (1901): 46–47. Weber to a colleague, 22 Dec. 1865 and 5

young physicists at Marburg, Knoblauch, Kohlrausch, Wüllner, and Melde, went on to become ordinary professors of physics at universities or technical institutes.

The Problem

The hiring practices that led to the physicists' difficulties at the Prussian provincial universities, the frequent absence of any junior physicists at the smaller southern universities, and the successful accommodation of physicsts at Bonn and Marburg were all attempts to deal with a difficult problem for physics at the universities. It was how to make good use of the institute for teaching and research and, at the same time, give the next generation of university teachers and institute directors the experience that would qualify them to succeed to ordinary professorships some day. The humanities, theology, and law could accommodate junior teachers whenever ministries or faculties considered such appointments desirable. In those fields, the principle of the Prussian ministry of culture that a Privatdocent's promotion to extraordinary professor was not to fill a gap in instruction but to recognize the candidate's qualification to become an ordinary professor some day (gaps in instruction were to be filled by an ordinary professor), could be met at no greater cost than a small salary.[122] But that principle was not well suited to the natural sciences and medicine because of the scientist's double responsibility as professor and institute director. As professor, a physicist could not do his job well if he did not have the material means provided by an institute; as administrator of a state institute, he could not do his job well if several professors had the right to use the institute.

Most physics institutes in this period, as we have seen, were limited to a few rooms, inadequate laboratory space—if there was any at all—and small budgets, not enough usually for one physicist and certainly not enough for more than one. The most important measuring instruments were expensive, so they could hardly be acquired in duplicate or triplicate. Often instruments were the handiwork of the institute director himself, designed specifically for his own researches and possibly even paid for with his own money; they were not in any case the kind of material he could be called upon to share with a colleague. Once the delicate measuring instruments were set up and adjusted for a particular experimental investigation, neither they nor the space they occupied could be shared with another physicist for the duration of the research, which might be months or even years. Given the material restraints on physics institutes, therefore, there was no way around the arrangement

---

Jan. 1866; Knoblauch to a colleague, 28 Jan. 1866; G. Weissenborn, "Separatvotum," 16 Feb. 1866, with an addendum dated 21 Feb. 1866; STA, Marburg, Bestand 305a, 1864/66, Melde.

122. The rule of promotion of the Prussian ministry of culture was discussed in a faculty debate at Bonn University, 16 Oct. 1827, Plücker Personalakte, Bonn UA. It was not generally accepted in Germany. Robert von Mohl, at Tübingen, gave the following definition in 1869: "Extraordinary professors: younger but already tried teachers for whom there is no ordinary position for the time being. Their uses are various: to fill gaps that do not allow for the establishment of a new chair; to supplement ordinary professors who are no longer fully capable of service; to multiply courses." In Württemberg, Statistisches Landesamt, Statistik . . . Tübingen, 25.

of putting university institutes at the complete disposal of one physicist. With specific reference to anatomical institutes, but applying equally to "every other collection," Helmholtz observed in 1860 that there was "always a considerable difficulty . . . if two teachers are to use the collection as ordinary professors, that is, with equal official entitlement."[123] For this among other reasons, Kirchhoff spoke of the "scientific versatility and depth" required of the "ordinary and lone representative of physics" at a university.[124] As the demands of physics teaching increasingly led to the appointment of a second, often already established, physicist to aid the director of the institute, the opportunities for "collisions" over the use of the facilities of the institute multiplied. In the same measure as the research needs of the second physicist were recognized, the arguments against the division of the director's sole responsibility for the institute were sharpened.[125]

At the same time, the needs of beginning physicists—instruments, laboratories, funds, to say nothing of salaries—had to be met, and yet they rarely could be. Prussian physics graduates had to wait for two, later for three, years after the doctorate before they could become Privatdocenten. Those who needed to earn money during the waiting time usually took a teaching job, preferably one near a university with a good institute; those with some money of their own or with unusual persistance, such as Ketteler, used the two or three years to do research in a university physics institute, if they could, and to publish as much as possible. Becoming a Privatdocent anywhere hardly improved a young physicist's financial situation, and it could deprive him of access to a university institute, reducing his chances for research. About the only chance a young physicist had of entering physics teaching was by lecturing on mathematical physics, Weber noted in 1873. But mathematical physics brought little in the way of student fees and did not prepare young physicists for their future duties. As a consequence, "even those who preferably wanted to devote themselves to physics nevertheless usually habilitated in . . . mathematics or, if they were somewhat removed from that, in . . . chemistry."[126] Their loss had

123. Riese, *Hochschule*, criticizes the German university structure for keeping young scholars from advancing. But he does not take account of the factors that set some fields such as physics apart from others; for example, the material limitations we have described, which made the continuation of that structure useful for the time being. See his chapter "Die Nichtordinarienfrage," 153–92, particularly the first two sections. Riese quotes Helmholtz on p. 115.

124. Kirchhoff to a colleague, 25 Dec. 1865, STA, Marburg, Bestand 305a, 1864/66 Melde.

125. Another argument against two physicists at one institute, especially with the second one in a junior position, was that it made it difficult to appoint the best man in case of a vacancy in the senior position. It usually meant bringing in someone from the outside and placing him above the physicist already at the institute. Under such circumstances the new physicist might hesitate to accept the job; the new combination might become troublesome because of the junior physicist's frustrated hopes of advancing to the senior position himself or because of his possible loss of earlier accesses to facilities, students, teaching subjects, and so on, which the new director might wish to claim for himself. Riese, *Hochschule*, 133.

126. Weber to Göttingen U. Curator Warnstedt, 26 Oct. 1873, Weber Personalakte, Göttingen UA, 4/V b/95a. Young physicists sometimes tried to combine university teaching with teaching at secondary or trade schools, as, for example, Hermann Schaeffer did at Jena, or Marbach at Breslau. When they received no offers of professorships from other universities and were passed up for the local professorship, they sometimes left academic life, as L. F. Ofterdinger did at Tübingen in 1851, reconciling themselves to a secondary school professorship. Others took paying jobs outside physics: Wilhelm Feussner

"proven to be detrimental for the experimental pursuit of physics at our universities," and only the increasing number of assistantships at physical institutes in the early 1870s gave Weber hope that the problem might be alleviated.[127] Gerling's idea, dating back to 1848, that the employment of assistants would constitute a "nursery" for physics was proving to be correct.[128] Assistantships allowed physicists waiting out their two or three years until habilitation to earn a small living without leaving research.

The training of physicists before the doctorate was not much affected by having only one ordinary physics professor at a university: students working toward doctorates in physics were still few in number at most universities, and their research was easily supervised by one professor. They were also encouraged to study at other universities with other physicists, who even welcomed them into their laboratories, particularly if it helped them in their doctoral research. Wüllner was one of the students who took advantage of this possibility, doing research with Magnus's method in Magnus's Berlin laboratory for a dissertation at Munich. Some of the better institutes could by this time specialize in the areas of research of their directors, which facilitated the work of students in these areas.[129]

The entry into physics through mathematical physics occurred because there were still young physicists unwilling to settle for mathematics or chemistry instead of physics. It also occurred because of the increasing teaching duties of the ordinary professor of physics, which often forced him to relegate those teaching duties that made least demand on the institute to a salaried junior colleague. At Giessen such an arrangement existed throughout the present period. An unsalaried extraordinary professorship was established in 1843 and given to F. G. K. Zamminer; by 1854 he was also receiving a small salary. Zamminer considered himself primarily a mathematical physicist in his researches, and he lectured on mathematical optics and on higher analysis in which he treated other branches of mathematical physics as applications.[130] He also required physical apparatus for teaching and doing experiments

---

at Marburg supported himself by working also as a librarian, O. J. Seyffer at Tübingen also worked as the editor of a newspaper, and C. H. Tielle at Kiel studied medicine while he was a Privatdocent for physics and then left physics to establish himself as a physician.

127. Weber to Göttingen U. Curator Warnstedt, 26 Oct. 1873. Under earlier conditions of physics institutes, there had been obstacles to the use of assistants: they presupposed ready-made instruments, hence a certain affluence of the institute, as Weber explained to the Göttingen U. Curator, 10 May 1851, Göttingen UA, 4/V h/21.

128. Gerling, Nachricht, 21.

129. In physics the existence of ordinary professorships for the whole field did not entail foregoing specialized research, as Riese claims it did (Hochschule, 159). The general lectures required of the ordinary professor were compatible with his specialization in research. The two usually required different kinds of instruments, so that as early as 1832 Weber distinguished between them. Of research instruments, Weber wrote that given the current state of physics, "it becomes less and less essential to strive for completeness in a higher scientific institute, which, the further science advances, can be achieved less and less often." Weber to Göttingen U. Curator, 15 Dec. 1832, Göttingen UA, 4/V h/16. Among the earliest physics institutes to be specialized in this way were not only Weber's at Göttingen and Leipzig but also those at Heidelberg and Bonn.

130. Buff to a colleague, 26 Oct. 1854; Zamminer to President Kern of the Swiss Education Council, 7 May 1855; both in A Schweiz. Sch., Zurich.

and money for adding to the collection. To begin with, he followed the institute director Buff's example of buying what he needed and then asking the state to reimburse him. That brought a reprimand, for state policy did not allow professors to spend the state's money without prior approval; but he was reimbursed all the same.[131] Zamminer gained a reputation for being a skilled and precise experimenter,[132] and at the same time he avoided any rivalry with Buff by teaching subjects that Buff did not. After Zamminer's early death in 1858, his professorship along with a teaching assignment for "mathematical-physical subjects" went to Johann Konrad Bohn, formerly Regnault's assistant and most recently Privatdocent at Munich University. Despite his strongly experimental background in physics, Bohn introduced himself to Giessen with a lecture on the value of mathematics for a general education, and he announced lecture courses on the theory of light, chapters of theoretical physics, elementary mathematics, and geodesy. In the Giessen physics seminar, he was put in charge of the mathematical-physical exercises. He received an auditorium, an adjacent laboratory, an office, money for instruments to be used as "aids for instruction in the mathematical-physical subjects," and free heat and light.[133] When Bohn moved to a technical school in 1866, the position went to Karl Zöppritz in 1867. Like his predecessors, Zöppritz taught optics, but in his main courses, for which he often found no students, he followed closely the model set by his teacher Franz Neumann: he covered mathematical physics and those parts of mathematics that were important to physicists, such as partial differential equations, and he conducted the mathematical-physical exercises in the seminar as Bohn had. Also like his predecessors, Zöppritz used the funds at his disposal to acquire instruments for his work, primarily for his teaching of optics.[134]

Over their twenty years of teaching at Giessen, these three extraordinary professors acted upon the understanding that their instruments, being the property of the state, belonged to the institute of the ordinary professor of physics. As a result, each in turn handed over his collection to the institute when he left Giessen; Zamminer, who enjoyed close personal relations with Buff, handed over the instruments all along. In this way, they prevented Giessen University from acquiring what might have become one of the early institutes for mathematical physics.

---

131. Hessen Academic Administration Commission in Giessen to Hessen Ministry of the Interior and of Justice, 10 May 1844, Giessen UA, Phil. H Nr. 35, Fasz. 6.

132. Weber to Kern, 1 Jan. and 9 May 1855; Weber to Zamminer, 8 Apr. 1855; and Buff to a colleague, 26 Oct. 1854; A Schweiz. Sch., Zurich.

133. Lorey, "Physik . . . Giessen," 92–93. Bohn to Academic Administration Commission, undated, received 28 Aug. 1860; the commission's reply to Bohn, 31 Aug. 1860; Giessen UA, Phil. H Nr. 35, Fasz. 7.

134. Lorey, "Physik . . . Giessen," 98. Zöppritz to Academic Administration Commission, 26 Oct. 1879, Giessen UA, Phil. H Nr. 35, Fasz. 6. For his brief stay as Privatdocent at Tübingen, Karl Zöppritz had been welcomed as a "younger teacher from the famous Königsberg school." Württemberg Minister of Religious and School Affairs to the King, 26 Aug. 1865, HSTA, Stuttgart, E11 Bü 63. But Zöppritz had actually been overwhelmed by the "mind-killing" calculations for his dissertation at Königsberg and had literally fled from there during Neumann's absence. He went to Kirchhoff at Heidelberg, where he was able to complete his doctorate almost immediately. Zöppritz to Franz Neumann, 30 Aug. 1864, Neumann Papers, Göttingen UB, Ms. Dept. His lectures at Giessen, listed in the semi-annual university calendar, *Deutsches Hochschulverzeichnis* (1872–1938), were unsuccessful.

We close our discussion of physics at provincial German universities by returning to two of our previous examples, Bonn and Marburg. They illustrate the change
that was taking place toward the end of our period, when faculties came to desire
an arrangement for physics similar to the one Giessen had enjoyed from early on.
After Plücker's death, the Bonn science faculty wanted to use the physics half of his
position to acquire an eminent experimental physicist who could secure for their
university an ample physics institute. To meet this "long felt need," the science
faculty looked to a "skilled and comprehensively trained director of the physical
laboratory." That meant someone who could organize a physics practice course for
elementary students and direct the laboratory research of advanced students. He was
also to be someone who, in addition to having mastered the art of experimental
physics, had mastered the theoretical methods of "fathoming the laws of nature"; he
was to be able to pass on the experimental and theoretical methods of physics to the
students and train them to be independent researchers. The candidates were Wüllner, the local physicist who had given Bonn students laboratory practice at the
agricultural academy where he taught, Wiedemann, and Quincke, all three of them
former students of Magnus.[135]

Lipschitz, the Bonn mathematician, agreed with most of what his colleagues
wanted, but he had a higher ambition for the university: he wanted a physicist who
"was opening new paths to scientific knowledge."[136] The three physicists who fit
that description best, in his view, were not those the faculty preferred but Helmholtz, Kirchhoff, and Clausius. The Bonn scientists considered his alternative list.
Helmholtz, they acknowledged, was a physicist of the first rank, but he was still
employed as a physiologist at Heidelberg University, and he had never headed a
physics institute. They noted that the physics researches that had gained Helmholtz
his reputation were "especially in a mathematical direction" rather than experimental. Moreover, they thought it was "very questionable" that Helmholtz would accept
a call to Bonn, and his "world reputation" as a physiologist would in any case make
him expensive, which might create problems.[137] Kirchhoff, the Bonn scientists
thought, was too tied to Heidelberg and to Bunsen to be lured to Bonn, so they
did not consider him further.[138] Clausius, they thought, was in no manner quali-

135. Draft of the report by the mathematics and natural sciences section of the Bonn U. Philosophical Faculty on a successor in physics to Plücker, July 1868, Plücker Personalakte, Bonn UA. Also there,
"Separatvotum als Erwiderung auf dasjenige des Herrn Professor Lipschitz vom 13ten Juli 1868," 14 July
1868.

136. Draft of Lipschitz's report on the same question, July 1868, Plücker Personalakte, Bonn UA.

137. Bonn U. faculty report in July 1868, "Separatvotum" of 14 July 1868, and Lipschitz's separate
vote, 13 July 1868. After Plücker's death, Lipschitz had written to Helmholtz to ask him if he wanted to
move to physics and to come to Bonn. Helmholtz answered yes, and Lipschitz proposed to the Bonn
philosophical faculty that Helmholtz appear in first place on the list of candidates for the physics chair.
Franz Neumann supported Lipschitz's efforts to get Helmholtz to Bonn, and Lipschitz reported to Neumann that the government had done "everything in its power" to get Helmholtz. Lipschitz to Neumann,
14 June 1868 and 15 Jan. 1869, Neumann Papers, Göttingen UB, Ms. Dept. Since Helmholtz had
already told the Bonn philosophical faculty of his willingness to come, their doubts about his availability
appear to have reflected more their disinclination toward him than the poor chance of getting him.
Helmholtz declined the call in the end because he felt that the Prussian ministry of culture was trifling
with him. Helmholtz to Carl Ludwig, 27 Jan. 1869, quoted in Koenigsberger, Helmholtz 2: 118–19.

138. Kirchhoff for that reason was never placed on the list of candidates at Bonn. Lipschitz to
Neumann, 14 June 1868.

fied for the main objective, the establishment of a physics institute at Bonn, since he had no experience in directing a laboratory and no experimental work to his credit.[139]

The disagreement within the Bonn science faculty resulted in a compromise: on the science faculty's list of candidates, the names of Helmholtz and Clausius would precede those of the three experimentalists. The intention of the majority of the science faculty appears to have been—and Lipschitz took it to be—that Wüllner's appointment would be assured in this way. Their arguments for Helmholtz and Clausius were flattering but brief, almost in the style in which faculties often mentioned the very best but unattainable men in the field before getting down to realistic proposals.[140] They no doubt assumed that if he were asked at all, Helmholtz would certainly refuse, and that Clausius would not be invited because he lacked laboratory experience. Helmholtz did refuse. The Prussian ministry of culture next went to Clausius, who accepted the call. Even though Clausius was a theorist in his research, he gave Bonn a physics institute of sorts, which is what the science faculty wanted of the man they acquired.[141] With Clausius's arrival at Bonn, the trained experimental physicist Ketteler found himself in the position—now becoming standard—of the second physicist responsible for theory.[142]

At Marburg, when the physics professorship fell vacant after Gerling's death, the faculty also wanted an experimental physicist who would direct student laboratory research. After several years of negotiations and disagreements over candidates' qualifications, the position went to Melde.[143] With an experimental physicist at the head of the physics institute, the second physicist at Marburg, the Privatdocent Feussner, who had earned a doctorate under Melde with an experimental dissertation and who had worked as an assistant at the Marburg physics institute, did what the second physicist at most other universities then did: he made mathematical physics his teaching specialty.[144]

139. Faculty reports cited above. Also Lipschitz to Neumann, 14 June 1868: in this letter, Lipschitz mentioned that he also suggested Meyer as a candidate, but the Bonn faculty rejected Meyer, as it did Clausius, for not being an experimental physicist. (The Bonn faculty did not consider Clausius's current, brief tenure as Würzburg's physics professor.)

140. Mathematics and natural sciences section of Bonn U. Philosophical Faculty to "Prodecan" Knoodt, 9 July 1868, and its "Separatvotum" in reply to Lipschitz, 14 July 1868, Plücker Personalakte, Bonn UA.

141. Clausius to Bonn U. Curator Beseler, 12 Mar. 1869, and documents giving details of Clausius's appointment, Clausius Personalakte, Bonn UA.

142. Ketteler to Dean of the Bonn U. Philosophical Faculty H. von Sybel, 27 June 1870, Ketteler Personalakte, Bonn UA. Ketteler's next publication was "of a more mathematical and critical nature," according to Clausius, who also said that Ketteler was "longing" for a physical cabinet. Clausius's recommendation of Ketteler for a position at the Karlsruhe Polytechnic, 29 Oct. 1870, Bad. GLA, 448/2355.

143. The Marburg philosophical faculty first asked for Wiedemann or Knoblauch. Wiedemann was offered the job and refused. Ignoring the faculty's second choice, Knoblauch, the ministry of the interior then proposed to the faculty three candidates of its own, Feilitzsch, Paalzow, and Quincke, all educated in Berlin and with connections to Magnus. These the faculty rejected. Documents dated 6 Feb., 10 and 17 Mar., and 3 June 1864, and 14, 16, and 21 Feb. 1866, STA, Marburg, Bestand 305a, 1864/66 Melde.

144. F. A. Schulze, "Wilhelm Feussner," Phys. Zs. 31 (1930): 513–14. Catalogus professorum academiae Marburgensis, 395.

10

Physics in Berlin: Relations to Secondary Education

When Altenstein, the newly appointed Prussian minister of culture, set out his program for the Prussian universities in 1818, he envisioned Berlin as the central, scientifically superior university of the nation; the Prussian provincial universities, by contrast, were to be restricted to meeting merely "practical needs" rather than undertaking "theoretical research." Altenstein's general scheme did not find much favor,[1] but he did not give up his hopes for Berlin's greatness. A few weeks before his death in 1840, he wrote to a friend of his great distress that the Prussian government was letting Berlin University slip more and more from its position of a "*world university* which impresses all of Europe." He believed that that was the "greatest misfortune that could befall the Prussian state."[2] In thinking that it ever had such esteem, he overlooked the refusal of some of the best German scholars, particularly in mathematics and the natural sciences, to accept his invitation to Berlin University, and he was painfully aware that Prussian ministers of finance could envision greater threats to Prussia than an inadequately endowed central university.[3]

Despite the limited provisions for physics and related sciences at Berlin University, throughout our present period the city of Berlin was already a central attraction for physicists. They came to Berlin to study, or they came there after their studies in search of a university career. They found in Berlin plenty of colleagues to support and encourage them in their research; there they had access to the physics literature, to laboratories, and to scientific societies. At the same time, they enjoyed the advantages of being in a city, the capital of the largest German state, with a good

---

1. Lenz, *Berlin*, vol. 2, pt. 1, pp. 11–12, 25.
2. Lenz, *Berlin*, vol. 2, pt. 1, p. 425.
3. With regard to foreign mathematicians and scientists, the Prussians' biggest disappointment was that despite their repeated efforts they could not draw Gauss to Berlin. See, for example, Lenz, *Berlin*, vol. 2, pt. 1, p. 375.

many gymnasiums and military and technical schools that could offer them a livelihood during their years of waiting and working for a university position.

Berlin Physics and the Berlin Gymnasiums

Each of the Berlin gymnasiums, of which there were six in this period, had at least two teachers for mathematics and physics; one teacher gave instructions in the lower grades and one in the two upper grades, *Secunda* and *Prima*, which together usually covered four years. Ministry regulations for gymnasiums prescribed that physics instruction was to be given in these last four years, and it was perhaps for this reason that the teacher for these years was more often a physicist than a mathematician. So young Berlin physicists could count on at least six gymnasium positions, more positions than any other kind of institution provided.[4]

The Berlin gymnasiums had reputations as distinguished as those of some German universities. When their physicists published research in national journals, they could identify their institution by giving only the name of the school without its location, whereas physicists at gymnasiums outside Berlin had to give both. To take a job at a gymnasium was to follow in the footsteps of Berlin University physics professors Paul Erman and Ernst Gottfried Fischer, who had held their university appointments and their gymnasium positions simultaneously for many years; it was no threat to a young physicist's hopes for an academic career to teach at a gymnasium.

A physicist at a gymnasium could hope to earn between 500 and 800 thaler a year, which was twice to three times what he would have earned as a salaried extraordinary professor. Beginning gymnasium teachers, who received less, could increase their income by becoming members of the seminar for gymnasium teachers at Berlin University, which paid its members 120, later 200, thaler annually, an arrangement that Clausius, for instance, took advantage of.[5] The time demanded of a physicist in return for his salary might be as much as twenty hours per week, which was Emil Wilde's load at the Gymnasium zum grauen Kloster in the 1830s, since he taught ten hours of Latin and religion in addition to mathematics and physics. Or it might be only twelve or fourteen hours per week, which was what Dove, for example, put in at the Friedrichs-Gymnasium auf dem Werder during the same period;

4. Rönne, *Unterrichts-Wesen* (a useful collection of regulations issued by the Prussian ministry of culture up to 1855) and Giese, *Quellen*, are the main general sources for our discussion of the gymnasiums. We have used them in conjunction with individual school histories and annual school programs, for the realization of the ministry regulations varied from school to school to some extent. We found the works of Friedrich Paulsen on this subject generally useless to a study of science and mathematics teaching at Prussian gymnasiums. Lexis, "Der Unterricht in den Naturwissenschaften," in *Reform*, provided us with a general introduction.

5. Rönne, *Unterrichts-Wesen*, 21. Karl-Ernst Jeismann, *Das preussische Gymnasium in Staat und Gesellschaft. Die Entstehung des Gymnasiums als Schule des Staates und der Gebildeten, 1787–1817*, vol. 15 of *Industrielle Welt, Schriftenreihe des Arbeitskreises für moderne Sozialgeschichte*, ed. W. Conze (Stuttgart: Ernst Klett, 1974), 100–101. Clausius's vita, 17 June 1855, A Schweiz. Sch., Zurich.

Dove taught mathematics and physics at other schools in Berlin in addition to the gymnasium and the university, altogether devoting as many as twenty-four to thirty hours per week to teaching, and increasing his income in this way.[6]

Particularly in the earlier part of the present period, several of the Berlin gymnasiums offered a physicist more than just an income: they offered him a stimulating setting for doing physics, as we shall see. The other gymnasiums did not attract the better physicists. The difference between them seems not to have been due to financial endowment, as one might suspect, but to the educational interests of the patrons of the gymnasiums. Of the six Berlin gymnasiums, three had been established under royal patronage and three under the patronage of the city of Berlin. The three royal gymnasiums—particularly two of them, the Friedrich-Wilhelms-Gymnasium and the Joachimsthalsches Gymnasium, which had annual budgets three times those of the others and approaching the budgets of the smaller Prussian universities—received generous financial support (along with oppressive solicitude) from the state.[7] In spite of their riches and no doubt because of the extra interest that the ministry took in these gymnasiums, to the disadvantage of the natural sciences, they did not contribute much to Berlin physics after the late 1820s. Pohl was the professor of mathematics and physics at the Friedrich-Wilhelms-Gymnasium in these years, and he taught none of the Berlin physicists who later dominated German university chairs; his successor, Dove, taught only one of them, Gustav Karsten. The Joachimsthalsches Gymnasium contributed to later Berlin physics before the ministry of culture imposed its directions on it; to understand what this means, we need to go back to the 1820s briefly.

The director of the Joachimsthalsches Gymnasium in the early 1820s was a teacher of mathematics and physics, Bernhard Moritz Snethlage. Snethlage belonged to a group of educators who were opposed to the educational policies of the ministry of culture and who in the early 1820s submitted their criticisms to the king, singling out for condemnation the intellectual trends of "speculation and criticism" and recommending a "useful direction" for studies through the "neglected practical, real, experimental sciences, the mechanical and fine arts."[8] While Snethlage was director, the gymnasium acquired Ernst Ferdinand August as a teacher in 1821. August had close ties to the physicist Fischer, his teacher and later his father-in-law. To qualify as a teacher August had concentrated on theology and philology at the uni-

6. *Programm . . . des Friedrichs-Gymnasium auf dem Werder, 1833* (Berlin, 1833). "Jahresbericht des Berlinischen Gymnasiums zum grauen Kloster von Ostern 1840 bis Ostern 1841," in Ferdinand Larsow, *De dialectorum linguae syriacae reliquiis* (Berlin, 1841), 29–62, on 29–30, 35. Alfred Dove, "Dove: Heinrich Wilhelm," *ADB* 48: 51–69, on 57.

7. Rönne, *Unterrichts-Wesen*, 9. Conrad Varrentrapp, *Johannes Schulze und das höhere preussische Unterrichtswesen in seiner Zeit* (Leipzig, 1889), 397–98. Varrentrapp quotes a student's account of a visit by Johannes Schulze, the powerful ministerial official, to one of the schools in which he took a special interest, this one outside Berlin: Schulze spent whole days examining all parts of the school, even the living quarters of the teachers and the student dormitory; "he missed no uncleanliness, no error, one could say no spider web." He interrupted classes by examining students or taking over the teaching himself. After classes he checked to see how the students occupied themselves in their rooms. Despite such testimony that gives a harsh picture of Schulze, Varrentrapp's biography is uncritical of him, if not completely adulatory.

8. Varrentrapp, *Schulze*, 329–30.

versity, but now, as he was teaching mathematics and physics under Snethlage, he studied these subjects at the university, earning a doctorate with a mathematical dissertation in 1823. He immediately started publishing tables of barometric observations, descriptions of instruments he invented or improved, and the like in the *Annalen*.[9] When Snethlage died in 1826, his opponent in the ministry Johannes Schulze went out of his way to replace him with a classical philologist.[10] Like its fellow royal gymnasiums, the Joachimsthalsches Gymnasium now played no further role in the lives of Berlin physicists; August moved to more fertile ground for his work, namely, to the city's new Real-Gymnasium.

As far as physics was concerned, the productive schools were the three Berlin city gymnasiums: the Friedrichs-Gymnasium auf dem Werder, the Gymnasium zum grauen Kloster, and after 1824 the Cöllnisches Real-Gymnasium. These schools received about a third of their budget from the city of Berlin and less than a tenth of it from the state. Because of its patronage, the city had a say in appointments and in the running of the schools.[11]

Gymnasium physics curricula reveal a difference between the Berlin city officials' views of the experimental sciences and those of the ministry of culture. Before 1837, the Prussian gymnasium curriculum, issued by the ministry, allowed for two hours of physics per week during the last four years of secondary school and for no hours in the lower grades. In 1837, the physics allowance was reduced to one hour per week for *Secunda*, the first half of the last four years. To this change the ministry added the recommendation that the one hour for physics be given over to natural history instead. Ignoring the recommendation, the Berlin city gymnasiums taught physics through all four years and then some. The Friedrichs-Gymnasium auf dem Weder in the 1830s taught two hours of physics per week for the last *six* years instead of the last four, while the Gymnasium zum grauen Kloster continued teaching two hours of physics through all four last years.[12]

From the appointments the city made to its schools, it would appear that city officials agreed with views such as Snethlage's favoring a greater emphasis on mathematics and the natural sciences. The lists of successive physicists on the faculties of the city schools read almost like those of university faculties. The lists even contain a chemist at the Cöllnisches Real-Gymnasium, although chemistry appears nowhere in the official gymnasium curriculum prescribed by the ministry. The physics teachers at the Friedrichs-Gymnasium auf dem Werder included August Seebeck, Dove, and Clausius; at the Gymnasium zum grauen Kloster, they included the physics educators Fischer and August and the physics researchers Wilde and Rudolph Franz, the collaborator of Knoblauch and Wiedemann.

The strongest indication of the city government's views was the creation of the

9. Moritz Cantor, "August: Ernst Ferdinand," *ADB* 1:683–84. August's first paper there was "Beschreibung eines neu erfundenen Differential-Barometers," *Ann.* 3 (1825): 329–40.

10. Varrentrapp, *Schulze*, 396.

11. Rönne, *Unterrichts-Wesen*, 19.

12. *Programm . . . des Friedrichs-Gymnasium auf dem Werder*, 1833. "Jahresbericht . . . Gymnasium zum grauen Kloster . . . 1840 . . . 1841." The curriculum proposed by the ministry in 1837 is given in Rönne, *Unterrichts-Wesen*, 156.

Cöllnisches Real-Gymnasium. Its forerunner, the Cöllnisches Gymnasium, had long been joined with the city's Gymnasium zum grauen Kloster; but in 1824, it was given a separate existence again, this time as a "Real-Gymnasium" on the strong insistence of the mayor of Berlin and against the wishes of the ministry of culture. The ministry consoled itself with the thought that the "Prussian state was strong enough and large enough to suffer such an experiment at *one* institution" (but when, more than forty years later, the Cöllnisches Real-Gymnasium reverted to the standard gymnasium program, Schulze read about it in the newspaper "with joy").[13]

Among physicists, the Cöllnisches Real-Gymnasium, which acquired August as its director in 1827 and August Seebeck as professor of physics in 1833, became something of a legend; Gustav Wiedemann recalled having been "captivated in the highest degree" by Seebeck, August, and the chemist Robert Hagen.[14] The plan for this unusual school was to give over more time to physics along with the other natural sciences, mathematics, and modern languages, without, however, giving up the humanistic gymnasium education. Instruction in the natural sciences began in the student's second year at the school, even before instruction in Latin began, and extended over seven years. From the third year on, six to eight hours were devoted to the natural sciences each week, four to six to mathematics, six to Latin, and the remaining fourteen hours were divided between German, Greek, modern languages, religion, history, and singing and drawing. Physics was briefly introduced in the third year along with chemistry as a preparation for mineralogy. For the next four years the physical sciences were taught together, two hours per week, with the remaining four hours for science going to botany and zoology. After that, the biological sciences were dropped from the curriculum, and the six hours for the natural sciences were divided equally between physics, chemistry, which included laboratory practice, and "technology." Physics, which August taught, consisted of "fundamental theories" of fluids and gases (the "main properties of bodies" having been included earlier), optics, and a complete review of all previous instruction in physics using the calculus this time, which August taught the year before, wherever possible. Also, in the last year, the mathematician Franz Herter added "applied mathematics" to his subjects, which meant the elements of hydrostatics and of spherical and theoretical astronomy. The year 1830–31 (the curriculum of which we have just described) saw the first qualifying examination, the *Abitur*, at the Cöllnisches Real-

13. Varrentrapp, *Schulze*, 412–13.

14. The programs of the city schools apparently appealed to businessmen, such as the fathers of Magnus, Riess, Knoblauch, and Franz, who sent their sons there. The program appealed, too, to a scientist such as Thomas Seebeck and to a physician such as Quincke's father. Cantor, "August," 684, and F. August, "Ernst Ferdinand August," in "Litterarischer Bericht CCIV," *Archiv d. Math. U. Physik* 51 (1870): 1–5, on August's activities there. On Seebeck: Kuno Fischer, *Seebeck*, 29, and K., "Seebeck: Ludwig Friedrich Wilhelm August," *ADB* 33 (1971): 559–60. On the students there, see, for example, Friedrich Kohlrausch, "Beetz," 1048; or Wiedemann, *Ein Erinnerungsblatt*, 6. Of the Cöllnisches Real-Gymnasium, Helmholtz wrote: "at that time," namely, when Wiedemann was a student there, this gymnasium "was already famous because of the excellent education of its students even in scientific and mathematical directions, which one knew how to unite with classical education there." Hermann von Helmholtz, "Gustav Wiedemann," *Ann.* 50 (1893): iii–xi, on iv. Friedrich Kohlrausch wrote: "With other contemporaries who went over to the natural sciences, Wiedemann shared the privilege of an education at the Cöllnisches Real-Gymnasium." Friedrich Kohlrausch, "Gustav Wiedemann. Nachruf," in *Ges. Abh.* 2:1064–76, on 1065–66.

Gymnasium, and August listed the examination questions in the school's annual report. In physics, the question was: "What is specific heat and what are the methods for determining it?"[15]

For the physicists who taught in them, the city schools had aspects of a physics institute. The professors usually lived together at the gymnasium; August described rushing to fetch his mathematical colleague Herter from his living quarters to confirm a new observation.[16] Students also lived at the school and so could be easily drawn into their teacher's work. August Seebeck, for example, used students to help in carrying out his many experiments; August provided the future *Annalen* editor Wiedemann with his first experience in handling scientific literature by letting him assist him with work on his books; Hagen had Wiedemann assist in the preparations for the chemical laboratory. The schools also provided material means for research. The Friedrichs-Gymnasium auf dem Werder, for example, had physical apparatus, which Dove apparently used for both teaching and research; in 1833 he devoted a good deal of his teaching there to electromagnetism, and at the same time he began publishing research on the subject. Wilde, at the Gymnasium zum grauen Kloster, wrote that it was the "rich library and the no less rich apparatus" at his disposal that led him to write his history of optics. The optical researches he published in the *Annalen* in the 1850s show that he was able to keep his means up to date.[17] By 1830–31, the Cöllnisches Real-Gymnasium, which was still adding to its building, already had a physical collection, a new "chemical auditorium" and laboratory, and scientific literature in its library.

August Seebeck's accounts of his work give us an idea of the possibilities of a gymnasium position. His first interest, going back perhaps to his days as Wilde's pupil at the Gymnasium zum grauen Kloster, was optics, which was the subject of his doctoral dissertation. He said that from the beginning of his scientific studies he had come to the conclusion that the main problems of physics were concentrated in the theory of cohesion, and that one of the most important approaches to this theory was through crystal physics.[18] His work at the gymnasium dealt with the same problems as the work of leading university physicists; he supervised the construction of apparatus for Neumann, exchanged long scientific letters with him, and furnished him with the observations without which, Neumann told Seebeck, it would not have been possible for him to dare approach a subject such as the influence of crystal surfaces on reflected light "with theoretical speculations."[19] Seebeck published re-

15. F. August, "August," 2. Also Cantor, "August," 684. Friedrich Köhler, *Ueber die Naturgeschichte des Kreuzsteins* (Berlin, 1831) includes August's annual program for the Cöllnisches Real-Gymnasium for 1830–31, on 12–44. The Cöllnisches Real-Gymnasium served the city not only as a gymnasium: for a number of years, August gave lectures on experimental physics in its lecture hall for "educated persons" (*"Gebildete"*). F. August, "August," 5.

16. Ernst Ferdinand August, "Ueber die vom Hrn. Dr. Wirth in Erlangen beobachtete Bewegung schwimmender Körpertheilchen auf der Oberfläche des ruhigen Wassers," *Ann.* 14 (1828): 429–37, on 431.

17. Heinrich Emil Wilde, *Geschichte der Optik, vom Ursprunge dieser Wissenschaft bis auf die gegenwärtige Zeit*, pt. 1 (Berlin, 1838), vii. Wilde's papers on optics appeared in the *Annalen* in 1850–53.

18. August Seebeck to Franz Neumann, 3 Jan. 1833, Neumann Papers, Göttingen UB, Ms. Dept.

19. August Seebeck to Franz Neumann, 3 Jan. and 11 May 1833, 5 Sept. 1837, and 13 Nov. 1840; Neumann to Seebeck, 23 June 1837; Neumann Papers, Göttingen UB, Ms. Dept.

search papers fairly frequently, on the average of once a year. Despite the demands of his teaching (beside teaching at the gymnasium and at the university as a Privat-docent, he also taught at the Berlin Allgemeine Kriegsschule), which at times kept him from making as extensive measurements as he needed to complete his investigations, his "calm and assurance of judgment" in scientific matters enabled him to maintain a good reputation as a researcher.[20] Seebeck had no difficulty in eventually moving from the gymnasium to positions in higher education: first to the director-ship of the Dresden Polytechnic and then to the chair of physics at Leipzig University.

After the 1840s, young Berlin physicists who went on to university careers did not teach physics at a Berlin gymnasium to earn a living as often as their predecessors. One reason was that other ways of earning a small living and of doing research while preparing for a university career appeared, as we will show. Another reason was that from the 1820s, Prussia began to have more gymnasium teachers than it could employ. To stop their numbers from growing, the ministry resorted to a number of new requirements, such as a trial year and more comprehensive examinations.[21] The result was that gymnasium teaching increasingly became a professional goal in its own right and less accessible as a temporary job for beginning physicists. Physics at the Berlin gymnasiums came to be taught by men who were satisfied to be gymnasium teachers only; Wilhelm Dumas at the Gymnasium zum grauen Kloster was one of these teachers, as was Kruse at the new Wilhelms-Gymnasium. Dumas studied in the Königsberg mathematical-physical seminar, earned a doctorate, and published one paper on physics in the *Annalen* and five other papers on mathematics and mechanics elsewhere, but he did not become a Privatdocent at Berlin University or have any kind of university career.[22] Kruse had a doctorate but never published in professional journals. Since by then, the 1860s, the gymnasium curriculum included only a total of three hours of physics a week for all classes, Kruse taught mainly elementary arithmetic and mathematics, with some natural history and religion thrown in. Physics was now taught according to a standard text prescribed by the ministry.[23]

Physics in Military Education in Berlin

During the period in which the Berlin gymnasiums attracted physicists, but extending beyond it, the Berlin military schools also took their physics teachers from the ranks of the university teachers. Three such schools had been in fairly regular existence since 1816 (they closed down and dismissed their civilian teachers during wars, threats of war, and internal disturbances): the Allgemeine Kriegsschule, the

20. Kuno Fischer, *Seebeck*, 31.
21. Varrentrapp, *Schulze*, 390, 391, 394.
22. Julius Heidemann, *Geschichte des Grauen Klosters zu Berlin* (Berlin, 1874), 307.
23. *K. Wilhelms-Gymnasium in Berlin. VI. Jahresbericht* (Berlin, 1866), "Schulnachrichten," 46–57, on 53–57. The new building of this gymnasium had a "physics classroom," apparently a new feature at gymnasiums.

military academy which trained the officers of the Prussian army; the Vereinigte Artillerie- und Ingenieurs-Schule, the artillery and engineering school which trained the technical military staff; and the school for cadets. The latter did not teach physics until after 1845 and so provided no jobs for physicists until then. A fourth military school for naval cadets was opened in Berlin in 1855, employing a physicist.[24]

The military academy was a three-year institution which devoted more time to mathematics, which included optics and mechanics, than to any other subject: from six to twelve hours per week. In the first year, more time was taken up by mathematics than in the second and third years, when physics and then chemistry took up four hours each week. The many hours given over to mathematics might suggest well-prepared students for physics and a level of physics instruction that did not, as a rule, exist. Because their students were officers, the civilian teachers of the academic subjects were not allowed, by school policy, to assert any authority over them or in any way offend their dignity; they could not, for example, ask direct questions of students, not even in examinations. The teachers regularly complained about the students' ignorance and absences. Physics teachers in the military academy had an additional problem: for many years it was customary for students, at their request, to be excused from taking academic subjects such as physics, mathematics, and chemistry, and as a consequence physics was usually not an examination subject. Physics was deemed of considerably less importance to the future officers at the military academy than, for example, the study of horses.[25]

All the same, the military academy provided the Berlin physicists with another place to do their research as well as earn 500 thaler for four hours of teaching per week. The plans for the school in 1809 included a collection of mathematical and physical instruments and models that was to meet not only the needs of instruction but also the "higher needs" of the teacher. But the plans came to nothing, and Erman, the physicist there, ended up providing his own materials. Since he had his living quarters at the academy, he accumulated a "considerable mass of physical apparatus" there.[26] After Erman's death, Dove lived at the academy, administered its "impressive" instrument collection, and did a fair amount of physical research with it, the greater part of it on meteorology; he even used the academy's instruments in his lectures at the university.[27] Both Erman and Dove made the military academy the center of their work.

Because of its technical nature, the combined artillery and engineering school, which was only a two-year school at first, gave over much less time to the "pure"

24. Our main source in this section is Bernhard Poten, *Geschichte des Militär-Erziehungs- und Bildungswesens in den Landen deutscher Zunge*, vol. 4, *Preussen*, vol. 17 of Monumenta Germaniae Paedagogica. Schulordnungen, Schulbücher und pädagogische Miscellaneen aus den Landen deutscher Zunge, ed. K. Kehrbach (Berlin, 1896). It lists in detail curricula and institutional arrangements, but only sometimes instructors by name. We have supplemented Poten's information by details taken from the biographical accounts of the Berlin physicists we cite throughout this chapter.

25. Poten, *Geschichte*, 258–59, 264–66, 280, 283.

26. Wilhelm Erman, "Paul Erman," 125, 212.

27. Alfred Dove, "Dove," 58.

sciences than did the military academy. Physics and chemistry were taught together, with time set aside for laboratory practice, only in the second year for four hours per week. Another four hours in the second year were devoted to "applied mathematics," which meant the "mechanical sciences" and analysis.[28] By the mid-1830s, the school's program had been lengthened by a year, and physics and chemistry were allotted twice as much time as before and were, eventually, separated.[29] For the practical exercises, the school had a new laboratory from the early 1820s and, from 1832, an instrument collection of its own. From 1832, an annual sum of 300 thaler was set aside for instruction in physics and chemistry.[30]

At the start, the physics instructors at the artillery and engineering school were apparently chosen for their technical knowledge: the first was the director of a gunpowder factory, Karl Daniel Turte, the second, from 1832, the Privatdocent for technology at Berlin University, Magnus. The next occupants of the job had long teaching experience to recommend them instead of their technical connections. After Magnus, the job went to Dove in 1840, to Clausius in 1850, and to Beetz in 1855.[31]

The artillery and engineering school was not used for experimental research by its physicists. But in the early 1850s, while working at the school, Clausius produced his important theoretical work on the mechanical heat theory. The school's contribution was limited to Clausius's salary of 500 thaler for eight hours per week of teaching, which gave him time for research.

Instruction at the school for cadets was at a secondary school level: there, as at the gymnasiums, physics was taught in the last two years for two hours per week. The job of teaching it was given to Magnus's assistant Wilhelm Beetz, who already had close personal ties to the school: he was born in it and grew up in it, since his father had taught geography there. For a decade Beetz taught physics at this school until moving to the artillery and engineering school in 1855.[32]

During his first years at the school for cadets, Beetz joined with other members of Magnus's colloquium to meet separately, as we have seen, in an informal group that was to become the Berlin Physical Society in 1845. That group first met in the reading room of the cadet school.[33] In this and other ways, the Berlin military schools, like the Berlin gymnasiums, helped sustain a number of beginning physicists. The military academy even provided what might be called the physics institute

28. Poten, Geschichte, 391–92.

29. The program for 1846, for example, specified that physics should treat the "general properties of bodies," the laws of equilibrium, heat, the application of steam, the measurement of heights and humidity, acoustics, optics, magnetism, electricity, electromagnetism, and magneto-electricity; the program included statics, geostatics, and hydrostatics in mathematics in the second year, and analytical mechanics and hydraulics, along with the calculus and higher geometry, in the third. Poten, Geschichte, 422–23.

30. Poten, Geschichte, 394, 408–9.

31. Poten, Geschichte, 392, 412. Hofmann, "Magnus," 81. Alfred Dove, "Dove," 57. Clausius's vita, 17 June 1855, A Schweiz. Sch., Zurich. Friedrich Kohlrausch, "Beetz," 1050.

32. Poten, Geschichte, 324, 329; Friedrich Kohlrausch, "Beetz," 1048, 1050.

33. Warburg, "Zur Geschichte der Physikalischen Gesellschaft," 35.

that Berlin University could not or would not provide for the university's ordinary professor of physics, first Erman and later Dove.

Physics at the Berlin Technical Institute

From about 1820, the Prussian ministry of culture and the Prussian ministry of trade had plans to establish a polytechnic school in Berlin, which was to have as its chief ornament the greatest German mathematician, Gauss. These plans were discussed for decades, but for various reasons—financial, personal, and other—the school could not be realized.[34]

Several lesser technical schools already existed in Berlin: the Bauakademie, established in 1799, which had the purpose of training the state's building and construction officials; a mining academy; and private technical schools, such as the one founded by the Prussian official C. P. W. Beuth in 1821, which in 1827 was transformed into a state institution, the so-called Gewerbeinstitut.[35] In a general reorganization of all Prussian trade schools in 1848–50, the Gewerbeinstitut was set above them as the "highest technical teaching institution of the state." Whereas the two-year trade schools were charged with the training of artisans, brewers, dyers, foremen for factories, and others, the Gewerbeinstitut was to train the technologists "who are capable of setting up and directing manufacturing plants." Its program consisted of three years of theoretical, that is, classroom, studies and some practical work in the institute laboratories.[36]

The curriculum of the Gewerbeinstitut and of the trade schools contained some physics. But the trade schools were much more concerned with applications than with "mere theoretical knowledge in mathematics and the natural sciences," which were regarded by the ministry as "of little use" to the practical man. Schools that taught analytical geometry and the calculus exceeded the limits set by the ministry for the trade school curriculum and were criticized for it. Teaching physics at these places was not the sort of work that attracted academic physicists. Students at the Gewerbeinstitut had graduated from a secondary school and had passed an examination in mathematics, and they all took a basic mathematics and science curriculum in addition to their technical specialties.[37] Even though the teaching was a little more demanding there than in the trade schools, few academic physicists during our present period were drawn to this school. This was in contrast to their attraction to polytechnic schools elsewhere in Germany.

34. Karl-Heinz Manegold, *Universität, Technische Hochschule und Industrie*, vol. 16 of Schriften zur Wirtschafts- und Sozialgeschichte, ed. W. Fischer (Berlin: Duncker und Humblot, 1970), 32, and "Eine École Polytechnique in Berlin," *Technikgeschichte* 33 (1966): 182–96. Gert Schubring, "On Education as a Mediating Element between Development and Application: The Plans for the Berlin Polytechnical Institute (1817–1850)," in H. N. Jahnke and M. Otte, eds., *Epistemological and Social Problems of the Sciences in the Early Nineteenth Century* (Dordrecht: Reidel, 1981), 269–84, on 270–72.

35. Manegold, *Universität*, 44.

36. Rönne, *Unterrichts-Wesen*, 327, 343–44.

37. Rönne, *Unterrichts-Wesen*, 327, 343–44.

Physicists in Berlin after 1840

Until the 1840s, all of the academic physicists who began—or, in some instances, even lived out—their careers in Berlin had at some stage relied on outside jobs to provide what the university could not. But from the 1840s, the majority of the beginning academic physicists did without these jobs. Gustav Karsten, Knoblauch, Kirchhoff, and Wiedemann, for instance, all spent two or three years doing nothing but research after receiving the doctorate; they became Privatdocenten at the end of the first year, but they needed to spend little time on teaching since their classes were small at best, and the subjects they taught came out of their research. They had either private means to support themselves or a stipend from the state, so that their main need was material support for their work. That now became available in Magnus's private laboratory.[38]

When a physicist arrived in Berlin for the first time in the late 1840s, as Kirchhoff did, for example, he would have found colleagues engaged in research in their private living quarters, at the secondary and military schools, at the academy, in Riess's private laboratory, and in the garden of Dirichlet's in-laws, the distinguished family of Mendelssohn-Bartholdy, who had supplied Humboldt with the site for his magnetic observatory. He would have found them discussing physics, for example, in the Berlin restaurant in which Helmholtz, Clausius, and Wiedemann regularly took their meals together in the winter of 1847, and in the meetings of the new Berlin Physical Society.[39]

He would also have found them meeting in private societies, such as the Society of the Friends of Humanity, in existence since 1797; the members of that particular society included Dove, Magnus, Poggendorff, and Turte, and other scientists such as Leopold von Buch, H. F. Link, the Roses, and Christian Gottfried Ehrenberg. At the meetings, the physicists gave talks on physics research, for example, on Melloni's experimental researches on heat, or on physicists they admired such as Faraday. They also expressed their contempt for and resentment of the current philosophical favorites of the government such as Schelling; a young physicist attending a talk there as a guest would quickly pick up the darker aspects of the life of Berlin physics. (We have a sample of Poggendorff's mocking of Schelling in 1844: having given an "empirical or experimental" lecture on heat the previous year, and having "always sensed a great talent" in himself for "philosophical speculations," Poggen-

---

38. Schmidt-Schönbeck, *300 Jahre Physik . . . Kieler Universität*, 65–66. Schmidt, "Knoblauch," 117. Robert Knott, "Knoblauch: Karl Hermann," *ADB* 51 (1971): 256–58, on 256. Koenigsberger, *Jacobi*, 365. Wiedemann, *Ein Erinnerungsblatt*, 7. Helmholtz, "Gustav Wiedemann," v.

39. Dove's paper "Correspondirende Beobachtungen über die regelmässigen stündlichen Veränderungen und über die Perturbationen der magnetischen Abweichung im mittleren und östlichen Europa," *Ann.* 19 (1830): 357–91, on 359, has an introduction by Humboldt that tells of the building of his "magnetic house" in the garden of city councillor Mendelssohn-Bartholdy in the fall of 1828. Dove and Humboldt were the regular observers at the observatory, and Dove wrote the reports on the observations; but on special dates, such as in October to December 1829, Dove and Humboldt might be joined by Encke, Poggendorff, Dirichlet, Magnus, and even a member of the Mendelssohn family. Sebastian Hensel, *The Mendelssohn Family (1729–1847). From Letters and Journals*, 2d rev. ed., trans. C. Klingemann (New York, 1882), 1:174. Helmholtz, "Clausius," 2.

dorff told his audience that he had wanted to try out such things for himself for once, particularly since he had learned that "the fate of philosophy is decided in Berlin." He had wanted to follow up his experimental talk with a philosophical part, and he had hoped to succeed because he flattered himself that he could establish a completely new, so far unheard-of science, thermo-philosophy. But, he said, he was stopped by the fear that someone might print his lecture behind his back and in so doing hurt his reputation as a philosopher, since the sublime structure of his philosophy had not yet been worked over sufficiently to hide its weaknesses. He did not need to remind his audience that just such troubles were then occupying Schelling or that Schelling might be drawing some comfort from the huge salary with which the ministry had brought him to Berlin only three years before, a salary well over 5000 thaler, or ten times the amount of the budget of the physics institute.)[40]

A newly arriving physicist was least likely to find physics research being done at the university, which had room only for lectures. If his connections were good, he would sooner or later find himself at the unofficial center of all physics activity for young physicists like himself; namely, at the Knobelsdorffsche Palais, Magnus's spacious and elegant home, where the Berlin colloquium met and where Magnus maintained his private laboratory. Magnus's invitation to young physicists extended beyond their student years, and by giving them laboratory space and equipment, he offered something of a research institute in his home.

The Berlin years of Gustav Karsten, Knoblauch, and Wiedemann, following their university studies, give a picture of the life of Berlin physics for the younger men who no longer took outside teaching jobs (as Clausius, Beetz, and Franz were still forced to do). Karsten received his doctorate in 1843, Knoblauch and Wiedemann theirs in 1847. Each of them then prepared to become a Privatdocent at Berlin University, which required more research and a publication. They took their time about it. Karsten at first briefly worked with his father on a scientific journal, then spent several months traveling, as he did again in 1846 when he went to England and met his idol, Faraday. When he returned to Berlin from his first trip abroad, Magnus offered him a place in his laboratory to do research. Magnus also invited Knoblauch to continue as a researcher in the laboratory; Knoblauch, who was in the midst of a comprehensive series of investigations when he graduated, completed the first phase of it before he left Berlin. Wiedemann, who had done the research for his dissertation in Magnus's laboratory, set up a modest place of his own to do experiments after his degree.

Two considerations governed Magnus's decision to accept a graduate or a student into his private laboratory: one was that the young researcher had selected a topic on his own that was not being worked on by anyone else; the other was that the topic was significant enough to be worth an experimental investigation.[41] That

40. Frommel, *Poggendorff*, 58. Lenz, *Berlin*, vol. 2, pt. 2, 42–51, describes Schelling's coming to Berlin in 1841 and his troubles in 1843 with H. E. G. Paulus, a former colleague, who had somehow acquired a copy of Schelling's unpublished lectures and published them along with his own voluminous criticisms.

41. Gustav Wiedemann and Adolph Paalzow described them in the anniversary volume of the

is, Magnus expected the beginning physicists to be mature enough to acquaint themselves thoroughly with the current literature and the state of the field as a whole. He helped prepare them through his colloquium and the literature he made available to them.

For his research in Magnus's laboratory, Karsten chose a subject that had this in common with much other research being done in Berlin then: it brought together two or more branches of physics. Karsten studied what he called "electrical images" and "heat images" in connection with efforts by physicists in these years to explain Moser's "invisible light."[42] Knoblauch, in his research in Magnus's laboratory, also investigated a connection between light and heat: starting from the analogy between light and heat radiation that Melloni and others had established in the 1830s, Knoblauch set out to establish the identity of the two by examining again the "optical" behavior of heat; that is, its double refraction, polarization, and diffraction. He was working on a fundamental problem; the connection of heat with light and the demonstration that heat radiation is subject to the laws of the wave theory of light were yet another reminder of the then generally recognized need for a new theoretical explanation of heat.[43] Knoblauch did not attempt to provide the theory himself, however; like Magnus, he separated experimental facts, which are "the only permanent things in science," from any "transitory" hypotheses, particularly since the latter "can only reach their goal if they are tied to a thorough mathematical treatment." He did hope that his observations would help guide heat theory to a "higher unity."[44]

Wiedemann met Helmholtz in Magnus's laboratory in 1847, about the time of his doctorate, when he was only twenty-one, five years younger than Helmholtz. Both were "stimulated by Gauss's magnetic investigations" and began meeting regularly to teach themselves mathematical physics, studying "some works by Poisson, especially his theory of elasticity."[45] But unlike Helmholtz, Wiedemann did not go on to distinguish himself in mathematical physics. Instead he became an experimentalist, although throughout his work he revealed his grasp of mathematical physics. In general the approach he took in his research was to establish the conditions under which known laws hold and to determine the form of new laws. In the research with which he qualified as Privadocent, he measured the rotation of the plane of polari-

Physical Society, *Verh. phys. Ges.* 15 (1896): 33 and 36–37. Their remarks are supported by accounts in other biographical sources of the Berlin physicists, such as those cited above.

42. Gustav Karsten, "Ueber elektrische Abbildungen," *Ann.* 58 (1843): 115–25, and 60 (1843): 1–17. He discussed the analogy between his electrical images and Moser's and his view that the two were identical. His first lecture course in the summer of 1845 was "Ueber die chemischen Wirkungen des Lichts"; in July of that year he gave a talk at the Physical Society, "Sonnenspektra und Mondbilder auf Papier und Daguerre'schen Platten; Bericht von Versuchen über die chemische Wirkung der Sonnenstrahlen." Schwalbe, "G. Karsten," 151.

43. Rosenberger, *Geschichte der Physik*, 386–90. Schmidt, "Knoblauch," 121–22.

44. Hermann Knoblauch, "Untersuchung über die strahlende Wärme," *Ann.* 71 (1847): 1–70, on 68–69.

45. Helmholtz, "Gustav Wiedemann," v–vi. Wiedemann said in 1896 of the early years of the Physical Society: "And we all were full of the undying achievements of Helmholtz. . . . " In the 1896 anniversary volume of the *Verhandlungen* of the society, 34.

zation of light by the magnetic forces of the galvanic current, a recent discovery of Faraday. Wiedemann confirmed Faraday's law that the rotation is proportional to the field intensity, and at the same time he established that there is no law, such as Biot had tried to find, describing the dependence of the magnetic rotation on the wavelength of light that is valid for all substances.[46] Two years later he investigated the mechanical actions of the galvanic current by which the current sets into motion the fluid matter through which it passes. By his experiments, he said, he proved that these actions follow exactly the same laws that Ohm had established for the distribution of electricity in the galvanic pile.[47] This study of the relationship between electrical and mechanical processes Wiedemann soon reformulated as the study of the relationship between magnetic and mechanical processes. In the new study, which he carried through at Basel University, in his first position after leaving Berlin, he exhibited a far-reaching parallelism between the magnetization and the mechanical deformation of iron and steel. The theoretical idea that guided him was that the magnetization of iron is a mechanical process effected by the rotation of the smallest particles.[48] Like Magnus, Wiedemann was a measuring expermentalist, but unlike Magnus, he chose to blend experiment and theory in his research, not keep them separate.

In addition to doing research, Wiedemann, Karsten, and Knoblauch participated in other aspects of Berlin physics such as Magnus's colloquium, the Berlin Physical Society, and teaching at the university. Karsten became Privatdocent in 1845, Knoblauch in 1848, and Wiedemann in 1850; it appears that they succeeded one another as Privatdocenten, for Karsten left Berlin for a university appointment in 1847, and Knoblauch left for Bonn in 1849. Wiedemann remained in Berlin twice as long as they, until 1854; but then he moved directly to an ordinary university professorship, which they had not done.

Yet another side of the Berlin physicists' activities involved the organization of the physics literature. That expressed their desire to stay on top of their subject, something Magnus always encouraged. Karsten became the first editor of the *Fortschritte der Physik*, the first of much similar work by him. Wiedemann, out of the feeling that he was insufficiently informed on the literature of the fields of physics he had chosen, began in his last three years in Berlin to collect notes on it, at first only for his own use but eventually, in 1861, to be worked into his great handbook, *Die Lehre vom Galvanismus und Elektromagnetismus nebst technischen Anwendungen.*[49] In 1877 Wiedemann became *the* organizer of the physics literature in Germany when he succeeded Poggendorff as editor of the *Annalen.*

During the next decade or so, the young physicists in Berlin differed from their predecessors in several respects. First, they were usually not natives of Berlin. Sec-

46. Wiedemann, *Ein Erinnerungsblatt*, 7. Helmholtz, "Gustav Wiedemann," vi.

47. Gustav Wiedemann, "Ueber die Bewegung von Flüssigkeiten im Kreise der geschlossenen galvanischen Säule," *Ann.* 87 (1852): 321–52, especially 321, 351–52.

48. Kohlrausch, "Wiedemann," 1071. Rosenberger, *Geschichte der Physik*, 526–27. Helmholtz, "Gustav Wiedemann," vii.

49. Wiedemann, *Ein Erinnerungsblatt*, 10–11.

ond, perhaps because they had grown up elsewhere, they got only part of their university education at Berlin University. Ketteler, for example, who was in Berlin from 1857 to 1861, spent his first two years of university study at Bonn before moving to Berlin to complete it. Similarly, Kundt came to Berlin from Leipzig in 1861, and Warburg from Heidelberg in 1865.[50] Among those who had grown up in Berlin, Paul du Bois-Reymond and Quincke began and completed their work at their home university, but they also spent several years elsewhere, principally at Königsberg.[51] After the doctorate, the young Berlin physicists in these years had to wait longer than their predecessors to habilitate, and as Privatdocenten they had to wait longer for professorships than the two or three years that Kirchhoff, Karsten, or Knoblauch had to wait. Adolph Paalzow and Rudolph Franz, for example, were Privatdocenten for eight years.[52] Quincke was Privatdocent for six years and then extraordinary professor for another seven. Kundt's and Warburg's rapid advancement was exceptional for then. Some of the young physicists in Berlin were even kept from habilitating there at all; graduates of other universities sometimes found that they could not meet the habilitation requirements at Berlin and after a while moved on.[53]

Berlin University had long tried to stop an overflow of Privatdocenten and extraordinary professors by making those positions harder to attain.[54] Physics had been less affected by the overflow than some other fields, since the university offered it so little material means. But at the same time, the spreading fame of Magnus's laboratory and the high reputation of the Berlin mathematicians could not fail to attract young physicists to Berlin. Now as before, Berlin had successful young experimentalists—such as Quincke, Wüllner, Ketteler, Kundt, and Warburg—who worked in Magnus's laboratory and who advanced through independent, significant researches.

50. Eduard Ketteler, "Vita," in his dissertation, *De refractoribus interferentialibus*, Ketteler Personalakte, Bonn UA. August Kundt, "Vita," 21 June 1867, A Schweiz. Sch., Zurich. Eduard Grüneisen, "Emil Warburg zum achtzigsten Geburtstage," *Naturwiss.* 14 (1926): 203–7, on 203.

51. Paul du Bois-Reymond had already published an important paper, in 1854, before he left Berlin for Königsberg, on the subject that eventually became his dissertation. F. H. du Bois-Reymond to Franz Neumann, 18 Mar. 1857; Quincke to Franz Neumann, 27 Mar. 1859; Neumann Papers, Göttingen UB, Ms. Dept. Alfred Kalähne, "Dem Andenken an Georg Quincke," *Phys. Zs.* 25 (1924): 649–59, on 650–51.

52. On Paalzow and Franz, see J. C. Poggendorff's *Biographisch-literarisches Handwörterbuch.* Also Adolf Wissner's article on Franz in *Neue deutsche Biographie* 5 (Berlin: Duncker und Humblot, 1961): 376–77, and Lenz, *Berlin*, vol. 2, pt. 2, 299.

53. Correspondence between O. E. Meyer and Carl Pape, our two examples, and Franz Neumann, cited below.

54. The overflow of Privatdocenten and extraordinary professors at Berlin University was due to the same ministry policy we have discussed in connection with appointments at the Prussian provincial universities; only it was more severe at Berlin because of Altenstein's big plans for this university. Lenz, *Berlin*, vol. 2, pt. 1, 407–8, writes that eventually the university was filled up with young scholars waiting for professorships, sometimes as many as five to ten in a field; the university lacked the money to maintain them as Wilhelm von Humboldt, who had initiated the policy, had intended. In the natural sciences, according to Lenz (p. 507), the rush of Privatdocenten stopped after 1834. We find that that was not true for physics, even if physics never became too burdened; before 1848 physics generally had one or two Privatdocenten, and only briefly, from 1832 to 1834, three; in 1848 their number increased to four and it remained at three or four until 1865, when it fell off for a few years, perhaps because of Magnus's declining health and the change in chairholder.

The countermeasures to the excessive influx of young scholars proposed by the faculty generally met with the ministry's approval, except for the measure that would have eliminated the problem easily; that was for the ministry to consult the faculty on appointments. Lenz, *Berlin*, vol. 2, pt. 1, 410–15.

Berlin also had physicists who were good enough to advance to university chairs eventually, but who in its now more competitive climate remained on the margins, without any affiliation, hoping for their chance. O. E. Meyer and Carl Pape are cases in point.

As Neumann's students, Meyer and Pape were given a cordial welcome by the Berlin physicists and mathematicians at the university, where they arrived with their Königsberg degrees in hand. Nothing would stand in the way of his habilitation, Pape was told, as soon as he had fulfilled the legal requirements. Everything Meyer heard or saw indicated that it would be easy to lecture there successfully; but given the number of people at Berlin, he also found that "no one pays any attention to anyone else."[55]

The way to get more than momentary attention was to produce good research or at least a good idea for research. Then the legal requirements, the habilitation research, the Latin dissertation, and the unanimous approval of the faculty, which meant in most cases only the unanimous approval of the physicists and related specialists in the faculty, were not difficult to obtain. Pape tried to take these hurdles with energy and directness but also without an appreciation of the competition he was up against. He spent eight weeks on the Latin dissertation using old student work on the combustion of gunpowder so as not to be detained too long. His habilitation research required "many numerical calculations" and was therefore "very strenuous and time-consuming," but after five months he was nearly ready to submit it to the Berlin faculty. That "unfortunately the experiments do not give the expected results" and "the conclusions that I wanted to draw from them cannot be drawn from them" did not loom as a real obstacle to him.[56] It did, however, to the professors who were to evaluate his research and recommend him for habilitation; they found that they could not support his application, and they advised him not even to try. He took their advice.[57]

To Meyer, Pape's difficulties seemed to stem from his frankness about his plans to habilitate in Berlin. So Meyer, who had come to Berlin with the intention of habilitating, used a subtler approach. It did him no good, however, as he clearly failed to impress the physicists there, and he apparently did not try to habilitate. In any case, what would have kept him out of Berlin University was not what he perceived as his mathematical superiority over the Berlin physicists, but the lack of direction in his research, which his letters about his Berlin year show. He picked up and tried to improve the work of other physicists—as he later wanted to develop a "decent mathematical theory" for Clausius's work on gases—rather than pursuing a course of his own. Nothing could have been more at odds with Magnus's requirements of his young colleagues. Two years after he had left Königsberg, Meyer still had not produced any publishable results.[58]

55. Pape to Franz Neumann, 6 June 1861; Meyer to Neumann, 6 Feb. and 6 Aug. 1861; Neumann Papers, Göttingen UB, Ms. Dept. Young physicists had felt superfluous and ignored in Berlin earlier, too, as we gather from Dove's letter to a Baden official on 31 Jan. 1844, Bad. GLA, 235/7525.
56. Pape to Franz Neumann, 6 June 1861.
57. Pape to Franz Neumann, 9 Jan. 1862, Neumann Papers, Göttingen UB, Ms. Dept.
58. Meyer wrote on Pape in his letter to Franz Neumann, 6 Aug. 1861. He reported on his research

What kept young men like Pape and, later, Albert Wangerin in Berlin, even though they could not get a position at the university, were the many opportunities that the city offered them. "Here in Berlin there are so very many higher educational institutions, some of which are not even completely organized yet," Pape wrote, noting that the technical school was about to be expanded and that there were some open positions.[59] Wangerin, who already supported himself with lesser teaching positions, wrote in 1867 that he had turned down a permanent position as mathematics teacher in a provincial town because it did not offer what Berlin did, the stimulation to "keep alive continuously an interest in science." Through the Physical Society and the associated journal circle, he could easily keep up to date on the new phenomena in science and even get suggestions for his work. While he still lacked sufficient time for research, he kept in touch with physics through the reports he contributed to the *Fortschritte der Physik.*[60]

To complete the picture of physics in Berlin in the last decade of Magnus's tenure—and of Dove's as well, for although Dove survived Magnus by about ten years, he was disabled by a stroke[61]—requires an account of the two physicists who took on a larger part of the responsibility for physics instruction than the many Privatdocenten whom we have discussed. They were Quincke and Kundt. After his promotion to extraordinary professor in 1865, Quincke introduced a four-semester course on theoretical physics; before that, the subject had been taught unsystematically by Privatdocenten such as Kirchhoff, Clausius, and Paalzow. From about the same time, Kundt gave much of the instruction in Magnus's laboratory.[62]

During his student days, moving from Berlin to Königsberg to Heidelberg and back to Berlin, Quincke had exposed himself to the best that the physical sciences had to offer in Germany: he worked in Magnus's and Mitscherlich's laboratories, he was in Neumann's seminar, he learned all there was to learn of Bunsen's methods, and he studied mechanics under Kirchhoff and elliptical functions under Clebsch.[63] Kundt conducted his studies in the same spirit, sampling from the best. From "earliest youth," Kundt had been strongly inclined to physics, but when he came to Berlin he spent the first two years working on mathematics and astronomy, making observations and calculations under an astronomer and studying mathematical phys-

in letters to Neumann on 6 Feb. and 6 Aug. 1861, and on the fruitlessness of his work in a letter to Neumann from Göttingen on 20 Feb. 1863. Meyer's reference to Clausius is in a letter to Neumann on 30 Mar. 1867. All letters in Neumann Papers, Göttingen UB, Ms. Dept.

59. Pape to Franz Neumann, 9 Jan. 1862.
60. A. Wangerin to Franz Neumann, 19 Oct. 1867, Neumann Papers, Göttingen UB, Ms. Dept.
61. Alfred Dove, "Dove," 68.
62. For several years after Magnus's death, Quincke conducted the colloquium. Kalähne, "Quincke," 653. Planck, "Das Institut für theoretische Physik," 276. Ferdinand Braun, "Hermann Georg Quincke," *Ann.* 15 (1904): i–viii, on ii. August Kundt, "Vita," 21 June 1867, A Schweiz. Sch., Zurich.
63. The best source of Quincke's experiences at the three universities is his correspondence with Franz Neumann in the Göttingen UB, Ms. Dept. E. H. Stevens, "The Heidelberg Physical Laboratory," *Nature* 65 (1902): 587–90, gives as reason for Quincke's move from Königsberg to Heidelberg that "Neumann allowed his pupils too little scope for originality," which is confirmed by the tone of much of the correspondence between Neumann and his students in the Neumann Papers.

ics on the side. He wanted to do experimental physics, too, because he wanted to find out which direction of physics he was especially suited for. Finding no opportunity at first, his "longed for" chance came when Magnus opened the official university laboratory in the spring of 1863. Kundt entered it at once. He became Magnus's assistant that year and published his first papers the following spring.[64] He stayed in Berlin for five years, until 1868, and he later returned to its chair of physics.

Although Quincke became the representative for mathematical physics at Berlin University, he had already decided to do experimental research by the time he started to teach. Of his efforts to learn mathematical physics, he said: my "capabilities unfortunately did not allow me also to develop my mathematical means as far as I had wished," even though "I try at least to drag myself along as well as I can."[65] Since he knew that he would not succeed by the same route as his teachers Neumann and Kirchhoff, he was reassured that expert experimentalists with whom he was in touch in Berlin had good reasons to be skeptical of certain mathematical theories of physics, particularly when they were not closely linked to experiment.[66] Early on, in 1858, Quincke experienced the excitement of making an important experimental discovery: constant electric currents arise, he found, when distilled water or any other fluid flows through a porous diaphragm, and the currents have the same direction as the flow of the water. His defensiveness about his experimenting, which characterized his reports on the progress of his dissertation,[67] gave way to pride over this discovery. "I only wanted to inform you briefly today," he wrote to Neumann, "that Professor Magnus yesterday presented excerpts, or rather a preliminary notice, of my new work to the local academy to secure me priority." Quincke speculated on the many ways in which his discovery might be of significance to science. "There must be many such currents present in the earth that modify earth magnetism"; "further, hydrogen must occur in bodies of water, for the water that seeps through porous layers of earth is decomposed, etc. To what extent

64. Kundt, "Vita." Rubens, "Das physikalische Institut," 281–82. Rubens's claim (p. 281) that Magnus set the subject and method of student research is contradicted by accounts by Magnus's students, as we have seen.

65. Quincke to Neumann, 14 Oct. 1861, Neumann Papers, Göttingen UB, Ms. Dept.

66. With regard to Quincke's work on capillarity, his main research subject in the early years, Eilhard Mitscherlich told him that he did not believe in Laplace's theory and that the disagreement between experiment and theory that Quincke found in his work was not the fault of his experimental methods. It was Mitscherlich's view, as Quincke wrote to Neumann, that "as soon as I used other equations than pure interpolation equations, I would no longer have pure observations. But mathematics could introduce, and already would have introduced, something wrong." Quincke to Neumann, 28 Feb. 1857, Neumann Papers, Göttingen UB, Ms. Dept. Quincke adopted that view in his dissertation, which he published as "Ueber die Capillaritätsconstanten des Quecksilbers," Ann. 105 (1858): 1–49: he came to the conclusion that the established capillarity theory cannot be shown to agree with any experimental phenomena since the theory starts from the assumption of a state of equilibrium for the mercury that cannot be achieved in reality. He reported the negative result to save other physicists the trouble of trying to prove capillarity theory by experiments.

67. "You will perhaps think . . . that I did not take up the matter in the right way and with the proper enthusiasm," Quincke wrote to Neumann on 28 Feb. 1857; "but if you had made the measurements yourself you would have seen for yourself how many details hamper one's progress; such details really don't belong to the investigation directly and take up the most time in experimenting."

physiology and botany are affected by it I don't as yet know, of course; but it might be possible that the variation of the muscle current during contraction of the muscle derives from it." Most important to Quincke was that this discovery was not accidental but that "so far everything has come out exactly as I had imagined it."[68]

In 1861 Quincke began a larger research topic. He had been studying capillarity (which was involved in his previous discovery, since he considered the pores of the diaphragm as so many capillaries), which led him to the study of surfaces and then to the study of the interaction between the electricity on the surface of a body with a ray of light. Nothing came of that, but it in turn led Quincke to a fundamental problem: "I would like . . . to discover what electricity is," he wrote. To be able to decide if it is oscillations and, if so, if it is transversal or longitudinal oscillations, Quincke designed an experiment analogous to an optical experiment on polarization. He reasoned that if electricity consists of waves, then it should be polarized in his experiment, and the polarization should appear as a change in intensity. His results did not satisfy him, "but for now," he said, "I will take the experiment as proof and now do experiments to prove that electricity is a fluid, perhaps identical with the light ether."[69]

Quincke set up his experimental equipment in his living quarters for a time after he had completed his doctoral work at the university—and gathered up twenty pounds of mercury from all over his room repeatedly whenever his pressure apparatus burst—but by 1861 he had a "pretty laboratory, together with another gentleman," and enough apparatus to use in his lectures as well as for research.[70] He had built some of the apparatus himself and some was lent to him by a friend. His private instrument collection allowed him to turn down offers from elsewhere to remain in Berlin awaiting his chances, carrying out research all the while. (Two other reasons may also have kept him there: in 1865, when he was promoted to extraordinary professor in Berlin, he was only thirty-one and could afford to wait; and he was married to Riess's daughter, which established an excellent connection with Berlin scientists.) Helmholtz's appointment to succeed Magnus in 1870, however, ended any hopes Quincke had for the Berlin chair, and he left in 1872 to become ordinary professor of physics in Würzburg.

Kundt, as we have seen, established himself in Magnus's Berlin laboratory at the start. He assisted Magnus during lectures, worked for him in the laboratory, and instructed students. His duties were soon reduced to laboratory teaching when Magnus acquired a second assistant, which allowed Kundt more time for his own research.[71] By 1867, after he had been in Magnus's laboratory only four years, during which time he had completed his university studies and his dissertation and qualified

68. Quincke to Franz Neumann, 29 Oct. 1858, Neumann Papers, Göttingen UB, Ms. Dept.

69. Quincke to Franz Neumann, 24 Dec. 1860 and 14 Oct. 1861, Neumann Papers, Göttingen UB, Ms. Dept.

70. Kalähne, "Quincke," 653. Quincke to Franz Neumann, 27 Mar. 1859; Rudolph Radau to Franz Neumann, 21 Oct. 1861; Neumann Papers, Göttingen UB, Ms. Dept.

71. Kundt, "Vita." Also introduction in August Kundt, "Untersuchungen über die Schallgeschwindigkeit der Luft in Röhren," Ann. 135 (1868): 337–72, 527–61.

as a Privatdocent, Kundt could claim fourteen publications, a record of work which suggests what it might have taken to succeed where Meyer and Pape had failed.

Kundt's researches from his years in Magnus's laboratory include work of considerable importance. Referring to the method Kundt invented for determining the velocity of propagation of sound in gases, Wilhelm von Bezold said that this work had won for Kundt a place among physicists of the first rank. Kundt's researches were primarily experimental, as Quincke's were, but he had more use for theory than Quincke, generally starting his work from the theoretical considerations of others.[72] While still in Berlin, Kundt found his future theoretical collaborator in his student Warburg.[73] With Kundt, the mixing of theory and experiment that Magnus had objected to entered Magnus's laboratory toward the end. It was a development to which Magnus was reconciled, as Helmholtz was to discover.[74] With Kundt, also, the use of the laboratory in the training of physicists changed from the way in which Magnus had conducted it, which had been to encourage independent student research. Kundt's collaboration with his student—soon his colleague—Warburg in his own work was to become a familiar pattern for advanced student research.

72. Wilhelm von Bezold, "Gedächtnissrede auf August Kundt," Verh. phys. Ges. 13 (1894): 61–80, on 67, 72. Rosenberger, Geschichte der Physik, 753–54.

73. Emil Warburg was, of course, primarily an experimentalist. He had begun his university studies at Heidelberg with the intention of becoming a chemist. Kirchhoff's lectures won him over to physics, and after his move to Berlin, Kundt's instruction decided Warburg to become an experimental physicist. Friedrich Paschen, "Gedächtnisrede des Hrn. Paschen auf Emil Warburg," Sitzungsber. preuss. Akad., Phil.-Hist. Kl., pt. 1 (1932), cxv–cxxiii. Grüneisen, "Warburg."

74. In 1870 Helmholtz was elected to the Prussian Academy of Sciences on Magnus's initiative. Helmholtz wrote to Emil du Bois-Reymond after Magnus's death that Magnus's action on his behalf was "a dear memory" to him, since he had always liked him greatly. "As I now see, I suspected him unjustly of feeling a certain opposition to my mathematical direction." Helmholtz to du Bois-Reymond, 17 May [1870], STPK, Darmst. Coll. F 1 a 1847.

11

Physics in Munich: Relations to Technology

Ohm's Return to Bavaria

In the sixteen years that Ohm spent abroad in Prussia, he had made himself known to physicists primarily through the mathematical law of physics that bears his name. Despite this recognized achievement in "pure" science, for years he tried in vain to get a suitable job in Bavaria. He succeeded at last when Bavaria reorganized its technical education, hiring Ohm, a physicist, to further the state's technical goals.[1] As it turned out, Ohm's job at a technical school was a stepping stone to what he regarded as a far more suitable job, a university professorship in Munich. Ohm's return to Bavaria from Prussia was, as we will see, just one example of the many connections between physics and technology in nineteenth-century Bavaria.

In the early 1830s Ohm could hope for a job in any one of Bavaria's three polytechnic schools: in Nuremberg's, in the new polytechnic school being planned for Augsburg, and in the one being reconstituted at Munich. The last interested Ohm especially, for he hoped to combine an appointment to its chair of physics,

---

1. Better to serve the needs of trade and industry, a new plan for Bavarian technical education was announced in 1833. This plan called for three tiers: the lowest tier consisted of three-year trade schools, or Gewerbeschulen, and agricultural schools, which taught a little science but no physics. They prepared students for an apprenticeship or for the second tier, the polytechnic schools, which included among their science courses a five-hour experimental physics course in the first year. The polytechnic schools, too, had a three-year program, after which their graduates either took jobs or went on to the third tier, the highest technical school. The latter was conceived as the central Bavarian technical university, or Technische Hochschule, an institution that had been proposed before at various times, for example, in 1823 by Fraunhofer and Reichenbach (see below). The central higher technical school that was actually adopted in 1833 was the then practically defunct political economic faculty of Munich University. In this faculty, ten new chairs were created for professors to train students for careers in civil engineering, forestry, mining, industry, agriculture, and construction, and to train teachers for these subjects in the trade and polytechnic schools. But the graduates of these specialties found no place in the state's administration of technical services, the principal place where they might have been employed, because the state continued its traditional use of law graduates there. The higher technical school seemed superfluous, and for this and other reasons, above all the then widespread opinion that, in principle, technical education did not belong at a university, the school was dissolved after a few years. The equality of education in technical fields with a university education was denied, a state of affairs that would remain for the next quarter century, until the founding of an autonomous technical university in Munich in 1868. Neuerer, *Das höhere Lehramt in Bayern*, 29–35, 249–50.

which had fallen vacant, with an extraordinary professorship at the university, a
favorable position for an eventual promotion to an ordinary university professorship.[2]
The death of the Munich physics professor Stahl in 1833 gave Ohm the immediate
occasion to apply to the Bavarian minister of the interior for both jobs. This time
his application was not filed away but referred to the university for expert opinion.
The physics professor Siber, who was then dean of the philosophical faculty, returned a favorable report: "a significant majority" of the philosophical faculty had
voted for granting Ohm's request, giving as their main reason his usefulness to technical teaching, the reason that had given Ohm enough hope to apply in the first
place. They stated, first, that they "hold it to be desirable to reacquire Dr. Ohm
because of what they have heard of the petitioner's former effectiveness as a
teacher"; second, they recommended Ohm as "a quiet, harmless, and industrious
man who . . . had acquired great literary fame through his book, 'The galvanic
circuit, mathematically treated 1827' "; third, they supported his request "especially
because he mainly asks for a teaching position at the polytechnic school and only
secondarily for an extraordinary professorship at the university and because he seems
to be completely qualified through his skill and knowledge."[3] Impressed by the praise
Ohm had received, the senate wanted to see him return to the "fatherland," Bavaria. The king now wanted to see Ohm return, too, and he appointed Ohm professor of physics at the polytechnic school in Nuremberg. Since Ohm had really
wanted an appointment at the polytechnic in Munich in connection with an appointment at the university, he deliberated; if he were to take the job at Nuremberg,
he would have to limit rather than expand his "literary field of activity," by which
he meant his research. In the end, Ohm accepted the offer.[4]

In Nuremberg, Ohm doubled the planned physics curriculum to ensure a thorough "scientific training" for future artisans and craftsmen. He soon added higher
mathematics to his teaching and doubled the hours of it, too, coordinating his
teaching in mathematics with that in physics. In 1839 he became rector of the
school. All of this left him with little time for research, as he had foreseen.[5]

During his first six years at Nuremberg, Ohm published no research. When he
began to publish again, it was not on electricity, the branch of physics he had
worked on until then, but on acoustics and optics, branches that belonged to an
encompassing theory of waves, as the Weber brothers had conceived of it in their
Wellenlehre. Ohm had no musical ear, but that did not keep him from working
experimentally in musical acoustics (he could and did call on a colleague with a
good musical ear). In any case, here as in his electrical studies his mathematical
reasoning proved decisive. In his work on tones, which he carried out from 1839 to

2. Ohm to E. Dingler, n.d. [1831]; Ohm to the Bavarian King, 1 Sept. 1831 and 29 July 1832; in
Ohms . . . Nachlass, 149–51, 151–54, 155–56, respectively.

3. Ohm's letter of inquiry to the Bavarian Minister of the Interior Prince von Wallerstein, 23 Feb.
1833; Siber's account of the faculty's discussion to Munich U. Senate, 4 Apr. 1833; in *Ohms . . .
Nachlass*, 157–59 and 159–60, respectively. Quotation on 160.

4. Rector Oberndorfer to the Bavarian King, 18 Apr. 1833; Ohm to the same, n.d. [1833]; in *Ohms
. . . Nachlass*, 160–61 and 177–80, respectively.

5. Bauernfeind, "Ohm," 193.

1844, he turned to Fourier again, this time for his representation of any function of time by an infinite series of trigonometric functions, a theorem which, he noted, had become "famous through its repeated and important applications." Just as the ear resolves a mass of musical sound into individual tones—an assumption that, according to Helmholtz, most mathematical physicists before Ohm had implicitly made but which he recognized as a fundamental law—Ohm resolved mathematically any sound impression into partial impressions, each expressible by a simple harmonic term in an infinite Fourier series. The ear, that is, performs the same Fourier analysis that the physicist carries out mathematically, revealing at once the mathematical order of the organ of hearing and the power of mathematical methods in physics and in physiological acoustics.[6]

Ohm's confidence in this simple correspondence between tones and terms in a Fourier series led him to doubt certain evidences of the senses that seemed to contradict it. August Seebeck, who was working on the same subject with a more empirical approach, thought that other tones contribute to the main tone of a sounding body, intensifying it; Ohm thought that the ear deceives us by making the main tone seem more intense than it really is and neighboring tones seem weaker, just as the eye presents a middle tint on a dark background as brighter and on a light background as darker than it really is. According to Seebeck, the ear is all we have to tell us what belongs to a tone, and without it there is no tone, only the motion of air; according to Ohm, Seebeck's new definition of tone leads us into a "new labyrinth."[7] Ohm soon withdrew from the controversy, leaving the field to Seebeck, and their disagreements remained unsolved until Helmholtz took them up shortly after Ohm's death.[8]

As an "experimenting theorist," as Ohm referred to himself, he did more experimental and theoretical research after his acoustics, but not much more. While at the Nuremberg polytechnic school, he published one more paper to make certain experimental facts "more useful for theoretical purposes" in galvanism.[9]

Fraunhofer's Work in Optical Instrument Manufacture

Physics, technology, and state-promoted industry rarely interacted as vigorously in Germany in the early nineteenth century as they did in Munich. As the interaction yielded results that benefited physical theory, physics in Munich brings the subject

6. Hermann von Helmholtz, "Ueber Combinationstöne," Ann. 99 (1856): 497–540, in Wiss. Abh. 1:263–302, on 287. Georg Simon Ohm, "Ueber die Definition des Tones, nebst daran geknüpfter Theorie der Sirene und ähnlicher tonbildender Vorrichtungen," Ann. 59 (1843): 513–65, in Ges. Abh., 587–633, on 592–93; "Noch ein paar Worte über die Definition des Tones," Ann. 62 (1844): 1–18, in Ges. Abh., 634–49, on 640–43.

7. Ohm, "Noch ein paar Worte," 646, 648. August Seebeck, "Ueber die Definition des Tones," Ann. 63 (1844): 353–68, on 361, 367.

8. Helmholtz championed Ohm's law and sought to refute Seebeck's objections to it. Helmholtz, "Ueber Combinationstöne," 287. R. Steven Turner, "The Ohm-Seebeck Dispute, Hermann von Helmholtz, and the Origins of Physiological Acoustics," Brit. Journ. Hist. Sci. 10 (1977): 1–24, on 10–11.

9. Georg Simon Ohm, "Galvanische Einzelheiten," Ann. 63 (1844): 389–405, in Ges. Abh., 650–64, on 650.

of the technical concerns of the state into the domain of the study of German theoretical physics.

By the time of Ohm's return to Bavaria, Munich had had a flourishing optical instrument establishment for about two decades. The guiding scientific spirit of the most eminent Munich optical "institute" was Joseph Fraunhofer, who not only provided scientists with optical instruments of unsurpassed accuracy but also made fundamental discoveries of his own in optics. Fraunhofer worked within a commercial firm, which introduces into our study a new site for research, one which offered different opportunities and constraints than those of the school, university, and academy.

The firm Fraunhofer belonged to was founded at the beginning of the nineteenth century. Georg Reichenbach, who was trained as an engineer, wanted to set himself up as an instrument maker, and he induced Joseph Liebherr, a clockmaker, to join him. To get enough capital, in 1804 they acquired a third partner, the businessman and high state official Joseph Utzschneider, who worked for the Bavarian topographical bureau. The state took an interest: the directors of the topographical bureau, recognizing the value of better measuring instruments in surveying, supported the venture with 1000 florins, and the Bavarian Academy of Sciences supplied a credit of 600 florins for erecting this "mathematical workshop" in Munich. Once they began manufacturing instruments, they soon saw the need for making their own optical glass and lenses. In 1807 Utzschneider and Reichenbach separated the optical from the mechanical part of their Munich institute and relocated it in a monastery in nearby Benediktbeuern, where glass for the telescopes of Reichenbach's instruments had been made. It was this addition of glass and optical manufacture that brought Fraunhofer into the firm. Hired in 1806 as a journeyman under an optics master, Fraunhofer moved to Benediktbeuern the following year.[10]

Unlike most of the physicists we discuss, Fraunhofer was not a university graduate. A quick and avid learner, he was largely self-taught in his chosen field. He gained practical experience in lens grinding in a friend's optical workshop, and on his own he studied Euler's theoretical optics in a simplified account in a German textbook, while on the job at Benediktbeuern he mastered the arts of making optical glass and lenses. With his practical skill and his superior theoretical knowledge of optics, he quickly advanced in the firm to become director of the optical section in 1809 and a salaried business partner in 1811. Reichenbach left the firm to begin his own in 1814. That year Utzschneider gave Fraunhofer 10,000 florins for investing in the firm, which entitled him to share in the profits of the renamed firm of "Utzschneider and Fraunhofer." Fraunhofer ran a busy shop: Benediktbeuern had separate glass furnaces for flint and crown glass along with eight glassmakers, two glass grinders, a glass cutter, two stokers, and a mechanical section, which was enlarged in 1814. To his work on problems of glass and lenses Fraunhofer now added the construction of entire optical instruments.[11]

The glass experiments of Fraunhofer and a co-worker, financed by Utzschneider,

10. Roth, Fraunhofer, 35–36.
11. Roth, Fraunhofer, 19, 27, 40, 50, 53, 63, 68–69, 71.

soon gave the Benediktbeuern workshop considerable advantage over its competi-
tors. To make better achromatic lens systems, for example, Fraunhofer needed precise determinations of the dispersion and refraction indices of flint and crown glass.
He first made the necessary measurements using as a source of monochromatic light
the bright yellow lines in the flame of a lamp. Then he tried sunlight with the same
purpose in mind, which led him to a major discovery:

> In a darkened room, through a small opening in the shutter approxi-
> mately 15 seconds wide and 36 minutes high, I let light fall on a prism
> of flint glass, which stood on the . . . theodolite. The theodolite was
> 24 feet from the shutter, and the angle of the prism measured approximately
> 60°. . . . . I wanted to determine if in the spectrum of sunlight a similar
> bright line was to be seen as in the spectrum of lamplight, but instead of
> that I found, with the telescope, almost countless strong and weak ver-
> tical lines, which are darker than the remaining part of the spectrum;
> some appeared to be almost completely black.

With these "Fraunhofer lines," as they came to be called, he had discovered the
ideal means for determining the optical constants of the various kinds of glass used
in the manufacture of optical instruments. He also presented to physicists, astronomers, and chemists a new phenomenon and a stimulus to develop the technique of
spectrum analysis.[12]

Fraunhofer's instruments and discoveries brought him into personal contact with
scientists, foreign as well as Bavarian. Gauss, for example, in asking the Hannover
government to pay for a trip to Munich in 1816, argued that it was advantageous to
meet with the instrument maker personally to discuss the advantages and disadvantages of different constructions.[13] At home, Fraunhofer was befriended by the Bavarian court astronomer Johann Georg Soldner, who frequently tested Fraunhofer's
and Reichenbach's instruments before they were shipped off to the purchaser. In
1817 Soldner proposed Fraunhofer as a corresponding member of the Bavarian Academy of Sciences, submitting Fraunhofer's paper on the dark lines in the solar spectrum, which, he said, showed what Fraunhofer could achieve as a "theoretical optician and experimenter." Fraunhofer was elected, and his paper was accepted for
publication.[14]

This was the first of a number of scientific papers by Fraunhofer. In 1821, he
published an influential paper on the diffraction of light, which he introduced with

12. Roth, *Fraunhofer*, 62, 64–65. Joseph Fraunhofer, "Bestimmung des Brechungs– und Farbenzer-
streuungs-Vermögens verschiedener Glasarten, in bezug auf die Vervollkommnung achromatischer Fern-
röhre," *Denkschriften der Königl. Akademie der Wissenschaften zu München für die Jahre 1814 und 1815* 5
(1817): 193–226; reprinted almost unchanged in *Ann.* 56 (1817): 264–313; reprinted again in the series
Ostwald's Klassiker der exakten Wissenschaften, Nr. 150, ed. A. von Oettingen (Leipzig: Wilhelm Engelmann, 1905), quotation on 12. The solar lines, a few of which had been observed and reported on by
W. H. Wollaston several years earlier, were mapped by Fraunhofer by the hundreds, the more prominent
of which he labeled by capital letters, A, B, C, D, . . .

13. Since 1813 Gauss had been buying instruments from Benediktbeuern, and he engaged in correspondence with Fraunhofer for years. Roth, *Fraunhofer*, 74.

14. Roth, *Fraunhofer*, 86–87.

a characteristic reference to the dependence of the advance of science on precision instruments: it is well known, he said, that all researches carried out by scientists whose eyes are equipped with "optical tools" are distinguished by a "high degree of accuracy." In the case of researches on diffraction, he said, adequate tools did not exist, which he thought was a likely reason why this part of physical optics was retarded and "so few of the laws of this modification of light" were known. "If through a small opening in a darkened room," Fraunhofer began his account once again. For readers who were unfamiliar with it, he described the elementary phenomenon of diffraction: if the ray of light admitted into the darkened room is intercepted by a dark screen, itself containing a small opening, and if the light passing through it is allowed to fall on a white surface, the illuminated part of the surface is larger than the opening and exhibits colored fringes at the edges. He went on to give an account of his new experiments, which were of a measuring nature: "To receive in the eye all the light diffracted through a small opening and to see the phenomena greatly enlarged and, still more, to be able to measure directly the angle of inflection of the light, I put a screen containing a narrow vertical opening, which could be made wider or narrower by means of a screw, in front of the lens of a theodolite telescope. In a dark room, by means of a heliostat, I let sunlight fall through a narrow opening onto the screen, at an opening of which it was consequently diffracted. Through the telescope I could then observe the phenomena produced by the diffraction of light, enlarged and yet with sufficient brightness, and at the same time measure the angles of inflection with the theodolite."[15] By this means, Fraunhofer determined that the angle of bending of light in diffraction is inversely proportional to the width of the opening. Likewise, using gratings of parallel fibers, such as silver or gold wires, he determined that the diffraction of light is inversely proportional to the separation of the wires. His gratings required fine workmanship to make the separation extremely small; with his grating of 260 wires, the separation was only about 0.003862 Paris inch and the thickness of the wires about 0.002021 inch. Later he ruled very fine gratings of glass covered with gold foil. By examining the dark solar lines with his gratings, he was able to calculate the wavelengths of specific colors of the spectrum. The precision he achieved with this "optical tool" in physical optics was impressive.[16]

By this time Fraunhofer was back in Munich, since for financial reasons Utzschneider had had to sell the monastery in Benediktbeuern. By then he was also "Royal Professor," a title bestowed on him in recognition of his work, and the government had taken to calling on him for technical services.[17] Soon after completing

15. Joseph Fraunhofer, "Neue Modification des Lichtes durch gegenseitige Einwirkung und Beugung der Strahlen, und Gesetze derselben," *Denkschriften der Königl. Akademie der Wissenschaften zu München für 1821 und 1822* 8: 1–76, in *Joseph von Fraunhofer's Gesammelte Schriften*, ed. Eugen Lommel (Munich, 1888), 51–111, on 55.

16. Fraunhofer, "Neue Modification des Lichtes," in *Gesammelte Schriften*, 58, 67–68.

17. For example, in 1822 the government appointed Fraunhofer and Siber to a commission to look into the question of technical education. For several years at the beginning of the nineteenth century, Bavaria had a parallel set of educational institutions representing the division between the natural and the humanistic sciences. After a common primary schooling, students either went to the gymnasial school and then on to the gymnasial institute, or they went to the Realschule and then on to the Real- or

his paper on diffraction, in 1823 he asked the king for, and was granted, a salary as a member of the Bavarian Academy, which was to help him continue his theoretical and practical work. Later in 1823, he was named "second curator" of the mathematical-physical collection of the academy. His duties included lectures for the educated public, a program the academy started in 1824. At Utzschneider's place, to an audience of his choice, Fraunhofer lectured twice weekly on "mathematical-physical optics, accompanied by experiments." Around this time there was some discussion of the state acquiring the optical institute, but the idea was dropped when Fraunhofer died in 1826. After Fraunhofer, the institute continued as a commercial firm under Utzschneider and later Siegmund Merz.[18]

After Reichenbach left, Fraunhofer stopped making reading glasses, opera glasses, and the like and instead concentrated solely on scientific instruments, such as telescopes, microscopes, and trigonometric measuring instruments. Although in some ways Fraunhofer's firm increasingly took on a purely scientific character, it remained a commercial firm. Fraunhofer's astronomer friend Soldner thought Fraunhofer had an advantage working in that setting. He was, Soldner said, more independent than many a university physicist. He had at hand whatever apparatus and materials he required, something a university physicist could not count on; he had an excellent workshop; and Utzschneider happily paid the expenses of Fraunhofer's experiments. "Who else has such favorable relationships?" Solder asked. Without them, he added, even the "greatest zeal" for research would not get one very far. Fraunhofer was not completely convinced of this argument, since he regarded it as a burden always to have to produce instruments for the market. Further, since he did research within a firm, he was not free to publish what could be regarded as trade secrets. And, as Fraunhofer saw when he wanted to take part in the academy's sessions, his commercial exploitation of science put in question his acceptability in scholarly circles; as a manufacturer without formal scientific credentials, he and his work did not meet the academy's standards in the eyes of some members.[19] But

Physiko-technisches Institut. The remarkable feature of this system was that the two educational tracks had equal standing, each qualifying its graduates to go on to a university; that is, classics was not regarded as superior to science and modern languages in secondary education. For political reasons, the Realinstitute did not long survive, and Bavarian educators wanted to replace them with higher-level schools that would provide a professional technical training rather than a general education with a modern emphasis. The commission on which Fraunhofer and Siber sat drew up plans for what they called the Polytechnic Central School, modeled after the Paris Polytechnic School; the school opened in Munich in 1827 with Utzschneider as its director. Its official purpose was to train persons intending to enter those trades and industries that were "based on mathematics, physics, mechanics, and natural history." For political and financial reasons, the school got off to a slow start, and it was closed six years later, in 1833, when Bavarian technical education underwent another reorganization. Siegmund Günther, "Ein Rückblick auf die Anfänge des technischen Schulwesens in Bayern," in Munich Technical University, ed., Darstellungen aus der Geschichte der Technik, der Industrie und Landwirtschaft in Bayern (Munich: R. Oldenbourg, 1906), 1–16, quotation on 10. Franz Zwerger, Geschichte der realistischen Lehranstalten in Bayern, vol. 53 of Monumenta Germaniae Paedagogica (Berlin: Weidmannsche Buchhandlung, 1914), 2.

18. From 1823 Fraunhofer received a salary of 600 florins as member of the academy; he received no further salary as second curator. His income from the optical institute was over 2500 florins. Roth, Fraunhofer, 94, 99, 102. Eugen Lommel, "Vorwort," in Fraunhofer's Gesammelte Schriften, v–xiv, on viii–ix.

19. Roth, Fraunhofer, 87, 95, 99.

others saw his successful approach of joining physical theory, experiment, and technology as an example to follow. His direct successors included optical scientists in Munich, such as Steinheil and Ludwig Seidel, as well as scientists and technicians at Germany's other great optical center, Jena. The Jena physicist Ernst Abbe recognized Fraunhofer as the first to have had the idea that was to raise the German optical industry to world leadership. Abbe characterized the "rational method of construction of technical products for physical effects in the most general sense [as] Fraunhofer's method."[20]

Physics at Munich University and the Bavarian Academy of Sciences

The leading jobs in physics in Bavaria, as in Prussia, were at the universities, of which Bavaria had about as many as Prussia around 1800, and at the academy of sciences in Munich, the state capital. In Munich, as in Berlin, the academy of sciences was then, for a time, still the principal scientific institution in the service of the state. That changed in Prussia in 1810 with the founding of Berlin University; in Bavaria, the obstacles to establishing a university in Munich took another sixteen years to overcome, and when Munich at last acquired a university in 1826, it was not a new university, but one that moved there from another Bavarian city, Landshut.

Before 1826, various proposals to move the university to Munich had been rejected. The king did not like the idea of the capital being overrun with unruly students. Besides, it was argued, Munich did not need a university in addition to the Bavarian Academy of Sciences. The academy, founded in the middle of the eighteenth century, was a corporate body privileged and financed by the state and outfitted, as generally only a state institution could be, with extensive collections of research materials. To staff this central scientific institution, the government under King Maximilian I attracted some of the best people away from the Bavarian universities. In the event, the academy took on certain functions of a university; in particular, in the 1820s it founded an excellent medical school with the right to grant doctorates, which led certain medical professors to want to unify the Munich clinics with a university in Munich. For this and other reasons, the new king, Ludwig I, decided in 1826 to move the university from Landshut to Munich, where for a time it was located in the same building as the academy of sciences before it acquired its own quarters in the city. With the university and academy now both in Munich, the task of the academy was redefined, and it had to hand over custody of the scientific collections to a newly formed state office, the General Conservatorium.[21]

20. Reese V. Jenkins, "Fraunhofer, Joseph," *DSB* 5:142–44, on 144. Ernst Abbe, "Gedächtnisrede zur Feier des 50jährigen Bestehens der optischen Werkstätte," in *Gesammelte Abhandlungen*, vol. 3 (Jena: Fischer, 1906), 60–95, on 66.

21. Rainer Schmidt, "Landshut zwischen Aufklärung und Romantik," in *Ludwig-Maximilians-Universität, Ingolstadt, Landshut, München, 1472–1972*, ed. L. Boehm and J. Spörl (Berlin: Duncker und Humblot, 1972), 195–214. Harald Dickerhof, "Aufbruch in München," in *Ludwig-Maximilians-Universität*, 215–50, on 218–22.

One of the advantages to the university in moving to Munich was that its scientific resources were enhanced at no extra cost. Members of the academy were now also members of the philosophical faculty of the university, which meant that the number of professors in the natural sciences was increased without additional expense to the university and also that superfluous chairs could be left vacant when their holders relinquished them.[22] In the case of physics, as we will see, because of Munich University's new connection to the academy, the philosophical faculty acquired two ordinary professors of physics in place of its original one.

In Munich certain of the scientific collections belonging to the university, including the physical instruments, were combined with the collections of the academy of sciences, which were the property of the state. For this reason a number of professors at the university received part or all of their salary as curators of the state collections of their fields contained in the academy. Because of this combination of collections, K. D. M. Stahl, the professor of physics who had moved with the university from Landshut to Munich, was at the same time director of the university's physical cabinet and second curator, succeeding Fraunhofer, of the state's mathematical-physical collection at the academy. Stahl received his salary from the General Conservatorium, and in official documents his membership in the academy was always noted before his university title. The small sum he also received for maintaining the university's physical cabinet came from the state, too. (Munich University at this time was almost entirely self-sufficient and only later became largely reliant on the state; but some early state support came to it, as we see here, through the scientific collections and through the salaries for the science professors.)[23] In addition to Stahl, Munich University had a second physicist, Siber, the physics professor at the Munich Lyceum before 1826 and an author of textbooks on physics and mathematics.[24] Siber gave up his lyceum job to become ordinary professor of mathematics and natural sciences, meaning physics, and first curator of the mathematical-physical collection at the academy, replacing Yelin who died that year. In this way, Siber acquired a sizable collection, as he promptly determined by taking an inventory, counting over six hundred pieces of apparatus for physics; in addition to the

22. Dickerhof, "Aufbruch in München," 230.

23. Appointed ordinary professor for mathematics and natural sciences at Munich in 1826, Stahl received the same salary as he had at Landshut, 1600 florins; for the university physical cabinet under his charge, the university received 400 florins in its budget. Stahl Personalakte, Bay. HSTA, MInn 23588. The Bavarian state contributed only 8,000 florins to the university's budget of 64,000 in 1819 and 20,000 florins out of 104,000 in 1837; by 1876 the state's contribution was over half, and by 1919 over two-thirds. Clara Wallenreiter, *Die Vermögensverwaltung der Universität Landshut-München: Ein Beitrag zur Geschichte des bayerischen Hochschultyps vom 18. zum 20. Jahrhundert* (Berlin: Duncker und Humblot, 1971), 146, 176. G. von Mayr, "Die Königl. Bayerische Ludwig-Maximilians-Universität zu München," in Lexis, ed., *Die Universitäten im Deutschen Reich,* 452–68.

24. In addition to Siber, the mathematics teacher Leonhard Späth also moved to Munich University from the Munich Lyceum in 1826. The Munich Lyceum and other lyceums in Bavaria were not very different from universities, and, in fact, some of them had been universities. Their professors were equal in rank to university extraordinary professors and their rectors to university ordinary professors. From 1834, candidates for professorships at lyceums had to be Privatdocenten at a university. Supported by the Catholic church, Bavaria's several lyceums competed with the universities for students intended for the clergy. They usually had two sections, a theological and a philosophical, which had five professorships, including one for physics. Neuerer, *Das höhere Lehramt in Bayern,* 63–67, 69, 103.

familiar abundance of apparatus for demonstrating the principles of mechanics, he found the collection to be especially rich in optical and electrical apparatus.[25]

The future development of physics at Munich University depended on the existence of the two (later three) physics collections, the university's and the academy's, which ultimately insured the existence of two physics professorships. Stahl died in 1833, and for a time the philosophical faculty could not agree on the need for a replacement, since Siber taught the same subject. Meanwhile, Stahl's courses were taught by two Privatdocenten, while gymnasium professors applied in vain for his job. When in 1835 the faculty decided to retain Stahl's position, it was filled by a man, Steinheil, who did not lecture at the university and had no connection with its physical cabinet. Steinheil was appointed second curator of the academy's collection and drew his salary from the General Conservatorium. Siber remained first curator, but from the time of Steinheil's appointment he voluntarily withdrew, leaving the collection entirely in Steinheil's hands. Siber was compensated by succeeding to Stahl's old directorship of the university's cabinet. That left each of Munich's physicists with his own collection of apparatus, a harmonious, if a somewhat confusing, arrangement. The juggling of responsibilities between the university and the academy continued throughout the century.[26]

Steinheil, like Fraunhofer, fostered the spirit of exact measurement in Bavaria. His model was the best of its kind, the work of Bessel and Gauss: as a student he had gone from Erlangen to Göttingen to study with Gauss (who happened to be away measuring degrees in Hannover) and from there to Königsberg, where he stayed for two years, impressing his teacher Bessel with his "exactness." Upon leaving Königsberg, Steinheil set up a small observatory of his own on his father's estate near Munich. He took up researches in optics and optical instruments; for example, he followed up Fraunhofer's discoveries by working to improve flint glass. (He became involved with Utzschneider in negotiations, which Bessel instigated, for him to succeed Fraunhofer as director of the optical institute, but they proved inconclusive.) He also worked on problems outside of optics; for example, he improved the chemical balance so that in a single weighing the load could be determined to one ten-millionth part. This and other pure and applied scientific work, such as military ballistics, were officially recognized by his appointment as curator of the state mathematical-physical collection in 1835.[27]

Steinheil had ambitious plans for the proper use of the collection. He was concerned above all that physics be "productive." Likening physics to art—Steinheil was an accomplished landscape painter—he said that physics should aim at "creative

25. "Verzeichniss der physikalischen Apparate des Staates aufgenommen und fortgesetzt von dem Conservator Prof. Siber," 1827, Ms. Coll., DM, 1954-52/5.

26. Neuerer, *Das höhere Lehramt in Bayern,* 104. Siber's curatorial practices were explained to Ohm in letters from K. F. P. Martius, 13 Nov. 1849, and General Curator F. W. Thiersch, 28 Nov. 1849, in *Ohms . . . Nachlass,* 203–4, 206–8.

27. Steinheil left several biographical, probably all third-person autobiographical, sketches, written at different times, which are now in his file in the Bavarian State Archive. In one of these, probably written soon after May 1833, he quoted from Bessel's letters to him; the one quoted here is dated 3 June 1824.

ideas," which result in something "new." For that to happen, the use of the existing apparatus of a physical collection is insufficient in itself, since it was called into existence by old ideas. What is needed, he argued, is a "physical observatory," in which the academy's collection would be used to make observations in astronomy, optics, acoustics, and so on, together with a workshop for making new instruments. Physics progresses only if its observations "assume the character of scientific exactness as in astronomy," and this "instrumental physics" can only be pursued by the researchers themselves, not by mechanics. From the point of view of the state, this physical observatory has the purpose not only of teaching and research but also of applying research to life in the form of technology. Technology, Steinheil said, was often neglected by scholars or looked down on as unscientific; that is wrong. Steinheil believed that the "final purpose of all knowledge and instruction" is their "reaction on life—expansion of sense perception—subduing natural forces to our purposes." "That is productive physics," he said.[28]

Steinheil brought this same emphasis to his plans for reorganizing the Bavarian Academy of Sciences. Whereas foreign academies gave weight to those sciences, the physical, that stand closest to life, to technology, the Bavarian Academy had let its mathematical class fall into neglect. Dominated by natural historians, it did not even have a member from the side of mechanics, the "most important field with regard to technology." He recommended that the mathematical and physical sciences be separated off. Because these sciences did not present their results in a way that was "directly" applicable to technology, he recommended, as a middle step between the academy and life, the Polytechnic Union, where the appropriate researches could be carried out with the right equipment.[29]

In his position at the academy, Steinheil worked to advance the exact sciences and to promote technology, which, he believed, depended on the exact sciences. We see an example of how he brought these interests together in his activity in the academy on behalf of earth-magnetic researches in Bavaria. After his return from a visit with Gauss and Weber in Göttingen, in 1835 Steinheil proposed a new use for the state's physical collection. He asked for, and received, money to buy apparatus similar to what Gauss used in his galvano-magnetic investigations. To justify the purchase to the Bavarian government, he explained that of all the recent work in Germany, Gauss's had received "the greatest notice and the most general participation." Gauss had observed magnetic forces with an "exactness previously known only in astronomy," which he as able to do only through "new more complete apparatus and more appropriate methods of observation." For Gauss to be able to order the entire phenomenon under "fundamental laws of the highest simplicity," observations like his had to be carried out at other locations. Steinheil was determined that Munich should be one of them. In one of the rooms of the physical collection he

28. Steinheil, "Meine Ideen über Repraesentation der physikalischen Wissenschaften durch Königl. Sammlungen," n.d. [1835?], Steinheil Akte, Bay. HSTA.

29. Draft of a letter to "Ew. D[urchlaucht]," n.d., Steinheil Akte, Bay. HSTA. The Polytechnic Union was an organization in 1815–30, with its own journal, which advocated the advancement of crafts and industry through polytechnic schools.

set up Gauss's magnetic apparatus and with it determined the absolute magnetic force, the magnetic declination, and the periodic variations of the declination for Munich. Typically, Steinheil looked forward to realizing the great technological possibilities inherent in the galvanic telegraph that Gauss and Weber had built for scientific purposes in pursuit of their earth-magnetic measurements.[30]

Soon after introducing Gauss's apparatus and methods for earth-magnetic researches in Munich, at Gauss's request Steinheil took up the problem of giving the telegraph a "practical form" for use in "civil life." His greatest telegraphic innovation was the use of only one wire to connect a pair of stations, using the earth in place of the second wire to complete the circuit, halving the cost of installation. He invented a way to cause sufficiently strong mechanical motion at the receiving end of a telegraph, requiring only one-tenth of the galvanic force that Gauss's way had required. He also introduced a new mode of reception: by Gauss's method, the receiver observed small motions of magnetic needles through a telescope, by Steinheil's, the receiver listened to high and low tones excited by a hammer and bell, or he read a script written by the same hammer, which impressed groups of points on a moving paper strip driven by clockwork. Before thousands of witnesses, in 1837 he demonstrated his telegraph, using this combination of coded speech and writing: with copper wires strung along the towers and highest public buildings, Steinheil sent telegraphic messages across the three-quarter mile distance between the royal observatory in Bogenhausen, the academy, and his own observatory in Munich. As the local authority on telegraphy, in 1849 Steinheil was offered an appointment in the new Bavarian telegraph administration. But as he had just agreed to head the telegraph section of the Austrian ministry of trade, he temporarily moved his activities from Munich to Vienna. In less than two years, he organized the installation of over a thousand miles of telegraphic lines in Austria. When he left, he went on to advise the Swiss government on their telegraphic system linking over forty stations and eighty post offices.[31]

More than any other Munich physicist of our period, Steinheil united scientific work with wide-ranging technical accomplishments. As we have seen, he did scientific research in astronomy and optics, he developed optical instruments for research, and he did extensive practical work in telegraphy. In addition, he worked on practical problems of weights and measures, alcohol content in beer and wine, the daguerreotype, power machines, and locomotives, to mention several other examples. As a technical consultant and administrator, his work was wide-ranging: he served on committees for industrial exhibitions held in several countries; he worked

30. "Doctor Carl August Steinheil. Lebens-Skizzen," dated between 1867 and 1870; draft of a letter by Steinheil to the General Conservator, n.d. [1835], "Betreff: Ansuchen des Conservators Steinheil um Bewilligung des Betrages für die magnetischen Apparate . . ."; approval of funds for the purchase of earth-magnetic apparatus for the state mathematical-physical collection: Bavarian Ministry of the Interior to the General Conservator, 2 Nov. 1825; draft by Steinheil: "Kurzer Bericht an die königliche Akademie über die ersten Beobachtungen mit den magnetischen Apparaten von Gauss, angestellt im physikalischen Staatskabinet," n.d. [1835]; Steinheil Akte, Bay. HSTA.

31. Biographical sketch of Steinheil, dated from the late 1860s; drafts of letters from Steinheil to the King of Bavaria, n.d. [1837 or 1838] and 12 Feb. 1838; entries for 3–7 and 10 Nov. 1849; Steinheil Akte, Bay. HSTA. Robert Knott, "Steinheil: Karl August," ADB 35:720–24, on 724.

on the reorganization of Bavarian technical and polytechnic schools and was the
ministerial testing commissioner for them for several years; he advised the ministry
of trade and public works; and he sat on many state technical commissions dealing
with such questions as the use of railway tracks as telegraph conductors. With his
combination of interests, abilities, and jobs, Steinheil served the needs both of the
state and of the measuring sciences.[32]

    Unlike Steinheil, Munich University's other physicist, Siber, devoted himself
to teaching. He was a popular lecturer—in 1827 his classes attracted nearly five
hundred—and he gave interested students seminar-like exercises and encouraged
them in their extra-curricular study of mathematics and physics.[33] For most students,
Siber's physics course was a part of their general education, but for a few, it was also
their professional education. Siber gave the only instruction in physics that future
teachers of mathematics and physics at secondary and technical schools could get at
Munich University.[34]

Ohm and Steinheil in Munich

In late 1849, a secretary of the Bavarian Academy of Sciences wrote informally to
Ohm at the Nuremberg Polytechnic that Ohm was going to be called to replace
Steinheil as second curator of the academy's collection for mathematics and physics.
In part because there was no one else, Ohm was also going to replace Steinheil as
the ministerial director of the telegraph bureau located in the academy's building.
The only difference between Ohm and Steinheil was that Ohm would lecture, while
Steinheil did not. One of Ohm's former pupils, Carl Max von Bauernfeind, wrote
to him, welcoming his participation in university affairs because it would give people
at Munich a chance to see with their "own eyes how a physicist and mathematician
should be and teach."[35]

32. Draft of a letter from Steinheil to the Bavarian Ministry of the Interior, n.d.; draft of a letter
from Steinheil to the Bavarian King, 16 Mar. 1838; draft of a letter from the Ministry of the Interior to
an official of the Ministry of Trade and Public Works, concerning Steinheil as technical advisor to the
latter and summarizing his technical accomplishments, 7 July 1867; Steinheil Akte, Bay. HSTA.
    33. Neuerer, *Das höhere Lehramt in Bayern*, 103, 111. Eight persons, some if not all students, signed
a letter to the Senate of Munich University requesting permission to form a "mathematical-physical
society" under the protection of Siber. They also asked for a room in the university for their meetings.
The senate noted at the bottom of the request: "Let it rest." "Gehorsamste Bitte der Unterzeichneten um
die gütigste Erlaubniss, einen mathematisch-physikalischen Verein gründen zu dürfen," date received 26
Nov. 1834, Munich UA, Sen. 209.
    34. During Siber's time, it was possible for Munich students to take physics courses also from the
occasional extraordinary professor such as Joseph Reindl or Franz Eduard Desberger, who was very concerned with improving "realistic" schools in Bavaria and who was a rigorous examiner of teaching candidates, or the occasional Privatdocent such as Karl Dempp or Peter Lackerbauer. And, of course, the
ordinary professor of physics Stahl taught alongside Siber for the first several years after the founding of
Munich University.
    35. K. F. P. von Martius to Ohm, 13 Nov. 1849; Carl Max von Bauernfeind to Ohm, 27 Nov.
1849; General Curator F. W. Thiersch to Ohm, 28 Nov. 1849; in *Ohms . . . Nachlass*, 203–4, 205–6,
and 206–8, respectively; quotation on 205. On 23 Nov. 1849, the Bavarian king, Maximilian II, named
Ohm second curator of the state's collection; as ordinary professor for mathematics and physics, he was

Although Siber remained first curator at the academy, he left Ohm in charge, content to go on directing the university's physical cabinet. The division of responsibilities was convenient for both: Siber's cabinet was next to his lecture room at the university, which since 1840 had a building separate from the academy's, while Ohm's cabinet was next to his lecture room at the academy. Ohm took charge, and took good care, of Steinheil's former physics laboratory at the academy.[36]

One of the tasks awaiting Ohm at the academy was to take an inventory of the state collection, a complicated task because Steinheil's own instruments were mixed in with the academy's and had to be separated out.[37] The burden—or, perhaps, the satisfaction—of working on the collection was the occasion for Ohm's last published research: "My lecturing on optics at this university in the summer semester of 1851," he explained at the beginning of his publication, "imposed on me the duty to put in order and complete the necessary apparatus for this purpose." His particular subject was interference phenomena with uniaxial crystal plates, the theory of which he developed in the most general way. Once again he used methods from the "higher calculus [Rechnung] since Fourier": by viewing complicated light waves as a sum of plane waves, he greatly simplified the analysis, just as he had simplified the analysis of sounds by resolving them into tones.[38]

Ohm's teaching at Munich also led to another kind of publication. At Nuremberg, he had been approached by his publisher to write a textbook on physics; he had been too busy then, but at Munich he returned to the idea, prompted by difficulties he encountered in his teaching. He spent much of his time preparing physics lectures, which he found hard to get across. First of all, the lecture room was long and narrow like a "towel," so that a third of the auditors could not see the blackboard, and besides that the room had no desks. The greatest problem was that many students came from the humanistic gymnasiums and so were poorly prepared in mathematics. To alleviate these difficulties, Ohm had his lectures lithographed and handed out to the students. Eventually, out of necessity, he gave them to his publisher, who published them almost unchanged as a textbook.[39]

---

required to give lectures without receiving lecture fees. On 5 Dec. 1849, he was appointed scientific-technical advisor on telegraphic matters to the ministry of trade. His income was identical to Steinheil's down to the payment in goods, which was a certain yearly measure of grain worth about 100 florins; as curator his salary was 1400 florins, and as scientific-technical advisor to the state he received an additional 400. *Ohms . . . Nachlass*, 202.

36. F. W. Thiersch to Ohm, 28 Nov. 1849; Ohm to General Curator, 18 Feb. 1850; in *Ohms . . . Nachlass*, 207, 214.

37. Seidel, "Instruction für die mathematisch-physikalische Sammlung des Staates," 1852, Ms. Coll., DM, 5477. Under the title of an inventory made in 1850, Ohm inserted a note about his subsequent work on it in 1851–52: "Catalog der physikalisch-mathematischen Sammlung des Staates aufgenommen von Franz Schleicher im Jahre 1850," Ms. Coll., DM, 1954–52.

38. Georg Simon Ohm, "Erklärung aller in einaxigen Krystallplatten zwischen geradlinig polarisirtem Lichte wahrnehmbaren Interferenz-Erscheinungen," *Abh. bay. Akad.* 7 (1853): 43–149, 267–370, in *Ges. Abh.*, 665–855, quotations on 665 and 679. In a request, which was granted, for a two-month vacation to study French and English writings on optics, Ohm spoke of coming across new facts about light in the course of giving lectures that semester; he believed they would have an "influence" on the wave theory of light. Letter from Ohm to the Bavarian King, 16 July 1851, Bay. HSTA, MInn. 40636.

39. Letter from Ohm to his publisher Johann Leonhard Schrag, 9 Feb. 1842, in *Ohms . . . Nachlass*, 231. Jolly described the lecture room he inherited from Ohm to the Administrative Board of the

Ohm's initial arrangements in Munich lasted only two years. When Steinheil's work abroad on the telegraph was completed, the Bavarian king looked for ways to induce him to return to Munich. Neither the ministry's suggestion to give him Siber's job as professor of physics and director of the university's physical cabinet nor the king's to place him in an administrative position was workable. To begin with, Siber's position was not available, and then Steinheil lacked the experience for an administrative job. Furthermore, his technical experience with the telegraph was no longer needed, since the Bavarian telegraph was considered to be in good shape. Ohm, who was paid to work on it, was "in fact unoccupied." In any event, Steinheil had informed Bavaria that he did not want to work in a government bureau any more than he wanted to lecture at the university; he wanted a job that left him free to do scientific work. The Bavarian government found a way to accommodate him; they gave him a government advisory job, leaving deliberately vague his duties and title, "technical advisor at the minister's disposal." (His salary was not left vague.) Steinheil was also given back his old job as second curator at the academy, replacing Ohm.[40]

Upon his return, Steinheil worked to advance the art of optical and astronomical instruments. At the king's wish, in 1854 he established an optical and astronomical workshop in Munich, through which he extended the fame of Fraunhofer and Reichenbach. After 1862 Steinheil's son took over the workshop and ran it successfully.[41]

Now Ohm, after being dismissed as curator in 1852 to make room for Steinheil, had to be given something else to do. For the next two years, he served as ordinary professor of physics at the university, with a salary equal to his old income. He also served as director of the university's physical cabinet, the position Siber had relinquished.[42] In June 1854, owing to poor health, Ohm was relieved of both the big experimental physics lectures and the direction of the physical cabinet. In their place, he was given "mathematical physics as his assigned subject."[43] Ohm died that same year, and so it was only briefly, and for reasons of personal disability, that Munich University had an ordinary professor for mathematical physics. Not until forty years later would it establish this position on a regular basis.

Bavarian Academy of Sciences, 24 Mar. 1855, Acta . . . physicalisches Cabinet, Munich UA, Nr. 289. Ohm's Munich lectures appeared as *Grundzüge der Physik als Compendium zu seinen Vorlesungen* (Nuremberg, 1854).

40. The king was quoted by the Bavarian Minister of the Interior Friedrich Ringelmann, 22 Mar. 1852; Bavarian Minister of Trade and Public Works Ludwig Pfordten to Ringelmann, 28 or 29 Mar. 1852; Ringelmann to Pfordten, 24 Apr. 1852; Pfordten to Ringelmann, 16 May 1852; Steinheil Akte, Bay. HSTA. Steinheil's new salary as "technical advisor" was the same as his old salary as telegraph advisor. One of Steinheil's autobiographical sketches from the late 1860s says that after his return from Vienna, his "opponents" tried to force him out of public activity. Steinheil Akte, Bay. HSTA.

41. Knott, "Steinheil," 724.

42. Ringelmann to Pfordten, 24 Apr. 1852, Ohm's second appointment by the king is dated 11 June 1852, in Ohm Akte, Munich UA, Stand 1870, Littera E, Abt. II, Fascikel Nr. 226.

43. Bavarian Ministry of the Interior to Munich U. Senate, 28 June 1854, Munich UA, E II-N, Boltzmann. Wilhelm Wien, "Das physikalische Institut und das physikalische Seminar," in *Die wissenschaftlichen Anstalten der Ludwig-Maximilians-Universität zu München*, ed. K. A. von Müller (Munich: R. Oldenbourg and Dr. C. Wolf, 1926), 207–11, on 208.

Physics in Munich after Ohm

In 1854, shortly before Ohm, Siber also died. The astronomer Johannes Lamont proposed the Freiburg physicist Johann Müller as Siber's replacement. On his own, Heinrich Alexander, the rector and physicist at the Munich Polytechnic, applied to the university senate for Siber's job, pointing out that he already had university students in his lectures at the polytechnic school and that he would bring to the university an up-to-date laboratory.[44] The possibility of a separate instrument collection was relevant to the appointment, since the philosophical faculty recognized that their own physical cabinet, still headed by Ohm, could not be shared by two ordinary professors. The university senate, acknowledging that the appointment of a second physicist was one of their "most pressing needs," regarded material considerations as secondary to scientific ones: accordingly, they preferred Müller with his good reputation as a "teacher and author" over Alexander. The philosophical faculty agreed.[45] Despite their preference, however, it was not Müller who was appointed but Heidelberg's ordinary professor of physics since 1846, Philipp Jolly.[46]

When Ohm was restricted to mathematical physics later that year, Jolly was at first provisionally assigned Ohm's positions, then permanently.[47] As ordinary professor for experimental physics at the university and as an experimentalist in his research, Jolly took a good deal of interest in the university's physical cabinet under his charge. Pointing to the physics institutes at Berlin, Göttingen, Heidelberg, and Jena, he argued for the improvement of Munich's, which to his thinking did not represent the "advances in physics in the last 25 years." He got what he wanted: an assistant and funds for remodeling the institute within its modest accommodations in the north wing of the university building.[48]

In his research during his first years at Munich, as in his previous research at Heidelberg, Jolly addressed a fundamental problem, the law of the decrease with distance of the attractive force between molecules. The principles of this attraction, which he derived from his experiments on solutions, he presented to the Bavarian Academy of Sciences in 1857, but later he apparently came to doubt them and did

---

44. Joseph Reindl, Alexander's predecessor at the polytechnic school, had been an extraordinary professor, too, and in that capacity he had used the polytechnic's physical collection for his university lectures. Neuerer, *Das höhere Lehramt in Bayern*, 126–27.

45. Munich U. Senate to Philosophical Faculty, 20 May 1854, "Akten des k. akad. Senats der Ludwig-Maximilians-Universität München. Betreffend Dr. Ludwig Boltzmann," Munich UA, E II-N, Boltzmann.

46. Jolly's official appointment was in the summer of 1854, but as early as 19 Feb. of that year, while the senate and philosophical faculty was deliberating, Jolly wrote to Liebig, who had recommended him, that he had received the call to Munich. Liebigiana, Bay. STB, 58 (Jolly, Philipp v.), Nr. 3. On 11 July 1854, Jolly informed the Baden Ministry of the Interior that he had accepted the Munich offer: Bad. GLA, 235/3135.

47. Jolly's provisional appointment, at a salary of 2500 florins, to Ohm's old positions: Bavarian Ministry of the Interior to Munich U. Senate, 28 June 1854.

48. With Jolly's appointment came an extraordinary grant of 2500 florins for the physical cabinet and a salary of 200 florins for an assistant for the cabinet, to be selected by Jolly. The remodeled physical cabinet consisted of a lecture room, the collection in two rooms, a new laboratory, and a passageway. Wien, "Das physikalische Institut und das physikalische Seminar," 208.

not return to the subject. He concentrated instead on the improvement of measuring instruments and methods, a field for which Munich was now famous. He measured, for example, the specific weights of ammonia and other substances, the expansion coefficient of gases, and the density of the earth. The latter measurement—a measurement of great precision—has been judged his most important work in physics.[49]

Despite his considerable work in experimental physics, Jolly did not regard research as his main task. Teaching, he often remarked, gave him his greatest satisfaction. His lectures on experimental physics, which according to a Munich tradition were open to students of all faculties to further their general education, were attended by the largest number of students of any university lectures then.[50]

Shortly before Jolly came to Munich, the duties of the philosophical faculty had been redefined. In the first half of the nineteenth century, all students had to take a number of required courses in the philosophical faculty. These included more or fewer courses in the natural sciences depending on the statutes in effect at the time, and natural scientists such as the physics professor Siber were often dissatisfied with the statutes and the ministers responsible for them. From the middle of the nineteenth century, the philosophical faculty no longer had to provide a general education by giving required courses. Like the other faculties, it acquired professional training responsibilities of its own, which included improved instruction for secondary school teachers. In connection with the latter, Jolly founded a seminar for physics.[51]

After the departure in 1847 of the Bavarian minister of the interior Karl von Abel, who for ten years had deprived natural science professors of many students because of his statutes for general education, proposals were made for improving education in the natural sciences. These included early proposals for seminars at Munich University, among them a proposal in 1848 by Steinheil and Seidel for a mathematical-physical seminar.[52] A seminar of this description was officially established in 1856; organized in two sections, the physical under Jolly and the mathematical under Seidel, the seminar's formal purpose was the "training of teachers for

49. C. Voit, "Philipp Johann Gustav von Jolly," *Sitzungsber. bay. Akad.* 15 (1885): 119–36, on 126, 132. D. R., "Jolly: Philipp Johann Gustav von," *ADB* 55: 807–10, on 809. For serving as curator of the newly created physical-metronomical institute, Jolly received a salary of 500 florins. The annual budget of the institute was 500 florins, and in the early years it regularly received extraordinary grants. From documents in Bay. HSTA, Ad. Nr. 5418.
50. Voit, "Jolly," 134–35. D. R., "Jolly," 809.
51. Dickerhof, "Aufbruch in München," 233, 244. Neuerer, *Das höhere Lehramt in Bayern,* 118.
52. Dickerhof, "Aufbruch in München," 241–44. In 1847 Abel's bitter critic the Munich botanist Philipp von Martius drew up a new study plan, which took into account the increased importance of the natural sciences due to industrialization. The changed situation, he argued, ought to be reflected in the training of secondary school teachers, and for this purpose he thought that the Freiburg seminar, established the year before, would be the best model for Munich. Neuerer, *Das höhere Lehramt in Bayern,* 110. In a letter to Hause on 28 Feb. 1848, Seidel described the mathematical-physical seminar he and Steinheil planned. The seminar was clearly not intended to train school teachers but to assist the two seminar directors in their scientific work and at the same time give students a chance to do a bit of research. Helmuth Gericke and Hellfried Uebele, "Philipp Ludwig von Seidel und Gustav Bauer, zwei Erneuerer der Mathematik in München," in *Die Ludwig-Maximilians-Universität in ihren Fakultäten,* vol. 1, ed. L. Boehm and J. Spörl (Berlin: Duncker und Humblot, 1972), 390–99, on 394. Neither Martius's nor Seidel and Steinheil's seminar was approved.

mathematics in the higher teaching institutes." It served the scientific purposes of the seminar directors as well; in it Jolly introduced students such as Adolph Wüllner and Eugen Lommel to physical research.[53]

Jolly, like other Munich physicists, was called on for technical services by the state, such as advising on the metric system of weights and measures. Having established experimentally a law of molecular forces that was "as simple as it was far reaching," Jolly was delayed in publishing his results—to his "great sorrow"—by the government's request that he write a paper on the reorganization of technical schools.[54] He soon threw himself into this new work. Later, as head of the commission for the reorganization, he advocated curtailing the function of the trade schools as preparation for the polytechnic schools; he successfully argued for a new kind of well-rounded, but still officially "technical," school, the Realgymnasium.[55]

After Steinheil's death, in 1871, a so-called physical-metronomical institute was separated from the state mathematical-physical collection. Jolly became director of the new institute, and Seidel became director of the remaining mathematical-physical collection of the academy, acquiring Steinheil's old title of second curator. Seidel was Steinheil's heir in his research as well; he studied with Bessel, who recommended him to Steinheil, and under Steinheil, Seidel became a specialist in theoretical and experimental optics. Even though Seidel was professor of mathematics at the university, optics remained his favorite area of research. This Munich tradition was continued by Lommel, Jolly's successor in 1886, whose specialty too was optics.[56]

53. Oskar Perron, Constantin Carathéodory, and Heinrich Tietze, "Das Mathematische Seminar," in Die wissenschaftlichen Anstalten . . . zu München, 206. D. R., "Jolly," 809. The Munich mathematical-physical seminar, like the historical seminar, was outside the philosophical faculty. The directors were instructed to communicate with the ministry through the university senate, leaving out the philosophical faculty; this arrangement was regarded at the university as "abnormal." Neuerer, Das höhere Lehramt in Bayern, 129. In the gymnasiums, physics and mathematics were regarded as one teaching field and were the responsibility of the school's mathematics teacher. With the development of professional training of teachers in the philosophical faculty and the seminar, the question arose of whether their training should be directed more toward teaching elementary subjects or more toward scientific depth, or research. Secondary school students were not prepared for the advanced work that their teachers had learned at the university. For most of the second half of the nineteenth century, the question was not resolved. Mathematics was apparently more affected by it than physics. Neuerer, Das höhere Lehramt in Bayern, 118–19.

54. Jolly to F. G. J. Henle, 22 Apr. 1859, Riemann Personalakte, Göttingen UA, 4/V b/137.

55. Voit, "Jolly," 135. Four Realgymnasiums were started in 1864. Their students were graduates of the now five-year Latin school; at the Realgymnasiums they studied four more years of Latin as well as modern languages, mathematics, and the natural sciences, including five hours of physics in their third year. Critics of Jolly's plan called the Realgymnasium an extension of the humanistic gymnasium instead of what they wanted, a narrower, new kind of gymnasium for "mathematical-scientific-technical" studies. Neuerer, Das höhere Lehramt in Bayern, 36–37, 81, 252.

56. Seidel received a salary of 500 florins as curator of the state's mathematical-physical collection with a budget of 1000 florins. He had the right to borrow such instruments as he needed in his research from Jolly's physical-metronomical collection, and Jolly had the same right to borrow from Seidel's collection. Wilhelm von Bezold to General Conservator, 18 July 1871, Bay. HSTA, Ad. Nr. 5418. Neuerer, Das höhere Lehramt in Bayern, 125. Wien, "Das physikalische Institut und das physikalische Seminar," 210. The separation of the institute into two institutes had less to do with the nature of the institute than with the wish to treat Jolly and Seidel equally. J. A. von Müller, "Das physikalisch-metronomische Institut," in Die wissenschaftlichen Anstalten . . . zu München, 278–79, on 278.

The emergence of Munich as a center for precision optical instruments in the first half of the nineteenth century took place at the same time as a comparable emergence of mathematical work elsewhere in Germany. Precision instruments no less than mathematics were the tool of mathematical physics, and German mathematical physicists, such as Kirchhoff, looked to Munich for their instruments. As if to summarize the development of this field, Ohm, the physicist whose mathematical work began our account, concluded his career in Munich, the home of excellent instruments.

In Munich, as we have seen, physics had extensive connections with technical concerns, commercial, educational, and governmental. These connections continued and multiplied to the end of the century and beyond, lending substance to a modern view of progress. Addressing the German Association meeting in 1899, which was held in the Munich Technical University, one of the professors correctly drew attention to their location as a "symbol of the unity of technology with research in natural science, generated by the closest relationships and liveliest interactions between [this research] and technology."[57]

57. Remark made by Hoyer in *Verh. Ges. deutsch. Naturf. u. Ärzte* 71 (1899): 16.

12

Kirchhoff and Helmholtz at Heidelberg: Relations of Physics to Chemistry and Physiology

Throughout the period covered in this volume, physicists sometimes worked on subjects belonging to other sciences, while other scientists sometimes worked on subjects belonging to physics; in addition, certain other subjects were more or less shared by physics and neighboring sciences. Later in the nineteenth century, some of the border areas of physics were to be organized as disciplines in their own right, for example, physical chemistry, astrophysics, and geophysics. The work of Kirchhoff and Helmholtz at Heidelberg University in the middle years of the century is an example of the earlier mutual reinforcement of scientific fields; in their work we see physics pursued with evident connections to chemistry and physiology.

Kirchhoff and Helmholtz were not the first to connect physics with other sciences at Heidelberg. Jolly, Kirchhoff's predecessor, had joined the Heidelberg anatomist Theodor Bischoff in a chemical-physiological investigation of the respiratory process.[1] It was an activity that universities should encourage, Jolly explained to the Baden government in 1846 in an appeal for the establishment of a physics laboratory at Heidelberg: the absence of such a laboratory "completely prevents the profitable cooperation between teachers of related subjects, of chemistry and physiology" and the "undertaking of joint, more comprehensive experimental investigations," which had already begun at other universities.[2] When Jolly left Heidelberg in 1854, the medical faculty recommended as candidates for his replacement Magnus and Weber (and a secondary school teacher in Mannheim).[3] Since both Magnus and Weber, like Jolly, included physiological researches in their work, the medical faculty, by implication, wished to see that kind of work continue at Heidelberg.

The philosophical faculty at Heidelberg appears to have been guided by similar criteria. The one candidate they recommended for Jolly's replacement was Kirchhoff; Kirchhoff was to rejoin the chemist Robert Bunsen, alongside whom he had worked

1. D. R., "Jolly," 809. Voit, "Jolly," 122.
2. Jolly to Baden Ministry of the Interior, 12 June 1846, Bad. GLA, 235/3135.
3. Report by Heidelberg U. Senate to Baden Ministry of the Interior, 2 Aug. 1854, Bad. GLA, 235/3135.

briefly in Breslau. Weber, who was asked for his opinion of Kirchhoff, made a strong case for him partly on the grounds of the cooperative research he would ensure at Heidelberg: "Since we in Germany have no center for mathematics and the natural sciences such as Paris was for a long time, two scientists who by working together multiply their achievements are a rare phenomenon, which lends a special radiance to the university where it is successfully achieved." Kirchhoff's "great superiority" in physical theory and mathematics over other German physicists together with his talent as an "exact experimenter" promised "especially great success" if he were to work with Bunsen, for then the physicist's store of experimental problems, means, and methods would be enriched by the chemist's.[4]

Heidelberg before Kirchhoff

In the second half of the nineteenth century, as earlier, university faculties exploited the rivalry between the German states to gain support for scientific institutes. In addition, a new element increasingly entered their arguments for support of this sort; the competition for outstanding scientists. Successful teaching and research by university physicists had become associated with the availability of well-equipped laboratories. Formerly the measure of a state's investment in physics was its showpiece collection of physical instruments; a second measure was the salary a state could afford to entice the physicist of *literary* renown to one of its universities. The two measures gradually came to merge with the difference that the physics collection was no longer primarily for show but for work, and the physicist had to have *scientific* renown; the measure of a university, particularly the main univesity of a state, now was whether or not it could offer a satisfactory institute to the best physicist.

Shaming the government into giving more support for the physics institute by reporting on advances elsewhere, particularly at universities less important than their own, continued to be a tactic used by Heidelberg physicists. When Muncke's failing health allowed the junior physicist at Heidelberg, Jolly, to speak for physics there in 1846, he argued as Muncke had: "For a number of years now one sees at most German universities, even at those that are not equal to [Heidelberg] University either in attendance or in significance, the means for . . . physical and natural scientific studies growing apace with the quick development of these sciences." The "rise" of small Giessen University and the remnant of "splendor" that Göttingen University still had (following the unfortunate dismissal of Weber) were "largely if not solely due to the excellent aids, the rich collections, and grand institutes that are offered there to teachers and students in equal measure."[5]

In his description of the needs of the Heidelberg physics institute, Jolly moved beyond Muncke's plan of ten years before of involving a few advanced students in earth-magnetic observations. Jolly said he found an "extremely noticeable gap" in

4. Report, 2 Aug. 1854. After consulting with the philosophical faculty and the medical faculty, the Heidelberg U. Senate recommended Kirchhoff in "primo loco" and "Professor Schröder in Mannheim secundo loco." Weber to Bunsen, 12 Mar. 1854, Bad. GLA, 235/3135.
5. Jolly to Baden Ministry of the Interior, 12 June 1846.

the provisions made for studying physics: Heidelberg University "lacks a laboratory, a place for expanding the teacher's work and for student practice, a facility that nowadays, if anything is to be achieved at all in these subjects, is an inescapable requirement." Because Heidelberg lacked this, its eager and more capable students "were offered nothing," and experimental physics lay "fallow."[6] Jolly, who had taught the subject side by side with, and often in place of, Muncke for several years, had privately acquired a collection of physics instruments, "truly rich and worth seeing."[7] However, it contained only the instruments he needed for teaching: "for the purpose of independent researches, for the purpose of forming a school, a goal that at least at universities must not be overlooked," his instruments were insufficient. He asked the government for annual support for setting up and running a physics laboratory.[8] When no action was taken for several months, his solution to the problem was to transform his apartment into a physics institute of sorts by removing a wall to obtain a lecture hall and by turning the kitchen into a laboratory. He requested money with which he might rent a second apartment, this one for his family, since he paid half of his salary, 400 out of 800 florins, in rent for the flat in which he had set up his physics institute. "Physics has to be taught in Heidelberg," the Heidelberg curator remarked when he forwarded Jolly's request to the government, and Jolly cannot "experiment in the street."[9] Muncke was now too old and too ill to resume his duties, retiring after Jolly was promoted to ordinary professor toward the end of 1846 and given permission to use the physical cabinet of the university.[10] The gain in space Jolly received was not much; the official cabinet was too small for his many students, and it was not suited for physics experiments. However, Jolly did receive an annual fund now, and with it he managed to set up a small laboratory for students, which also accommodated experimental researches of his own.[11] For six years the government was given some respite. In any case, to improve any of Heidelberg's institutes significantly was a strain on Baden's resources, since it supported another university besides Heidelberg and a polytechnic school as well.[12]

Jolly was given an unusual opportunity when he was allowed to teach experimental physics in competition with the ordinary professor at Heidelberg. It proved

6. Jolly to Baden Ministry of the Interior, 12 June 1846.

7. Heidelberg U. Curator to Baden Ministry of the Interior, 1 Aug. 1846, Bad. GLA, 235/3135.

8. Jolly to Baden Ministry of the Interior, 12 June 1846.

9. Heidelberg U. Curator to Baden Ministry of the Interior, 24 Sept. 1846, Bad. GLA, 235/3135.

10. Jolly's appointment, 28 Sept. 1846, Bad. GLA, 235/3135. His new salary as ordinary professor was 1000 florins. Jolly Personalakte, Heidelberg UA, III, 5b, Nr. 233.

11. Heidelberg U. Curator to Baden Ministry of the Interior, 24 Sept. 1846. D. R., "Jolly," 808. Voit, "Jolly," 123–24.

12. Mohl, Lebens-Erinnerungen 1:221. Institute by institute, school by school, circumstances gradually improved for the natural sciences after the middle of the century. By the end of the period this chapter covers, in part because of the increase in numbers of students but more because of changes in instruction, Baden's expenditure on its three institutions of higher learning was rapidly growing. Lectures were now recognized as insufficient instruction, so that money had to be made available for seminars for humanistic studies and for well-equipped institutes for the natural sciences. Baden's expenditure on its three institutions increased by around 100 percent in the twenty years following the academic year 1868–69. Eugen von Philippovich, Der badische Staatshaushalt in den Jahren 1868–1889 (Freiburg i. Br., 1889), 93–94.

to be a mixed blessing. To supplement his salary to support his physics teaching, Jolly had to offer many so-called private lecture courses for which students paid fees; he worked in this way for a dozen years, dissipating his energies. In 1846, when he at last asked for state assistance, he explained that because of the burden of his teaching, he found time to publish research only recently, "much too late." More-over, he had had to treat "less fruitful, purely theoretical mathematical speculations" and to forego "his field," experimental physics, because his private means had been insufficient "for productive work in physics, for independent researches and experi-mental discoveries, which alone can entice one to [produce] written communications . . . in the present state of the science."[13]

When Jolly left for Munich University in 1854, Heidelberg had arrived at the moment of truth for a university; Heidelberg acknowledged that it could no longer attract a first-rate physicist because of the inadequacy of its physics institute. The philosophical faculty opened its report to the Baden ministry of the interior on pos-sible replacements for Jolly with a list of physicists who were out of reach for this reason: "As much as the faculty wished to see its . . . representative of the physical subjects replaced by another of the first notables of science, it nevertheless had to resign itself to forego this wish; for it cannot conceal from itself the fact that the excellent positions that the most outstanding physicists, who would be considered first, occupy not only as academic teachers but also in part as influential directors of important state institutes would probably thwart the success of any intended call in that direction, even if it were attempted with great sacrifices." On their list of such "notables" were Magnus and Dove in Berlin, Weber in Göttingen, Neumann in Königsberg, and Ettingshausen in Vienna.[14]

Kirchhoff at Heidelberg

The procedures by which candidates were selected for the Heidelberg chair of physics in 1854, in contrast with those in effect in 1816 when Muncke was appointed, show an increased use of specialists instead of local authorities. In 1816, of the three academics who were consulted for advice by the ministry of the interior, only one was a physicist, and he was an employee of the state of Baden; the other two were members of the Heidelberg faculty.[15] In 1854, in preparing their list of candidates, the Heidelberg faculty consulted the best-known physicists at large, recommending that the government, too, seek their advice if it should have any doubts about the proposed candidates.[16]

If we compare the philosophical faculty's report of 1854 with that of 1816, we see that the important qualification of being an experienced teacher, which carried

13. Jolly to Baden Ministry of the Interior, 12 June 1846.
14. Dean of Heidelberg U. Philosophical Faculty Bunsen to Baden Ministry of the Interior, 26 July 1854, Bad. GLA, 235/3135.
15. "Die Wiederbesetzung der Lehrstelle der Physik zu Heidelberg betrf.," 7 Dec. 1816, Bad. GLA, 235/3135.
16. Bunsen to Baden Ministry of the Interior, 26 July 1854.

as much weight as having a good scientific reputation in 1816, had almost completely disappeared in 1854. What had become decisive, and what was not explicitly mentioned in 1816, was original research, preferably experimental research. Only after a candidate was found to be superior in his research and therefore the man best suited for the position did the faculty add that he was also an effective teacher.[17]

Heidelberg's philosophical faculty, whose dean and spokesman in 1854 was Bunsen, did not take for granted that the ministry would understand or even expect their strong emphasis on research. Before discussing any of the candidates, they explained the assumptions on which their selection was based. The literature of physics, they wrote, points in two directions: it may give an account, in compendiums and annual reports, of scientific results and of the means by which they were obtained; or it may aim at enriching individual areas of science through original investigations. Since experience has shown, the faculty said, that one direction almost excludes the other, teachers of physics must be grouped in two categories. They listed three professors belonging to the first category, alongside their successful textbooks, and nine physicists belonging to the second. It was only the second that they would consider; as they explained: "The faculty must start from the conviction that *at universities* successful teaching in its true significance is unthinkable without work that is primarily directed to the expansion and development of science."[18]

Heidelberg's determination to fill its physics position with a productive researcher was regarded as the only proper course by German physicists. To provide support for researchers was now the raison d'être of physics chairs, Weber wrote to Heidelberg in 1854. For in physics as opposed to, say, chemistry, teaching was the only kind of work by which a researcher could hope to make a living: "In chemistry there are all kinds of positions outside of the university circle in which successful scientific work is possible, but which so far are still very much lacking in physics. It is all the more important for the growth of this science to see to the filling of the few professorships in this field and to act with the intention of reserving them for the most outstanding talents in this field who otherwise will not find any base for the development of work that would essentially further the science."[19]

In 1854 Kirchhoff was only thirty, but he had distinguished himself over many years as a researcher, which placed him in the right category from Heidelberg's point of view. Fortunately for Kirchhoff, it was no disqualification for a director of a phys-

17. Bunsen to Baden Ministry of the Interior, 26 July 1854.
18. Bunsen to Baden Ministry of the Interior, 26 July 1854. The philosophical faculty's explanation may have had an ulterior motive. The three professors who were dismissed, in respectful terms, as textbook writers were Wilhelm Eisenlohr, Johann Müller, and Heinrich Buff. The first two were employees of the state of Baden, at the Karlsruhe Polytechnic and at Freiburg University, respectively, and the third was a colleague and relative of Liebig at Giessen, to whom Jolly was beholden for a recommendation to Munich University and for whom Jolly was trying to secure the Heidelberg position. The faculty's explanation appears designed to counteract, on the one hand, the state's possible intention to fill the Heidelberg position cheaply by promoting one of the two physicists at the other Baden institutions of higher learning and, on the other hand, to prevent Jolly from bringing about Buff's appointment. Jolly's relationship to Liebig in this connection can be seen in Jolly's letter to Liebig, 19 Feb. 1854, Liebigiana, Bay. STB, 58 (Jolly, Philipp v.) Nr. 3.
19. Weber to Bunsen, 12 Mar. 1854, Bad. GLA, 235/3135.

ics institute to be known principally as a mathematical physicist, especially if he did experimental work, instead of as an experimental physicist. This can be seen from Ettingshausen's strong endorsement of Kirchhoff for the post at Heidelberg: Kirchhoff, he said, was simply "one of the best mathematical physicists in Germany."[20] From this and similar recommendations that Bunsen solicited in support of Kirchhoff, he could report that Kirchhoff was "considered one of the most talented of the younger physicists of the exact Gaussian school."[21] Bunsen's efforts were rewarded, as we have seen, by the faculty's sole recommendation of Kirchhoff for the Heidelberg physics chair.

Kirchhoff had encouraged Bunsen's efforts on his behalf, since for a number of reasons he wanted to move. He missed his close contact with Bunsen, which had been interrupted by Bunsen's move from Breslau to Heidelberg in 1852. In addition the new job meant a promotion and paid much more than his present one. Most important, at Heidelberg Kirchhoff would have his own institute where he could develop his teaching and research unhindered, as he could not in his subordinate position at Breslau.[22] His one worry was that his lectures would not be as successful as Jolly's "extraordinarily attractive" ones.[23] This worry was of secondary importance, at least as far as Heidelberg was concerned. Kirchhoff's two decades at Heidelberg from 1854 to 1874 were to prove the most productive of his career.[24]

The work that brought Kirchhoff and Bunsen their greatest scientific fame was spectrum analysis. This work also did much to put Heidelberg on the scientific map in the middle of the nineteenth century, an outcome that was gratifying from the Baden government's point of view. For Baden wanted to make Heidelberg University a "center for the study of the natural sciences and medicine . . . for Germany," according to Liebig, who was in a position to know. The state already gave preferential treatment to chemistry, paying Bunsen the second highest salary in the university when he arrived and building for him a new chemistry laboratory, which was to draw a large number of new students each year to prepare for what was now a profession outside of teaching.[25] Within a few years, preparations began for the badly

20. Ettingshausen to Bunsen, 14 Mar. 1854, Bad. GLA, 235/3135.

21. Bunsen to Liebig, 4 Nov. 1854, Liebigiana, Bay. STB, 58 (Bunsen, Robert), Nr. 15.

22. As extraordinary professor at Breslau, Kirchhoff got a salary of 1050 florins; as ordinary professor at Heidelberg, he got 1600 florins plus another 400 florins for housing. Kirchhoff Personalakte, Heidelberg UA, III, 5b, Nr. 244. Letter from Kirchhoff to his brother Carl, 18 Oct. 1854, quoted in Warburg, "Kirchhoff," 208. When Neumann recommended Kirchhoff for the Heidelberg professorship, he wrote to Bunsen that he was sorry to see Kirchhoff leave a Prussian university, Breslau; but Neumann wanted the "freer scientific activity" of Heidelberg for Kirchhoff because at Breslau he worked with difficulty under Frankenheim. Neumann to Bunsen, 20 Mar. 1854, Bad. GLA, 235/3135.

23. Kirchhoff to his brother Carl, 18 Oct. 1854. Bunsen to Baden Ministry of the Interior, 26 July 1854.

24. Robert Helmholtz, "A Memoir of Gustav Robert Kirchhoff," trans. J. de Perott, *Annual Report of the . . . Smithsonian Institution . . . to July, 1889*, 1890, 527–40, on 529.

25. Letter from Bunsen to Ministerial Counselor Lutz, 13 July 1851, quoted in Borscheid, *Naturwissenschaft*, 62. While Kirchhoff was at Heidelberg, chemistry there attracted more than twenty new students a year and in one year as many as fifty. Borscheid, 13, 50, 60–67. Baden had considered Liebig for the professorship to which it eventually appointed Bunsen.

needed new physics institute. A plan dating from about 1859, the time of Kirchhoff and Bunsen's work on spectrum analysis, described the location of the then existing institute as "generally speaking precarious, very unsuitable, and very strongly exposed to vibration." The plan called for a "laboratory (40' in length, 12' in breadth)" with smaller, specialized rooms for certain classes of experiments together with the traditional auditorium and an apartment for the director, Kirchhoff. It also called for a very large room "(42' in length and 40' in breadth)" for housing Heidelberg's impressive physical cabinet, containing "very beautiful apparatus" mainly for lecture purposes.[26] In 1863, after nine years in Heidelberg, Kirchhoff moved into the new institute building, the "Friedrichsbau."

By the time of the new Heidelberg physics institute, the need for laboratory practice and research was widely accepted: it no longer had to be given special justification in requests to the government for financing; the need could itself serve as a justification for institute requirements. In 1863 Kirchhoff reported to the ministry that every summer semester he directed physics exercises in which "young people, taking turns, work in the cabinet almost daily, often from early morning to late in the evening"; and he mentioned as a matter of course other accepted uses of the institute: "more advanced young people who work not merely for their education but carry out investigations of scientific interest" were using the institute, and he himself was doing experimental work there.[27]

It was not until close to the end of his stay at Heidelberg that Kirchhoff had an official seminar to direct. The Heidelberg philosophical faculty, until relatively late, viewed seminars as institutions for training secondary school teachers for which philological seminars sufficed. In time this understanding proved unworkable there as elsewhere.

From the late 1850s, Heidelberg's natural scientists were unhappy with their position in the philosophical faculty. With the proliferation of chairs, their humanistic colleagues acquired a widening numerical advantage over them. The gulf between the two faculty groups was generally seen as unbridgeable, since it was attrib-

---

26. "Universität Heidelberg. Neubau für naturwissenschaftliche Institute. II. Physikalisches Institut," ca. 1859, Bad. GLA, 235/352. Heidelberg U. Faculty to Baden Ministry of the Interior, 19 Oct. 1859, Bad. GLA, 235/352. The remark about the apparatus is Quincke's to Neumann, 9 Nov. 1854, Neumann Papers, Göttingen UB, Ms. Dept. Kirchhoff to "Grossherzogliche Bau- und Oekonomie-Commission," 26 Jan. 1864, Heidelberg UA, III, 5b, Nr. 244. At Heidelberg, Kirchhoff made a new inventory of the instrument collection, reorganized it, and updated it by requesting permission to sell what was useless or else break it up into pieces to make new instruments. The records for the Heidelberg physics institute under Kirchhoff's direction are misplaced or lost and with them the record of his administrative activities. There is indirect evidence that Kirchhoff did not see the need to exploit his scientific fame at Heidelberg to substantially improve the instrument collection or the institute generally. When he received a call to Berlin University in 1870, he asked for an increase in the budget of the Heidelberg physics institute, but it was only for 200 to 300 florins for a salary for an assistant. His main reward for refusing the call was a raise of 1100 florins to bring his salary to 3500. In the next four years, he received two other calls, before he accepted a third, and each time his salary was increased by a considerable amount, to 6000 florins in the end, but he did not use the later offers to get anything for his institute. Even the small improvement of the institute's circumstances he asked for in 1870 aided him personally, since he had suffered a foot injury that interfered with his work.

27. Kirchhoff to Baden Ministry of the Interior, 28 May 1863, Bad. GLA, 235/352.

uted to fundamental differences between their respective methods of training and research. In the new Baden testing regulations for teaching candidates in 1867, the earlier goal.of producing gymnasium teachers with a rounded philological-historical and natural-scientific education was finally abandoned. The reorganized Heidelberg philological seminar dropped its claim to be the only institution qualified to train teachers, opening the way for specialized seminars for mathematics and physics and other subjects.[28]

The appointment in 1869 of Kirchhoff's and Bunsen's good friend Leo Koenigsberger as mathematics professor provided an opportune occasion for the establishment of a mathematical-physical seminar at Heidelberg. Together Kirchhoff and Koenigsberger appealed for a seminar on the generally accepted grounds that secondary school teachers needed to do independent scientific research and to practice lecturing on scientific topics. The seminar they proposed had a familiar organization, consisting of sections for pure and applied mathematics and mathematical physics.[29] In the mathematical physics section in the summer semester, the routine went like this. Students would be given a weekly problem, part experimental and part theoretical, and in the accompanying lecture Kirchhoff would explain the problem and the methods to be used. Each member of the seminar would be given one morning or afternoon to carry out the prescribed experiment; the student would appear at the scheduled hour, adjust the apparatus, and take the necessary readings. Kirchhoff would look in on him once. At home, the student would do the calculations and write up a paper he would submit. Then at the next meeting of the seminar, Kirchhoff would discuss the accuracy of the results of the set of papers. The seminar was useful: the state examiners were expected to take into account the disciplines that the candidates studied and did research on in the seminar, and the papers the students prepared for the seminar often led to dissertations. Kirchhoff's physical half of the seminar in the summer semester of 1870 drew thirteen members, a manageable number for the procedure he designed for it.[30]

In addition to directing work in the seminar and laboratory, Kirchhoff gave regular lectures, the traditional responsibility of the chair holder. These were both on experimental physics, often with demonstration apparatus he assembled himself,

28. Riese, Hochschule, 88–90, 194–96. By Kirchhoff's time, the presumed intellectual unity of the philosophical faculty was widely disputed and debated. The Staatswissenschaften, in the 1860s, were the first to separate off at Heidelberg. In 1890, at the initiative of the natural scientists, and after inquiring of universities—Tübingen, Strassburg, and Leipzig—at which a division of the philosophical faculty had already occurred, the Heidelberg natural sciences and mathematics faculty also separated off (p. 90). In 1900, the Heidelberg mathematical-physical seminar divided; in light of the impending call of a professor for mathematical physics, the natural sciences and mathematics faculty wanted Heidelberg, like other universities, to "divide completely the mathematical and physical seminar." "Prodecan" Pfitzer to Heidelberg U. Senate, 25 Jan. 1900, Bad. GLA, 235/3228.

29. By the wording of the proposal for a mathematical-physical seminar—the request for "official" recognition—it sounds as if an unofficial seminar may have been in existence. Kirchhoff and Koenigsberger's proposal to "Excellency," 14 Apr. 1869, Bad. GLA, 235/3228.

30. Kirchhoff and Koenigsberger's annual report on the seminar for the academic year 1869–70, Bad. GLA, 235/3228. The rigid procedure followed in Kirchhoff's seminar was observed firsthand by Arthur Schuster, The Progress of Physics During 33 Years (1875–1908) (Cambridge: Cambridge University Press, 1911), 13–14.

and on theoretical physics, which included lectures at an advanced level.[31] As a teacher he was concise, elegant, exact, a "very precise man who weighed every word." To follow him, students needed a proper mathematical training, for which reason he placed great value on Koenigsberger's teaching, regarding it as the condition for the success of his own. Koenigsberger described their close cooperation at Heidelberg in the years 1869–74: "Kirchhoff and I worked hand in hand, so that sometimes in the same semester we both lectured to the same audience on mechanics, he more from the physical, I from the purely mathematical, point of view, and daily we spoke together about the subject of the coming lecture. To me it was an indescribable joy to see such an active scientific life expand."[32]

From all over Germany and from abroad, many young physicists came to Heidelberg because of Kirchhoff;[33] they often came because of Bunsen, too. For example, Heinrich Wild, in the summer semester of 1857, after receiving his doctorate in physics from Zurich University, went to Heidelberg to hear Bunsen lecture on experimental chemistry and to work in his laboratory. He also came to make measuring observations in Kirchhoff's laboratory; these concerned thermoelectric currents and electromotive force and resistance in conductors according to absolute measures. Quincke, another example, while still a physics student spent three semesters at Heidelberg, beginning in 1854. There he immediately joined the forty students in the chemistry laboratory, where Bunsen supervised work from eight in the morning to five in the evening. When Quincke was not working in Bunsen's laboratory, he was studying mechanics, and when he got stuck he would go to Kirchhoff, who was always willing to help him. He also worked in Kirchhoff's laboratory, investigating the lines of flow of electric current between two points on a metal plate; this work, close to Kirchhoff's own, resulted in what Quincke regarded as his first paper, which he duly sent off to Poggendorff's *Annalen.*[34]

While Kirchhoff was accessible to young physicists such as Wild and Quincke,

31. Kirchhoff gave the six-hour lecture course on experimental physics and supervised practical work in the laboratory. He also offered a three-hour survey course on theoretical physics, which treated mainly mechanics in the "wider sense" and concluded with the mechanical theory of heat. In addition, he gave a one-hour course on separate branches of theoretical physics such as the "mechanics of elastic and fluid bodies" and the "theory of heat and electricity." In the summer semester of 1870, for the first time, Kirchhoff's "physical seminar" was listed among the courses of the philosophical faculty. From then on, he offered in alternate semesters his seminar and his three-hour theoretical physics course. His teaching of theoretical physics was supplemented by that of the Privatdocent Friedrich Eisenlohr, who regularly offered a course in his specialty, theoretical optics, in addition to courses on mechanics, potential theory, and other mathematical subjects. *Anzeige der Vorlesungen . . . auf der Grossherzoglich Badischen Ruprecht-Carolinischen Universität zu Heidelberg,* the published list of courses offered each semester at Heidelberg. Pockels, "Kirchhoff," 248. Lorey, *Das Studium der Mathematik,* 72–73.

32. Leo Koenigsberger, *Mein Leben* (Heidelberg: Carl Winters, 1919), 101. Schuster, *Progress of Physics,* 14.

33. Kirchhoff's laboratory or lectures attracted not only gifted German physicists such as Eilhard Wiedemann and E. Bessel-Hagen but also many gifted foreign physicists such as Boltzmann and Lang from Austria, Gabriel Lipmann from France, H. Kamerlingh Onnes from Holland, and Schuster from Britain.

34. Wild to Neumann, 1 Feb. 1858; Quincke to Neumann, 9 Nov. 1854 and 23 Mar. 1856; Neumann Papers, Göttingen UB, Ms. Dept.

he did not try to draw them close to him. He was formal in manner, exacting in his standards, and given to cross-examining students when they had questions. He hesitated to pass judgment on new problems or to set students to work on them. Among his favorite words were "probably" and "perhaps," which he used unless he was absolutely certain of something. His extreme caution might be admired, but it did not create followers. His influence on his contemporaries came to be exerted mainly through his published lectures and, above all, his published researches.[35] His researches were not many by contemporary practice, needing only one modest volume together with a slender supplement to contain them; but they were choice, and they were the work of a physicist who had "mastered experiment as well as mathematics," the characteristic, one of Kirchhoff's biographers observed, of the "greatest physicist nowadays."[36]

In their recommendation of Kirchhoff for the Heidelberg physics chair, the philosophical faculty singled out for praise several of his researches in elasticity and electricity.[37] In addition to this work, his work on radiation was included for praise in the proposal in 1861 for his election as a corresponding member of the Prussian Academy of Sciences.[38] Kirchhoff worked in all three of these subjects—elasticity, electricity, and radiant heat—and in others as well, especially the mechanical theory of heat, at more or less the same time. As his publications show, the results he derived for one subject suggested to him analogies for developing another; theoretical methods and guiding ideas about the motions and energies of the physical world reappeared in widely different contexts. Kirchhoff was advancing the entire field of physics, not just this or that part of it.[39]

Kirchhoff's theoretical and experimental works were recognized by his contemporaries as models of accuracy and thoroughness. If in his experiments he made fewer observations than many physicists, he made them only after he was certain of their theoretical basis. In his theories, he revealed his great mathematical proficiency and his cautious attitude toward physical hypotheses. He preferred, for example, to treat matter as a continuum rather than as a molecular aggregate not because he regarded the molecular constitution of matter as improbable but because molecular hypotheses lacked rigor. His aim was to build equations that correspond to the phenomenal world as accurately as possible and with as little dependence as possible on anything hypothetical.[40]

35. Boltzmann, "Kirchhoff," 53. Woldemar Voigt, "Zum Gedächtniss von G. Kirchhoff," Abh. Ges. Wiss. Göttingen 35 (1888), 3–10, on 9–10. Schuster, Progress of Physics, 14–15.

36. Robert Helmholtz, "Kirchhoff," 528. The volume Kirchhoff edited himself, Gesammelte Abhandlungen, runs to 641 pages; the posthumous volume edited by Ludwig Boltzmann, Nachtrag to Kirchhoff's Gesammelte Abhandlungen (Leipzig, 1891), runs to 137.

37. Bunsen to Baden Ministry of the Interior, 26 July 1854.

38. "Wahlvorschlag für Gustav Robert Kirchhoff (1824–1887) zum KM," in Kirsten and Körber, Physiker über Physiker, 75–76.

39. Kirchhoff arranged the order of the papers for his collected works following the customary practice of scientists; he grouped papers by theme rather than by strict chronology, which made the edition convenient for scientific reference but obscured the historical connections of the various researches it contained.

40. Voigt, "Kirchhoff," 9. Pockels, "Kirchhoff," 261. Boltzmann, "Kirchhoff," 24–25.

Kirchhoff's Researches in Elasticity and Electricity

From early in his career, in 1848 and on and off for much of the rest of it, Kirchhoff worked on problems in elasticity. This work illustrates as well as any the general character of his physics. In his researches in elasticity, he often treated the relations that this branch of theoretical physics has with other branches. He developed, for example, equations for the deformation of bodies by electric and magnetic forces; he developed electrical theory by analogy with elastic theory; and he applied elastic theory to optics to derive a new law for the passage of light between transparent bodies.[41] He also worked on the general theory of elasticity as a part of mechanics, and it is this work that we discuss here.

In papers published in 1850 and 1858, Kirchhoff constructed equations for the equilibrium and motion of elastic plates and rods.[42] This work was highly regarded as one of the first exact treatments of the difficult subject of the elastic relations of bodies with one or two of their dimensions assumed to be infinitely small.[43] Kirchhoff's point of departure was work done by the French, who had developed elastic theory extensively. Poisson's theory of the deformation of elastic plates by an external load was deficient, however, and A. J. C. Barré de Saint-Venant's theory of the elastic rod, itself an improvement over Poisson's, was unduly limiting. Rejecting Poisson's molecular point of view in favor of the view of elastic matter as continuously filling the space of bodies, Kirchhoff derived general equations, in agreement with Cauchy's, for the interior and the surface of an elastic body. He emphasized the great generality of his derivation, which proceeded from a single variational equation.[44] Drawing on a "principle of mechanics," he introduced kinetic energy into the equation to attain the vibratory motion of an elastic body.[45] Specializing to the cases of an infinitely thin circular plate and an infinitely thin rod and invoking appropriate boundary and initial conditions, Kirchhoff arrived at equations of motion and solutions that, mathematically speaking, had "considerable interest" and, indeed, were published in a mathematical journal.[46]

41. Voigt, "Kirchhoff," 6.

42. Gustav Kirchhoff, "Ueber das Gleichgewicht und die Bewegung einer elastischen Scheibe," *Journ. f. d. reine u. angewandte Math.* 40 (1850): 51–88, in *Ges. Abh.*, 237–79; "Ueber das Gleichgewicht und die Bewegung eines unendlich dünnen elastischen Stabes," *Journ. f. d. reine u. angewandte Math.* 56 (1859): 285–313, in *Ges. Abh.*, 285–316. Kirchhoff's 1850 and 1858 papers are closely related, and we discuss them together here. But they have some important differences; Kirchhoff remarked that the first paper could be developed in a stronger way by following the method of the second (*Ges. Abh.*, 311).

43. Isaac Todhunter, *A History of the Theory of Elasticity and of the Strength of Materials from Galilei to the Present Time*, vol. 2, *Saint-Venant to Lord Kelvin*, pt. 2 (Cambridge, 1893), 54. Kirchhoff's 1858 paper—his "most important" elasticity paper, according to Todhunter (p. 68)—was judged by William Thomson and P. G. Tait, *Natural Philosophy*, pt. 2, §609, as the "first thoroughly general investigation of the equations of equilibrium and motion of an elastic wire."

44. In his 1850 paper, Kirchhoff's variational equation reads $0 = \delta P - K\delta\Omega$; it expresses the equality of the moments of the external force, and of the internal elastic forces for the equilibrium state. Here P is the moment of the external forces, K is a constant, and Ω is a volume integral of a homogeneous function of the main dilations. His 1858 paper proceeds from a similar variational equation. Earlier George Green had given the equation but had not expressed it in terms of principal dilations. Todhunter, *Elasticity*, 41, 56.

45. Kirchhoff, "Ueber das Gleichgewicht und die Bewegung eines . . . Stabes," 295.

46. This is Todhunter's comment on Kirchhoff's solution for the vibrations of the plate, which were expressed as "doubly-infinite series of functions akin to Bessel's functions." Todhunter, *Elasticity*, 45, 43.

Kirchhoff's theory had a physical interest as well as a mathematical one. "Physically" the theory connected with experiments, his and others', which Kirchhoff discussed in related papers in the *Annalen*.[47] Drawing upon Chladni's measurements of tones and more recent measurements of nodal lines on carefully prepared circular glass and metal plates, and after undertaking a "very great amount of laborious calculation," Kirchhoff concluded that his theory agreed remarkably well with experiment, all things considered.[48] The theory contained a constant, θ, to which Poisson had given the value of $1/2$ and more recent experiments the value 1. Tones and nodes of vibrating plates depended on this constant, but not sensitively enough for Kirchhoff to be able to decide between the two values from the measurements at hand. He came closer to the value of the constant through his theory of thin rods and the exacting experiments he carried out in connection with it. To long, thin, hardened metal rods, he applied a weight that produced both bending and twisting. His measurements of the two distortions yielded, through a constant constructed from it, the mean value of θ; it fell midway between the other two values, corresponding to common expectations then.[49] Altogether it was an impressive work. Neumann recommended Kirchhoff to Heidelberg by pointing out that his former student had improved upon his great French predecessors in mathematical physics: Kirchhoff had "uncovered errors, which are connected with names such as Poisson."[50]

Simultaneously with his "great theoretical and experimental investigation" of the elastic properties of metals, as Boltzmann described this work of Kirchhoff's, Kirchhoff continued to work on problems in electrical theory. Although the observed phenomena of elasticity and electricity are widely different, their mathematical descriptions are often remarkably similar. This Kirchhoff remarked on in two papers in 1857, in which he derived equations of motion of electricity in one-dimensional and three-dimensional conductors.[51] With these papers, he carried through the task he had envisioned in 1849: to derive the laws of currents in closed circuits from Weber's fundamental law of electric action.

Adopting Weber's understanding of current as the motion of opposing electric fluids, Kirchhoff viewed the production of a current at a point in a conductor as the

47. Todhunter, *Elasticity*, 45. Gustav Kirchhoff, "Ueber die Schwingungen einer kreisförmigen elastischen Scheibe," *Ann.* 81 (1850): 258–64, in *Ges. Abh.*, 279–85; "Ueber das Verhältniss der Quercontraction zur Längendilatation bei Stäben von federhartem Stahl," *Ann.* 108 (1859): 369–92, in *Ges. Abh.*, 316–39.

48. Todhunter, *Elasticity*, 46–47. Measurements of the radii of the circular nodes belonging to the different tones on glass and metal plates agreed in an "excellent way" with each other and—generally accurate to two places—with the values calculated from Kirchhoff's theory: "Ueber die Schwingungen," 285.

49. With thin rods, the physical meaning of the constant θ can easily be seen: when an elastic cylindrical rod is stretched in the direction of its length, its cross section is contracted; the ratio of that contraction to the increase in the length of the rod is $θ/(1 + 2θ)$, or, by the values for θ of $1/2$ and 1, $1/4$ and $1/3$.

50. Neumann to Bunsen, 20 Mar. 1854.

51. Boltzmann, "Kirchhoff," 22. Gustav Kirchhoff, "Ueber die Bewegung der Elektricität in Drähten," *Ann.* 100 (1857): 193–217, in *Ges. Abh.*, 131–54; "Ueber die Bewegung der Elektricität in Leitern," *Ann.* 102 (1857): 529–44, in *Ges. Abh.*, 154–68.

separation of opposing electricities there. He calculated the electromotive force responsible for the separation from a sum of the potential of the electrostatic force of the free electricity in the conductor and the potential of the induced electromotive force due to changing currents in the conductor. In the solutions to the equations of motion of electricity under the action of this electromotive force, he recognized a "remarkable analogy" between the propagation of electricity in a closed wire and the propagation of a wave in a longitudinally vibrating elastic rod. In the limit of vanishing resistance in the wire, he found that electricity is propagated analogously to waves in a taut string and, "to be sure, with the velocity that light has in empty space." He also treated the other limit, that of infinite resistance, in which electricity propagates analogously to heat, rather than to elastic waves.[52]

Kirchhoff's "extraordinary failure," as it has been called, to develop the electrical significance of the velocity of light has to do, at least in part, with the theory he worked within. By Weber's electrical theory, the velocity in question is the relative velocity of two electric particles when they exert no force on one another. It does not suggest optical phenomena, least of all to a physicist as wary of physical hypotheses as Kirchhoff.[53] Kirchhoff recognized formal analogies between the motion of electricity and the motion of rods, strings, heat, and light. For Kirchhoff, all natural phenomena arise ultimately from motions, and as he and others at the time were demonstrating, a few kinds of differential equations suffice to describe most kinds of motion; mathematical and numerical similarities in different parts of physics were commonly encountered and did not necessarily imply a physical connection. Eventually Kirchhoff's laws of the motion of electricity entered work on the electrical theory of light, but it was work by others, notably Ludwig Lorenz and Helmholtz, who took seriously an electrical theory of light for reasons other than Kirchhoff's elastic analogy.

Kirchhoff and Bunsen: Researches in Spectrum Analysis and Radiant Heat

In 1858 Kirchhoff turned to a new subject of research, the mechanical theory of heat. In his applications of this theory to problems such as the absorption of gases, the solution of salts, and the evaporation of mixtures of sulphuric acid and water, he developed theoretical methods of significance for physical chemistry.[54] In this new work, he made frequent references to his colleague Bunsen's work. Soon Kirchhoff joined Bunsen in what was to be the principal work in chemistry for them both: the development of spectrum analysis, on which they began publishing in 1859.

In the first half of the nineteenth century, efforts were made to recognize chem-

52. Kirchhoff, "Ueber die Bewegung der Elektricität in Drähten," 146–47; "Ueber die Bewegung der Elektricität in Leitern," 164.

53. Rosenfeld, "The Velocity of Light," 1635, 1640, attributes Kirchhoff's failure to develop the analogy between light and electricity to his phenomenology. Kirchhoff's avoidance of risky physical hypotheses would have made it difficult for him to anticipate a physical basis for the coincidence of the two velocities.

54. Gustav Kirchhoff, "Ueber einen Satz der mechanischen Wärmetheorie und einige Anwendungen desselben," Ann. 103 (1858): 177–206; in Ges. Abh., 454–82. Pockels, "Kirchhoff," 250–51.

ical substances by placing them in a flame and observing their characteristic colors through prisms or by observing the spectra of electric arcs produced by electrodes fashioned from the substances. For a time, Bunsen studied the flames of salts, using colored glasses and solutions to help him distinguish the colors. The gas burner he introduced in the 1850s facilitated this general approach to chemical analysis; by giving a flame that was hot but not bright, it did not interfere with the flame of the substance under observation. Bunsen discussed his work on this problem with Kirchhoff, who pointed the way to a method based on the prismatic resolution of the colors of flames into their separate parts.

With Bunsen's burner and with Kirchhoff's fine spectral apparatus, which he constructed of a prism equipped with telescopes and a scale for the delicate measurements, Bunsen and Kirchhoff extended the principle of characteristic spectra from gases and metals, where it was already established, to salts, as they systematically examined the spectra of alkalies and alkaline earths to identify the metals they contain. They found that the location of the discrete bright lines in the spectrum of a given metal is the same regardless of how the metal is combined in salts or how hot the flame is. They developed a technique for analytic chemistry of unsuspected sensitivity, as Bunsen soon demonstrated by discovering two new metals with it.[55]

Late in 1859, Bunsen wrote to his friend and colleague the chemist Henry Roscoe: "At the moment I and Kirchhoff are occupied with a common work that does not let us sleep. That is to say that Kirchhoff has made a wonderful, entirely unexpected discovery, in which he has found the cause of the dark lines in the spectrum of the sun. . . . By this means the way is given for identifying the material constitution of the sun and the fixed stars with the same certainty with which we determine S, Cl, and so forth through our reagents. On earth, substances can be differentiated and identified by this method with the same sharpness as in the sun."[56] Kirchhoff came upon his explanation for the dark lines in the solar spectrum in the course of comparing the dark D lines that Fraunhofer had measured in the solar spectrum with the two close, bright yellow lines of the spectrum of sodium, as observed in flames in the laboratory. When Kirchhoff simultaneously passed sunlight and light from a sodium flame through the slit of the spectral apparatus, he confirmed that the D lines and the sodium lines coincide, as expected. He also found results that optical theory did not account for: with strong sunlight, an interposed sodium flame does not lighten the D lines but makes the dark lines even more

55. According to Boltzmann, Kirchhoff's first flint glass prism, which he obtained in 1857, had been ground by Fraunhofer himself. Boltzmann, "Kirchhoff," 60. Gustav Kirchhoff and Robert Bunsen, "Chemische Analyse durch Spectralbeobachtungen," *Ann.* 110 (1860): 160–89; in *Ges. Abh.*, 598–625. Bunsen told Wilhelm Ostwald the history of the discovery of spectrum analysis, which Ostwald reported in the "Anmerkungen," 71–72, appended to his edition of *Chemische Analyse durch Spectralbeobachtungen von G. Kirchhoff und R. Bunsen* (1860), vol. 72 of Ostwald's Klassiker der exakten Wissenschaften (Leipzig, 1895). William McGucken, *Nineteenth-Century Spectroscopy* (Baltimore: Johns Hopkins University Press, 1969), 26–28, 34, 50. Daniel M. Siegel, "Balfour Stewart and Gustav Robert Kirchhoff: Two Independent Approaches to 'Kirchhoff's Radiation Law,' " *Isis* 67 (1976): 565–600, on 568–69. Pockels, "Kirchhoff," 252–53.

56. Henry Roscoe, "Gedenkrede auf Bunsen," in *Gesammelte Abhandlungen von Robert Bunsen*, ed. Wilhelm Ostwald and M. Bodenstein (Leipzig: W. Engelmann, 1904), 1:xv–lix, on xxxiv.

distinct; by contrast, with weak sunlight, the D lines appear bright. Taken by complete surprise by this observation, he had no immediate explanation. But by the following day, he had come to recognize a fundamental principle behind the reversal of the spectral lines: any luminous body absorbs the same rays it emits. In particular, sodium, which emits bright lines of the same wavelengths as the dark D lines in the solar spectrum, also absorbs the same wavelengths, producing dark lines like the sun's. From this understanding, Kirchhoff attributed the Fraunhofer D lines to sodium in the cooler atmosphere of the sun, which absorbs just those wavelengths from the continuous spectrum of the hotter core of the sun. By measuring the exact positions of spectral lines, other terrestrial chemical elements, such as iron, were identified in the solar atmosphere by the same reasoning.[57] When Roscoe visited Heidelberg in 1860, he found himself "in the thick of it." "I shall never forget," he recalled, "the impression made upon me by looking through Kirchhoff's magnificent spectroscope, arranged in one of the back rooms of the old building in the Hauptstrasse, which then served for the Physical Institute, as I saw the coincidence of the bright lines in the iron spectrum with the dark Fraunenhofer's [sic] lines in the solar spectrum. The evidence that iron, such as we know it on this earth, is contained in the solar atmosphere, struck one instantly as conclusive."[58]

Early in 1860, Kirchhoff wrote to his brother Otto, a "half chemist like me," to tell him that he was "very passionately occupied with chemistry": "I want to analyze nothing less than the sun and perhaps later also the fixed stars."[59] Over the next years he planned to complete his "drawing of the spectrum of the sun," though he pursued the project so avidly that later in 1860 he temporarily had to interrupt his observations of spectra because they strained his eyes.[60]

While at first spectrum analysis interested chemists and astronomers mainly, it soon began to interest physicists, too. They used it in their work, and they also recognized its contribution to a uniform understanding of physical nature, always a matter of interest to physicists. The method of analysis revealed the "unity of the universe," Woldemar Voigt said, by disclosing the chemical constitution of the heavenly bodies. Belonging to the "boundary of physics, chemistry, and astronomy," Boltzmann said, spectrum analysis contributed to the recognition of the "unity of natural forces everywhere," the main goal of the natural sciences.[61]

Kirchhoff followed up his paper on the chemical composition of the solar atmosphere a few weeks later with the first of two theoretical papers on the subject of radiant heat. They contained the proof of a "general law" applying to all bodies that emit and absorb light and heat, the "theoretical foundation," he believed, of his

57. Ostwald, "Anmerkungen," 72. Siegel, "Balfour Stewart and Gustav Robert Kirchhoff," 570–71. Pockels, "Kirchhoff," 253–55. Revealing his characteristic caution, Kirchhoff calculated the probability that the sixty known lines of the spectrum of iron would coincide with Fraunhofer lines by mere chance as less than one in a trillion; he concluded that the identification of iron in the sun has as much certainty as any conclusions in natural science. Pockels, "Kirchhoff," 255.

58. *The Life and Experiences of Sir Henry Enfield Roscoe, D.C.L., LL.D., F.R.S.* (London and New York: Macmillan, 1906), 69.

59. Kirchhoff to his brother Otto, 11 May 1860, quoted in Warburg, "Kirchhoff," 209.

60. Kirchhoff to Neumann, 18 Dec. 1860, Neumann Papers, Göttingen UB, Ms. Dept.

61. McGucken, Spectroscopy, 35. Voigt, "Kirchhoff," 8. Boltzmann, "Kirchhoff," 4.

explanation of the Fraunhofer lines. The starting point of his proof was the experimentally proven law that the ratio of thermal radiating power to absorbing power is the same for all bodies at the same temperature. By imagining a body that emits and absorbs heat rays of only one wavelength, Kirchhoff derived on the basis of the "general fundamental laws of the mechanical theory of heat" the following law: for heat rays of the same wavelength and for a given temperature, the ratio of emissive power to absorptive power is the same for all bodies. The ratio is a function only of wavelength and temperature.[62] The immense richness of facts that spectrum analysis provided did not, the physicists and mathematicians of the Berlin Academy of Sciences agreed ten years later, "attain the importance of that simple physical law."[63]

Kirchhoff soon published another, more rigorous proof of his law. By regarding light and radiant heat as differing only in wavelength, a common assumption by then, he used the laws of optical absorption and reflection in the proof. He started from the laws of the mechanical theory of heat: he associated "vis viva," or kinetic energy, with heat rays, subordinating them to the "law of equivalence of heat and work," or the first fundamental law of the mechanical theory of heat. When a body emits heat rays it loses to the ether a quantity of heat equal to the vis viva of the heat rays; conversely, when a body absorbs heat rays it gains the equivalent of the vis viva of the rays. The second fundamental law of the mechanical theory of heat, or Carnot's theorem, entered Kirchhoff's proof in his discussion of heat equilibrium: by this law, the temperature of a body in equilibrium with its surroundings stays the same unless the body loses or gains heat, so that in a given time the vis viva of the heat rays emitted by a body must equal the vis viva of the rays it absorbs.[64]

Kirchhoff imagined a "perfectly black" enclosure, which absorbs all of the rays that strike it. Inside it are a "perfect mirror" that reflects all rays and a plate that is "perfectly diathermanous" for rays of a given wavelength and polarization but completely reflecting for all other rays. Kirchhoff's proof of his law depends on the assumption that the three ideal bodies—perfectly black, perfectly transparent, perfectly reflecting—are "conceivable." However unrealizable these bodies are in the laboratory, they are conceivable in thought, which is sufficient; for a law of nature cannot depend on our artificial means of realizing bodies and processes in the laboratory.[65]

In his proof, Kirchhoff did not introduce elementary laws between pairs of points and hypotheses about the structure of matter. Rather by an artful arrangement of

62. Gustav Kirchhoff, "Ueber den Zusammenhang zwischen Emission und Absorption von Licht und Wärme," *Monatsber. preuss. Akad.* (1859), 783–87; in *Ges. Abh.*, 566–71, on 567, 569–70. Kirchhoff's understanding of absorption and emission was reached independently and at about the same time by Balfour Stewart, resulting in a priority dispute. Siegel, "Balfour Stewart and Gustav Robert Kirchhoff." Gustav Kirchhoff, "Zur Geschichte der Spectral-Analyse und der Analyse der Sonnenatmosphäre," *Ann.* 118 (1863): 94–111; in *Ges. Abh.*, 625–41.
63. "Wahlvorschlag für Gustav Robert Kirchhoff (1824–1887) zum AM," 10 Mar. 1870, in Kirsten and Körber, *Physiker über Physiker*, 77–79, on 79.
64. Gustav Kirchhoff, "Ueber das Verhältniss zwischen dem Emissionsvermögen und dem Absorptionsvermögen der Körper für Wärme und Licht," *Ann.* 109 (1860), 275–301; in *Ges. Abh.*, 571–98, on 571–73.
65. Kirchhoff, "Ueber das Verhältniss," 573–74. Pockels, "Kirchhoff," 256–57.

conceivable bodies, he analyzed the exchange of vis viva between radiant heat and matter in thermal equilibrium. The result was a law as simple as Ohm's in its mathematical expression: $E/A = e$. It says that the ratio of emissive power E to absorptive power A of any body is the same as the ratio e for a blackbody; in other words, the ratio is the same for all bodies, a function only of wavelength and temperature.[66] From the identification of light with radiant heat and from the mechanical theory of heat, Kirchhoff derived a universal property of the relationship between matter and radiation. It was a testimony to the power of theoretical reasoning in physics from general principles.

As an experimental consequence of his law, Kirchhoff showed that heat rays inside a hollow, opaque body have the same properties as rays from a blackbody, which offered a means for closely approximating a blackbody in practice; blackbodies of this sort were later constructed. The radiation that leaves such a *Hohlkörper*, or *Hohlraum*, as it came to be called, by a tiny opening has the properties of blackbody radiation, and laboratory measurements of this radiation yield the ratio of emissive to absorptive power of a blackbody as a function of temperature and wavelength. The laws of this radiation were recognized as having "fundamental significance" for physics, since by Kirchhoff's law they determine the ratio of emissive to absorptive power for all bodies.[67]

Kirchhoff was not the only one to state the law of radiation that bears his name, but he was the first to derive it rigorously from energy considerations. He recognized the essential point in the mass of information scattered in the scientific reports and raised it "through theoretical proof and systematic observation to a scientific theorem." Kirchhoff's work on the theory of radiant heat was characteristic: his inclination was not to begin but to complete a line of research.[68]

According to Koenigsberger, Kirchhoff was always eager to engage in mathematical and philosophical discussion. By contrast, he said, Bunsen was "no mathematical head," but he was capable of rational analysis and had a fine intuition and aesthetic sense. Bunsen did not so much explain phenomena through an "exact intellectual process" as grasp them through "sense perception."[69] By knowledge and ability, Kirchhoff and Bunsen complemented one another, the chemist A. W. Hofmann observed: "It was a kind fate that joined the paths of these two researchers;

66. Kirchhoff defined the "emissive power" E of a body in terms of the vis viva it transfers to the ether through heat rays of a given polarization: the intensity or vis viva of the rays emitted by the body in the wavelength interval λ to $\lambda + d\lambda$ in a unit of time is $E\,d\lambda$. He defined the "absorptive power" A of the body as the ratio of the intensity of the absorbed rays to that of the incident rays. Whereas E or A individually depends not only on wavelength but also on the polarization, on the geometry of the slits used in observing the emission and absorption, and on the condition of the body, the ratio E/A is the same for all bodies for a given temperature and for rays of a given wavelength. Kirchhoff, "Ueber das Verhältniss," 574, 592.

67. Kirchhoff, "Ueber das Verhältniss," 597–98. Pockels, "Kirchhoff," 257.

68. That, at least, was how Kirchhoff's achievement appeared to a German theoretical physicist of the next generation. Voigt, "Kirchhoff," 8–9.

69. Koenigsberger told his impressions of Kirchhoff and Bunsen to Roscoe, "Gedenkrede auf Bunsen," lix.

for only through the intimate association of a man at the top of chemical knowledge and ability with a master of the entire domain of physical phenomena could a work be realized that shaped the results of earlier research, which in their own untiring work they surveyed, completed, and expanded, into a new system of chemical analysis; only through such association could we obtain an apparatus that, far superior to the most powerful microscope, is capable of making visible traces of matter that had evaded every previous observation."[70]

After their work on spectrum analysis, Kirchhoff and Bunsen were cited in arguments to gain support for physical chemistry, a field of growing interest. An early instance of this was the Leipzig philosophical faculty's move in the late 1860s to secure one of its two chemistry chairs for physical chemistry:

> It must arouse a painful and uncomfortable feeling to see how the natural sciences (as consequence of an inner necessity) in the course of time increasingly branch out and splinter, to see how scientific researchers follow their different courses, every one of them trying to research a *single* area, every one of them driven by the need for the time being to gain a survey of the phenomena of at least a *single* area. We must appreciate it all the more when vis-à-vis this *tendency toward splintering* the opposite trend, the *tendency toward unification*, shows itself, namely, when this tendency toward unification shows up in men who belong to the most outstanding and most famous natural scientists of our time.
>
> Such efforts of unification are appearing at present with regard to the areas of chemistry and physics. Through the partly theoretical, partly experimental investigations of Bunsen, Kirchhoff, Clausius, Kopp, Graham, Frankland, St. Claire Deville, Berthelot a. o., in the last years there has developed at the border between chemistry and physics an increasingly growing activity that seems to be destined gradually to fill the chasm between chemistry and physics and gradually to fuse those two areas into *one* higher and more general science, which equally profits by the treasures collected in the one as in the other area.[71]

Kirchhoff joined a number of other physicists, who included Clausius, Weber, and Franz Neumann, in warmly encouraging this plan for a chair of physical chemistry. From personal experience Kirchhoff could assure the Leipzig faculty that "research in those areas that lie on the border of physics and chemistry is of the highest importance for both sciences."[72]

70. A. W. Hofmann, "Gustav Kirchhoff," *Berichte der deutschen chemischen Gesellschaft*, vol. 20, pt. 2 (1887), 2771–77, on 2774. Apropos of Bunsen's and Kirchhoff's collaboration, Bunsen was heard to say that "a chemist who is no physicist is nothing at all." Roscoe, "Gedenkrede auf Bunsen," lix.

71. Leipzig U. Philosophical Faculty to Saxon Ministry of Culture and Public Education, undated draft, ca. 1869, Wiedemann's Personalakte, Leipzig UA, PA 1060, Bl. 5–8.

72. Quotation from Kirchhoff's letter to the Leipzig U. Philosophical Faculty, inserted in the draft letter from the faculty to the Saxon Ministry of Culture, ca. 1869.

Kirchhoff on Mechanics

To Kirchhoff, there was a deeper unity to the universe than that of its chemical constituents, as revealed by spectrum analysis. It was a physical, or more specifically a mechanical, unity, as he explained in his rector's address at Heidelberg University in 1865. He introduced his topic, the goal of the natural sciences, by asserting that all natural processes consist in the motion of unchanging matter and that every advance in the understanding of nature has confirmed this. For this reason, mechanics, or the science of motion in general, bears fundamentally on all the natural sciences. From mechanical laws we can, in principle, determine the state of matter for all future time if we know the state of matter at any one time and all the forces acting on it. It follows, Kirchhoff said, that the highest goal of the natural sciences is to realize the conditions for carrying out that task: to determine the forces and the state of matter or, in other words, to reduce all natural phenomena to mechanical processes. The natural sciences were far from having realized this goal, Kirchhoff conceded, since there remained many areas of ignorance. He named them: there was as yet no understanding of molecular forces, nor of the forces between electricity and bodies, nor of the forces that produce heat and chemical decomposition, nor of the molecular structure of matter, nor, of course, of the distribution and velocities of all matter, ponderable and, as in the case of the ether and electric fluids, imponderable alike. But, he said, scientists had already learned a good deal about nature through their understanding of its motions. The imponderable fluids of magnetism and heat had been eliminated from physics and replaced by motions, and now there was talk of eliminating electrical fluids, too. In this development, the recent understanding of heat as a mode of motion was especially important, since heat enters into all phenomena. This understanding includes the identification of heat rays with light rays, and in general it implies that "nowhere in nature is there any rest." In the inorganic and organic world alike, "no true understanding is achieved as long as the reduction to mechanics has not been accomplished." Kirchhoff concluded that this goal will "never be completely reached, but even the fact that it has been recognized as such offers a certain satisfaction, and in approaching this goal one finds the greatest enjoyment that the occupation with the phenomena of nature can offer."[73]

For Kirchhoff, then, mechanics provided the reductive goal of all natural science. In his own research, he applied mechanical principles throughout physics, and he worked on difficult mechanical problems such as the motions of elastic bodies discussed above. Toward the end of his Heidelberg years, he worked on difficult mechanical problems in yet another area, the motions of fluids.

Although Kirchhoff had a few more years of teaching and research in Heidelberg and a few more after that in Berlin, his most important work was behind him. It included his mathematical and experimental researches on the forces and motions

73. Gustav Kirchhoff, *Ueber das Ziel der Naturwissenschaften* (Heidelberg, 1865). Quotation on 24.

of matter, electricity, and ether, stations along the way toward the ideal of a complete scientific comprehension of the natural world.

Helmholtz at Heidelberg: Physiological Researches

In 1848, a year after publishing his major work on the conservation of force, Helmholtz resigned his position as army surgeon to succeed his friend the physiologist Brücke, first as teacher of anatomy at the Berlin Art Academy and then, a year later, as teacher of physiology and general pathology at Königsberg University. Although then and for many years after, he worked principally in physiology and anatomy, he retained the interest in physics that had bound him with Brücke and du Bois-Reymond within Magnus's circle and after that within the Berlin Physical Society. Helmholtz moved to Bonn in 1855 to teach physiology and anatomy and then to Heidelberg in 1858 to teach physiology for the last time. Throughout his professional career in physiology, Helmholtz did a certain amount of theoretical and experimental physics, usually on topics closely related to his physiology.

Helmholtz's early physiological work dealt mainly with the muscles and their exciting nerves. By the time he moved to Heidelberg, his principal research topics were the senses and perception. He studied the human eye as an optical instrument and the human ear as an acoustical instrument, he perfected theories of color mixtures and of combination tones, and he extended the physiological principle of specific energies of nerve fibers to explain the perception of color and sound.

For his physiological research, Helmholtz improved or invented various apparatus and instruments, the most valuable of which was the ophthalmometer, "an instrument of astronomical refinement," as du Bois-Reymond characterized it. The ophthalmometer permitted exact measurements to be made of images in the interior of the eye and of the variable curvatures of its refracting surfaces. Helmholtz introduced into his physiology, along with instruments and measuring methods, a rigorous form of reasoning, strongly mathematical and physical. His papers were filled with mathematical-physical excursions, which aided the qualified reader in viewing the subject as Helmholtz did. No other physiologist at the time brought to his subject such a thorough knowledge of mathematical physics.[74]

In the mid-1860s, Helmholtz published his great physiological texts, *Sensations of Tone as a Physiological Basis for the Theory of Music* and *Treatise on Physiological Optics*. They present the two subjects in a systematic and complete form, and they contain Helmholtz's own extensive experimental and theoretical research, much of which he undertook to test the conclusions of previous writers. The organization of the two texts is parallel, each having three parts: the first part contains the physics of the human ear or eye and the associated anatomy and physiology, while the second and third parts contain the study of the sensation of sound or sight and the perception of tones or vision. The thorough study of any sense organ, Helmholtz

74. L. Hermann, "Hermann von Helmholtz," *Schriften der Physikalisch-ökonomischen Gesellschaft zu Königsberg* 35 (1894), 63–73, on 67. Emil du Bois-Reymond, *Hermann von Helmholtz. Gedächtnissrede* (Leipzig, 1897), 29.

believed, must be at the same time physical, physiological, and psychological. Of the two texts he wrote, the one on physiological acoustics was for the wider audience, but it too contains mathematics and experiments intended for the "physicist," here relegated to appendices.[75] After these books, Helmholtz published occasionally on physiology, but from this time on his research centered increasingly on physics, especially on theoretical physics.[76]

It is an indication of the kind of physiology Helmholtz did that the writers he cited include, in addition to physiologists and anatomists, many physicists. He worked with Thomas Young's theory of color preception, with James Clerk Maxwell's theory of color blindness, and with G. G. Stokes's theory of fluorescence, to mention three of the British physicists he cited.[77] He tested and used extensively Listing's law of eye motions, and he discussed other work of Listing's, such as his model of the "schematic eye" and his work on the magnification of microscopes.[78] He used Fraunhofer's measurements of the wavelengths of spectral lines and his research on the dispersion of the eye.[79] He confirmed Fechner's theory of afterimages of the eye.[80] In his work on the oscillations of the drum and the small bones of the ear, which Riemann had anticipated, he used Kirchhoff's conditions of equilibrium of an infinitely thin, elastic rod.[81] And in his work on combination tones, he adopted Ohm's law, according to which the ear analyzes the periodic motions of the air into simple harmonic oscillations, or individual tones.[82]

In his teaching at Heidelberg, Helmholtz could concentrate on physiology without having to combine it, as he had before, with anatomy or pathology.[83] Since the

75. Hermann von Helmholtz, *Die Lehre von den Tonempfindungen, als physiologische Grundlage für die Theorie der Musik* (Braunschweig, 1863). Translated from the 4th German edition of 1877 by A. J. Ellis as *Sensations of Tone as a Physiological Basis for the Theory of Music*, 2d English ed. (London, 1885). Helmholtz's treatise on physiological optics began as a contribution, which he completed in 1856, to Gustav Karsten's *Allgemeine Encyclopaedie der Physik* (Leipzig, 1856–63). Helmholtz completed the second part in 1860 and the third in 1866. It appeared in three volumes as *Handbuch der physiologischen Optik* (Leipzig, 1856–67). Translated and edited by J. C. P. Southall from the 3d German edition, ed. A. Gullstrand, J. von Kries, and W. Nagel (Hamburg and Leipzig: Voss, 1909–11), as *Treatise on Physiological Optics*, 3 vols. (Rochester: Optical Society of America, 1924–25).

76. This statement needs qualification: Helmholtz returned several times to his work on optical perception, he did some work later in electrophysiology, and at the beginning of the 1870s he directed some physiological work. Hermann, "Helmholtz," 83 n. 45.

77. Helmholtz, *Treatise* 2:143–45; "Ueber Farbenblindheit," *Verhandlungen des naturhistorisch-medicinischen Vereins zu Heidelberg* 2 (1859): 1–3, in *Wiss. Abh.* 2:346–49; "Ueber die Empfindlichkeit der menschlichen Netzhaut für die brechbarsten Strahlen des Sonnenlichtes," *Ann.* 94 (1855): 205–11, in *Wiss. Abh.* 2:71–77.

78. Hermann von Helmholtz, "Ueber die normalen Bewegungen des menschlichen Auges," *Archiv für Ophthalmologie* 9:2 (1863): 153–88, in *Wiss. Abh.* 2:360–419; *Treatise* 1:94–96, 112; "Die theoretische Grenze für die Leistungsfähigkeit der Mikroskope," *Ann.*, Jubelband (1874): 557–84, in *Wiss. Abh.* 2:185–212.

79. Hermann von Helmholtz, "Ueber die Zusammensetzung von Spectralfarben," *Ann.* 94 (1855): 1–28, in *Wiss. Abh.* 2:45–70; "Ueber die Empfindlichkeit der menschlichen Netzhaut."

80. Helmholtz, *Handbuch der Physiologischen Optik*, 3d ed., 2:219–21.

81. Hermann von Helmholtz, "Die Mechanik der Gehörknöchelchen und des Trommelfells," *Archiv für Physiologie* 1 (1868): 1–60, in *Wiss. Abh.* 2:515–81.

82. Hermann von Helmholtz, "Ueber Combinationstöne," *Ann.* 99 (1856): 497–540, in *Wiss. Abh.* 1:263–302.

83. Du Bois-Reymond, *Helmholtz*, 72.

physiology institute had insufficient laboratory space for the number of students he had to teach, he soon set about working on plans for a new institute, which was to accommodate thirty-two students and researchers in addition to his own needs. In 1863 he moved into the new institute, which was housed in the same building as Kirchhoff's, the Friedrichsbau.[84]

From Helmholtz's laboratory at Heidelberg came a good deal of published research, Helmholtz's own and that of others.[85] As at Königsberg, at Heidelberg Helmholtz occasionally allowed his laboratory to be used for physics experiments related to his own work.[86] But for the most part, Helmholtz devoted his laboratory to physiology, for which it was intended. The physiology there, apart from some work on muscles, dealt with the eye; it was reported on regularly in papers appearing in the *Archiv für Ophthalmologie*, a new journal begun in 1854. The researchers in his laboratory often came from abroad and were there for only a short time; one of them, for example, had carried out experiments in his native Kiev before applying to Helmholtz, the "genial physiologist and specialist in the theory of accommodation," for advice and for permission to work in the Heidelberg laboratory, where upon being admitted he repeated his experiments in the presence of Helmholtz and an assistant.[87] Usually researches carried out in the laboratory were on subjects that Helmholtz was, or had been, working on, for example, the fluorescence of the retina, the curvature of the cornea, color blindness, and the accommodation of the eye. The methods were usually Helmholtz's; the frequent appearance in laboratory publications of the phrase "at the suggestion of Professor Helmholtz" conveys an idea of the way he conducted the laboratory. Nearly everyone associated his own work with Helmholtz's: one researcher, for example, intended his experiments to provide "one more support for Young's theory, which Helmholtz has perfected in such an admirable way."[88] Publications from Helmholtz's laboratory were experimental, lacking the strong theoretical development and the language of mathematical physics that characterized Helmholtz's own publications.

84. Koenigsberger, *Helmholtz* 1:318. "Universität Heidelberg. Neubau für naturwissenschaftliche Institute. I. Physiologisches Institut," probably 1859, Bad. GLA, 235/352.

85. "Verzeichniss der Arbeiten, die aus Helmholtz Laboratorium hervorgegangen und publicirt sind," in "Anlage" to Lipschitz, draft, n.d. [1868], in Plücker Personalakte, Bonn UA. This list of publications by thirteen researchers working in Helmholtz's Heidelberg laboratory may be incomplete, but it is adequate for the purposes of the present discussion.

86. At Königsberg, Helmholtz placed his physiology institute and a quartz apparatus at the disposal of Ernst Esselbach, "Eine Wellenmessung im Spectrum jenseits des Violetts," *Ann.* 98 (1856): 513–46. At Heidelberg, Gustav von Piotrowski did hydrodynamic experiments for his and Helmholtz's publication, "Ueber Reibung tropfbarer Flüssigkeiten," *Sitzungsber. österreichische Akad.* 40 (1860): 607, in *Wiss. Abh.* 1:172–222. Further hydrodynamic experiments were done in the Heidelberg physiology laboratory by Alexis Schklarewsky, as reported by Helmholtz, "Zur Theorie der stationären Ströme in reibenden Flüssigkeiten" (1868), *Verhandlungen des naturhistorisch-medicinischen Vereins zu Heidelberg* 5 (1871): 1–7, in *Wiss. Abh.* 1: 223–30.

87. D. von Trautvetter, "Ueber den Nerv der Accommodation," *Archiv für Ophthalmologie* 12:1 (1866), 95–149, on 131–32.

88. Rudolph Schelske, "Zur Farbenempfindung," *Archiv für Ophthalmologie* 9:2 (1863), 39–62, on 49.

Helmholtz's Physical Researches

Beginning in 1859, a series of physics experiments was carried out in Helmholtz's physiological laboratory at his suggestion by Gustav von Piotrowski. The experiments dealt with the friction of liquids against rigid containing walls, the mathematical theory of which Helmholtz had laid down with the help of equations worked out by Poisson, Navier, and Stokes. Helmholtz hoped to arrive at the fundamental hydrodynamic equations that include the effect of friction. If he succeeded, he wrote to his friend Ludwig, "every special problem of fluid motion would be reduced to a mathematical problem." In their joint publication, Helmholtz and Piotrowski observed that the friction encountered by liquids sufficiently influences the form of their motion that it cannot be ignored in technical problems or in "physiological investigations."[89]

The year before, Helmholtz had published a purely theoretical study of vortex motions in water, in which he discussed the difficulty of defining the effect of friction and of measuring it, which he attributed to ignorance of the forms of motion of water experiencing friction. Here he did not investigate friction directly but motions, of which frictional motion is an example, for which no velocity potential exists, which in hydrodynamic studies was an uncommon assumption.[90] He determined that a velocity potential does not exist if water particles rotate, a form of motion he called "vortical." For this motion, he derived a law of conservation of vortices analogous to the law of conservation of matter, which suggested (to others) that atoms may be represented by vortices in a continuous ether. In the course of this work, Helmholtz came upon a "remarkable analogy" between vortex motions in liquids and electromagnetic actions of electric currents. The analogy made accessible to the imagination this new form of motion, and in analyzing it Helmholtz spoke of "magnetic masses or electric currents" thereby attaching familiar expressions to the unfamiliar mathematical functions describing vortex motions.[91] Helmholtz used a similar analogy in a purely theoretical paper in 1859; in this paper he dealt not with hydrodynamics but with acoustics, which bore directly on his physiological acoustics. Here he treated the motion of air in open-ended tubes, or organ pipes, a kind of motion for which a velocity potential can be assumed. There had been no major advances in the theory since Daniel Bernoulli and Euler, Helmholtz said, though Poisson and others had worked on it. The theory remained incomplete in its han-

89. Helmholtz and Piotrowski, "Ueber Reibung," 172. Helmholtz to Ludwig, 13 June 1859, quoted in Koenigsberger, *Helmholtz* 1:343.

90. Hermann von Helmholtz, "Ueber Integrale der hydrodynamischen Gleichungen welche den Wirbelbewegungen entsprechen," *Journ. f. d. reine u. angewandte Math.* 55 (1858): 25–55, in *Wiss. Abh.* 1:101–34.

91. If the components of the velocity of each water particle can be written as the differential quotients of a certain function, the function is called the "velocity potential." Quotations from Helmholtz, "Ueber Integrale," 103–4. Albert Wangerin, "Anmerkungen," in his edition of *Zwei hydrodynamische Abhandlungen von H. v. Helmholtz*, vol. 79 of Ostwald's Klassiker der exakten Wissenschaften (Leipzig, 1896), 53, 55. Volkmann, "Helmholtz," 74–75.

dling of the passage into free space of plane sound waves excited in the depth of the tube. Helmholtz gave a complete solution to the problem without having to make assumptions about the state of air at the open end, as previous investigators had. His analysis introduced mathematical functions identical with the electric potential function, which enabled him to apply to his acoustical problem certain well-known results from electrical theory; by analogy he could associate electric mass-points with excitation-points of sound and the electric potential with the velocity potential of air.[92] These two papers on hydrodynamics and acoustics at the close of the 1850s, with their solutions of difficult technical problems and their wealth of analogies, belonged, in Kirchhoff's opinion, to Helmholtz's most important contributions to mathematical physics. Helmholtz wrote them while employed as a physiologist.[93]

Upon completing the acoustical theory of organ pipes and comparing it with experiment, Helmholtz was satisfied that the most striking disparities had been removed. But since the agreement was still imperfect, he improved on it by introducing the complicating factor of friction again.[94] In a series of researches around 1860, Helmholtz invesigated the tones produced by various classes of musical instruments. Woodwinds, or reed pipes, were one such class: Weber, he noted, was the first to explain properly the mechanics of reed pipes, but Weber had restricted his study to metal reeds, and Helmholtz developed the mathematical laws of the tones of reeds made of lighter materials, which correspond to clarinet and oboe reeds and to the human lips.[95] In turn he examined organ pipes, as we have seen, and violins and the human voice. Helmholtz's physiological work suggested to him problems not only in acoustics and optics but in electricity as well. In 1869 he wrote to his friend Ludwig: "At the moment I am again at electrical studies on the time and propagation of discharges, which I became interested in through physiological researches and questions."[96]

92. Hermann von Helmholtz, "Theorie der Luftschwingungen in Röhren mit offenen Enden," *Journ. f. d. reine u. angewandte Math.* 57 (1860): 1–72, in *Wiss. Abh.*, 1:303–82.

93. Koenigsberger, *Helmholtz* 1:312. Acoustical studies, as those of organ pipes, suggested to Helmholtz the solution to another problem in fluid motion with implications for other branches of physics, which he published in 1868. The same differential equations govern the interior motions of fluids, electric currents, and heat conduction, but a fluid escaping through an opening behaves differently than electricity or heat. He showed that a fluid flowing around a sharp edge is torn apart, and the motion is discontinuous. Highly mathematical again, this study had "great interest for the theory of functions" as well as for physics. Helmholtz, "Ueber discontinuirliche Flüssigkeits-Bewegungen," *Monatsber. preuss. Akad.* (1868), 215–28, in *Wiss. Abh.* 1:146–57. Leo Koenigsberger, "The Investigations of Hermann von Helmholtz on the Fundamental Principles of Mathematics and Mechanics," *Annual Report of the . . . Smithsonian Institution . . . to July, 1896,* 1898, 93–124, on 106–7. Helmholtz's 1868 paper provides another example of related work by Heidelberg colleagues: in 1869 Kirchhoff published a paper on stationary currents in an incompressible fluid, which he based directly on Helmholtz's paper. Gustav Kirchhoff, "Zur Theorie freier Flüssigkeitsstrahlen," *Journ. f. d. reine u. angewandte Math.* 70 (1869): 289–98, in *Ges. Abh.*, 416–27.

94. Hermann von Helmholtz, "Ueber den Einfluss der Reibung in der Luft auf die Schallbewegung," *Verhandlungen des naturhistorisch-medicinischen Vereins zu Heidelberg* 3 (1863): 16–20, in *Wiss. Abh.* 1:383–87.

95. Hermann von Helmholtz, "Zur Theorie der Zungenpfeifen," *Ann.* 114 (1861): 321–27, in *Wiss. Abh.* 1:388–94.

96. Helmholtz's letter to Ludwig is quoted in Koenigsberger, *Helmholtz* 2:162.

Physiology led Helmholtz in still another direction, beyond physics to pure mathematics. In the late 1860s he published on the axioms of geometry, initially unaware that Riemann had once again been there before him, arriving at much the same conclusions as his own. "My investigations of the spatial perceptions in the field of vision," Helmholtz explained at the opening of his geometrical work, "have also caused me to undertake investigations into the origins and the nature of our general perceptions of space." He argued that it is a result of experience that our spatial intuitions seem to agree with the axioms of Euclidean geometry instead of with those of, say, spherical or pseudospherical geometry; that is, the agreement is empirical, not a necessity of thought. He explained that to acquire real significance, the axioms of geometry must be conjoined to the mechanical properties of solid bodies, such as compasses, by which we make our spatial measurements. The resulting systems of propositions that describe the geometry of our intuition, Helmholtz concluded, cannot be taken as a Kantian "transcendental form of intuition" unless we assume, without justification, some "preestablished harmony between form and reality."[97]

It was under the heading "epistemology" in his collected works that Helmholtz included his research on geometry, to which his research on physiological optics had directed him. His student Heinrich Hertz summed up the epistemological meaning for Helmholtz of the physiological study of the senses: "Within our consciousness we find an inner intellectual world of conceptions and ideas: outside our consciousness there lies the cold and alien world of actual things. Between the two stretches the narrow borderland of the senses." That borderland, the subject of Helmholtz's investigations, is essential to the question of "the possibility and the legitimacy of all natural knowledge."[98]

Helmholtz on the Relations between Sciences

Helmholtz said that with his *Sensations of Tone*, he connected the "boundaries of two sciences, which, although drawn toward each other by many natural affinities, have hitherto remained practically distinct—I mean the boundaries of *physical and physiological acoustics* on the one side, and of *musical science and aesthetics* on the other."[99] This work, like Bunsen and Kirchhoff's work on spectrum analysis, re-

97. Hermann von Helmholtz, "Ueber die Thatsachen, die der Geometrie zu Grunde liegen," *Gött. Nachr.* (1868), 193–221, in *Wiss. Abh.* 2:618–39, on 618. A brief publication on this subject appeared earlier, in 1866: *Wiss. Abh.* 2:610–17. Helmholtz's popular lecture delivered in Heidelberg in 1870, "Ueber den Ursprung und die Bedeutung der geometrischen Axiome," translated by E. Atkinson and revised by R. Kahl as "The Origin and Meaning of Geometric Axioms (I)," in *Selected Writings*, 246–65, on 265.

98. Heinrich Hertz, "Hermann von Helmholtz," from the supplement to the *Münchener Allgemeine Zeitung*, 31 Aug. 1891, in Hertz, *Miscellaneous Papers*, trans. D. E. Jones and G. A. Schott (London, 1896), 332–40, on 335, 337. Helmholtz distinguished clearly between what belonged to one world and what belonged to the other; what was susceptible to physical and physiological approaches and what belonged to psychology and philosophy. Turner, "The Ohm-Seebeck Dispute," 18–21.

99. Helmholtz, *Sensations of Tone*, 1.

cently "invented in our own university," illustrated the subject of his address as prorector at Heidelberg University in 1862. The address dealt with the "interrelationships" and the "vigorous cooperation" between the sciences, the fostering of which was the "great office of the universities." Different as the methods are by which the different sciences arrive at their results, they all have "one common aim," Helmholtz said, which is "to establish the rule of intellect over the world."[100]

100. Hermann von Helmholtz, "Ueber das Verhältniss der Naturwissenschaften zur Gesammtheit der Wissenschaften," Prorector's address on 22 Nov. 1862; English translation: "The Relation of the Natural Sciences to Science in General," by R. Kahl, ed., *Selected Writings*, 122–43, on 122–23, 141–43.

Bibliography

Archives

A Schweiz. Sch., Zurich: Archiv des Schweizerischen Schulrates, ETH Zürich
Bad. GLA: Badisches Generallandesarchiv Karlsruhe
Bay. HSTA: Bayerisches Hauptstaatsarchiv, München
Bay. STB: Bayerische Staatsbibliothek München
Bonn UA: Archiv der Rheinischen Friedrich-Wilhelms-Universität Bonn
Bonn UB: Universitätsbibliothek Bonn
Breslau UB: Biblioteka Uniwersytecka Wrocław (Breslau)
DM: Bibliothek des Deutschen Museums, München
Erlangen UA: Universitäts-Archiv der Friedrich-Alexander-Universität Erlangen
Erlangen UB: Universitätsbibliothek Erlangen-Nürnberg
ETHB: Bibliothek der ETH Zürich
Freiburg SA: Stadtarchiv der Stadt Freiburg im Breisgau
Freiburg UB: Universitäts-Bibliothek Freiburg i. Br.
Giessen UA: Universitätsarchiv Justus Liebig-Universität Giessen
Göttingen UA: Archiv der Georg-August-Universität Göttingen
Göttingen UB: Niedersächsische Staats- und Universitätsbibliothek Göttingen
Graz UA: Archiv der Universität in Graz
Heidelberg UA: Universitätsarchiv der Ruprecht-Karls-Universität Heidelberg
Heidelberg UB: Universitätsbibliothek Heidelberg
HSTA, Stuttgart: Württembergisches Hauptstaatsarchiv Stuttgart
Jena UA: Universitätsarchiv der Friedrich-Schiller-Universität Jena
LA Schleswig-Holstein: Landesarchiv Schleswig-Holstein, Schleswig
Leipzig UA: Archiv der Karl-Marx-Universität Leipzig
Leipzig UB: Universitätsbibliothek der Karl-Marx-Universität Leipzig
Munich UA: Archiv der Ludwig-Maximilians-Universität München
Münster UA: Universitäts-Archiv der Westfälischen Wilhelms-Universität Münster

N.-W. HSTA: Nordrhein-Westfälisches Hauptstaatsarchiv Düsseldorf
Öster. STA: Österreichisches Staatsarchiv, Wien
STA K Zurich: Staatsarchiv des Kantons Zürich
STA, Ludwigsburg: Staatsarchiv Ludwigsburg
STA, Marburg: Hessisches Staatsarchiv Marburg
STPK: Staatsbibliothek Preussischer Kulturbesitz, Berlin
Tübingen UA: Universitätsarchiv Eberhard-Karls-Universität Tübingen
Tübingen UB: Universitätsbibliothek Tübingen
Würzburg UA: Archiv der Universität Würzburg

East Germany refuses us permission to consult its state archives. Fortunately, much of what they contain that bears on physics can be learned from other documents and, in some cases, from copies of their documents in collections accessible to us.

Printed Sources

We give scientific articles in the footnotes but because of their great number we do not give them again in this bibliography.

Works on universities and other schools are arranged by location: Berlin, Göttingen, etc.

Aachener Bezirksverein deutscher Ingenieure. "Adolf Wüllner." *Zs. d. Vereins deutsch. Ingenieure* 52 (1908): 1741–42.
Abbe, Ernst. "Gedächtnisrede zur Feier des 50jährigen Bestehens der optischen Werkstätte." In *Gesammelte Abhandlungen*, vol. 3, 60–95. Jena: Fischer, 1906.
Allgemeine deutsche Biographie. Vols. 1–56. 1875–1912. Reprint. Leipzig: Duncker und Humblot, 1967–71. *(ADB)*
Assmann, Richard, et al. "Vollendung des 50. Jahrganges der 'Fortschritte.' " *Fortschritte der Physik des Aethers im Jahre 1894* 50, pt. 2 (1896): i–xi.
Auerbach, Felix. "Ernst Abbe." *Phys. Zs.* 6 (1905): 65–66.
———. *Ernst Abbe, sein Leben, sein Wirken, seine Persönlichkeit.* Leipzig: Akademische Verlagsgesellschaft, 1918.
———. *The Zeiss Works and the Carl Zeiss Foundation in Jena: Their Scientific, Technical and Sociological Development and Importance.* Translated by R. Kanthack from the 5th German edition, 1925. London: Foyle, n.d.
August, Ernst Ferdinand. *Zwei Abhandlungen physicalischen und mathematischen Inhalts. . . .* Berlin, 1829.
August, F. "Ernst Ferdinand August." In "Litterarischer Bericht CCIV," *Archiv d. Math. u. Physik* 51 (1870): 1–5.
Baerwald, Hans. "Karl Schering." *Phys. Zs.* 26 (1925): 633–35.
Band, William. *Introduction to Mathematical Physics.* Princeton: Van Nostrand, 1959.
Baretin, W. "Johann Christian Poggendorff." *Ann.* 160 (1877): v–xxiv.
———. "Ein Rückblick." *Ann.*, Jubelband (1874): ix–xiv.

Bauernfeind, Karl Max. "Ohm: Georg Simon." *ADB* 24 (1970): 187–203.

Baumgarten, Fritz. *Freiburg im Breisgau.* Berlin: Wedekind, 1907.

Baumgartner, Andreas von, and Andreas von Ettingshausen. *Die Naturlehre nach ihrem gegenwärtigen Zustande mit Rücksicht auf mathematische Begründung.* 6th ed. Vienna, 1839.

Becherer, Gerhard. "Die Geschichte der Entwicklung des Physikalischen Instituts der Universität Rostock." *Wiss. Zs. d. U. Rostock, Math.-Naturwiss.* 16 (1967): 825–30.

Beer, August. *Einleitung in die höhere Optik.* Braunschweig, 1853.

Benzenberg, J. F. *Ueber die Daltonsche Theorie.* Düsseldorf, 1830.

Berkson, William. *Fields of Force: The Development of a World View from Faraday to Einstein.* New York: Wiley, 1974.

Berlin. Berlinisches Gymnasium zum grauen Kloster. "Jahresbericht des Berlinischen Gymnasiums zum grauen Kloster von Ostern 1840 bis Ostern 1841." In *De dialectorum linguae syriacae reliquiis,* by Ferdinand Larsow. Berlin, 1841.

———. See Julius Heidemann.

Berlin. Cöllnisches Real-Gymnasium. E. F. August's annual program for 1830–1831. In *Ueber die Naturgeschichte des Kreuzsteins,* by Friedrich Köhler. Berlin, 1831.

Berlin. Friedrichs-Gymnasium auf dem Werder. *Programm . . . des Friedrichs-Gymnasium auf dem Werder, 1833.* Berlin, 1833.

Berlin. K. Französisches Gymnasium. *Festschrift zur Feier des 200jährigen Bestehens des königlichen Französischen Gymnasiums.* Edited by the director and teachers. Berlin, 1890.

———. *Programme d'invitation à l'examen public du Collége Royal Français.* Berlin, 1858.

Berlin. K. Wilhelms-Gymnasium. *K. Wilhelms-Gymnasium in Berlin. VI. Jahresbericht.* Berlin, 1866.

Berlin. Technical University. *Die Technische Hochschule zu Berlin 1799–1924. Festschrift.* Berlin: Georg Stilke, 1925.

Berlin. University. *Forschen und Wirken. Festschrift zur 150-Jahr-Feier der Humboldt-Universität zu Berlin 1810–1960.* Vol. 1. Berlin: VEB Deutscher Verlag der Wissenschaften, 1960.

———. *Idee und Wirklichkeit einer Universität. Dokumente zur Geschichte der Friedrich-Wilhelms-Universität zu Berlin.* Edited by Wilhelm Weischedel. Berlin: Walter de Gruyter, 1960.

———. *Index Lectionum.* Berlin, n.d.

———. See Kurt-R. Biermann; Ilse Jahn; Rudolf Köpke· Max Lenz.

Bernhardt, Wilhelm. *Dr. Ernst Chladni, der Akustiker.* Wittenberg, 1856.

Bessel, F. W. *Populäre Vorlesungen über wissenschaftliche Gegenstände.* Edited by H. C. Schumacher. Hamburg, 1848.

Bezold, Friedrich von. *Geschichte der Rheinischen Friedrich-Wilhelms-Universität von der Gründung bis zum Jahr 1870.* Bonn: A. Marcus und E. Weber, 1920.

Bezold, Wilhelm von. "Gedächtnissrede auf August Kundt." *Verh. phys. Ges.* 13 (1894): 61–80.

Biermann, Kurt-R. "Humboldt, Alexander von." *DSB* 6 (1972): 549–55.

————. *Die Mathematik und ihre Dozenten an der Berliner Universität 1810–1920. Stationen auf dem Wege eines mathematischen Zentrums von Weltgeltung.* Berlin: Akademie-Verlag, 1973.

Biermer, M. "Die Grossherzoglich Hessische Ludwigs-Universität zu Giessen." In *Das Unterrichtswesen im Deutschen Reich*, edited by Wilhelm Lexis, vol. 1, 562–74.

Biot, Jean Baptiste. *Lehrbuch der Experimental-Physik, oder Erfahrungs-Naturlehre.* 3d ed. Translated by Gustav Theodor Fechner. 4 vols. Leipzig, 1824–25.

Blackmore, John T. *Ernst Mach. His Work, Life, and Influence.* Berkeley, Los Angeles, and London: University of California Press, 1972.

Böhm, Walter. "Stefan, Josef." *DSB* 13 (1976): 10–11.

Boltzmann, Ludwig. "Eugen von Lommel." *Jahresber. d. Deutsch. Math.-Vereinigung* 8 (1900): 47–53.

————. *Gustav Robert Kirchhoff.* Leipzig, 1888. Reprinted in *Populäre Schriften*, 51–75.

————. "Josef Stefan." Rede gehalten bei der Enthüllung des Stefan-Denkmals am 8. Dez. 1895. In *Populäre Schriften*, 92–103.

————. *Populäre Schriften.* Leipzig: J. A. Barth, 1905.

————. *Wissenschaftliche Abhandlungen.* Edited by Fritz Hasenöhrl. 3 vols. Leipzig: J. A. Barth, 1909. Reprint. New York: Chelsea, 1968.

Bonn. University. *Geschichte der Rheinischen Friedrich-Wilhelm-Universität zu Bonn am Rhein.* Edited by A. Dyroff. Vol. 2, *Institute und Seminare, 1818–1933.* Bonn: F. Cohen, 1933.

————. *150 Jahre Rheinische Friedrich-Wilhelms-Universität zu Bonn 1818–1968. Bonner Gelehrte. Beiträge zur Geschichte der Wissenschaften in Bonn. Mathematik und Naturwissenschaften.* Bonn: H. Bouvier, Ludwig Röhrscheid, 1970.

————. *Vorlesungen auf der Königlich Preussischen Rhein-Universität Bonn.*

————. See Friedrich von Bezold.

Bonnell, E., and H. Kirn. "Preussen. Die höheren Schulen." In *Encyklopädie des gesamten Erziehungs- und Unterrichtswesens*, edited by K. A. Schmid, vol. 6, 180 ff. Leipzig, 1885.

Borscheid, Peter. *Naturwissenschaft, Staat und Industrie in Baden (1848–1914).* Vol. 17 of *Industrielle Welt, Schriftenreihe des Arbeitskreises für moderne Sozialgeschichte*, edited by Werner Conze. Stuttgart: Ernst Klett, 1976.

Brandes, Heinrich Wilhelm. "Mathematik." In *Johann Samuel Traugott Gehler's Physikalisches Wörterbuch*, vol. 6, pt. 2, 1473–85. Leipzig, 1836.

————. *Vorlesungen über die Naturlehre zur Belehrung derer, denen es an mathematischen Vorkenntnissen fehlt.* 3 vols. Leipzig, 1830–32.

Braun, Ferdinand. "Hermann Georg Quincke." *Ann.* 15 (1904): i–viii.

Brendel, Martin. "Über die astronomischen Arbeiten von Gauss." Third treatise in vol. 11, pt. 2 of *Carl Friedrich Gauss's Werke.* Berlin and Göttingen: Springer, 1929.

Breslau. University. *Festschrift zur Feier des hundertjährigen Bestehens der Universität Breslau. Pt. 2, Geschichte der Fächer, Institute und Ämter der Universität Breslau 1811–1911.* Edited by Georg Kaufmann. Breslau: F. Hirt, 1911.

Broda, Engelbert. *Ludwig Boltzmann. Mensch, Physiker, Philosoph.* Vienna: F. Deuticke, 1955.

Brüche, E. "Aus der Vergangenheit der Physikalischen Gesellschaft." *Phys. Bl.* 16 (1960): 499–505, 616–21; 17 (1961): 27–33, 120–27, 225–32, 400–410.

———. "Ernst Abbe und sein Werk." *Phys. Bl.* 21 (1965): 261–69.

Bruhns, Karl. "Brandes: Heinrich Wilhelm." *ADB* 3 (1967): 242–43.

———. "Gerling: Christian Ludwig." *ADB* 9 (1968): 26–29.

———, ed. *Alexander von Humboldt. Eine wissenschaftliche Biographie.* 3 vols. Leipzig, 1872.

Brush, Stephen G. "Boltzmann, Ludwig," *DSB* 2 (1970): 260–68.

———. "Irreversibility and Indeterminism: Fourier to Heisenberg." *Journ. Hist. of Ideas* 37 (1976): 603–30.

———. *The Kind of Motion We Call Heat: A History of the Kinetic Theory of Gases in the 19th Century.* Vol. 1, *Physics and the Atomists.* Vol. 2, *Statistical Physics and Irreversible Processes.* Vol. 6 of Studies of Statistical Mechanics. Amsterdam and New York: North-Holland, 1976.

———. *Kinetic Theory.* Vol. 1, *The Nature of Gases and of Heat.* Vol. 2, *Irreversible Processes.* The Commonwealth and International Library; Selected Readings in Physics. Oxford and New York: Pergamon, 1965–66.

———. "Randomness and Irreversibility." *Arch. Hist. Ex. Sci.* 12 (1974): 1–88.

———. "The Wave Theory of Heat." *Brit. Journ. Hist. Sci.* 5 (1970): 145–67.

Buchheim, Gisela. "Zur Geschichte der Elektrodynamik: Briefe Ludwig Boltzmanns an Hermann von Helmholtz." *NTM* 5 (1968): 125–31.

Buff, Heinrich. *Grundzüge der Experimentalphysik mit Rücksicht auf Chemie und Pharmacie, zum Gebrauche bei Vorlesungen und zum Selbstunterrichte.* Heidelberg, 1843.

Bunsen, Robert. *Gesammelte Abhandlungen von Robert Bunsen.* Edited by Wilhelm Ostwald and M. Bodenstein. Vol. 1. Leipzig: W. Engelmann, 1904.

———. See Gustav Kirchhoff.

Caneva, Kenneth L. "From Galvanism to Electrodynamics: The Transformation of German Physics and Its Social Context." *HSPS* 9 (1978): 63–159.

Cantor, G. N., and M. J. S. Hodge, eds. *Conceptions of Ether: Studies in the History of Ether Theories 1740–1900.* Cambridge: Cambridge University Press, 1981.

Cantor, Moritz. "August: Ernst Ferdinand." *ADB* 1 (1967): 683–84.

———. "Pfaff: Johann Friedrich." *ADB* 25 (1887): 592–93.

———. "Richelot: Friedrich Julius." *ADB* 28 (1970): 432–33.

———. "Snell: Karl." *ADB* 34 (1892): 507.

———. "Stahl: Konrad Dietrich Martin." *ADB* 35 (1893): 402–3.

Carus, C. G. *Lebenserinnerungen und Denkwürdigkeiten, nach der zweibändigen Originalausgabe von 1865/66.* Edited by Elmar Jansen. 2 vols. Weimar: Kiepenheuer, 1966.

Cawood, John. "Terrestrial Magnetism and the Development of International Collaboration in the Early Nineteenth Century." *Annals of Science* 34 (1977): 551–87.

Clausius, Rudolph. *Abhandlungen über die mechanische Wärmetheorie. Erste Abtheilung.* Braunschweig, 1864.

———. *Die mechanische Wärmetheorie.* 2d rev. and completed ed. of *Abhandlungen über die mechanische Wärmetheorie.* Vol. 1. Second title page reads *Entwickelung der Theorie, soweit sie sich aus den beiden Hauptsätzen ableiten lässt, nebst Anwendungen.* Braunschweig, 1876. Vol. 2, *Die mechanische Behandlung der Electricität.* Second title page reads *Anwendung der der mechanischen Wärmetheorie zu Grunde liegenden Principien auf die Electricität.* Braunschweig, 1879.

———. *Die Potentialfunction und das Potential. Ein Beitrag zur mathematischen Physik.* Leipzig, 1859.

———. *Über das Wesen der Wärme, verglichen mit Licht und Schall.* Zurich, 1857.

Clebsch, Alfred. "Zum Gedächtniss an Julius Plücker." In *Julius Plückers Gesammelte Mathematische Abhandlungen,* edited by A. Schoenflies, vol. 1, ix–xxxv. Leipzig, 1895.

Conrad, Johannes. *Das Universitätsstudium in Deutschland während der letzten 50 Jahre. Statistische Untersuchungen unter besonderer Berücksichtigung Preussens.* Jena, 1884.

Craig, Gordon. *Germany, 1866–1945.* New York: Oxford University Press, 1978.

Daub, Edward E. "Atomism and Thermodynamics." *Isis* 58 (1967): 293–303.

———. "Clausius, Rudolf." *DSB* 3 (1971): 303–11.

———. "Entropy and Dissipation." *HSPS* 2 (1970): 321–54.

———. "Probability and Thermodynamics: The Reduction of the Second Law." *Isis* 60 (1969): 318–30.

———. "Rudolf Clausius and the Nineteenth Century Theory of Heat." Ph.D. diss., University of Wisconsin-Madison, 1966.

Dedekind, Richard. "Bernhard Riemann's Lebenslauf." In *Bernhard Riemann's gesammelte mathematische Werke,* 507–26.

Degen, Heinz. "Die Gründungsgeschichte der Gesellschaft deutscher Naturforscher- und Ärzte." *Naturwiss. Rundschau* 8 (1955): 421–27, 472–80.

Des Coudres, Theodor. "Ludwig Boltzmann." *Verh. sächs. Ges. Wiss.* 85 (1906): 615–27.

Deutscher Universitäts-Kalender. Or *Deutsches Hochschulverzeichnis; Lehrköper, Vorlesungen und Forschungseinrichtungen.* Berlin, 1872–1901. Leipzig, 1902– .

Dickerhof, Harald. "Aufbruch in München." In *Ludwig-Maximilians-Universität, Ingolstadt, Landshut, München, 1472–1972,* 215–50.

Dictionary of Scientific Biography. Edited by Charles Coulston Gillispie. 15 vols. New York: Scribner's, 1970–78. *(DSB)*

Dirichlet, Gustav Lejeune. *G. Lejeune Dirichlet's Werke.* Edited by L. Kronecker and L. Fuchs. 2 vols. Berlin, 1889–97.

———. *Vorlesungen über die im umgekehrten Verhältniss des Quadrats der Entfernung wirkenden Kräfte.* Edited by F. Grube. Leipzig, 1876.

Dove, Alfred. "Alexander von Humboldt auf der Höhe seiner Jahre (Berlin 1827–59)." In *Alexander von Humboldt,* edited by Karl Bruhns, vol. 2, 93–189.

———. "Dove: Heinrich Wilhelm." *ADB* 48 (1971): 51–69.

Dove, Heinrich Wilhelm. *Darstellung der Farbenlehre und optische Studien.* Berlin, 1853.

———. "Ueber Maass und Messen." In *Programm . . . des Friedrichs-Gymnasium auf dem Werder.* Berlin, 1833.

Dove, Heinrich Wilhelm, and Ludwig Moser, eds. *Repertorium der Physik.* Vol. 1. Berlin, 1837.

Drake, Stillman. *Galileo at Work.* Chicago: University of Chicago Press, 1978.

Drobisch, Moritz Wilhelm. *Philologie und Mathematik als Gegenstände des Gymnasialunterrichts betrachtet, mit besonderer Beziehung auf Sachsens Gelehrtenschulen.* Leipzig, 1832.

Drude, Paul. "Wilhelm Gottlieb Hankel." *Verh. sächs. Ges. Wiss.* 51 (1899): lxvii–lxxvi.

Du Bois-Reymond, Emil. *Hermann von Helmholtz. Gedächtnissrede.* Leipzig, 1897.

Dugas, René. *A History of Mechanics.* Translated by J. R. Maddox. New York: Central Book, 1955.

———. *La théorie physique au sens de Boltzmann et ses prolongements modernes.* Neuchâtel-Suisse: Griffon, 1959.

Dunnington, Guy Waldo. *Carl Friedrich Gauss, Titan of Science; A Study of His Life and Work.* New York: Exposition Press, 1955.

Ebert, H. "Die Gründer der Physikalischen Gesellschaft zu Berlin." *Phys. Bl.* 6 (1971): 247–54.

Ebert, Hermann. *Hermann von Helmholtz.* Stuttgart: Wissenschaftliche Verlagsgesellschaft, 1949.

Eggeling. "Fries: Jakob Friedrich." *ADB* 8 (1967): 73–81.

Eggert, Hermann. "Universitäten." In *Handbuch der Architektur,* pt. 4, sect. 6, no. 2aI, 54–111.

Einstein, Albert. "Emil Warburg als Forscher." *Naturwiss.* 10 (1922): 824–28.

———. *Ideas and Opinions.* New York: Dell, 1973.

———. "Maxwell's Influence on the Development of the Conception of Physical Reality," 1931. In *Ideas and Opinions,* 259–63.

Elkana, Yehuda. "Helmholtz' 'Kraft': An Illustration of Concepts in Flux." *HSPS* 2 (1970): 263–98.

Engel, Friedrich. *Grassmanns Leben.* Vol. 3, pt. 2 of *Hermann Grassmanns gesammelte mathematische und physikalische Werke.* Leipzig: B. G. Teubner, 1911.

Erlangen. University. See Theodor Kolde.

Erman, Wilhelm. "Paul Erman. Ein Berliner Gelehrtenleben 1764–1851." In *Schriften des Vereins für die Geschichte Berlins* 53 (1927): 1–264.

"Ernst Abbe (1840–1905). The Origin of a Great Optical Industry." *Nature,* no. 3664 (20 Jan. 1940): 89–91.

Ernst Mach. Physicist and Philosopher. Vol. 6 of Boston Studies in the Philosophy of Science. Edited by R. S. Cohen and R. J. Seeger. Dordrecht-Holland: Reidel, 1970.

Ettingshausen, Andreas von. *Anfangsgründe der Physik.* Vienna, 1844.

———. See Andreas von Baumgartner.

Eulenburg, Franz. *Der akademische Nachwuchs; eine Untersuchung über die Lage und die Aufgaben der Extraordinarien und Privatdozenten.* Leipzig: B. G. Teubner, 1908.

——. "Die Frequenz der deutschen Universitäten." *Abh. sächs. Ges. Wiss.* 24, pt. 2 (1904): 1–323.

Fechner, Gustav Theodor. *Elementar-Lehrbuch des Elektromagnetismus, nebst Beschreibung der hauptsächlichsten elektromagnetischen Apparate.* Leipzig, 1830.

——. *Massbestimmungen über die galvanische Kette.* Leipzig, 1831.

——. *Repertorium der Experimentalphysik, enthaltend eine vollständige Zusammenstellung der neuen Fortschritte dieser Wisenschaft.* Vol. 3. Leipzig, 1832.

——. *Ueber die physikalische und philosophische Atomenlehre.* 2d rev. ed. Leipzig, 1864.

Ferber, Christian von. *Die Entwicklung des Lehrkörpers der deutschen Universitäten und Hochschulen 1864–1954.* Göttingen: Vandenhoeck und Ruprecht, 1956.

Fischer, Ernst Gottfried. *Lehrbuch der mechanischen Naturlehre.* 3d ed. 2 vols. Berlin and Leipzig, 1826–27.

Fischer, Kuno. *Erinnerungen an Moritz Seebeck, wirkl. Geheimerath und Curator der Universität Jena, nebst einem Anhange: Goethe und Thomas Seebeck.* Heidelberg, 1886.

Folie, F. "R. Clausius. Sa vie, ses travaux et leur portée metaphysique." *Revue des questions scientifiques* 27 (1890): 419–87.

Francis, W. See J. Tyndall.

Franck, James. "Emil Warburg zum Gedächtnis." *Naturwiss.* 19 (1931): 993–97.

Frankfurt am Main. Physical Society. *Jahresbericht des Physikalischen Vereins zu Frankfurt am Main.* Frankfurt am Main, 1831– .

Fraunhofer, Joseph (von). *Joseph von Fraunhofer's Gesammelte Schriften.* Edited by Eugen Lommel. Munich, 1888.

Freiburg i. Br. *Freiburg und seine Universität. Festschrift der Stadt Freiburg im Breisgau zur Fünfhundertjahrfeier der Albert-Ludwigs-Universität.* Edited by Maximilian Kollofrath and Franz Schneller. Freiburg i. Br.: n.p., 1957.

Freiburg. University. *Aus der Geschichte der Naturwissenschaften an der Universität Freiburg i. Br.* Edited by Eduard Zentgraf. Freiburg i. Br.: Albert, 1957.

——. *Statuten des Seminars für Mathematik und Naturwissenschaften an der Universität zu Freiburg im Breisgau.* Freiburg i. Br., 1846.

——. *Die Universität Freiburg seit dem Regierungsantritt Seiner Königlichen Hoheit des Grossherzogs Friedrich von Baden.* Freiburg i. Br. and Tübingen, 1881.

——. See Fritz Baumgarten.

Frey-Wyssling, A., and Elsi Häusermann. *Geschichte der Abteilung für Naturwissenschaften an der Eidgenössischen Technischen Hochschule in Zürich 1855–1955.* [Zurich], 1958.

Frick, Joseph. *Die physikalische Technik, oder Anleitung zur Anstellung von physikalischen Versuchen und zur Herstellung von physikalischen Apparaten mit möglichst einfachen Mitteln.* 2d rev. ed. Braunschweig, 1856.

Fricke, Robert. "Die allgemeinen Abteilungen." In *Das Unterrichtswesen im Deutschen Reich*, edited by Wilhelm Lexis, vol. 4, pt. 1, 49–62.

Fries, Jakob Friedrich. *Entwurf des Systems der theoretischen Physik; zum Gebrauche bey seinen Vorlesungen*. Heidelberg, 1813.

———. *Die mathematische Naturphilosophie nach philosophischer Methode bearbeitet. Ein Versuch*. Heidelberg, 1822.

Frommel, Emil. *Johann Christian Poggendorff*. Berlin, 1877.

Füchtbauer, Heinrich von. *Georg Simon Ohm; ein Forscher wächst aus seiner Väter Art*. 2d ed. Bonn: Ferdinand Dümmler, 1947.

Galle, A. "Über die geodätischen Arbeiten von Gauss." First treatise in vol. 11, pt. 2 of Carl Friedrich Gauss's *Werke*. Berlin and Göttingen: Springer, 1924.

Garber, Elizabeth Wolfe. "Clausius and Maxwell's Kinetic Theory of Gases." *HSPS* 2 (1970): 299–319.

———. "Maxwell, Clausius and Gibbs: Aspects of the Development of Kinetic Theory and Thermodynamics." Ph.D. diss., Case Institute of Technology, 1966.

———. "Rudolf Clausius' Work in Meteorological Optics." *Rete* 2 (1975): 323–37.

Gauss, Carl Friedrich. *Allgemeine Lehrsätze in Beziehung auf die im verkehrten Verhältnisse des Quadrats der Entfernung wirkenden Anziehungs- und Abstossungs-Kräfte* (1840). Edited by Albert Wangerin. Vol. 2 of Ostwald's Klassiker der exakten Wissenschaften. Leipzig, 1889.

———. *Die Intensität der erdmagnetischen Kraft auf absolutes Maass zurückgeführt* (1832). Edited by Ernst Dorn. Vol. 53 of Ostwald's Klassiker der exakten Wissenschaften. Leipzig, 1894.

———. *Werke*. Vol. 5. Edited by Königliche Gesellschaft der Wissenschaften zu Göttingen. N.p., 1877. Vol. 11, pt. 2, *Abhandlungen über Gauss' wissenschaftliche Tätigkeit auf den Gebieten der Geodäsie, Physik und Astronomie*, edited by Gesellschaft der Wissenschaften zu Göttingen. Berlin and Göttingen: Springer, 1924–29.

———. See Alexander von Humboldt.

Gebhardt, Willy. "Die Geschichte der Physikalischen Institute der Universität Halle." *Wiss. Zs. d. Martin-Luther-U. Halle-Wittenberg, Math.-Naturwiss.* 10 (1961): 851–59.

Gehlhoff, Georg. "E. Warburg als Lehrer." *Zs. f. techn. Physik* 3 (1922): 193–94.

Gehrcke, E. "Warburg als Physiker." *Zs. f. techn. Physik* 3 (1922): 186–92.

Gericke, Helmuth, *Zur Geschichte der Mathematik an der Universität Freiburg i. Br.* Freiburg i. Br.: Albert, 1955.

Gericke, Helmuth, and Hellfried Uebele. "Philipp Ludwig von Seidel und Gustav Bauer, zwei Erneuerer der Mathematik in München." In *Die Ludwig-Maximilians-Universität in ihren Fakultäten* 1:390–99.

Gerling, Christian Ludwig. *Christian Ludwig Gerling an Carl Friedrich Gauss. Sechzig bisher unveröffentlichte Briefe*. Edited by T. Gerardy. Göttingen: Vandenhoeck und Ruprecht, 1964.

————. *Nachricht von dem mathematisch-physicalischen Institut der Universität Marburg.* Marburg, 1848.

German Physical Society. Fiftieth anniversary issue. *Verh. phys. Ges.* 15 (1896): 1–40.

————. Foreword. *Die Fortschritte der Physik im Jahre 1845* 1 (1847).

Gibbs, Josiah Willard. "Rudolf Julius Emanuel Clausius." *Proc. Am. Acad.* 16 (1889): 458–65.

Giese, Gerhardt. *Quellen zur deutschen Schulgeschichte seit 1800.* Vol. 15 of Quellensammlung zur Kulturgeschichte, edited by Wilhelm Treue. Göttingen: Musterschmidt-Verlag, 1961.

Giessen. University. *Ludwigs-Universität, Justus Liebig-Hochschule, 1607–1957. Festschrift zur 350-Jahrfeier.* Giessen, 1957.

————. *Statuten des physikalischen Seminars an der Grossherzoglichen Landes-Universität zu Giessen.* N.p., 1862.

————. *Die Universität Giessen von 1607 bis 1907. Beiträge zu ihrer Geschichte. Festschrift zur dritten Jahrhundertfeier.* Edited by Universität Giessen. Vol. 1. Giessen: A. Töpelmann, 1907.

————. See M. Biermer; Wilhelm Lorey.

Gilbert, L. W. "Vorrede." *Ann.* 1 (1799).

Goethe, Johann Wolfgang (von). *Goethes Gespräche mit J. P. Eckermann.* Edited by Franz Deibel. Vol. 1. Leipzig: Insel-Verlag, 1908.

————. *Goethes Sämtliche Werke.* Jubiläums-Ausgabe. Vol. 30, *Annalen.* Stuttgart and Berlin: J. G. Cotta, n.d.

————. *Goethes Werke.* Weimar, 1887– .

————. *Neue Mittheilungen aus Johann Wolfgang von Goethe's handschriftlichem Nachlasse.* Vols. 1–2, *Goethe's Naturwissenschaftliche Correspondenz (1812–1832).* Edited by F. T. Bratranek. Leipzig, 1874.

Göttingen. University. *Die physikalischen Institute der Universität Göttingen.* Edited by Göttinger Vereinigung zur Förderung der angewandten Physik und Mathematik. Leipzig and Berlin: B. G. Teubner, 1906.

————. "Statuten des mathematisch-physikalischen Seminars zu Göttingen." *Gött. Nachr.,* 1850, 75–79.

————. *Statuten des mathematisch-physikalischen Seminars zu Göttingen.* Göttingen, 1886.

————. See Johann Stephan Pütter.

Goldstein, Eugen. "Aus vergangenen Tagen der Berliner Physikalischen Gesellschaft." *Naturwiss.* 13 (1925): 39–45.

Gollwitzer, Heinz. "Altenstein, Karl Sigmund Franz Frhr. vom Stein zum." *Neue deutsche Biographie* 1 (1953): 216–17.

Grailich, Josef. *Krystallographisch-optische Untersuchungen.* Vienna and Olmüz, 1858.

"Grailich, Josef." *Österreichisches Biographisches Lexikon 1815–1950* 2 (1959): 46–47.

Grassmann, Hermann. *Hermann Grassmanns gesammelte mathematische und physikalische Werke.* Edited by Friedrich Engel. 3 vols. in 6. Leipzig: B. G. Teubner, 1894–1911.

Gregory, Frederick. *Scientific Materialism in Nineteenth Century Germany.* Dordrecht
  and Boston: Reidel, 1977.
Greifswald. University. *Festschrift zur 500-Jahrfeier der Universität Greifswald.* Vol. 2.
  Greifswald: Universität, 1956.
Gren, F. A. C. Foreword. *Journal der Physik* 1 (1790).
Gross, Edward. *Work and Society.* New York: Thomas Y. Crowell, 1967.
Grüneisen, Eduard. "Emil Warburg zum achtzigsten Geburtstage." *Naturwiss.* 14
  (1926): 203–7.
Gümbel, von. "Schmid: Ernst Erhard." *ADB* 31 (1970): 659–61.
Günther. "Mayer: Johann Tobias." *ADB* 21 (1885): 116–18.
Günther, Siegmund. "Ein Rückblick auf die Anfänge des technischen Schulwesens
  in Bayern." In *Darstellungen aus der Geschichte der Technik, der Industrie und
  Landwirtschaft in Bayern,* edited by the Munich Technical University, 1–16.
Guggenbühl, Gottfried. "Geschichte der Eidgenössischen Technischen Hochschule
  in Zürich." In *Eidgenössische Technische Hochschule 1855–1955,* 3–260.
Guttstadt, Albert, ed. *Die naturwissenschaftlichen und medicinischen Staatsanstalten
  Berlins. Festschrift für die 59. Versammlung deutscher Naturforscher und Aerzte.*
  Berlin, 1886.
Häusermann, Elsi. See A. Frey-Wyssling.
Halle. University. *Bibliographie der Universitätsschriften von Halle-Wittenberg 1817–
  1885.* Edited by W. Suchier. Berlin: Deutscher Verlag der Wissenschaften,
  1953.
―――. *450 Jahre Martin-Luther-Universität Halle-Wittenberg.* Vol. 2. [Halle, 1953?]
―――. *Vorläufiges Reglement für das Seminar für Mathematik und die gesammten Na-
  turwissenschaften auf der Universität Halle-Wittenberg.* Halle, 1840.
―――. See Willy Gebhardt; Wilhelm Schrader.
Handbuch der Architektur. Pt. 4, *Entwerfen, Anlage und Einrichtung der Gebäude.* Sect.
  6, *Gebäude für Erziehung, Wissenschaft und Kunst.* No. 2a, *Hochschulen, zugehö-
  rige und verwandte wissenschaftliche Institute. I. Hochschulen im allgemeinen, Uni-
  versitäten und Technische Hochschulen. Naturwissenschaftliche Institute.* Edited by H.
  Eggert, C. Junk, C. Körner, and E. Schmitt. 2d ed. Stuttgart: A. Kröner, 1905.
Handbuch der bayerischen Geschichte. Vol. 4, *Das neue Bayern 1800–1970.* Edited by
  Max Spindler. Pt. 2. Munich: C. H. Beck, 1975.
Hankel, Wilhelm. *Grundriss der Physik.* Stuttgart, 1848.
Harig, G., ed. *Bedeutende Gelehrte in Leipzig.* Vol. 2. Leipzig: Karl-Marx-Universität,
  1965.
Harman, P. M. *Energy, Force, and Matter: The Conceptual Development of Nineteenth-
  Century Physics.* Cambridge: Cambridge University Press, 1982.
―――. *Metaphysics and Natural Philosophy: The Problem of Substance in Classical
  Physics.* Brighton: Harvester Press, 1982.
Harnack, Adolf, ed. *Geschichte der Königlich preussischen Akademie der Wissenschaften
  zu Berlin.* 3 vols. Berlin: Reichsdruckerei, 1900.
Heidelberg. University. *Anzeige der Vorlesungen . . . auf der Grossherzoglich Badischen*

Ruprecht-Carolinischen Universität zu Heidelberg. . . . Heidelberg.

———. *Heidelberger Professoren aus dem 19. Jahrhundert. Festschrift der Universität zur Zentenarfeier ihrer Erneuerung durch Karl Friedrich.* Vol. 2. Heidelberg: C. Winter, 1903.

———. *Ruperto-Carola. Sonderband. Aus der Geschichte der Universität Heidelberg und ihrer Fakultäten.* Edited by G. Hinz. Heidelberg: Brausdruck, 1961.

———. *Die Ruprecht-Karl-Universität Heidelberg.* Edited by G. Hinz. Berlin and Basel: Länderdienst, 1965.

———. *Zusammenstellung der Vorlesungen, welche vom Sommerhalbjahr 1804 bis 1886 auf der Grossherzoglich Badischen Ruprecht-Karls-Universität zu Heidelberg angekündigt worden sind.* Heidelberg.

———. See Reinhard Riese; Georg Weber.

Heidemann, Julius. *Geschichte des Grauen Klosters zu Berlin.* Berlin, 1874.

Heimann, P. M. "Conversion of Forces and the Conservation of Energy." *Centaurus* 18 (1974): 147–61.

———. "Helmholtz and Kant: The Metaphysical Foundations of *Über die Erhaltung der Kraft.*" *Stud. Hist. Phil. Sci.* 5 (1974): 205–38.

———. "Mayer's Concept of 'Force': The 'Axis' of a New Science of Physics." *HSPS* 7 (1976): 277–96.

Heinrichs, Joseph. "Ohm im mathematisch-naturwissenschaftlichen Gedankenkreis seiner Zeit." In *Georg Simon Ohm als Lehrer und Forscher in Köln 1817 bis 1826*, edited by Kölnischer Geschichtsverein, 254–70.

Heller, Karl Daniel. *Ernst Mach: Wegbereiter der modernen Physik.* Vienna and New York: Springer, 1964.

Helm, Georg. "Oskar Schlömilch." *Zs. f. Math. u. Phys.* 46 (1901): 1–7.

Helmholtz, Anna von. *Anna von Helmholtz. Ein Lebensbild in Briefen.* Edited by Ellen von Siemens-Helmholtz. Vol. 1. Berlin: Verlag für Kulturpolitik, 1929.

Helmholtz, Hermann (von). "Autobiographical Sketch." In *Popular Lectures on Scientific Subjects*, vol. 2, 266–91.

———. *Epistemological Writings.* Edited by Paul Hertz and Moritz Schlick. Translated by M. F. Lowe. Vol. 37 of Boston Studies in the Philosophy of Science. Dordrecht and Boston: Reidel, 1977.

———. "Gustav Magnus. In Memoriam." In *Popular Lectures on Scientific Subjects*, 1–25.

———. "Gustav Wiedemann." *Ann.* 50 (1893): iii–xi.

———. *Handbuch der physiologischen Optik.* 3 vols. Leipzig, 1856–67. Translated as *Treatise on Physiological Optics* and edited by J. C. P. Southall from the 3d German ed. of 1909, edited by A. Gullstrand, J. von Kries, and W. Nagel. 3 vols. Rochester: Optical Society of America, 1924–25.

———. *Die Lehre von den Tonempfindungen, als physiologische Grundlage für die Theorie der Musik.* Braunschweig, 1863. Translated as *Sensations of Tone as a Physiological Basis for the Theory of Music* by A. J. Ellis from the 4th German ed. of 1877. 2d English ed. London, 1885.

———. *Popular Lectures on Scientific Subjects.* Translated by E. Atkinson. London,

1881. New ed. in 2 vols. London: Longmans, Green, 1908–12.

———. *Selected Writings of Hermann von Helmholtz*. Edited by R. Kahl. Middletown, Conn.: Wesleyan University Press, 1971.

———. *Ueber die Erhaltung der Kraft, eine physikalische Abhandlung*. Berlin, 1847.

———. *Vorlesungen über theoretische Physik*. Vol. 1, pt. 1, *Einleitung zu den Vorlesungen über theoretische Physik*. Edited by Arthur König and Carl Runge. Leipzig: J. A. Barth, 1903.

———. *Wissenschaftliche Abhandlungen*. 3 vols. Leipzig, 1882–95.

———. "Zur Erinnerung an Rudolf Clausius." *Verh. phys. Ges.* 8 (1889): 1–7.

———. *Zwei hydrodynamische Abhandlungen von H. v. Helmholtz*. Vol. 79 of Ostwald's Klassiker der exakten Wissenschaften. Leipzig, 1896.

Helmholtz, Robert, "A Memoir of Gustav Robert Kirchhoff." Translated by J. de Perott. *Annual Report of the . . . Smithsonian Institution . . . to July, 1889*, 1890, 527–40.

Hensel, Sebastian. *The Mendelssohn Family (1729–1847). From Letters and Journals*. Translated by C. Klingemann. 2d rev. ed. New York, 1882.

Hermann, Armin. "Physiker und Physik—anno 1845." *Phys. Bl.* 21 (1965): 399–405.

Hermann, L. "Hermann von Helmholtz." *Schriften der Physikalisch-ökonomischen Gesellschaft zu Königsberg* 35 (1894): 63–73.

Hertz, Heinrich. "Hermann von Helmholtz." In supplement to *Münchener Allgemeine Zeitung*, 31 Aug. 1891. Reprinted and translated by D. E. Jones and G. A. Schott in *Miscellaneous Papers*, 332–40.

———. *Miscellaneous Papers*. Translation of *Schriften vermischten Inhalts* by D. E. Jones and G. A. Schott. London, 1896.

Hess, W. "Lichtenberg: Georg Christoph." *ADB* 18 (1883): 537–38.

Heunisch, A. J. V. *Das Grossherzogthum Baden, historisch-geographisch-statistisch-topographisch beschrieben*. Heidelberg, 1857.

Heydweiller, Adolf. "Friedrich Kohlrausch." In Friedrich Kohlrausch's *Gesammelte Abhandlungen*, vol. 2, xxxv–lxviii.

———. "Johann Wilhelm Hittorf." *Phys. Zs.* 16 (1915): 161–79.

Hiebert, Erwin N. "Ernst Mach." *DSB* 8 (1973): 595–607.

———. "The Genesis of Mach's Early Views on Atomism." In *Ernst Mach. Physicist and Philosopher*, 79–106.

Hildebrandt, Friedrich. *Anfangsgründe der dynamischen Naturlehre*. N.p. [Erlangen], 1807.

Hodge, M. J. S. See G. N. Cantor.

Hölder, O. "Carl Neumann." *Verh. sächs. Ges. Wiss.* 77 (1925): 154–80.

Hofmann, A. W. "Gustav Kirchhoff." *Berichte der deutschen chemischen Gesellschaft*, vol. 20, pt. 2 (1887): 2771–77.

———. "Magnus: Heinrich Gustav." *ADB* 20 (1970): 77–90.

Holborn, Hajo. *A History of Modern Germany, 1840–1945*. New York: Alfred A. Knopf, 1969.

Hoppe, Edmund. *Geschichte der Elektrizität*. Leipzig, 1884.

Hoppe, Günter. "Goethes Ansichten über Meteorite und sein Verhältnis zu dem Physiker Chladni." *Goethe Jahrbuch* 95 (1978): 227–40.

Humboldt, Alexander von. *Briefe zwischen A. v. Humboldt und Gauss. Zum hundertjährigen Geburtstage von Gauss am 30. April 1877.* Edited by Karl Bruhns. Leipzig, 1877.

Jacobi, C. G. J., and M. H. Jacobi. *Briefwechsel zwischen C. G. J. Jacobi und M. H. Jacobi.* Edited by W. Ahrens. Leipzig: B. G. Teubner, 1907.

Jaeckel, Barbara, and Wolfgang Paul. "Die Entwicklung der Physik in Bonn 1818–1968." In *150 Jahre Rheinische Friedrich-Wilhelms-Universität zu Bonn 1818–1968,* 91–100.

Jäger, Cajetan. "Wucherer, Gustav Friedrich." In *Literärisches Freiburg i. Br.,* 200–207. Freiburg i. Br., 1839.

Jäger, Gustav. "Der Physiker Ludwig Boltzmann." *Monatshefte für Mathematik und Physik* 18 (1907): 3–7.

Jahn, Ilse. "Über die Einwirkung Alexander von Humboldts auf die Entwicklung der Naturwissenschaften an der Berliner Universität." *Wiss. Zs. d. Humboldt-U. Berlin, Math.-Naturwiss.* 21 (1972): 131–44.

Jahnke, H. N., and M. Otte, eds. *Epistemological and Social Problems of the Sciences in the Early Nineteenth Century.* Dordrecht: Reidel, 1981.

Jeismann, Karl-Ernst. *Das preussische Gymnasium in Staat und Gesellschaft. Die Entstehung des Gymnasiums als Schule des Staates und der Gebildeten, 1787–1817.* Vol. 15 of Industrielle Welt, Schriftenreihe des Arbeitskreises für moderne Sozialgeschichte, edited by Werner Conze. Stuttgart: Ernst Klett, 1974.

Jena. University. *Beiträge zur Geschichte der Mathematisch-Naturwissenschaftlichen Fakultät der Friedrich-Schiller-Universität Jena anlässlich der 400-Jahr-Feier.* Jena: G. Fischer, 1959.

———. *Geschichte der Universität Jena 1548/58–1958. Festgabe zum vierhundertjährigen Universitätsjubiläum.* 2 vols. Jena: G. Fischer, 1958.

Jenkins, Reese V. "Fraunhofer, Joseph." *DSB* 5 (1972): 142–44.

Johann Samuel Traugott Gehler's Physikalisches Wörterbuch. Edited by Heinrich Wilhelm Brandes, L. Gmelin, J. C. Horner, Georg Wilhelm Muncke, C. H. Pfaff, J. J. von Littrow, and K. L. von Littrow. 11 vols. in 22. Leipzig, 1825–45.

Jolly, Philipp. *Ueber die Physik der Molecularkräfte. Rede in der öffentlichen Sitzung der Königl. Akademie der Wissenschaften am 28. März 1857.* Munich, 1857.

Jungnickel, Christa. "The Royal Saxon Society of Sciences: A Study of Nineteenth Century German Science." Ph.D. diss., Johns Hopkins University, 1978.

Junk, Carl. "Physikalische Institute." In *Handbuch der Architektur,* pt. 4, sect. 6, no. 2a1, 164–236.

K. "Reich: Ferdinand." *ADB* 27 (1967): 607–11.

———. "Riess: Peter Theophil." *ADB* 28 (1970): 584–86.

———. "Schweigger: Johann Salomo Christoph." *ADB* 33 (1891): 335–39.

———. "Seebeck: Ludwig Friedrich Wilhelm August." *ADB* 33 (1971): 559–60.

Kalähne, Alfred. "Dem Andenken an Georg Quincke." *Phys. Zs.* 25 (1924): 649–59.

Karlsruhe. Technical University. *Festgabe zum Jubiläum der vierzigjährigen Regierung Seiner Königlichen Hoheit des Grossherzogs Friedrich von Baden.* Karlsruhe, 1892.

Karsten, Gustav, ed. *Allgemeine Encyclopaedie der Physik.* Leipzig, 1856–63.

Kastner, Carl Friedrich August Theodor. *Die Physik.* Pt. 1. Rostock, 1829.

Kastner, Carl Wilhelm Gottlob. *Grundriss der Experimentalphysik.* 2 vols. Heidelberg, 1810. 2d rev. ed. 1820–21.

———. *Grundzüge der Physik und Chemie zum Gebrauch für höhere Lehranstalten und zum Selbstunterricht für Gewerbtreibende und Freunde der Naturwissenschaft.* Bonn, 1821. 2d ed. in 2 vols. 1832–33.

Kelbg, Günter, and Wolf Dietrich Kraeft. "Die Entwicklung der theoretischen Physik in Rostock." *Wiss. Zs. d. U. Rostock* 16 (1967): 839–47.

Kiel. University. *Geschichte der Christian-Albrechts-Universität Kiel, 1665–1965.* Vol. 6, *Geschichte der Mathematik, der Naturwissenschaften und der Landwirtschaftswissenschaften.* Edited by Karl Jordan. Neumünster: Wachholtz, 1968.

———. See Charlotte Schmidt-Schönbeck.

Kirchhoff, Gustav. *Gesammelte Abhandlungen.* Leipzig, 1882. *Nachtrag.* Edited by Ludwig Boltzmann. Leipzig, 1891.

———. *Ueber das Ziel der Naturwissenschaften.* Heidelberg, 1865.

Kirchhoff, Gustav, and Robert Bunsen. *Chemische Analyse durch Spectralbeobachtungen von G. Kirchhoff und R. Bunsen* (1860). Vol. 72 of Ostwald's Klassiker der exakten Wissenschaften. Edited by Wilhelm Ostwald. Leipzig, 1895.

Kirn, H. See E. Bonnell.

Kirsten, Christa, and Hans-Günther Körber, eds. *Physiker über Physiker.* Berlin: Akademie-Verlag, 1975.

Kistner, Adolf. "Meyer, Oskar Emil." *Biographisches Jahrbuch und Deutscher Nekrolog* 14 (1912): 157–60.

Klein, Felix. "Ernst Schering." *Jahresber. d. Deutsch. Math.-Vereinigung* 6 (1899): 25–27.

———. *Vorlesungen über die Entwicklung der Mathematik im 19. Jahrhundert.* Pt. 1 edited by R. Courant and O. Neugebauer. Pt. 2, *Die Grundbegriffe der Invariantentheorie und ihr Eindringen in die mathematische Physik,* edited by R. Courant and St. Cohn-Vossen. Reprint. New York: Chelsea, 1967.

Klein, Martin J. "Gibbs on Clausius," *HSPS* 1 (1969): 127–49.

———. "Mechanical Explanation at the End of the Nineteenth Century." *Centaurus* 17 (1972): 58–82.

———. *Paul Ehrenfest.* Vol. 1, *The Making of a Theoretical Physicist.* Amsterdam and London: North-Holland, 1970.

Klemm, Friedrich. "Fischer, Ernst Gottfried." *Neue deutsche Biographie* 5 (1961): 182–83.

Kline, Morris. *Mathematical Thought from Ancient to Modern Times.* New York: Oxford University Press, 1972.

Klüpfel, Karl. *Die Universität Tübingen in ihrer Vergangenheit und Gegenwart dargestellt.* Leipzig, 1877.

Knott, Robert. "Hankel: Wilhelm Gottlieb." *ADB* 49 (1967): 757–59.

———. "Knoblauch: Karl Hermann." *ADB* 51 (1971): 256–58.

———. "Steinheil: Karl August." *ADB* 35 (1893): 720–24.

———. "Weber: Wilhelm Eduard." *ADB* 41 (1967): 358–61.

Kölnischer Geschichtsverein, ed. *Georg Simon Ohm als Lehrer und Forscher in Köln 1817 bis 1826. Festschrift zur 150. Wiederkehr seines Geburtstages.* Köln: J. P. Bachem, n.d. [1939].

König, Walter. "Georg Hermann Quinckes Leben und Schaffen." *Naturwiss.* 12 (1924): 621–27.

Königsberg. University. See Hans Prutz.

Koenigsberger, Leo. *Carl Gustav Jacob Jacobi.* Leipzig: B. G. Teubner, 1904.

———. *Hermann von Helmholtz.* 3 vols. Braunschweig: F. Vieweg, 1902–3.

———. "The Investigations of Hermann von Helmholtz on the Fundamental Principles of Mathematics and Mechanics." *Annual Report of the . . . Smithsonian Institution . . . to July, 1896,* 1898, 93–124.

———. *Mein Leben.* Heidelberg: Carl Winters, 1919.

Köpke, Rudolf. *Die Gründung der Königlichen Friedrich-Wilhelms-Universität zu Berlin.* Berlin. 1860.

Körber, Hans-Günther. "Hankel, Wilhelm Gottlieb." *DSB* 6 (1972): 96–97.

———. See Christa Kirsten.

Körner, Carl. "Technische Hochschulen." *Handbuch der Architektur,* pt. 4, sect. 6, no. 2al, 112–60.

Kohlrausch, Friedrich. *Gesammelte Abhandlungen.* Edited by Wilhelm Hallwachs, Adolf Heydweiller, Karl Strecker, and Otto Wiener. 2 vols. Leipzig: J. A. Barth, 1910–11.

———. "Gustav Wiedemann. Nachruf." In *Gesammelte Abhandlungen,* vol. 2, 1064–76.

———. "Wilhelm v. Beetz. Nekrolog." In *Gesammelte Abhandlungen,* vol. 2, 1048–61.

Kolde, Theodor. *Die Universität Erlangen unter dem Hause Wittelsbach, 1810–1910.* Erlangen and Leipzig: A. Deichert, 1910.

Konen, Heinrich. "Das physikalische Institut." In *Geschichte der Rheinischen Friedrich-Wilhelm-Universität zu Bonn am Rhein,* vol 2, 345–55.

Kraeft, Wolf Dietrich. See Günter Kelbg.

Krause, Martin. "Oscar Schlömilch." *Verh. sächs. Ges. Wiss.* 53 (1901): 509–20.

Kuhn, Thomas S. "Energy Conservation as an Example of Simultaneous Discovery." In *Critical Problems in the History of Science,* edited by M. Clagett, 321–56. Madison: University of Wisconsin Press, 1959. Reprinted in *The Essential Tension,* 66–104.

———. *The Essential Tension: Selected Studies in Scientific Tradition and Change.* Chicago: University of Chicago Press, 1977.

———. "The Function of Measurement in Modern Physical Science." In *Quantification,* edited by Harry Woolf, 31–63. New York: Bobbs-Merrill, 1961.

———. "Mathematical versus Experimental Traditions in the Development of Physical Science." *Journal of Interdisciplinary History* 7 (1976): 1–31. Reprinted in *The Essential Tension,* 31–65.

Kummer, E. E. "Gedächtnissrede auf Gustav Peter Lejeune Dirichlet." In G. *Lejeune Dirichlet's Werke*, vol. 2, 311–44.

Kuntze, Johannes Emil. *Gustav Theodor Fechner, Dr. Mises; ein deutsches Gelehrten-leben*. Leipzig, 1892.

L., von. "Müller: Johann Heinrich Jakob." *ADB* 22 (1970): 633–34.

Lamont, Johannes. "Rede zur Feier des hohen Geburtsfestes Sr. Majestät des Königs Maximilian II. von Bayern" including obituaries of Thaddäus Siber and G. S. Ohm. *Gelehrte Anzeigen der k. bayerischen Akademie der Wissenschaften, Historische Classe* 40 (1855): cols. 25–34.

Lampa, Anton. "Ludwig Boltzmann." *Biographisches Jahrbuch und Deutscher Nekrolog* 11 (1908): 96–104.

Lampe, Hermann. *Die Entwicklung und Differenzierung von Fachabteilungen auf den Versammlungen von 1828 bis 1913*. Vol. 2 of *Schriftenreihe zur Geschichte der Versammlungen deutscher Naturforscher und Ärzte*. Hildesheim: Gerstenberg, 1975.

———. *Die Vorträge der allgemeinen Sitzungen auf der 1.–85. Versammlung 1822–1913*. Vol. 1 of *Schriftenreihe zur Geschichte der Versammlungen deutscher Naturforscher und Ärzte*. Hildesheim: Gerstenberg, 1972.

Lang, Victor von. Obituary of Ludwig Boltzmann. *Almanach österreichische Akad.* 57 (1907): 307–9.

Lasswitz, Kurd. *Gustav Theodor Fechner*. 2d rev. ed. Stuttgart: F. Frommann, 1902.

Laue, Max (von). "Über Hermann von Helmholtz." In *Forschen und Wirken. Festschrift . . . Humboldt-Universität zu Berlin*, vol. 1, 359–66.

Lehmann, Otto, ed. *Dr. J. Fricks Physikalische Technik; oder, Anleitung zu Experimentalvorträgen sowie zur Selbstherstellung einfacher Demonstrationsapparate*. 7th rev. ed. 2 vols. in 4. Braunschweig: F. Vieweg, 1904–9.

———. "Geschichte des physikalischen Instituts der technischen Hochschule Karlsruhe." In *Festgabe* by the Karlsruhe Technical University, 207–65.

———. "Vorrede." In *Dr. J. Fricks Physikalische Technik*, vol. 1, pt. 1, v–xx.

Leipzig. University. *Festschrift zur Feier des 500jährigen Bestehens der Universität Leipzig*. Vol. 4, *Die Institute und Seminare der Philosophischen Fakultät*. Pt. 2, *Die mathematisch-naturwissenschaftliche Sektion*. Leipzig: S. Hirzel, 1909.

———. *Die Universität Leipzig, 1409–1909. Gedenkblätter zum 30. Juli 1909*. Leipzig: Press-Ausschuss der Jubiläums-Kommission, 1909.

———. *Verzeichniss der . . . auf der Universität Leipzig zu haltenden Vorlesungen*. Leipzig.

———. See Otto Wiener.

Lemaine, Gerard, Roy Macleod, Michael Mulkay, and Peter Weingart, eds. *Perspectives on the Emergence of Scientific Disciplines*. The Hague: Mouton, 1976.

Lenz, Max. *Geschichte der Königlichen Friedrich-Wilhelms-Universität zu Berlin*. 4 vols. in 5. Halle a. d. S.: Buchhandlung des Waisenhauses, 1910–18.

Lexis, Wilhelm, ed. *Die Reform des höheren Schulwesens in Preussen*. Halle a. d. S.: Buchhandlung des Waisenhauses, 1902.

———, ed. *Das Unterrichtswesen im Deutschen Reich*. Vol. 1, *Die Universitäten im Deutschen Reich*. Berlin: A. Asher, 1904.

Liebmann, Heinrich. "Zur Erinnerung an Carl Neumann." *Jahresber. d. Deutsch. Math.-Vereinigung* 36 (1927): 174–78.

"Life and Labors of Henry Gustavus Magnus." *Annual Report of the . . . Smithsonian Institution for the Year 1870,* 1872, 223–30.

Listing, J. B. "Zum Andenken an A. von Ettingshausen." *Gött. Nachr.,* 1878, 516.

Littrow, K. L. von. "Versuch." In *Johann Samuel Traugott Gehler's Physikalisches Wörterbuch,* vol. 9, pt. 3, 1813–57. Leipzig, 1840.

Lommel, Eugen. "Chladni: Ernst Florens Friedrich." *ADB* 4 (1968): 124–26.

———. "Erman: Paul." *ADB* 6 (1968): 229–30.

———. "Vorrede und Einleitung." In G. S. Ohm's *Gesammelte Abhandlungen,* v–xviii.

Lorentz, H. A. "Ludwig Boltzmann." *Verh. phys. Ges.* 9 (1907): 206–38. Reprinted in *Collected Papers,* vol. 9, 359–91. The Hague: M. Nijhoff, 1934–39.

Lorey, Wilhelm. "Paul Drude und Ludwig Boltzmann." *Abhandlungen der Naturforschenden Gesellschaft zu Görlitz* 25 (1907): 217–22.

———. "Die Physik an der Universität Giessen im 19. Jahrhundert." *Nachrichten der Giessener Hochschulgesellschaft* 15 (1941): 80–132.

———. *Das Studium der Mathematik an den deutschen Universitäten seit Anfang des 19. Jahrhunderts.* Leipzig and Berlin: B. G. Teubner, 1916.

Losch, P. "Melde, Franz Emil." *Biographisches Jahrbuch und Deutscher Nekrolog* 6 (1901): 338–40.

Lüdicke, Reinhard. *Die preussischen Kultusminister und ihre Beamten im ersten Jahrhundert des Ministeriums, 1817–1917.* Stuttgart: J. G. Cotta, 1918.

Lummer, Otto. "Physik." In *Festschrift . . . Breslau,* vol. 2, 440–48.

McCormmach, Russell. *Night Thoughts of a Classical Physicist.* Cambridge, Mass.: Harvard University Press, 1982.

McGucken, William. *Nineteenth-Century Spectroscopy.* Baltimore: Johns Hopkins University Press, 1969.

McGuire, J. E. "Forces, Powers, Aethers and Fields." *Boston Studies in the Philosophy of Science* 14 (1974): 119–59.

McKnight, John L. "Laboratory Notebooks of G. S. Ohm: A Case Study in Experimental Method." *Am. J. Phys.* 35 (1967): 110–14.

Macleod, Roy. See Gerard Lemaine.

McRae, Robert J. "Ritter, Johann Wilhelm." *DSB* 11 (1975): 473–75.

Manegold, Karl-Heinz. "Eine École Polytechnique in Berlin." *Technikgeschichte* 33 (1966): 182–96.

———. *Universität, Technische Hochschule und Industrie.* Vol. 16 of Schriften zur Wirtschafts- und Sozialgeschichte, edited by W. Fischer. Berlin: Duncker und Humblot, 1970.

Marburg. University. *Catalogus professorum academiae Marburgensis; die akademischen Lehrer der Philipps-Universität in Marburg von 1527 bis 1910.* Edited by F. Gundlach. Marburg: Elwert, 1927.

———. *Die Philipps-Universität zu Marburg 1527–1927.* Edited by H. Hermelink and S. A. Kaehler. Marburg: Elwert, 1927.

Maxwell, James Clerk. "Hermann Ludwig Ferdinand Helmholtz." *Nature* 15 (1877): 389–91.

Mayer, Johann Tobias. *Anfangsgründe der Naturlehre zum Behuf der Vorlesungen über die Experimental-Physik.* 2d rev. ed. Göttingen, 1805. 3d rev. ed. 1812. 4th rev. ed. 1820. 7th rev. ed. 1827.

Merz, John Theodore. *A History of European Thought in the Nineteenth Century.* 4 vols. 1904–12. Reprint. New York: Dover, 1965.

Minkowski, Hermann. *Gesammelte Abhandlungen.* Edited by David Hilbert. 2 vols. Leipzig and Berlin: B. G. Teubner, 1911.

————. "Peter Gustav Lejeune Dirichlet und seine Bedeutung für die heutige Mathematik." In Minkowski's *Gesammelte Abhandlungen,* vol. 2, 447–61.

Mohl, Robert von. *Lebens-Erinnerungen.* Vol. 1. Stuttgart and Leipzig: Deutsche Verlags-Anstalt, 1902.

Moser, Ludwig. See Heinrich Wilhelm Dove.

Müller, J. A. von. "Das physikalisch-metronomische Institut." In *Die wissenschaftlichen Anstalten der Ludwig-Maximilians-Universität zu München,* 278–79.

Müller, Johann. *Bericht über die neuesten Fortschritte der Physik. In ihrem Zusammenhange dargestellt.* 2 vols. Braunschweig, 1849.

————. *Grundriss der Physik und Meteorologie. Für Lyceen, Gymnasien, Gewerbe- und Realschulen, sowie zum Selbstunterrichte.* 5th rev. ed. Braunschweig, 1856.

Mulkay, Michael. See Gerard Lemaine.

Muncke, Georg Wilhelm. "Beobachtung." In *Johann Samuel Traugott Gehler's Physikalisches Wörterbuch,* vol. 1, pt. 2, 884–912.

————. "Physik." In *Johann Samuel Traugott Gehler's Physikalisches Wörterbuch,* vol. 7, pt. 1, 493–573.

————. *System der atomistischen Physik nach den neuesten Erfahrungen und Versuchen.* Hannover, 1809.

Munich Technical University, ed. *Darstellungen aus der Geschichte der Technik, der Industrie und Landwirtschaft in Bayern.* Munich: R. Oldenbourg, 1906.

Munich. University. *Die Ludwig-Maximilians-Universität in ihren Fakultäten.* Vol. 1. Edited by L. Boehm and J. Spörl. Berlin: Duncker und Humblot, 1972.

————. *Ludwig-Maximilians-Universität, Ingolstadt, Landshut, München, 1472–1972.* Edited by L. Boehm and J. Spörl. Berlin: Duncker und Humblot, 1972.

————. *Die wissenschaftlichen Anstalten der Ludwig-Maximilians-Universität zu München.* Edited by Karl Alexander von Müller. Munich: R. Oldenbourg und Dr. C. Wolf, 1926.

————. See Clara Wallenreiter.

Nernst, Walther. "Rudolf Clausius 1822–1888." In *150 Jahre Rheinische Friedrich-Wilhelms-Universität zu Bonn 1818–1968,* 101–9.

Neuerer, Karl. *Das höhere Lehramt in Bayern im 19. Jahrhundert.* Berlin: Duncker und Humblot, 1978.

Neumann, Carl. *Der gegenwärtige Standpunct der mathematischen Physik.* Tübingen, 1865.

―――. "Worte zum Gedächtniss an Wilhelm Hankel." *Verh. sächs. Ges. Wiss.* 51 (1899): lxii–lxvi.

Neumann, Franz. *Franz Neumanns Gesammelte Werke.* Edited by his students. 3 vols. Leipzig: B. G. Teubner, 1906–28.

―――. *Die mathematischen Gesetze der inducirten elektrischen Ströme*, 1845. Edited by Carl Neumann. Vol. 10 of Ostwald's Klassiker der exakten Wissenschaften. Leipzig. 1889.

―――. *Vorlesungen über mathematische Physik, gehalten an der Universität Königsberg.* Edited by his students. Leipzig, 1881–94. The individual volumes are as follows: *Einleitung in die theoretische Physik.* Edited by Carl Pape. Leipzig, 1883. *Vorlesungen über die Theorie der Capillarität.* Edited by Albert Wangerin. Leipzig, 1894. *Vorlesungen über die Theorie der Elasticität der festen Körper und des Lichtäthers.* Edited by Oskar Emil Meyer. Leipzig, 1885. *Vorlesungen über die Theorie des Magnetismus, namentlich über die Theorie der magnetischen Induktion.* Edited by Carl Neumann. Leipzig, 1881. *Vorlesungen über die Theorie des Potentials und der Kugelfunctionen.* Edited by Carl Neumann. Leipzig, 1887. *Vorlesungen über elektrische Ströme.* Edited by Karl Von der Mühll. Leipzig, 1884. *Vorlesungen über theoretische Optik.* Edited by Ernst Dorn. Leipzig, 1885.

Neumann, Luise. *Franz Neumann, Erinnerungsblätter von seiner Tochter.* 2d ed. Tübingen: J. C. B. Mohr (P. Siebeck), 1907.

Obituary of Heinrich Wilhelm Brandes. *Neuer Nekrolog der Deutschen* 12, pt. 1 (1834): 396–98.

Obituary of L. W. Gilbert. *Ann.* 76 (1824): 468–69.

Obituary of L. W. Gilbert. *Neuer Nekrolog der Deutschen* 2 (1825): 483–93.

Obituary of Hermann von Helmholtz. *Nature* 50 (1894): 479–80.

Obituary of Eduard Ketteler. *Leopoldina* 37 (1901): 35–36.

Obituary of Franz Melde. *Leopoldina* 37 (1901): 46–47.

Oersted, Hans Christian. *Correspondance de H. C. Örsted avec divers savants.* Edited by M. C. Harding. 2 vols. Copenhagen: H. Aschehoug, 1920.

Österreichisches Biographisches Lexikon 1815–1950. Graz and Cologne: H. Böhlaus, 1959.

Ohm, Georg Simon. *Aus Georg Simon Ohms handschriftlichem Nachlass. Briefe, Urkunden und Dokumente.* Edited by Ludwig Hartmann. Munich: Bayerland-Verlag, 1927.

―――. *Beiträge zur Molecular-Physik.* Vol. 1, *Grundriss der analytischen Geometrie im Raume am schiefwinkligen Coordinatensysteme.* Nuremberg, 1849.

―――. *Die galvanische Kette, mathematisch bearbeitet.* Berlin, 1827. Reprinted in Ohm's *Gesammelte Abhandlungen*, 61–186.

―――. *Gesammelte Abhandlungen.* Edited by Eugen Lommel. Leipzig, 1892.

―――. *Grundzüge der Physik als Compendium zu seinen Vorlesungen.* Nuremberg, 1854.

Olbers, Wilhelm. *Wilhelm Olbers, sein Leben und seine Werke.* Vol. 2, *Briefwechsel zwischen Olbers und Gauss.* Pt. 2. Edited by C. Schilling. Berlin: J. Springer, 1909.

Olesko, Kathryn Mary. "The Emergence of Theoretical Physics in Germany: Franz Neumann and the Königsberg School of Physics, 1830–1890." Ph.D. diss., Cornell University, 1980.

Oppenheim, A. "Heinrich Gustav Magnus." *Nature* 2 (1870): 143–45.

Ostwald, Wilhelm. "Gustav Wiedemann." *Verh. sächs. Ges. Wiss.* 51 (1899): lxxvii–lxxxiii.

Otte, M. See H. N. Jahnke.

Paalzow, Adolph. "Stiftungsfeier am 4. Januar 1896." *Verh. phys. Ges.* 15 (1896): 36–37.

Parrot, Georg Friedrich. *Grundriss der theoretischen Physik zum Gebrauche für Vorlesungen.* 3 parts. Riga and Leipzig, 1809–15.

Paschen, Friedrich. "Gedächtnisrede des Hrn. Paschen auf Emil Warburg." *Sitzungsber. preuss. Akad., Phil.-Hist. Kl.*, pt. 1 (1932), cxv–cxxiii.

Paul, Wolfgang. See Barbara Jaeckel.

Paulsen, Friedrich. *Die deutschen Universitäten und das Universitätsstudium.* Berlin: A. Asher, 1902.

Perron, Oskar, Constantin Carathéodory, and Heinrich Tietze. "Das Mathematische Seminar." In *Die wissenschaftlichen Anstalten . . . zu München,* 206.

Pfaff, C. H. *Der Elektro-Magnetismus, eine historisch-kritische Darstellung der bisherigen Entdeckungen auf dem Gebiete desselben, nebst eigenthümlichen Versuchen.* Hamburg, 1824.

———. *Revision der Lehre vom Galvano-Voltaismus, mit besonderer Rücksicht auf Faraday's, De la Rive's, Becquerels, Karstens u. a. neueste Arbeiten über diesen Gegenstand.* Altona, 1837.

Pfaff, Johann Friedrich. *Sammlung von Briefen gewechselt zwischen Johann Friedrich Pfaff und Herzog Carl von Würtemberg, F. Bouterwek, A. v. Humboldt, A. G. Kästner, und Anderen.* Edited by Carl Pfaff. Leipzig, 1853.

Pfannenstiel, Max, ed. *Kleines Quellenbuch zur Geschichte der Gesellschaft Deutscher Naturforscher und Ärzte.* Berlin, Göttingen, and Heidelberg: Springer, 1958.

Philippovich, Eugen von. *Der badische Staatshaushalt in den Jahren 1868–1889.* Freiburg i. Br., 1889.

Pisko, F. J. "Andreas Freiherr v. Baumgartner." *Archiv d. Math. u. Physik* 45 (1866): 1–13.

Planck, Max. "Helmholtz's Leistungen auf dem Gebiete der theoretischen Physik." *ADB* 51 (1906): 470–72. Reprinted in *Physikalische Abhandlungen und Vorträge,* 3:321–23.

———. "Das Institut für theoretische Physik." In *Geschichte der . . . Universität zu Berlin,* edited by Max Lenz, vol. 3, 276–78.

———. *Physikalische Abhandlungen und Vorträge.* 3 vols. Braunschweig: F. Vieweg, 1958.

Plücker, Julius. *Gesammelte physikalische Abhandlungen.* Edited by Friedrich Pockels. Leipzig, 1896.

Pockels, Friedrich. "Gustav Robert Kirchhoff." In *Heidelberger Professoren aus dem 19. Jahrhundert,* vol. 2, 243–63.

Poggendorff, Johann Christian. Foreword. *Ann.* 1 (1824): v–viii.

———. *J. C. Poggendorff's biographisch-literarisches Handwörterbuch zur Geschichte der exacten Wissenschaften.* Leipzig, 1863– .

———. "Meine Rede zur Jubelfeier am 28. Februar 1874." In *Johann Christian Poggendorff* by Emil Frommel, 68–72.

———. "Oeffentliche Anerkennung der Ohm'schen Theorie in England." *Ann.* 55 (1842): 178–80.

Poten, Bernhard. *Geschichte des Militär-Erziehungs- und Bildungswesens in den Landen deutscher Zunge.* Vol. 4, *Preussen.* Vol. 17 of Monumenta Germaniae Paedagogica. Schulordnungen, Schulbücher und pädagogische Miscellaneen aus den Landen deutscher Zunge, edited by K. Kehrbach. Berlin, 1896.

Pringsheim, Peter. "Gustav Magnus." *Naturwiss.* 13 (1925): 49–52.

Prutz, Hans. *Die Königliche Albertus-Universität zu Königsberg i. Pr. im neunzehnten Jahrhundert. Zur Feier ihres 350jährigen Bestehens.* Königsberg, 1894.

Pütter, Johann Stephan. *Versuch einer academischen Gelehrten-Geschichte von der Georg-Augustus-Universität zu Göttingen.* Pt. 3, *1788–1820.* Hannover, 1820.

Quintus Icilius, Gustav von. *Experimental-Physik. Ein Leitfaden bei Vorträgen.* Hannover, 1855.

R., D. "Jolly: Philipp Johann Gustav von." *ADB* 55 (1971): 807–10.

Reich, Ferdinand. *Leitfaden zu den Vorlesungen über Physik an der Bergakademie zu Freiberg.* 2d ed. 2 vols. Freiberg, 1852–53.

Reindl, Maria. *Lehre und Forschung in Mathematik und Naturwissenschaften, insbesondere Astronomie, an der Universität Würzburg von der Gründung bis zum Beginn des 20. Jahrhunderts.* Neustadt an der Aisch: Degener, 1966.

Reinganum, Max. "Clausius: Rudolf Julius Emanuel." *ADB* 55 (1971): 720–29.

Riecke, Eduard. "Plücker's physikalische Arbeiten." In Julius Plücker's *Gesammelte physikalische Abhandlungen,* xi–xviii.

———. "Rudolf Clausius." *Abh. Ges. Wiss. Göttingen* 35 (1888): appendix, 1–39.

———. "Wilhelm Weber." *Abh. Ges. Wiss. Göttingen* 38 (1892): 1–44.

Riemann, Bernhard. *Bernhard Riemann's gesammelte mathematische Werke. Nachträge.* Edited by M. Noether and W. Wirtinger. Leipzig: B. G. Teubner, 1902.

———. *Bernhard Riemann's gesammelte mathematische Werke und wissenschaftlicher Nachlass.* Edited by Heinrich Weber, with the collaboration of Richard Dedekind. Leipzig, 1876.

———. *Partielle Differentialgleichungen und deren Anwendung auf physikalische Fragen.* Edited by Karl Hattendorff. Braunschweig, 1869.

———. *Schwere, Elektricität und Magnetismus, nach den Vorlesungen von Bernhard Riemann.* Edited by Karl Hattendorff. Hannover, 1876.

Riese, Reinhard. *Die Hochschule auf dem Wege zum wissenschaftlichen Grossbetrieb. Die Universität Heidelberg und das badische Hochschulwesen 1860–1914.* Vol. 19 of Industrielle Welt, Schriftenreihe des Arbeitskreises für moderne Sozialgeschichte, edited by Werner Conze. Stuttgart: Ernst Klett, 1977.

Riewe, K. H. *120 Jahre Deutsche Physikalische Gesellschaft.* N.p., 1965.

Rönne, Ludwig von. *Das Unterrichts-Wesen des Preussischen Staates.* Vol. 2, *Die höhern Schulen und die Universitäten des Preussischen Staates.* Berlin, 1855.

Röntgen, W. C. *Zur Geschichte der Physik an der Universität Würzburg*. Festrede. Würzburg, 1894.

Ronge, Grete. "Die Züricher Jahre des Physikers Rudolf Clausius." *Gesnerus* 12 (1955): 73–108.

Roscoe, Henry. "Gedenkrede auf Bunsen." In *Gesammelte Abhandlungen von Robert Bunsen*, vol. 1, xv–lix.

————. *The Life and Experiences of Sir Henry Enfield Roscoe, D.C.L., LL.D., F.R.S.* London and New York: Macmillan, 1906.

Rosenberg, Charles E. "Toward an Ecology of Knowledge: On Discipline, Context and History." In *The Organization of Knowledge in Modern America 1860–1920*, edited by A. Oleson and J. Voss, 440–55. Baltimore: Johns Hopkins University Press, 1979.

Rosenberger, Ferdinand. *Die Geschichte der Physik*. Vol. 3, *Geschichte der Physik in den letzten hundert Jahren*. Braunschweig, 1890. Reprint. Hildesheim: G. Olms, 1965.

Rosenfeld, Leon. "Kirchhoff, Gustav Robert." *DSB* 7 (1973): 379–83.

————. "The Velocity of Light and the Evolution of Electrodynamics." *Nuovo Cimento*, supplement to vol. 4 (1957): 1630–69.

Rostock. University. See Günter Kelbg.

Roth, Günter D. *Joseph von Fraunhofer, Handwerker—Forscher—Akademiemitglied 1787–1826*. Vol. 39 of Grosse Naturforscher, edited by Heinz Degen. Stuttgart: Wissenschaftliche Verlagsgesellschaft, 1976.

Rubens, Heinrich. "Das physikalische Institut." In *Geschichte der . . . Universität zu Berlin*, edited by Max Lenz, vol. 3, 278–96.

Salié, Hans. "Carl Neumann." In *Bedeutende Gelehrte in Leipzig*, edited by G. Harig, vol. 2, 13–23.

Schachenmeier, R. See A. Schleiermacher.

Schacher, Susan G. "Bunsen; Robert Wilhelm Eberhard." *DSB* 2 (1970): 586–90.

Schaefer, Clemens. "Über Gauss' physikalische Arbeiten (Magnetismus, Elektrodynamik, Optik)." Second treatise in vol. 11, pt. 2 of Carl Friedrich Gauss's *Werke*. Berlin and Göttingen: Springer, 1929.

Schagrin, Morton L. "Resistance to Ohm's Law." *Am. J. Phys.* 31 (1963): 536–47.

Scheel, Karl. "Die literarischen Hilfsmittel der Physik." *Naturwiss.* 16 (1925): 45–48.

Schering, Ernst. "Bernhard Riemann zum Gedächtniss." *Gött. Nachr.*, 1867, 305–14.

Schiff, Julius. "J. S. C. Schweigger und sein Briefwechsel mit Goethe." *Naturwiss.* 13 (1925): 555–59.

Schimank, Hans. "Beiträge zur Lebensgeschichte von E. F. F. Chladni." *Sudhoffs Archiv* 37 (1953): 370–76.

Schleiermacher, A., and R. Schachenmeier. "Otto Lehmann." *Phys. Zs.* 24 (1923): 289–91.

Schmidt, Georg Gottlieb. *Handbuch der Naturlehre zum Gebrauche für Vorlesungen*. 2d rev. ed. Giessen, 1813.

Schmidt, Gerhard C. "Eilhard Wiedemann." *Phys. Zs.* 29 (1928): 185–90.

———. "Wilhelm Hittorf." *Phys. Bl.* 4 (1948): 64–68.

Schmidt, Karl. "Carl Hermann Knoblauch." *Leopoldina* 31 (1895): 116–22.

Schmidt, Rainer. "Landshut zwischen Aufklärung und Romantik." In *Ludwig-Maximilians-Universität, Ingolstadt, Landshut, München, 1472–1972,* 195–214.

Schmidt-Ott, Friedrich. *Erlebtes und Erstrebtes, 1860–1950.* Wiesbaden: Franz Steiner, 1952.

Schmidt-Schönbeck, Charlotte. *300 Jahre Physik und Astronomie an der Kieler Universität.* Kiel: F. Hirt, 1965.

Schmitt, Eduard. "Hochschulen im allgemeinen." In *Handbuch der Architektur,* pt. 4, sect. 6, no. 2aI, 4–53.

Schneider, Ivo. "Rudolph Clausius' Beitrag zur Einführung wahrscheinlichkeitstheoretischer Methoden in die Physik der Gase nach 1856." *Arch. Hist. Ex. Sci.* 14 (1975): 237–61.

Schrader, Wilhelm. *Geschichte der Friedrichs-Universität zu Halle.* 2 vols. Berlin, 1894.

Schulze, F. A. "Wilhelm Feussner." *Phys. Zs.* 31 (1930): 513–14.

Schulze, Friedrich. *B. G. Teubner 1811–1911. Geschichte der Firma in deren Auftrag.* Leipzig, 1911.

Schulze, O. F. A. "Zur Geschichte des Physikalischen Instituts." In *Die Philipps-Universität zu Marburg 1527–1927,* 756–63.

Schuster, Arthur. *The Progress of Physics During 33 Years (1875–1908).* Cambridge: Cambridge University Press, 1911.

Schwalbe, B. "Nachruf auf G. Karsten." *Verh. phys. Ges.* 2 (1900): 147–59.

Seifert, Karl-Friedrich. "Frankenheim, Moritz Ludwig." *Neue deutsche Biographie* 5 (1961): 350.

Siegel, Daniel M. "Balfour Stewart and Gustav Robert Kirchhoff: Two Independent Approaches to 'Kirchhoff's Radiation Law.' " *Isis* 67 (1976): 565–600.

Siemens, Werner von. *Personal Recollections.* Translated by W. C. Coupland. New York, 1893.

Snell, Karl. *Lehrbuch der Geometrie.* Leipzig, 1841.

———. *Philosophische Betrachtungen der Natur.* Dresden, 1839.

Sommerfeld, Arnold. "Oskar Emil Meyer." *Sitzungsber. bay. Akad.* 39 (1909): 17.

Stähelin, Christoph. "Wilhelm Weber in seiner allgemeinen Bedeutung für die Entwicklung und die Fortschritte der messenden und experimentirenden Naturforschung." In *Principien einer elektrodynamischen Theorie der Materie* by J. C. F. Zöllner, vol. 1, xcix–cxxiv.

Stefan, Josef. Obituary of Andreas von Ettingshausen. In *Almanach österreichische Akad.* 28 (1878): 154–59.

Stevens, E. H. "The Heidelberg Physical Laboratory." *Nature* 65 (1902): 587–90.

Sticker, Bernhard. "Benzenberg, Johann Friedrich." *DSB* 1 (1970): 615–16.

Stieda, L. "Seebeck, Thomas Johann." *ADB* 33 (1971): 564–65.

Sturm, Rudolf. "Mathematik." In *Festschrift . . . Breslau,* vol. 2, 434–40.

Süss, Eduard. Obituary of Josef Stefan. *Almanach österreichische Akad.* 43 (1893): 252–57.

Täschner, Constantin. "Ferdinand Reich, 1799–1884. Ein Beitrag zur Freiberger Gelehrten- und Akademiegeschichte." *Mitteilungen des Freiberger Altertumsvereins*, no. 51 (1916): 23–59.

Tammann, G. "Wilhelm Hittorf." *Gött. Nachr.*, 1915, 74–78.

Taylor, Richard, ed. *Scientific Memoirs, Selected from the Transactions of Foreign Academies of Science and Learned Societies, and from Foreign Journals*. 5 vols. London, 1837–1852. Reprint. New York: Johnson, 1966.

Todhunter, Isaac. *A History of the Theory of Elasticity and of the Strength of Materials from Galilei to the Present Time*. Vol. 2, *Saint-Venant to Lord Kelvin*. Pt. 2. Cambridge, 1893.

Truesdell, C. "History of Classical Mechanics, Part II, the 19th and 20th Centuries." *Naturwiss.* 63 (1976): 119–30.

Tübingen. University. *Festgabe zum 25. Regierungs-Jubiläum seiner Majestät des Königs Karl von Württemberg*. Tübingen, 1889.

———. *Quellen zur Gründungsgeschichte der Naturwissenschaftlichen Fakultät in Tübingen 1859–1863*. Edited by Wolf von Engelhardt and Hansmartin Decker-Hauff. Tübingen: J. C. B. Mohr (Paul Siebeck), 1963.

———. See Karl Klüpfel.

Turner, R. Steven. "The Growth of Professorial Research in Prussia, 1818 to 1848—Causes and Context." *HSPS* 3 (1971): 137–82.

———. "Helmholtz, Hermann von." *DSB* 6 (1972): 241–53.

———. "The Ohm-Seebeck Dispute, Herman von Helmholtz, and the Origins of Physiological Acoustics." *Brit. Journ. Hist. Sci.* 10 (1977): 1–24.

Tyndall, J., and W. Francis, eds. *Scientific Memoirs, Natural Philosophy*. London, 1853. Reprint. New York: Johnson, 1966.

Uebele, Hellfried. See Helmuth Gericke.

"Universitätsnachrichten. Leipzig." *Leipziger Repertorium* 1 (1843): 223–24.

Varrentrapp, Conrad. *Johannes Schulze und das höhere preussische Unterrichtswesen in seiner Zeit*. Leipzig, 1889.

Vienna. University. *Geschichte der Wiener Universität von 1848 bis 1898*. Edited by the Akademischer Senat der Wiener Universität. Vienna, 1898.

Voigt, Woldemar. "Ludwig Boltzmann." *Gött. Nachr.*, 1907, 69–82.

———. *Physikalische Forschung und Lehre in Deutschland während der letzten hundert Jahre. Festrede im Namen der Georg-August-Universität zur Jahresfeier der Universität am 5. Juni 1912*. Göttingen, 1912.

———. "Zum Gedächtniss von G. Kirchhoff." *Abh. Ges. Wiss. Göttingen* 35 (1888): 3–10.

———. "Zur Erinnerung an F. E. Neumann, gestorben am 23. Mai 1895 zu Königsberg i/Pr." *Gött. Nachr.*, 1895, 248–65. Reprinted as "Gedächtnissrede auf Franz Neumann" in *Franz Neumanns Gesammelte Werke*, vol. 1, 3–19.

Voit, C. "August Kundt." *Sitzungsber. bay. Akad.* 25 (1895): 177–79.

———. "Eugen v. Lommel." *Sitzungsber. bay. Akad.* 30 (1900): 324–39.

———. "Philipp Johann Gustav von Jolly." *Sitzungsber. bay. Akad.* 15 (1885): 119–36.

————. "Wilhelm von Beetz." *Sitzungsber. bay. Akad.* 16 (1886): 10–31.

Volkmann, H. "Ernst Abbe and His Work." *Applied Optics* 5 (1966): 1720–31.

Volkmann, Paul. "Franz Neumann als Experimentator." *Phys. Zs.* 11 (1910): 932–37.

————. *Franz Neumann. 11. September 1798, 23. Mai 1895.* Leipzig, 1896.

————. "Hermann von Helmholtz." *Schriften der Physikalisch-ökonomischen Gesellschaft zu Königsberg* 35 (1894): 73–81.

Wagner, Rudolf. *Taschenbuch der Physik.* Leipzig, 1851.

Wagner, Rudolph. "Schriften über Universitäten. Dritter Artikel." *Gelehrte Anzeigen* 3 (1836): cols. 993–97, 1001–6, 1013–16.

Wallenreiter, Clara. *Die Vermögensverwaltung der Universität Landshut-München: Ein Beitrag zur Geschichte des bayerischen Hochschultyps vom 18. zum 20. Jahrhundert.* Berlin: Duncker und Humblot, 1971.

Wangerin, Albert, *Franz Neumann und sein Wirken als Forscher und Lehrer.* Braunschweig: F. Vieweg, 1907.

Warburg, Emil. "Das physikalische Institut." In *Die Universität Freiburg,* 91–96.

————. "Zur Erinnerung an Gustav Kirchhoff." *Naturwiss.* 13 (1925): 205–12.

————. "Zur Geschichte der Physikalischen Gesellschaft." *Naturwiss.* 13 (1925): 35–39.

Weber, E. H., and Wilhelm Weber. *Wellenlehre auf Experimente gegründet oder über die Wellen tropfbarer Flüssigkeiten mit Anwendung auf die Schall- und Lichtwellen.* Leipzig, 1825.

Weber, Eduard. See Wilhelm Weber.

Weber, Georg. *Heidelberger Erinnerungen, am Vorabend der fünften Säkularfeier der Universität.* Stuttgart, 1886.

Weber, Heinrich. *Die partiellen Differential-Gleichungen der mathematischen Physik. Nach Riemann's Vorlesungen.* 4th rev. ed. 2 vols. Braunschweig: F. Vieweg, 1900–1901.

Weber, Heinrich. *Wilhelm Weber. Eine Lebensskizze.* Breslau, 1893.

Weber, Leonhard. "Gustav Karsten." *Schriften d. Naturwiss. Vereins f. Schleswig-Holstein* 12 (1901): 63–68.

Weber, Wilhelm. "Lebensbild E. F. F. Chladni's." In *Wilhelm Weber's Werke,* vol. 1, 168–97.

————. *Wilhelm Weber's Werke.* Edited by Königliche Gesellschaft der Wissenschaften zu Göttingen. Vol. 1, *Akustik, Mechanik, Optik und Wärmelehre.* Edited by Woldemar Voigt. Berlin, 1892. Vol. 2, *Magnetismus.* Edited by Eduard Riecke. Berlin, 1892. Vol. 3, *Galvanismus und Elektrodynamik, erster Theil.* Edited by Heinrich Weber. Berlin, 1893. Vol. 4, *Galvanismus und Elektrodynamik, zweiter Theil.* Edited by Heinrich Weber, Berlin, 1894. Vol. 5, with E. H. Weber, *Wellenlehre auf Experimente gegründet oder über die Wellen tropfbarer Flüssigkeiten mit Anwendung auf die Schall- und Lichtwellen.* Edited by Eduard Riecke. Berlin, 1893.

————. See E. H. Weber.

Weber, Wilhelm, and Eduard Weber. *Mechanik der menschlichen Gehwerkzeuge.* Göttingen, 1836.

Weiner, K. L. "Otto Lehmann, 1855–1922." In *Geschichte der Mikroskopie,* edited by H. Freund and A. Berg, vol. 3, 261–71. Frankfurt a. M.: Umschau, 1966.

Weingart, Peter. See Gerard Lemaine.

Weis, E. "Bayerns Beitrag zur Wissenschaftsentwicklung im 19. und 20. Jahrhundert." In *Handbuch der bayerischen Geschichte,* vol. 4, pt. 2, 1034–88.

Whittaker, Edmund. *A History of the Theories of Aether and Electricity.* Vol. 1, *The Classical Theories.* Vol. 2, *The Modern Theories, 1900–1926.* Reprint. New York: Harper and Brothers, 1960.

Wiedemann, Gustav. *Ein Erinnerungsblatt.* Leipzig, 1893.

———. "Hermann von Helmholtz' wissenschaftliche Abhandlungen." In Helmholtz's *Wissenschaftliche Abhandlungen,* vol. 3, xi–xxxvi.

———. "Stiftungsfeier am 4. Januar 1896." *Verh. phys. Ges.* 15 (1896): 32–36.

———. "Vorwort." *Ann.* 39 (1890): first four unnumbered pages.

Wiederkehr, K. H. *Wilhelm Eduard Weber. Erforscher der Wellenbewegung und der Elektrizität 1804–1891.* Vol. 32 of Grosse Naturforscher. Stuttgart: Wissenschaftliche Verlagsgesellschaft, 1967.

Wien, Wilhelm. "Helmholtz als Physiker." *Naturwiss.* 9 (1921): 694–99.

———. "Das physikalische Institut und das physikalische Seminar." In *Die wissenschaftlichen Anstalten . . . zu München,* 207–11.

Wiener, Otto. "Das neue physikalische Institut der Universität Leipzig und Geschichtliches." *Phys. Zs.* 7 (1906): 1–14.

Wilde, Heinrich Emil. *Geschichte der Optik, vom Ursprunge dieser Wissenschaft bis auf die gegenwärtige Zeit.* Pt. 1. Berlin, 1838.

Wise, M. Norton. "German Concepts of Force, Energy, and the Electromagnetic Ether: 1845–1880." In *Conceptions of Ether: Studies in the History of Ether Theories 1740–1900,* edited by G. N. Cantor and M. J. S. Hodge, 269–307.

Wissner, Adolf. "Franz: Johann Carl Rudolph." *Neue deutsche Biographie* 5 (1961): 376–77.

Wolkenhauer, W. "Karsten, Gustav." *Biographisches Jahrbuch und Deutscher Nekrolog* 5 (1900): 76–78.

Woodruff, A. E. "Action at a Distance in Nineteenth Century Electrodynamics." *Isis* 53 (1962): 439–59.

———. "The Contributions of Hermann von Helmholtz to Electrodynamics." *Isis* 59 (1968): 300–311.

Württemberg. Statistisches Landesamt. *Statistik der Universität Tübingen.* Edited by the K. Statistisch-Topographisches Bureau. Stuttgart, 1877.

Würzburg. University. *Verzeichniss der Vorlesungen welche an der Königlich-Bayerischen Julius-Maximilians-Universität zu Würzburg . . . gehalten werden.* Würzburg, n.d.

———. See Maria Reindl; W. C. Röntgen.

Wundt, Wilhelm. "Zur Erinnerung an Gustav Theodor Fechner." *Philosophische Studien* 4 (1888): 471–78.

Ziegenfuss, Werner. "Helmholtz, Hermann von." In *Philosophen-Lexikon*, vol. 1, 498–501. Berlin: de Gruyter, 1949.

Zöllner, J. C. F. *Erklärung der universellen Gravitation aus den statischen Wirkungen der Elektricität und die allgemeine Bedeutung des Weber'schen Gesetzes. Mit Beiträgen von Wilhelm Weber.* 2d ed. Leipzig, 1886.

———. *Principien einer elektrodynamischen Theorie der Materie.* Vol. 1, *Abhandlungen zur atomistischen Theorie der Elektrodynamik.* Leipzig, 1876.

Zurich. ETH. *Eidgenössische Technische Hochschule 1855–1955.* Zurich: Buchverlag der Neuen Zürcher Zeitung, 1955.

———. *Festschrift zur Feier des fünfzigjährigen Bestehens des Eidg. Polytechnikums.* Pt. 1, *Geschichte der Gründung des Eidg. Polytechnikums mit einer Übersicht seiner Entwicklung 1855–1905* by Wilhelm Oechsli. Frauenfeld: Huber, 1905.

———. *100 Jahre Eidgenössische Technische Hochschule. Sonderheft der Schweizerischen Hochschulzeitung* 28 (1955).

———. See A. Frey-Wyssling.

Zwerger, Franz. *Geschichte der realistischen Lehranstalten in Bayern.* Vol. 53 of Monumenta Germaniae Paedagogica. Berlin: Weidmannsche Buchhandlung, 1914.

Acknowledgments

We are grateful to the National Science Foundation for the award of two major grants to support our research and to the many historians of science who supported it through their evaluations of the proposal for this book. We are especially grateful to Martin J. Klein and Thomas S. Kuhn for their encouragement and help. We want to thank the owners of manuscripts and photographs who granted us permission to use them, and we want to thank the archivists and librarians of the many manuscript collections here and abroad who assisted us in our work.

Index

Yelin, Julius Konrad, 39, 43, 274
Young, Thomas, 305

Zach, Franz Xaver von, 64
Zamminer, F. G. K., 242–43
Zeitschrift für Physik und Mathematik, 32, 37–38
Zöppritz, Karl, 243

Zoology, 11–12, 81, 117
Zurich Kantonsschule, 187, 201
Zurich Polytechnic: founding of, 186; new positions in physics, 186–90; physics teaching at, 190–93; Clausius's researches at, 193–96;
Zurich University, 190